Standards, Principles, and Techniques

in

QUANTITY

FOOD

PRODUCTION

Standards, Principles, and Techniques

in

QUANTITY
FOOD
PRODUCTION

Second Edition

by

LENDAL H. KOTSCHEVAR, Ph.D.

*Professor, School of Hotel, Restaurant,
and Institutional Management,
Michigan State University, East Lansing, Michigan*

McCutchan Publishing Corporation
2526 Grove Street
Berkeley, California 94704

Preface

This book is written to state some of the standards, principles, and techniques required to produce food in quantity. It is not a recipe book but a book that attempts to give the *what, why,* and *how* behind the use of recipes. It is written for managers and supervisors who must bear the responsibility for food production and for students who must learn how to bear this responsibility. It is intended as a working manual. Management will find the illustrations and explanations helpful not only to itself but also as a training guide for workers. The main emphasis of this book is on standards and how they are achieved. While the young manager close to food production will find this book helpful in his immediate problems of administration, he will find it continually useful as he rises in management responsibilities and becomes less and less involved in the actual production of food, for it should remain a constant source of reference in food production.

The operation of a quantity food kitchen cannot be learned, however, from a book. For this knowledge, the student must work with foods, see actual reactions in large quantity cooking, and to learn to use food production equipment by operating it. Menu planning, scheduling of employees, ordering and storing of foods, preparation, service, and the application of management principles must be related to actual conditions. The dynamic flow of food production under the stress of meeting a meal deadline can only be learned when work situations are real and not hypothetical.

As a text, this material should be related to lectures, demonstrations, and actual work experiences. Many of the illustrations found in this book have been duplicated in color on film strips along with recordings which explain the principles and techniques illustrated on the strips. It is hoped that the visual and oral joining of textual materials, along with lectures, demonstrations, and laboratory experiences, will vastly improve learning and interest as well as allow students to study more on their own.

While many people have assisted in the production of this book, special thanks are due to Mr. Michael Palmer, Research Chef of Procter and Gamble, and Mr. Stan Rosswurm, Field Baker for Pillsbury Company, for their assistance in making many of the illustrations in the chapters on cakes and breads.

This book is dedicated to my students who have inspired and encouraged me to write it.

Seeley Lake, Montana
June 1963

LENDAL H. KOTSCHEVAR, Ph.D.

Contents

Section I

Management in Quantity Food Production

1 Planning

Responsibility for food production in food services rests with management. The day when management could delegate this responsibility to the chef, the steward, or other food service worker and concentrate only on front-of-the-house problems has passed. Highly competitive conditions, increasing costs, and the lack of skilled workers have made it necessary that management concern itself with the details of producing food.

The production of good food at a proper cost requires not only a knowledge of how to produce it but also the application of successful management principles. A kitchen and a dining room are run by an organization of people, and the problem of managing them and achieving satisfactory production and service demands managerial talent. The rules of personnel management must be artfully applied, and management must also directly concern itself with planning, forecasting, merchandising, purchasing, accounting, financing, control, and other management functions. The menu offerings, the amount and quality of food prepared, its cost, the methods of production, and service require management decision. Unless management assumes this responsibility, low worker productivity, over- or underproduction, high costs, and poor quality food result.

Good selection and training of a food production staff, plus its proper organization, is management's responsibility. Standardized recipes, purchase specifications, outlined work procedures and training programs and other modes of operation must be followed. Management must be alert to utilize new management tools. Large or chain operations may find it desirable to place their entire operation and control systems on punch cards with the result that much food production planning is far less under human control and far more under machine control. Operations are now functioning very successfully under such systems of machine and punch card control. Undoubtedly, we shall see further extension in the future in this field. In addition, as more and more convenience foods are introduced into the kitchen, the quantity of labor required and the degree of skill and importance of labor will decline, and management will assume a role of growing importance. Management will be able to concentrate then less on problems of pro-

RESTAURANT ORGANIZATION

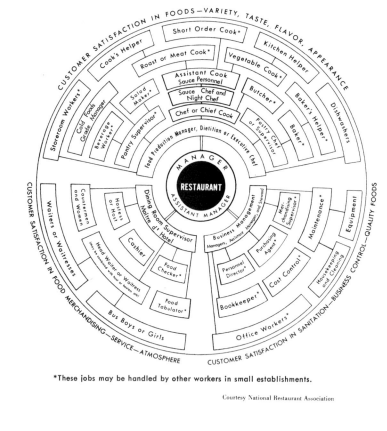

*These jobs may be handled by other workers in small establishments.

Courtesy National Restaurant Association

FIG. 1-1 Organization is necessary to the success of any food service, but a different type of organization set-up will be required for each type of operation. This organization chart from the National Restaurant Association would suit many different types of operation. While organizations may differ in detail, basically they will be the same, and the same principles of control will apply to all.

duction and more on the problems of merchandising and service. Standards and principles for the production of good food must still be known, however, for without these the success of a food service cannot be guaranteed, and the need for management to concern itself directly with food production will never be completely eliminated. The nature of the food service industry will make it impossible to convert completely to machine production and eliminate entirely the need for a personalized food production system.

CONTROLS

One of the most important factors that management must establish in quantity food production is controls. Cost, quality, and quantity controls are those most frequently used. To control does not mean to establish a measure; to control means to direct. Measures are necessary to control, for a part of control is evaluation, and measures of values are implicit in evalua-

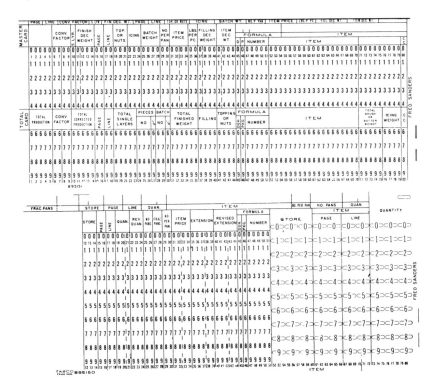

FIG. 1-2 These two simple cards are used to control the entire ordering and production of foods for a chain of 34 units of quick lunch, candy, and ice cream operations. Data processing systems such as this can materially reduce costs and strengthen management control.

tion. Accounting information provides measures, but other systems and guides must be established to accomplish complete control. Controls are guides established to direct an organization to its goals; these guides should be simple and quick to use, give desired results, and cost relatively little to employ.

Cost Control

Until recently food and labor costs have received most emphasis in quantity food operation control. Spiraling non-food and non-labor costs, however, have awakened many operators to the fact that cost control involves the control of all costs, not just food and labor. Establishment of controls over all costs should be the aim of management.

Before a cost can be controlled, one must be aware that it exists, why it exists, and how to control it. Accounting information, the costing of recipes, yield studies, and time studies on labor are some of the means of gaining this information. But knowing this information does not control. It is merely a basis upon which to act to control, just as a barometer tells us that a storm is brewing or a thermometer informs a doctor that a patient is ill. Once informed, the control or cure must be used. The elimination of waste, increase in labor efficiency, reduction of equipment use, and other similar factors are the actual controls.

Food Cost

Many means are used to control food costs. Good purchasing and receiving procedures, correct forecasting, wise use of carry-over foods, alert supervision, adequate storage, efficiently operating equipment, skilled employees, portion control, and other factors will lower food costs. Excessive inventories, failure to take advantage of discounts or favorable market prices, lack of security of assets, and many other factors may increase food costs. Constant search for new material which will produce a product as good or better at a lower cost is required. Controlling costs by lowering quality or reducing sizes of portions is of doubtful value.

Recipe costing aids in controlling food costs by giving advance information on costs. Tables which list the costs of common foods in quantities used make it easy for planners to estimate costs. Accounting departments can make up such tables and revise them periodically. A knowledge of the AP (as purchased), EP (edible portion), and AS (as served) costs and their relationship to one another is helpful in giving management an indication of the true cost of items used in manufacture. Most authorities recommend that recipe costs be reviewed every six months. Precosting information of food cost may be obtained also by totals obtained from purchase orders and requisitions written at the time the menu is planned. These, if forwarded to the accounting department, can give a precost, and the menu can be revised, if necessary, to control costs.[1]

LABORATORY REPORT

Recipe for _____ Date _____

Ingredients	Weight or Measure	Price per Unit	Cost

YIELD: Expected_____ Actual _____   COST: Total Cost _____

Size of Portion_____   Volume or Units _____

AP Weight_____   Cost Per Unit _____

Trim Loss _____   Selling Price _____

Shrinkage _____   Percentage Food Cost _____

EP Weight_____

Percentage of Loss_____

Name of Student _____

Remarks _____

_____

_____
Supervisor

FIG. 1-3 An example of a recipe cost form for use in calculating total and portion costs.

[1]See "Analyze Your Food Costs" and "Allocating Labor Costs to Individual Food Items" by John M. Welch, Agricultural Extension Service, University of Missouri, Columbia, Missouri.

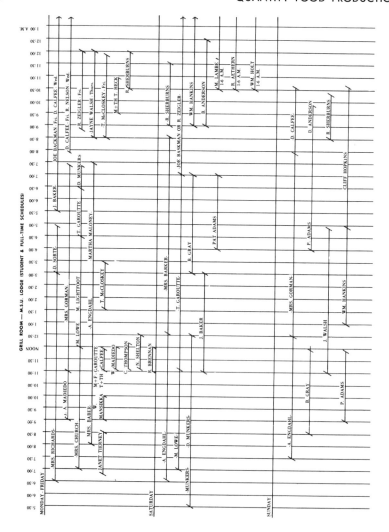

FIG. 1-4 The importance of scheduling labor properly to achieve desirable costs and quality in quantity food production cannot be over-stressed. Bring the worker on the job when production re-quires. A line schedule shown here gives a supervisor and management a good grasp of coverage of positions dur-ing all phases of production and service.

WORK SHEET

Food Quantities

BREAKFAST	Total Prepared Weight or Count	Carry Over or Run Out Time	Total Used Weight or Count	Meal Count
LUNCH				
DINNER				
Bread				
Butter				
Milk				
Cream				
Coffee				

FIG. 1-5   The work sheet shown here is a valuable record to food production managers in informing management of over- or under-production.

Labor Cost

In many operations labor cost is higher than food cost. For this reason, increasing emphasis is being given to methods for controlling it. A study of the quantity of labor used gives management a measure, and, once a measure is established, performance can be evaluated. Increasing worker productivity is considered so important that one entire chapter in this book reviews methods used to study workers and establish work standards. If recipes state the production time and the total time required to produce given items, management has better means for controlling labor costs. Production time is that time a worker spends in producing a food item, and from this figure labor cost can be calculated. Total time is reckoned from the start of a product to its finish and includes time a worker does not work on the item. It informs management when to start production, how long equipment will be involved, and when to schedule labor to meet production demands.

Correct forecasting of quantities required and precise scheduling of labor to meet production needs will prevent labor waste. Many planners find it advisable to establish a labor budget. Shifting of labor between departments is allowed providing the overall labor budget is not exceeded.

Production schedules should be used to inform employees of what and how much is to be produced and to allow management to control the amount of labor used. Each operation must set up a scheduling system that suits its needs. In large operations, departmental schedules may be desirable rather than one schedule for the entire kitchen. On the schedule it is advisable to list the day, date, and other general information at the top. List together at the left the menu items to be produced according to sections that must produce them and, if necessary, the names of workers who will produce them. Next to the menu items, list the recipe to be used by a code or file number. Most planners also indicate next the quantity required, batch times, portion size, times for starting and completing production, and perhaps run-out time and selling price. Indicate clearly how work is to be co-ordinated between departments, such as vegetable preparation for salad units or cooks, patty shells from the bakeshop for creamed chicken, and so forth.

The planning of the menu should occur sufficiently in advance of production so labor scheduling is efficient. Watch carefully prepreparation requirements and schedule this work in sufficient time so the work proceeds smoothly. Know production times. These will vary according to the item, layout, equipment, skill of workers, and other factors. Roasts need to set thirty minutes at least before slicing. Gelatin mixtures normally take four hours to set. Rolled-in doughs must rest between turns. Balance work loads so that workers on easy days do jobs that make busy days less busy. Work carefully on schedules for days off and reliefs. Plan banquets and parties so foods on the regular menu are served, thus avoiding extra work. Keep records of production for future reference. Add vital information to production schedules so this may be available later. Cycle menus make it possible to set up repetitive procedures that reduce work.

Quality Control

It is the responsibility of management to establish food standards and to see that these are maintained. Employees cannot be expected to establish standards on their own; therefore management must take the lead in seeing that they are established. A standard is a measure that establishes a value. Without values, management and employees have no yardsticks with which to evaluate the quality of the foods produced. Employees must be thoroughly indoctrinated with the standards of an operation. These should be communicated to employees in every way possible: by pictures, meetings, discussions, panels, and so forth. Quality control in food services is more difficult to establish and maintain than in a factory, where standard items are mass produced by machines and objective measures may be applied. Food services produce a variety of items spasmodically, using much hand labor, which causes variability. Furthermore, the products are usually highly perishable. Good quality control is therefore frequently a matter of good on-the-job supervision.

There are, however, aids in quantity production for controlling quality. Recipes, thermometers, clocks, portion scales, and other measuring devices aid in producing standard items. Score sheets can be used to judge foods, and management and employees working together can agree on a desirable standard. Well planned menus, standardized recipes, precise purchase specifications, and exacting receiving procedures are parts of a good quality control program. Equipment that is in good working order, well planned work areas, good working conditions, and well trained personnel are also essential. Proper quality ingredients must be used. Good supervision is required along with good preparation procedures. Customer reactions, plate waste, the number of items sold, and other means of determining popularity of menu items is of assistance in checking on quality. Constant evaluation and criticism is necessary on the part of management and employees if a satisfactory quality control program is to be achieved.

Quantity Control

Proper forecasting of the correct quantity required and portion control in serving this quantity are two essentials toward achieving good quantity control. The amount prepared will depend upon the number of portions required multiplied by the portion size, but if the number or size of portions varies from that planned, production is thrown off. Establish portion sizes and see that they are achieved. There are many factors to be considered in doing this.

Portion size will vary according to the type of food served, the type of meal, the type of patron, cost of the food, and portion appearance. Food served as a snack, a one-dish meal, a heavy breakfast, a light luncheon, or a moderate supper will differ in portion size. The richness or lightness of the food may be a factor. A very rich dessert will be dished lightly, while a non-rich one will be dished more heavily. A fruit cocktail will be smaller than a fruit compote served as a dessert. Tradition has established some

FIG. 1-6   (a) Here are some standards commonly accepted in our commercial dealings: a quart measure, silver dollars, a ruler, a pound weight, a clock, and a graded measure to check the color of butter. Standards such as these bring order out of chaos on the market.

standard sizes for portions, such as a pat of butter, a portion of coffee cream, gravy on mashed potatoes, and so forth.

Know your customer and his wants. Adults, teen-agers and small children consume different quantities as well as different kinds of food. Men consume more calories than women, and people doing hard work consume more food than those doing more sedentary tasks. Certain ethnic groups eat different size portions and different types of food. Cost may be a factor in deciding portion size. A large steak may be too expensive to serve when the budget is limited, but a smaller steak with more liberal portions of accompanying food may be satisfactory. Serving a liberal quantity of low-cost foods such as soup or appetizers before more expensive food may give satisfaction without complaint, even though the expensive food portions are smaller than they would have otherwise been. If patrons serve themselves, it may be necessary to devise ways to guide them in selecting portions.

In any food service, portions must appear ample; and the size of the

FIG. 1-6   (b) These are some of the measuring devices that can be used to bring food production up to standards in quantity cookery.

serving dish, decoration and width of the rim, and color of the dish, along with the food arrangement, may affect the appearance of the portion size. A garnish or sauce may be used to make a portion appear larger. The quantity of other foods served with a particular food may affect the portion size. A thick piece of Swiss steak may appear small, but if cut thinner so it occupies a greater surface area it may appear ample. Tightly packed food versus food that is lightly packed will require different portion weights, even though their size may appear the same.

It is possible to do a good job of production planning and still fail to meet production needs because of a failure to control serving. Portion control actively starts when the menu is planned. List on it the portion size, or indicate a recipe giving the desired size. Use purchase specifications, preparation instructions, and other means to see that foods are sized properly. Planning that contemplates the serving of two wieners 10 to the pound will not be achieved if frankfurters six to the pound are received, accepted, prepared, and served; nor if pears 25 count per No. 10 can are served instead of a planned 40 count. A cook who marks a 12 by 20 inch pan of meat pie three by six instead of four by six may cause a last-minute frantic rush to prepare more when the supply is exhausted during the peak of service.

Calculation of production requirements may be challenging to food planners. Each operation usually needs its own system of forecasting. Serving a fixed population and a non-selective menu may make forecasting simple. Patient counts in hospitals, weekend absentee predictions by dormitory staffs, and other means may be used to estimate variations in counts. Restaurants and other establishments with variable drop-in trade find it desirable to keep records of past experience and the effect of menu items, season, day, weather, and other factors for reference. Maintaining flexibility to meet fluctuating conditions is desirable. For banquets or parties, guarantees are frequently required. Sometimes 5 to 10% over or under the guarantee is allowed.

Total production needs should be stated to production people in meaningful units: pounds, quarts, gallons, or other measures used in production. It may be simple to estimate the number of pies required, but when one must calculate how many five-ounce cube steaks are to be obtained from AP rounds of beef, the amount to calculate may be somewhat more difficult than the number of pies. Tables of quantities required for given numbers based on standard portions are helpful. Tested recipes assist in this, and also in giving correct quantities required. The U.S. Department of Agriculture Handbooks, No. 16, *Planning Food for Institutions*, and No. 102, *Food Yields*, are good references.

Not only must production planners forecast total quantities correctly but oftentimes they must break the total quantity required into batches and then indicate times at which batches will be required. Workers need to be trained to keep a steady, even flow of fresh products to the service areas. Freshly cooked vegetables should reach service stations every 20 minutes.[2] Batch cooking, besides being an important factor in controlling quality,

[2]See batch cookery in the chapter on vegetables, pp. 280–81.

acts as a brake against overproduction.

In setting up the quantity control system, see that servers and other employees are informed on portion sizes. Establish lists of portion sizes and place them in work areas for quick reference. These should list portions per pound, package, piece, or other unit. For instance, indicate that 45 size melons are to be cut in halves, that one-third cup of fruit cup or $1\frac{1}{2}$ ounces of crab meat are standard portions for cocktails, and that slicing machines should be set at specified gage numbers to give the right size portions. List the number of pieces on arranged salads or other dishes. Wherever possible show pictures of foods as they should be served. All recipes should indicate portion size and the number of portions to be obtained. Recipes should give exact panning instructions. Indicate how many servings should be obtained from each pan. Use geometric markings on pans to indicate portions. Establish the raw deposit weight for cookies, cream puffs, or other items. Mark pans with their own tare weights so calculation of total quantities in the pans can be made rapidly. List sizes of scoops, spoons, ladles, and other tools that are used for portioning specific foods. Mark stainless steel rulers so the quantity in a mixer, steam-jacketed kettle, or pot can be quickly ascertained. Use portion scales and correctly sized dishes, souffle cups, and so forth to portion foods. Preportion so that in a busy period the correct amount is given. Check frequently the portioning equipment to see it is in good working order and is being used properly. Be practical. It is easier and less exacting when working at high speed to use a rounded six-ounce scoop than to measure a level eight-ounce scoop for an eight-ounce portion. See that servers are informed before service about the size of the portion by weight, volume, or count, the dish in which it is to be served, the serving tool to use, and other information necessary so a proper size portion is given.

THE MENU

The menu authorizes production. In this respect, it is like a production order in a factory. Its writing sets in motion a series of procurement and manufacturing functions that culminate in a finished product. Once the menu is written, many production requirements are established — what is to be produced and how much, type of preparation and service, cost, and selling price. Menus sent to the production department should include production information not presented in menus that patrons see. There are two steps in planning any menu: (1) selecting the menu offerings, and (2) the writing.

Selecting Menu Offerings

It is frequently advisable to have more than one staff member participate in selecting items for the menu; one of these should be experienced in planning and know the management's policies. Search widely for good and new menu suggestions. Do not ignore employee and patron comments. Menu selectors, tallies of item popularity, lists of popular food combinations, ideas gleaned from magazines, cook books, advertisements, published articles, or even competitors' menus may be helpful. In some cases, specialty items always appear on a menu and there is little problem in their selection. Some selections are traditional for the season, holiday or locale. Keep a reminder on these.

The type of menu should suit the operation and the patron. Simplicity and rapid comprehension in reading should be sought. A menu may be written for a meal, a day, a week, or longer. Some menus never change while others change at every meal, and no meal or day is ever the same as another. Each type of food service will require a menu designed to suit its specific needs; a hospital plans a general menu and from this makes selections for its special diets. Some food services may want simple menus with few selections, while others will want many. Special occasions require special planning, and details of service and other arrangements may have to accompany the menu. Catering requires special organization and planning as well as special arrangements in food production.

An *a la carte* menu lists and sells foods separately. On a *du jour* menu some foods are served with an item; it is preferable but not essential that such foods be named. A *table d'hote* menu has a fixed price for an entire meal or a group of foods. An a la carte menu may be used on heavy paper which never changes as a backing for a lighter sheet of paper attached to it, a table d'hote menu that is changed with each meal. Some menus list items with a table d'hote price for a complete meal, and then in a column to the right list an a la carte price also. It is becoming more and more common to price the main entree and include foods with it, such as a vegetable, salad, roll, butter, and beverage, and then allow selection of appetizer, soup, and dessert at extra cost, if desired. Selling meals and lodging at one price is called the American plan, while selling meals separately from lodging is called the European plan. A table setting for one person is called a cover.

Considerations for Planning

One of the first rules to observe in planning a successful sales program is to know the market. Menu planners should know the economic, regional, ethnic, religious, and social backgrounds of those who will eat the food. Observe traditional food patterns and note changing dietary patterns of peoples. While it may be desirable to offer new foods to give variety to a menu, variety at the expense of old favorites or too much originality will mean failure. Teen-agers want their hot dogs, hamburgers, French fries, and other favorites, and rebel against artichokes, lobster curry, and other foods with which they have little acquaintance. The southerner wants

Luncheon Menu

SALAD

Crisp Lettuce Wedge, Roquefort Dressing 45
Pear, Pineapple and Cottage Cheese, Chantilly Sauce 35

SOUPS

Tomato Madrilene 25   Boston Clam Chowder 25
Davenport Onion Soup 25

ENTREES

ALL VEGETABLE HEALTH PLATE - Western Carrots,   𝍲
Green Beans, Spinach, Mexican Corn, Tiny Whole Beets........... 1.40 **5**

ALASKAN SHRIMP NEWBURG - Served over Golden Baked Rice, 𝍲 𝍲
Western Carrots, Crisp Green Salad 1.75 **10**

ROAST TOP ROUND OF CHOICE BEEF AU JUS - Mexican Red Beans, 𝍲 ///
Baby Pearl Onions with Garden Green Peas 1.95 **8**

WESTERN SALAD BOWL - Julienne of Turkey, Avocado and Bacon - 𝍲 /
tossed with Crisp Greens and Caesar Dressing 1.60 **6**

BUTTERED SPAGHETTI with Ripe Olives and Fresh Mushrooms Saute - 𝍲 𝍲/
topped with Grated Parmesan Cheese, Tossed Green Salad......... 1.45 **11**

Coffee, Tea or Milk - - Roll and Butter

SANDWICHES

Deviled Egg .. 𝍲 /.......	75	**6**	Tuna Fish .. 𝍲. 𝍲 /.......	1.05	**11**
Baked Ham .. ///	1.05	**3**	Swiss Cheese .. ////	80	**4**
Chicken.. 𝍲 .. .:	1.35	**5**	Beef or Pork .... ///	1.05	**3**
American Cheese . 𝍲 / ..	75	**6**	Baked Ham & Cheese.. ////	1.20	**4**
Lettuce & Tomato. 𝍲 /// ..	80	**8**	Early Birds Club.. 𝍲	1.60	**5**
Chicken Salad . ///	1.20	**4**			

Choice of- Potato Salad, Cottage Cheese, Potato Chips or
Fruit Salad with above Sandwiches

DESSERTS

Assorted Pies 35   Chocolate or White Layer Cake 35
French Vanilla or Chocolate Ice Cream 35
Rice or Bread Pudding with Cream 35
Choice of Sherbet 30   Cup Custard 30

Executive Chef - Dean Atkinson   Friday

EARLY BIRDS

FIG. 1-7 An easily read menu. Note how the number of each item sold has been tallied by the cashier from her sales slips.

hominy grits at breakfast and black-eyed peas on New Year's Day. The Bostonian likes his clam chowder with milk, and the Philadelphian wants it with tomatoes and no milk.

Where selection is offered, the menu should make it possible to select an adequate diet, but when little or no choice is offered, the menu should be written to assure adequacy. Some menus should be planned with special restrictions. A general hospital menu may not only have to yield low-residue, low-salt, low-calorie, and other special diets, but must be satisfactory for service to the doctors, nurses, and general staff. A school lunch menu must conform to Type A requirements if it is to qualify for federal subsidy. Aged, ill or mentally disturbed patients may need enriched foods because of low food intake. In-plant cafeterias may have to emphasize lunches and coffee-break foods. Religious rules may have to be observed. The psychological factors behind food acceptance should be understood by menu planners. Food services catering to "captive audiences" have problems in menu planning which other types of operations do not have. Building interest in the food served must receive special emphasis under such circumstances. Foods in institutions may be rejected not because of quality but because familiar and loved surroundings associated with food are missing. Supplying adequate substitutes for these missed factors brings special challenges.

Budgetary limitations may restrict menu offerings. Menu planners frequently wish to set up guides on what can be spent on various foods and yet stay within the budget. For instance, of the total cost for a meal, 8 to 10% might be allowed for appetizer, 50 to 55% for the entree, 10 to 15% for potato and vegetable, 12 to 15% for dessert, and 10% for beverage, bread, and butter. Many institutions find that offering a choice in vegetables, salads, and beverages assists in creating satisfaction. At times it is desirable to plan foods which are quickly prepared, served, and consumed so a satisfactory turnover is obtained.

Menu prices should be within the price range the customer wants to pay. Vary your price offerings so that at least several selections are in the lower price range. Selling prices may be obtained by dividing the percentage of food cost desired into the cost of food, but this is not always to be recommended.[3] It is oftentimes desirable, not to establish a standard markup for all foods, but to vary them because of varying costs of labor in production or for merchandising or other reasons. Raising prices is difficult once a level has been established. Experience has shown that it is easier to change prices on popular items than it is on less popular ones. If prices are raised a small amount at a time on one item and another small amount on another until

---

[3]See "A New Marketing Approach to Profits," Thompson and Kotschevar, *Institutions Magazine*, February 1960.

the desired change is obtained, it will be noticed less by patrons.

Some menu items may be frequently repeated, such as specialties of the house, but too frequent a repetition may lead to dissatisfaction. Maintaining files to remind one of past offerings and using seasonal foods will assist in giving good food rotation. On the other hand, surprise and interest may be obtained when foods are offered out of season, providing menu prices support it. Variety may not be as much a matter of changing foods as clever and novel means of service. Use special care in presenting dishes made from carry-over foods. Weak disguises will bring customer rejection.

Planners should know what can and cannot be accomplished either by workers or with equipment. Menu offerings are limited oftentimes by

FIG. 1-8 Select foods according to this chart to assure dietary adequacy. Add extra quantities for growth and energy needs. Food services, while they may not be able to direct menu selections, must make possible the selection of nourishing foods which will assure an adequate diet. (Courtesy American Institute of Baking)

staff abilities. Balancing what is to be produced with available equipment is essential. Work loads should be geared to work force and equipment. Lists of capacities of equipment and production times and a knowledge of the skills and abilities of workers will assist in avoiding error here.

The type of service used may affect menu selections. Table, counter, cafeteria, buffet, drive-in, automatic, or vending service will influence what is offered. Each type of service is best suited to specific types of food. The occasion also may dictate food choices. A wedding breakfast will differ greatly in foods offered from a stag buffet.

Informal meal service may be Russian, family, or cafeteria style. In the former, foods are dished in the pantry or kitchen. When foods are dished onto platters or dishes and brought to the table where guests help themselves or someone at the table dishes up the food, a family type of service is achieved. But distinctions in service, especially in the informal types, are rapidly being lost. Vending, drive-in, self-service, and other types of service are rapidly changing many service patterns, and the foods produced must be adapted to this change.

Formal meal service may be French, Russian, or English; a fourth service, resembling Russian but having a slightly different course sequence, is known as American but is seldom used. Formal service is being used less and less because of labor cost. Modifications to reduce labor are being

FIG. 1-9 Catering is a significant part of the business done in some clubs, hotels, restaurants, and other operations. Here we see waiters at the Biltmore Hotel, Los Angeles, reporting for service at a catering function. In the background a captain explains the table setting for the meal.

introduced, such as a la Ritz, which is a simplification of formal French cart service. Many authorities feel that no more than eight courses are required at a formal meal except perhaps formal state dinners. These eight are:

1. Hors d'oeuvre, or appetizer.	5. Roast and vegetable.
2. Soup.	6. Salad.
3. Fish.	7. Dessert.
4. Entree.	8. Coffee.

Appetizers may be hors d'oeuvres, oysters, clams, fruit such as melon, fruit cup, juice, or a large canapé. If small canapés and hors d'oeuvres are served in the reception room with an alcoholic cocktail, aperitif, or juice, the first course may be omitted. Wine-type aperitifs are considered more appropriate than cocktails for a formal meal, but in this country the preference is for cocktails. Oftentimes Russian formal service has a buffet of hors d'oeuvres and canapés. Servers pass these as guests sip their aperitifs. A *buffet Russe* is a buffet in which appetizer-type foods are served from a glass or carved-ice piece centered on a table, with caviar being one of the foods. In a formal meal, the fourth course, the entree, may be a timbale, a creamed dish, or another cooked, hot, prepared food. A frozen punch or ice is proper with the roast. Dessert may be a sweet type, or cheese and fruit, or cheese and crisp wafers may be served before a sweet dessert. Liquors or brandy, candies and nuts may follow coffee. A different wine is frequently served with each of several courses. In Russian and French service, bread and butter plates and salts and peppers are not used. No bread or butter is served. Second servings are never offered. Finger bowls may be used. In all formal service, a service plate about 10 inches in diameter is used and this is left before the guest until the roast and vegetable are served. It may be returned again with the salad but removed when the dessert is served. Menus are frequently printed along with the program and placed next to the napkin. Place cards are proper. The following are the usually accepted course sequences for the formal type meals:

French

Three settings; each setting consists of a number of courses, and a number of foods are served with each setting. Foods either are brought to the table or are rolled in on carts, and servers dish up for the guests. Normally a table of eight requires two waiters and a captain in addition to a supervisor for each two or three tables. A bain-marie may be placed behind a screen close by for hot foods. The settings are quite elaborate and this service is used only for the most formal meal. This service is seldom used today.

Russian

Formal Russian service is basically like the Russian informal service in that foods are dished in the kitchen or pantry for guests. The course sequence follows that of the French formal service.[4] In some instances, foods may be dished in the kitchen or pantry and then brought to guests by waiters so selections can be made. This is known as Russian platter service. Occasionally cold foods may be on the table as decorations. These are removed and served and brought back either on individual plates or on platter service.

FIG. 1-10 A chef checks his buffet as foods are placed on the table for service.

[4]The foods offered in the three settings for French and Russian formal service are:

First Setting	*Second Setting*	*Third Setting*
Appetizer	Frozen punch or sherbet	Dessert
Soup	Roast	Cheese
Hors d'oeuvre	Chaudfroid	Ice
Fish		Fresh fruit
Solid joint		Coffee, possibly followed
Entree		by liqueurs and brandy

English

For formal English service, foods are brought to the table on platters or dishes. The host usually carves, but servers may do it from a side table if the gathering is large. Usually the host serves the meat and vegetables, and may serve the dessert if the hostess is serving the beverage. The appetizer and salad are usually at the covers when guests are seated. If not, the hostess serves these. She also usually serves the dessert and beverage. At times, only a part of the foods may be dished by the host and hostess, while others are passed to guests, who help themselves.

Careful consideration of the material and labor cost should be given before foods are placed on menus. Food prices should be watched by planners, and a knowledge of losses in preparation is essential so the final cost AS is known. If recipes are precosted, planners will have some knowledge of final costs. The time required to produce foods should be known so labor costs can be determined. At times it may be necessary to select items because of the rapidity with which they can be produced and the quickness with which they can be consumed. Some operations must have a rapid turnover during lunch periods or other mealtimes in order to operate successfully, and menu selections may affect turnover.

Careful consideration should be given in selecting menu items to secure

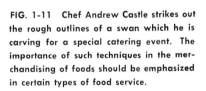

FIG. 1-11 Chef Andrew Castle strikes out the rough outlines of a swan which he is carving for a special catering event. The importance of such techniques in the merchandising of foods should be emphasized in certain types of food service.

contrasts in form, texture, flavor, color, and temperature in the foods offered. Planners should check these elements to see that pleasing food combinations are on the menu. Contrasts in service also may create appeal. See that crisp foods are contrasted with soft. Seek contrasts in flavors, too. Broccoli and coleslaw are too closely related in flavor to be served at the same meal. Tart, spicy foods such as mint jelly or applesauce with lamb or pork will heighten the flavor and lessen the fatty taste of these meats. See that foods also contrast in color, and avoid unnatural food colors. Seek temperature differences in foods. Consider weather conditions and season in selecting foods. During times when weather may be variable, select foods which would be suitable for any type of weather.

Menu Writing

After the items have been selected, the second step in menu planning occurs, the writing. The importance of the menu as a merchandising and advertising medium should not be forgotten. It is usually the first and best bit of advertising the customer sees. The menu offers an opportunity to impress the customer with the standards of the operation. Use colorful language but not language which confuses or embarrasses the patron because he does not understand it. Flavor, texture, color, or other important qualities which sell may be indicated by words such as "honey fruit dressing," "minted peas," "crisp brown potatoes," "topped with full ripe strawberries," and so forth. Menus should not be misleading and words should convey precise information. The patron should not be disappointed by getting something different from what he thinks he is to receive when he orders.

Menu Format

The format used should present items so the menu is simple to read, quick to grasp, and clear as to prices. Some menus may be just boards hung near points of service in a cafeteria. Certain menus may be designed for leisurely reading, while others should be designed for the patron who has limited time. Avoid cluttered or long menus that annoy patrons. The menu should be sufficiently large to be handled but not so large as to make it difficult to hold and read. Avoid fine print. Maintain levels of light so menus can be easily read. Main food items should stand out, with accompanying foods listed so the relationship is evident. Large and small type, indentations, boldface and italics in print, and variation in spacing should be used to give emphasis and simplify reading and interpretation. Do not list items single-spaced in a column, as this makes for difficult reading. Some authorities state that one-fourth to one-third of the menu should be blank space. If clip-ons are used, do not cover essential material with them. The paper on which the menu is printed should be stiff enough to hold firm while the patron is reading. Glazed paper will soil less. Unglazed paper may be enclosed in transparent stiff material.

Ideas for writing menus may be gained from studying the menus of others. Set up an evaluation score sheet and ask yourself: "Does the menu sell? Why? Is it simple to read? Why? Does it present food items properly?" and so forth. While simplified menus reduce food production requirements, eliminate waste, and minimize carry-overs, inventories, and capital involved, they must be constructed with care. Patrons must be satisfied with the limited number of offerings. Set up a check list to see that variety is obtained: Do you offer a beef item? Poultry? Fish? Non-meat item? Are vegetables and salads included? and so forth.

No hard and fast rules can be given for the writing of a menu. There are many variations and most are acceptable. The following rules may be helpful in setting some standards:

1. Capitalize all words except articles, prepositions, and descriptive material.

2. Arrange the foods in the order in which they are eaten in a meal or course.

3. Give consideration to symmetry and form. Group foods within a course together. Utilize space and print-size differentiation between main items of a course or between courses to assist in rapid comprehension.

4. The main item of a course or meal should be given the most prominent place (usually at the left). Accompaniments, in smaller print, should follow or be placed directly below, such as:

    Prospector's Stew with Parsley Dumplings......................................$1.35
    *(Selection of salad or juice, roll and butter, beverage,
    and dessert)*

5. Condiments, butter, cream, sugar, and similar items are not listed on the menu unless they are something special or unless it is desirable to remind those in charge of production and service that these items accompany the meal and should be served.

6. Use accurate descriptions and develop key words for identification of items. Unless the clientele knows the meaning of foreign words or phrases, do not use them.

7. Specialties, sandwiches, or other items may be listed in a separate group on the menu.

8. Do not arrange items by order of price. The first food of a group is more frequently selected than others providing it has the same degree of popularity as the other dishes offered. Place at the top the

item you want to sell.

Some of the most commonly used menu terms will be found in the glossary of this text, but no attempt has been made to be all-inclusive. References included in the bibliography may be consulted for a more complete list.

THE STANDARDIZED RECIPE

While the menu authorizes production and sets in motion activities which culminate in the production of foods, the standardized recipe *controls* production. No factory begins manufacture of a product until blueprints, purchase specifications, labor force, equipment use, materials, and methods of manufacture are set forth in detail. The standardized recipe is to the food service what these are to the other manufacturer. A standardized recipe produces a known quantity of food of a desired quality. It gives production control to management, who must be responsible for it. The standardized recipe also assists in eliminating human failure, and over a period of time it will give greater standardization of quality, quantity, and cost.

Three files of standardized recipes should be maintained: the master file in the manager's office, another file in the production supervisor's office, and a file of foods produced in each production section. To reduce soiling from handling of the latter, place the recipes in plastic cases.

Recipe Content

The lower the skill of the employee, the more information must be given to obtain a satisfactory product. Usually a recipe contains:

1. Name of food item and its file code.
2. Total quantity produced and number of portions of stated size obtained.
3. Ingredients by weight and measure, sometimes by count.
4. Procedures and times for combining ingredients.
5. Cooking or baking temperatures.
6. Times for cooking or baking.
7. Panning information.
8. Cost information.
9. Standard of quality expected.
10. Total and production time.

The name should be brief and descriptive and one that leads to immediate recognition. Place recipes on different-colored cards to assist in identification: entrees on white, breads on green, cakes on blue, for instance. State total quantities produced in terms related to portion size. Information such as "Yield: 192 portions, total weight 26 lb, scale 18 by 26 inch baking sheets 6½ lb each" relates well to the portion desired: "Portion: 3 by 3 inches square (2 oz), cut each pan 6 by 8". Portions may be stated in several ways, such as by count, size, weight, volume, or portioning tool used (such as "Portion: one No. 12 scoop rounded").

List ingredients on the recipe in the order used. State prepreparation procedures first. There is nothing so exasperating as to find in the middle of preparation that an item to be used should have been soaked 30 minutes before use. Precisely define ingredients, for there are many types. Do not say "season to taste" but indicate precisely quantities of seasoning to use; it is correct, however, to state "taste for correctness of seasoning." Give exact weight, measure, and sometimes count. It is usually preferable to scale rather than measure; scaling is more accurate and takes less time. State measures in full, not part, capacity. For instance, write "three cups", not "3/4 quart." Sirups, melted fat or oil, and many other fluids are best measured. Coat the inside of a measure lightly with oil to assist in emptying out thick liquids. Pour, do not dip, thick fluids into a measure. To obtain a full liquid measure see that liquids reach the measure mark at the edge and not at the center of the measure. Use methods that save time. Cutting a pound of butter into equal halves will give one cup in each half. Memorize volume and weight tables. Know common equivalents such as "16 T equals 1 c," "2 c equals 1 pt" and so forth. Dry ingredients are usually scaled and then sifted together. Scale small ingredients first and then the heavier ones; for best accuracy, scale items separately, especially those used in small quantity. If dry items must be measured, fill the measure lightly until overflowing, tap gently, and then level off. Some items may have to be sifted before measuring, such as flour; others are never sifted

BECHAMEL SAUCE   O. SAUCES No. 14

YIELD: 2 Gallons or 100 Portions				EACH PORTION: 1/4 Cup
INGREDIENTS	WEIGHTS	MEASURES	PORTIONS	METHOD
Stock, white........	....	1 1/2 gal.......	....	1. Cook together 20 minutes. Strain. There should be 4 quarts of liquid.
Onion, sliced........	2 oz............	1/4 cup........	....	
Carrots, chopped	1/2 lb............	1 1/2 cups......	....	
Bay leaves...........	....	2 leaves.......	....	
Butter, melted......	1 lb.............	2 cups.........	....	2. Blend butter and flour. Stir into strained stock.
Flour, sifted.........	1 lb.............	4 cups.........	....	
Milk, hot.............	....	1 gal..........	....	3. Add hot milk, salt, and pepper. Stir and cook until thick and blended.
Salt....................	1/2 oz...........	1 tbsp.........	....	
Pepper................	....	1 tsp..........	....	
Pepper, red..........	....	few grains...	....	

NOTE: 1. For a yellow sauce, stir the sauce into beaten yolks of 16 eggs.
   2. Serve with meat croquettes.

FIG. 1-12   An example of a good recipe form.

before measuring, such as dry milk, leavening agents, and sugar. Roll or heat brown sugar gently in an oven to remove the lumps. Pack brown sugar lightly into the measure until the sugar holds its shape. Ingredients that pack, such as baking powder, graham flour, and dry milk solids, should be lightly stirred before measuring. To measure by spoon or small measure, dip the measure into the container, heaping it without packing; then level off. Partial quantities of a teaspoon or tablespoon should be measured by using the correct measure, for it is difficult to divide small measures accurately. A pinch usually represents about 1/16 teaspoon. When measuring or scaling cannot be used, count is permissible, but is not recommended as a general practice. Avoid using count for eggs. Use volume and weight instead.

In procedures for handling ingredients, leave little to individual interpretation. Check your writing to see that it is clear and complete. Use terms which define precisely the type of manipulation desired, such as "fold" rather than "stir" if blending must include the preservation of a delicate foam. Mixing or baking times should be stated exactly. Time in baking or in cooking should be calculated from the time the oven comes up to proper temperature or the food begins to cook. Descriptions of how items should appear during different stages of production are helpful. Yields may vary on some foods because of variable preparation or cooking losses. This frequently cannot be avoided. It is therefore best to state quantities to use in a state as close to final use as possible. Giving EP rather than AP weight is preferred, but giving both is sometimes even more helpful.

Recipe Format

The form used in presenting a recipe should be that which gives the required information in the simplest and most practical manner. Some rules frequently followed are:

1. Select an arrangement that sets off clearly all essential information. Use large print to set off special directions. Use space arrangements to give emphasis. Use lines to separate groups of ingredients which are handled or treated together in procedures. Do not crowd.

2. Use 5 by 8 or 6 by 8 inch cards.

3. Center title at top, and place filing or index information to right of this at edge of card.

4. Below title on right-hand side, list portion size.

5. On left-hand side opposite portion size, list total yield and number of portions obtained.

6. List panning instructions below portioning information or at bottom of recipe.

7. State first the work that is done in advance.

8. List ingredients on the left-hand side in order of use. Put methods for combining ingredients on the right-hand side. Between these, list weights and measures. Count may be indicated beneath or beside measure in parentheses. Do not use abbreviations in methods. Number methods in sequence and arrange them opposite ingredients used.

9. Provide extra columns for increasing weights and measures when calculating batch size.

WORK SHEET FOR RECIPE STANDARDIZATION

RECIPE FOR (Name of Item)_____WORK ORDER NO._____

TESTED BY_____ DATE_____ APPROVED BY_____DATE_____

COSTED BY_____DATE_____CHECKED BY_____DATE_____

PRODUCTION RECIPE PREPARED BY_____DATE_____FIRST SERVED (date)_____

FOOD INGREDIENTS USED	WEIGHT AND/OR MEASURE For (Portions) (number) (Gallons) ( ) (other)	A/P or E/P	PRO-CEDURE No. (See back of this sheet for detailed procedure)	UNIT A/P	COST PER UNIT A/P	COST OF QUANTITY OF INGREDIENT USED IN THIS RECIPE
TOTAL COST OF FOOD USED						

FOOD PRODUCTION RECAPITULATION

YIELD: Weight and/or Measure_____Lbs_____oz,_____(Gallons) PORTIONS: No.____ Size:_____
                                                                                                    (No.) (Unit)

PANS: No. Counter pans (size:____"x____"x____")____Wt/pan____lbs____Oz No. Portions/pan_____

COST: Portion $____Selling Price/Portion $____Food Cost Percent (Cost/Portion) _____%
                                                                      (Selling Price)

FIG. 1-13 (a) Calculation of labor time may be one of the most significant factors in controlling costs in any operation. The three forms shown here have been helpful to many operations in obtaining such cost information. (Courtesy Mr. Jack Welch, University of Missouri Extension)

10. List pan sizes and quantities placed in each in scaling information. State any portioning information desired.

11. Follow the recipe at the bottom with notes and variations. Use the following as a guide for writing notes or variations:

    When only one:

    NOTE: Substitute 2 lb honey for 2 lb karo..

    VARIATION: Add 3 lb sugar instead of 2 lb honey........................

    When more than one:

    NOTE: 1. Substitute 2 lb honey for 2 lb karo...........................

    2. Add 1 oz baking powder instead of...........................

    VARIATION: 1. Add 3 lb sugar instead of 2 lb honey........................

    2. Add 5 lb shredded coconut for...........................

12. Write all abbreviations for weight and measure in the singular, such as: 4 qt, 3 gal, 2½ lb, 5 oz, except that *cups* may be written out and pluralized if more than one cup is indicated.

PROCEDURES USED

No.	PROCEDURE	TIME (Min.)	EMPLOYEE (Class No.)

REMARKS · OBSERVATIONS · RECOMMENDATIONS

FIG. 1-13 (b)

13. Do not put periods after abbreviations except for inches (in.) and number (No.).

14. Use t and T for teaspoon and tablespoon respectively.

15. Use 8 to 10 min or 8 by 10 in., not 8-10.

16. Use No. 10 can or No. 2 can instead of #10 or #2.

17. It is preferable to capitalize for emphasis rather than to underline.

18. All substitutions for ingredients and consequent changes in procedure should be included under notes.

19. Capitalize AP, EP and AS for *as purchased, edible portion* and *as served* respectively.

20. For shell eggs use this form:

Eggs, whole	1 lb	1 pt
		(10 eggs)

21. Many forms of milk are used in quantity food preparation. To simplify recipe construction quote all milk in usable liquid form. Then, if dry, evaporated, or whole milk are used, these can be brought to a liquid form by consulting the proper tables of equivalents.

    Milk, liquid, whole   8 lb   1 gal

22. Allow space on the card at the bottom or reverse side for instructions on garnishing, serving, holding time, storing, or use of the food as a carry-over. Indicate at the bottom that other information is to be found on the other side by using: (over); it is oftentimes preferable, however, to use a new card rather than the back.

LABOR COST RECAPITULATION				
OPERATION	TIME (min.)	EMPLOYEE (Class No.)	RATE (Hr.)	LABOR COST
ASSEMBLY OF MATERIALS AND EQUIPMENT REQUIRED				
PRE-PREPARATION OF FOODS (Washing, peeling, cutting, etc.				
FINAL PREPARATION OF FOODS (Mixing, cooking, baking, etc.				
GARNITURE AND/OR PORTIONING				
SERVICE				
DEAD TIME (Watching and waiting)				
TOTAL DIRECT TIME AND LABOR COST		XXXXXXXXXXXX		
OVERHEAD AND MANAGEMENT (%)				
TOTAL LABOR COST OF RECIPE				

LABOR COST/PORTION $_____LABOR COST: PERCENTAGE (Labor Cost/Portion)_____%
                                                        (Selling Price)
FOOD PLUS LABOR COSTS/PORTION $_____FOOD PLUS LABOR COSTS: PERCENT_____%

RECIPE REVIEW DATE_____

FIG. 1-13   (c)

Recipe Costing

Recipe costing is frequently as essential an operation as is testing for quality. There are many methods used. Figures 1-13a, 1-13b, and 1-13c illustrate one recommended method.[5] Figure 1-13a is used to calculate cost of ingredients, while Figure 1-13b summarizes procedures used and time spent by specific employees in accomplishing work. Figure 1-13c summarizes the cost of labor. Production time, as defined earlier, would be included in Figure 1-13c, the first four categories under "operation" up to time of service. To obtain total time, keep a record of the time each employee begins and ends work. This will include watching and waiting time, time foods are in equipment while the worker does other tasks, and so forth.

Most authorities recommend that in recipe costing, costs be calculated to the nearest $\frac{1}{2}\phi$, any cost less than $\frac{1}{4}\phi$ be omitted. Some omit seasoning costs and add the per cent that the total cost of seasonings purchased in a year is to total food cost of that year to the cost of the product. Thus, if 2% of the total food cost per year is for seasonings, the total ingredient cost of a recipe would be increased 2% for seasoning. Some operations avoid frequent recalculation of costs by increasing or lowering costs by the percentage the food index moves up or down. Most authorities recommend review of recipe costs every six months.

The selling price for a food can be calculated from these food and labor costs. By adding to the labor-plus-food cost of a portion of food or a meal (1) the profit desired, (2) fixed costs as a percentage of sales, and (3) semi-variable costs as a percentage of sales, a selling price is obtained. For instance, if food cost is 30ϕ and labor cost is 26ϕ, the labor-plus-food cost is 56ϕ. If the current profit and loss statement indicates that (1) fixed costs are 10% of sales, (2) semi-variable costs, other than labor, are also 10% of sales, and (3) you desire a net profit of 10%, the following calculation is made: 56ϕ plus 10% (fixed costs) plus 10% (semi-variable costs) plus 10% (profit) equals 100%; or 56ϕ equals 100% minus 10% (fixed costs) minus 10% (semi-variable costs) minus 10% (profit); or 56ϕ equals 70%, and 100% (selling price) equals $\dfrac{\$0.56}{.70}$ or \$0.80. It is now also possible to calculate the food cost from this selling price; in this instance it is $37\frac{1}{2}\%$ and the labor cost is $32\frac{1}{2}\%$.

Recipe Development

New ideas for recipes may come from many sources. Keep a file of recipe

[5]Examples taken from Journal Series Paper No. 2362, John M. Welch, Agricultural Economist, University of Missouri.

UNITED FRUIT and FOOD CORP.

30 ST. JAMES AVE., — BOSTON 16, MASS.

TECHNOLOGICAL EXAMINATION

NAME——————————————————— DATE——————————— 19———

ITEM———————————————————————

COLOR									
ODOR									
FLAVOR									
TEXTURE									
APPEARANCE									
SAMPLE NUMBER	EXTREMELY POOR	VERY POOR	POOR	BELOW FAIR ABOVE POOR	FAIR	BELOW GOOD ABOVE FAIR	GOOD	VERY GOOD	EXCELLENT

ITEM———————————————————————

COLOR									
ODOR									
FLAVOR									
TEXTURE									
APPEARANCE									
SAMPLE NUMBER	EXTREMELY POOR	VERY POOR	POOR	BELOW FAIR ABOVE POOR	FAIR	BELOW GOOD ABOVE FAIR	GOOD	VERY GOOD	EXCELLENT

REMARKS:

FIG. 1-14 An example of a judging sheet that makes possible later statistical evaluation of scores. (Courtesy United Fruit and Food Corporation)

SCORE SHEET

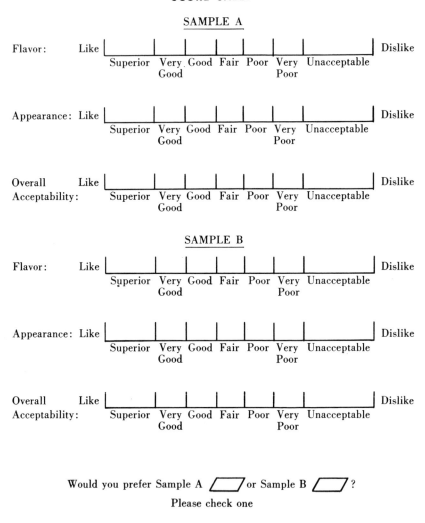

SAMPLE A

Flavor: Like |__|__|__|__|__|__|__|__| Dislike
              Superior Very Good Fair Poor Very Unacceptable
                      Good   Poor

Appearance: Like |__|__|__|__|__|__|__|__| Dislike
              Superior Very Good Fair Poor Very Unacceptable
                      Good   Poor

Overall   Like |__|__|__|__|__|__|__|__| Dislike
Acceptability: Superior Very Good Fair Poor Very Unacceptable
                      Good   Poor

SAMPLE B

Flavor: Like |__|__|__|__|__|__|__|__| Dislike
              Superior Very Good Fair Poor Very Unacceptable
                      Good   Poor

Appearance: Like |__|__|__|__|__|__|__|__| Dislike
              Superior Very Good Fair Poor Very Unacceptable
                      Good   Poor

Overall   Like |__|__|__|__|__|__|__|__| Dislike
Acceptability: Superior Very Good Fair Poor Very Unacceptable
                      Good   Poor

Would you prefer Sample A ☐ or Sample B ☐ ?
Please check one

Samples of the products we are testing today have been prepared by two different methods. Your help in filling out this questionnaire will aid our evaluation of these methods. Please indicate your appraisal of the three characteristics — flavor, appearance, and overall acceptability — of *both* samples A and B by checking the appropriate box. Then please check whether, all factors considered, you would prefer sample A or B.

FIG. 1-15 An evaluation sheet for use in comparing an experimental food with a control. This type of score sheet also lends itself to later statistical evaluation of scores.

ideas that seem practical and desirable. All food services need new recipes and every operation also needs constantly to revise old recipes. New foods, improved ingredients, and new equipment are constantly appearing on the market, making it necessary to make changes. Cost requirements make it desirable to check recipes frequently for possible savings. Progress and efficiency are achieved by instituting a good recipe development program. This is as essential to success of a food service as is development of a new-model car for an automobile manufacturer.

Recipe development is not a matter of merely checking quality or of increasing or decreasing quantities by mathematical calculation. A great deal of technical knowledge of how foods perform in quantity preparation must be applied to create a new product. It requires painstaking laboratory experimentation, testing, careful thought, and study. High standards and a creative imagination are required. It is necessary to have the ability to write clearly and simply. A product has to be visualized as it goes through production, and adequate information must be given to workers so production problems and employee mistakes can be avoided. Everything essential for proper production must be stated. A good sense of taste is required. There are subtle differences in flavors, and the experienced person with taste acuity will select those that are most pleasing and true. Combining foods so flavors are compatible is an art. One should not only remember flavors during a taste test but be able to carry them always in mind as a standard to evaluate other flavors. An accurate knowledge of what customers are apt to like or dislike is required. Too frequently the foods that appear on the menu are what the chef, or the manager, or someone else in authority likes.

Remember that cold foods must be more highly seasoned than hot foods, for flavors are not as prominent in cold foods as in hot. Flavor judgment is not only a matter of physiological competence or sense acuity but also a matter of experience. We have four sets of taste buds in our mouth: salt, bitter, sweet, and sour. These are properly called tastes and are located in small oval fields around the edge of the tongue and in a large, V-shaped field at the back of the tongue. The center of the tongue lacks taste buds. To taste, flavors must be dissolved in saliva, which flows into the pockets of the papillae, the bumpy pimples which cover the surface of the tongue. Sweet tastes are detected at the tip of the tongue, salty on either side of the sweet tasting buds, sour on the sides of the tongue at the back, and bitter in the V-shaped field of taste buds on the back of the tongue. Other sensory endings report on the texture and temperature of the food. A flavor is a combination of any of these four basic tastes and aroma. Most food has some odor, and sensory organs in the nose detect it. Aromas combined with

LABORATORY REPORT

Name_____Date_____

                                        Yield_____

Name of Product_____No. of Servings_____

Cooking Temperature and Time_____Preparation Time_____

Preparation Processes Used: Major Equipment Used:

Was Product Completed_____
                        (If not, list stage of completion)

Score Product   APPEARANCE   QUALITY

	Color	Form	Size	Arrangement	Odor	Flavor	Texture or Consistency
Excellent							
Good							
Fair							
Below Standard							

(If product scores less than excellent, list reasons:)

ORGANIZATION OF WORK: (Constructive Criticism)

(Use Other Side)

FIG. 1-16   An evaluation sheet for use in a quantity food laboratory where students produce food and evaluate it before sending it to service.

basic tastes, texture, and temperature make up flavor. The ability to evaluate flavor can be developed, and an educated taster is one who has learned to differentiate and identify the many flavors that exist in foods.

Tastes can be balanced and modified. Salt will subdue the taste of excessive sweetness, bitterness, or tartness. At the same time, it will assist in bringing out the subtle flavors of other ingredients that would have been masked by the excessive sweetness, bitterness, or tartness of the product. Sugar will in a similar manner subdue certain flavors and bring out others. A small quantity of sugar added to vegetables or a meat sauce will smooth out and blend flavors together. Only true flavors should be acceptable. Texture affects acceptability. Greasy soup, rubbery pie filling, overcooked meat, or soggy griddle cakes will be unpalatable because of undesirable

Material and Specifications	Recipe Quant.	Correc- tions	Gross Quant.	Unit Cost	Total Cost

FIG. 1-17   One form used by a production department to test recipes.

texture. Appearance, adequacy of portion, and other factors should also be judged. Score sheets should be used listing the factors to be judged. Remember that taste buds fatigue easily and it is not usually wise to taste more than six samples at any one time without resting for some time between tests. Judging should be done in a quiet room. Lighting is important and natural light or the conditions under which the food is consumed should be provided.

Frequently products are judged by a group or panel and not by one individual. Select the panel members carefully. They should possess good food standards and know something about quantity food production and how food is served in the operation. Have the panel include both men and women. Non-smokers usually have more taste acuity, but if an otherwise desirable judge does not smoke for two hours before a test, he may regain

SCORE SHEET FOR JUDGING VEGETABLES

Type of Vegetable————————————Judge————————————————

Date————————————————————

	Maximum Score	Score
Exterior Appearance	20	
Regular, unbroken, even-shaped pieces		
Correct size		
Good color, bright, even, clear, fresh; not dull, pale		
or muddy		
Proper moistness; not dry, watery, or shriveled		
Interior		
Texture: tender, slightly crisp, very crisp, mushy,	30	
stringy, tough, woody, hard		
Good color		
Palatability	45	
Flavor: pleasant, true, not lacking in flavor, raw or		
strong; well-seasoned, not burned		
Temperature proper		
Portion		
Adequacy of portion	5	
Attractiveness of serving	——	
	100	

FIG. 1-18   An example of a score sheet used to judge vegetables.

taste acuity. Colds, emotional disturbance, fatigue, a weakened sense of smell, or other factors may cause an otherwise competent judge to lose taste acuity, so all members of a panel will not be expert tasters at every test. Use methods to ascertain this temporary loss. Allow those that fail to pass to take the test and then eliminate their judgments for that test, but do not inform them of this fact. Build confidence in your judges. Use judges of different ages. Elderly people may still retain good taste sense, which, coupled with experience, makes them good judges. Eating two hours or later before tasting usually dulls the palate, and 11:30 AM and 4:30 PM have been found to be times when individuals possess highest taste acuity. Alcohol dulls the palate.

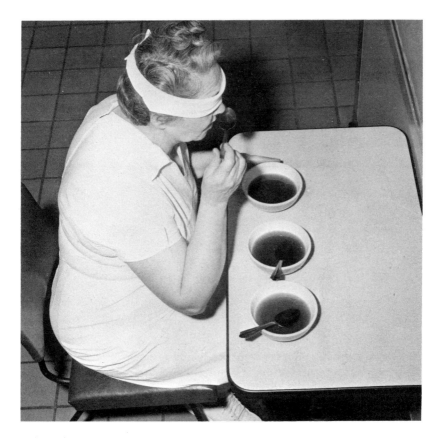

FIG. 1-19   Here an expert judge takes a blindfold test in an attempt to distinguish flavor differences in a food. Appearance in this case would indicate the difference.

Testing Recipes

Before testing a recipe, study it. Certain well-defined ratios are required in ingredients to make a successful product; adjust these if the ratio is not correct. Check the procedure to ascertain if the organization and sequence of work is correct and to reduce labor. Simplify, rearrange, combine, or eliminate. Why not use the dump method for making a cake? Why not blend flour with the sugar and eliminate making a milk and flour slurry? Why not combine all dry ingredients and all liquids and then blend? Why grease pans? Would not a new type of ingredient do as well?

If you wish to change the yield in a recipe, this should be done without a change in quality. Adjustment of ingredient ratios or methods in quantity

FIG. 1-20   A group of experts taste a food sample.

food production are frequently necessary to obtain the desired number of portions. Slight imbalances in a small quantity recipe may not show up until a large quantity is prepared, or cooking reactions may differ in small and large quantity preparation. Frequently we fail to realize that our quantity equipment and ingredients differ considerably from those used in the home, and for quantity work adjustments must be made in small quantity recipes to secure parallel results. A mass of food cooked in a steam-jacketed kettle must be handled differently from a batch in a small stewing pan. Yields may vary, too, because evaporative losses may differ as the mass of the food or the surface area vary.

After thoroughly checking the recipe, write it up for testing. Test first in the smallest quantity possible and judge the standard. Note all factors carefully in writing, for this may be helpful in subsequent tests. Obtain total yield and number of portions. Make changes on the recipe card in colored pencil. Then rewrite the recipe and, if required, test again. When you are satisfied with results, increase the recipe and test again, and repeat until desired yield and quality are obtained.

Losses in prepreparation, preparation, baking or cooking, and holding or serving should be considered and adjustment made in setting up final quantities for purchase, prepreparation, preparation, panning, and serving weights. To obtain pan weight, multiply the portion size by the number of portions desired from the pan. Casserole dishes will lose around 5% in baking; a 4% additional evaporation loss will usually occur in holding for

Current Grade Sheet on Laboratory Work _____Hall

Names					
Ability to work with others					
Ability to learn new skills					
Attitude toward criticism					
Efficiency — time and energy					
Initiative					
Interest in work					
Methods of cooking					
Personal neatness					
Punctuality					
Responsibility					
Standards of cleanliness and order					
Skills required					
Successful products					
Average					

To determine average:

A — 4
B — 3
C — 2
D — 1

Dietitian _____

Date _____

FIG. 1-21 An assignment sheet used to place students in quantity food units so that they can gain practical experience.

service, and serving losses have been found to run for all types of foods from 0 to 8%. Potatoes may lose 27% of their AP weight in paring, then increase about 2 to 5% in steaming and lose 3 to 4% in holding for service. Roasts may shrink from 10 to 35%, slicing may lose 5%, and serving losses may be around 5%. Baking losses vary from 4 to 16%. Consider such losses in calculating final yields desired.

To change the yield of a recipe, convert all weights to ounces.[6] If possible, ingredients given by count or volume should also be changed to ounces. If this cannot be done, establish a factor for the change and multiply by this. Multiply the ounce weights by the change. The following example indicates how this might be done in increasing a recipe from 50 to 250 portions, or in making an increase of five times:

Coconut Drop Cookies

Ingredients	Columns				
	(1)	(2)	(3)	(4)	(5)
Milk, condensed	1½ c	17 oz	85 oz	7½ c	(2¾ qt)
Coconut, shredded	1 lb	16 oz	80 oz	5 lb	(7½ lb)
Vanilla	1 T	½ oz	2½ oz	⅓ c	(½ c)
Nuts, chopped	8 oz	8 oz	40 oz	2½ lb	(3¾ lb)

In the first column after ingredients, the weights or measures as they appear in the recipe are listed. Column two shows the conversion to ounces. Since the recipe is being increased from 50 to 250 portions, the ounces in column two are multipled by five and the result is shown in column three. Reconversion is made in column four to original values stated on the recipe card. Corrections for variations in weights or measures are made so that these are even and stated in meaningful values. If the cookies were to be scaled at three-fourths of an ounce instead of a half ounce, the recipe would have to be increased one-half again. The quantities required to make this scaling weight change are shown in column five in parentheses. Testing of the final quantities should be done to check yield and quality of product.

Before using a new recipe, go over essential points with the worker who will make the product. If necessary, set up a work sheet for recording weights and measures, mixing or manipulation times, mixer speeds, type and size of tools and equipment used, and baking or cooking temperatures and times. Leave space for comments or observations. Evaluate the product with the worker or workers who have done the work. Gaining acceptance from workers is essential to success in recipe development. Methods which yield better products and make work easier go a long way in winning worker

[6]For those who work consistently with recipe calculations, see direct reading tables in appendix.

FOOD LABORATORY ASSIGNMENT

Name_____

You are to report to_____to perform
the following assignment:

Time of Reporting:_____

Date_____

Job Title_____

Your assigned duties_____

_____

_____

_____

Student Signature_____No. of hours of production_____

Comment_____
                                        Supervisor

FIG. 1-22   An example of an evaluation sheet used to judge the work done
in actual operating units by students in a quantity food class.

Table 1-1

Approximate Basic Proportions in Large Quantity Food Preparation

Item	Flour*	Liquid	Fat	Eggs	Sugar	Salt	Baking Powder**	Other Ingredients
BEVERAGES								
Cocoa		1 gal milk			6 to 8 oz			4 to 6 oz (1 to 1¼c) cocoa or 4 to 8 oz Choc.
Coffee		2 ½ gal						1 lb (1 qt) coffee
Tea		1 gal						1 oz (⅓ c)
BREADS								
Baking powder biscuits	1 lb	1⅓-1½ c	4 oz			1½ to 2 t	1 oz	
Griddle cakes	1 lb	3 to 4 c	2 to 3 oz	2	2 to 2½ oz	1 to 1½ t	¾ to 1 oz	
Muffins	1 lb	1½ to 2 c	2 to 4 oz	2	2 to 4 oz	1 to 1½ t	¾ to 1 oz	
Popover (pour batter)	1 lb	1 qt				1 to 1½ t		
Yeast breads	1 lb (bread)	1⅓ c	0 to 1 oz		¾ to 1½ oz	½ to 1 t		⅓ oz compressed yeast (varies)
CAKES								
Butter	1 lb (cake)	2 c	6 to 8 oz	2 to 4	1 to 1¼ lb	1 t	½ to ¾ oz	Flavoring
Pound	1 lb	0 to ½ c	¾ to 1 lb	1 lb	1 to 1¼ lb	1 to 1½ t		Flavoring
Angel	1 lb (cake)			1 to 1¼ lb (whites)	2 lb 9 oz	½ to 1 t		1T cream of tartar and flavoring
Sponge	1 lb (cake)	2 t		2 lb 6½ oz	1½ lb	½ to 1 t	0 to 2 t	
Cream Puffs (choux paste)	1 lb	1 qt	1 lb	1½ lb		1 t		Flavoring

*all-purpose unless stated otherwise   **double-acting

Table 1-1 (cont.)
Approximate Basic Proportions in Large Quantity Food Preparation

Item	Flour	Liquid	Fat	Eggs	Sugar	Salt	Baking Powder**	Other Ingredients
Doughnuts	1 lb	1 c	1 oz	2	8 oz	1 t	¾ oz	Flavoring
Pie dough	1 lb	½ to ¾ c	11 oz			1 t		
Cereal (hot)	1 lb	1 gal				1 T		
Macaroni, spaghetti, noodles, etc.	1 lb	1 gal				1 T		
Rice	1 lb	½ gal				½ to ¾ T		½ c Oil
Custards		1 gal			1¼ lb	2 t		Flavoring and 1 lb dry milk if water used as liquid
(Eggs as thickening agents—4 to 6 whole eggs, 8 to 12 yolks, or 10 to 16 whites per qt of liquid)								
Cornstarch pudding (Blanc Mange)		1 gal		3 c	1 lb	2 t		7 oz cornstarch Flavoring and 1 lb dry milk
SAUCES OR GRAVIES								
Thin	4 oz	1 gal	4 to 8 oz			2 T		1 lb dry milk***
Medium	8 oz	1 gal	½ to 1 lb			2 T		1 lb dry milk***
Thick (heavy)	1 lb	1 gal	1 to 1½ lb			2 T		1 lb dry milk***

* all-purpose unless stated otherwise

** double-acting

*** cream sauce only

Basic flour to liquid ratios	Measure	Weight
Pour batter (popovers, etc.)	1:1	1:2
Drop batter (cakes, muffins)	2:1	1:1
Soft dough (biscuit, dumplings, yeast rolls)	3:1	1½:1
Stiff dough (pie dough, cookies)	4:1	2:1

approval. Enlisting workers' cooperation will rouse their interest and enthusiasm for this work. Tell workers the aims, give them responsibility and credit for the work done, and they will quickly accept a recipe development program. Work at the same time through the heads of departments. The chef, head baker, head pantry worker, and supervisors should be close to the program, and their ideas and suggestions should receive consideration. Be sure to define standards of the product desired with all workers. New recipes may be introduced at group meetings or classes and employees given a chance to judge the new product.

Suggested laboratory experiences or work assignments for Chapter 1:
1. Set up an organization chart for a specific type of operation.
2. Write a menu and schedule employees for its production; give work to other class members for a critique.
3. Standardize and cost a recipe, obtaining also the selling price.
4. Calculate yields required from AP, EP, and AS.
5. Increase and decrease yield in a recipe.
6. Demonstrate proper methods for scaling and measuring foods.
7. Set up various types of service and discuss service requirements for different foods.
8. Set up a taste panel and evaluate a recipe that is being developed.

2 Work Methods

Achievement of satisfactory quality and cost in quantity food production will be affected substantially by the way the work is done. Much of this work must be done by hand. While many other industries have found ways to reduce labor through the use of machines, the food service industry has not been able to do likewise, either because too few units are produced or because machines are lacking which duplicate the worker skills required. The food service industry's products therefore carry a higher percentage of labor cost in their selling price than those of most other industries. While the food service industry employs more people than any other, it ranks as one of the poorest in utilizing worker effort. On the average, a worker in quantity food production produces 45% of the time, wasting or resting the remaining 55%. Good productivity should be 80 to 85%. Poor work planning, lack of training or skills, and the use of poor work methods are the main factors contributing to this low worker efficiency. Maintaining high labor productivity should be an important management objective in quantity food production.

PLANNING WORK

Two types of work planning must be done in order to obtain good worker productivity. Some aspects of the first type have been discussed in the preceding chapter. Management must adequately organize and plan for the work to be done; failure to do so may result in low productivity in spite of good worker effort. If materials are not ordered for proper arrival time, if production requirements are not clearly established, if production is not co-ordinated between different production sections and service, and if many other responsibilities of management are not carried out, then the worker contends with this failure and loses efficiency because of it.

Management also has the responsibility for providing a properly

(a)

(b)

(c)

(d)   (e)

FIG. 2-1   Mobile equipment makes work easier. (a) Foods protected by plastic wraps are easily transported when placed on carts. (b) Transport foods on inexpensive dollies, such as this, from the storeroom to work areas. (c) Equipment when mobile may be rolled out of the way when not required, as was this toaster. (d) On the average, women should not lift more than 35 pound loads and men 50. (e) Mobility in this scrubbing machine makes for lower labor costs.

planned layout and adequate equipment, tools, and materials to do the job.[1]
Too frequently management criticizes workers for their lack of productivity
when the real fault rests with management for not providing adequate facilities to achieve a satisfactory production standard. Equipment should be
grouped around the worker so that he becomes an island surrounded by
his equipment. If placement of equipment is correct, work will proceed
smoothly in proper sequence without backtracking or crisscrossing. Work
tables, sinks, and refrigerators should be within easy reach of the worker,
thus eliminating travel. Equipment should be near at hand during all phases
of production. For instance, in the pantry the sink should be easily available
for prepreparation, assembly, and clean-up, and refrigerators should be available for storage during any sequence of production. Space should be adequate for production needs; equipment should be appropriate in size for
the work to be accomplished. Production needs may vary, and production
for banquets and parties may be severely hampered by a failure to provide
enough space and equipment. Flexibility must be incorporated into the work
units, and mobile equipment may assist in providing it. See that work
heights are correct and that floors give good footing and comfort. Provide
good light. Fifty to 100 foot-candles is frequently recommended for work
areas. Quiet increases the productivity of workers; so do well-controlled
heat and humidity.

Assistance in good work organization, such as providing means for
keeping orders in proper sequence, will encourage higher worker productivity; so will providing workers with the right tools in proper condition.
Real concern and attention on the part of management to providing workers
with the facilities they need to do the work will pay off.

Storage, handling of foods, tools, and utensils, and transfers in production need study. Plan for one-motion storage. Send pots and pans to the
units where they will be used rather than to a central storage. Store utensils
and foods at their points of first use. Arrange work so that the shortest
possible distance exists between storage and the place where the items are
used. Plan for temporary storage in work areas so as to eliminate travel to
central storage. Most food service operators provide only for dead storage,
but if storage space is used as an important sequential part of the entire production process, much higher productivity will be achieved. Conveyors or
mobile storage units should be used to reduce handling of dishes, materials,
and utensils. Production should be planned so that as work is done, the
movement of goods and the production sequence occur close together.

It is desirable to use modular equipment so that food transfers can

[1]See *Kotschevar and Terrell, Food Service Planning* (Wiley & Sons, 1961), for further
information on layout planning to achieve high worker productivity.

be minimized. If the same pan can be used for refrigerated storage, baking, and steam table use, work motions will be eliminated. See that the most frequently used items have preference in storage. Heavy items should be placed where body strain is avoided in securing and using them. Hunting and searching should be minimized by planning work and by fixing the placement of equipment, tools, and materials. Avoid storing unlike items in front of one another. Plan work so that the movement from mobile to stationary equipment is at the same level and so that items that are poured from tilting equipment pour directly into containers on carts. Many work areas should have adjustable shelving so they can be adapted to different storage requirements. Management should instruct workers in the basic principles of one-motion storage so they can learn to use layouts properly.[2]

The second type of planning that must be done to achieve a high rate of production is planning the job itself. Work done haphazardly without plan or organization obviously takes longer to do than work done according to plan. It is a joy to watch a skilled worker come onto his station and in a short time set up his day's work. There is a sequence to work that leads to high productivity, and efficient workers learn this sequence quickly. Proper preparation must occur so work will proceed easily without delay and, when the service peak arrives, orders will move out easily and methodically without confusion. The need for lining up work is especially great in units where many items are produced to order. A good broiler man or pantry worker who organizes properly aptly demonstrates the adage "Success comes with adequate preliminary preparation."

Immediately upon coming on shift, a good worker notes from the work schedule what he must do. He checks ahead on materials, tools, equipment, and other requirements. Ovens and other units are turned on so that they are at proper temperature. He knows his production times and organizes production so that foods are ready at peak quality when required. Soups, roasts, and other items which require long cooking are started first, and then other work is done. Some foods must be prepared ahead, others not. Cakes must be cool to be frosted, and gelatin mixtures must be given time to set, while hot breads, French fries, and other highly perishable items should come directly from production to service with no delay. Proper organization and planning make it possible to do tasks with minimum effort. It would be good organization, for example, to make a white butter cake first and a chocolate one next, avoiding the washing of the mixer in between. Workers should learn to clean up as they go, for clutter can cause confusion, poor quality products, and loss of time.

Lining up work is very important in units where production must be

²*Ibid.*, pp. 51–52.

fast, especially if the product is highly perishable and requires considerable handwork. In the pantry, salad and sandwich items should be brought as close to finished production as possible, consistent with good product quality. Salad items need to be sliced, cut, or prepared in the form required, juices should be poured, bread placed close at hand convenient for use, butter or margarine softened, and meat and cheese portioned and prestacked in crisscross fashion for quick pickup. In the broiler section, where items need time for cooking, it is essential that everything be done to speed the task so that customers are not kept waiting. Prepreparation and organization for work must be considered two of the most important aspects of most jobs in the kitchen. All tools, utensils, and materials should be placed within the normal or maximum work areas, depending upon use. The principles of motion economy need to be observed.

Teach workers to organize work efficiently, such as placing dirty pots and pans on mobile carts until they accumulate in a batch and can be moved at one time rather than carrying them singly to pot-washing sinks. Why have workers receive celery, lettuce, and other bulky fresh items which require prepreparation, move them into refrigeration, move them out again to the prepreparation unit, and then take them back into storage? Why not send them directly to the prepreparation unit and then to storage? Why not set up deliveries, work schedules, and production plans so that items are received and sent directly to the production unit, by-passing storage altogether?

TRAINING

The skills and knowledge required for quality food production must be learned, but many workers today have failed to do so. Job training is therefore necessary. Standardized recipes and good supervision will reduce some training requirements, but the establishment of a good training program can reduce supervisory needs and pay for itself in improved product quality and production. Training should be considered an essential adjunct to any program in order to increase worker productivity.

Training starts with the selection of good workers. Establish job specifications for the type of worker you want to do the job. Deftness and rapidity of movement are requirements in places where foods must be assembled rapidly, such as in the pantry or broiler section. Establish needs for each job, such as education, personality, ability to plan and organize, experience, and so forth, so that workers selected will have the talents and capabilities necessary to do the job. Good employee selection provides a good base upon which to build the skills and knowledge required to do a good job.

Written descriptions of the work to be done, called job descriptions, are helpful in introducing workers to jobs and orienting them quickly to requirements. Provide for training of inexperienced workers under the more experienced, but be sure that the training given is what you want. Poor work methods may be passed along to new workers by the older ones. Set up special training programs and provide an opportunity for workers to acquire knowledge and skills, even if some freedom from work must be given. Demonstrations, visual aids, and other practical devices may be used as teaching aids. On-the-job training is especially good if supervisors understand the basic principles of learning[3]. Frequent discussion with workers on food standards, work methods, and other factors of importance in achieving satisfactory production will improve job proficiency. Establish standards for worker performance, such as the number of items to be produced in a given time, and occasionally evaluate workers and let them know their ratings. Workers need to know what is expected of them and how well they are doing their jobs. Use job performance as a standard for promotion and wage increases. Future chapters will discuss production requirements for specific foods, and workers may be encouraged to read these to gain knowledge and standards for doing their jobs correctly.

An operation that spends time and effort to train an employee should realize the investment it has in that employee and attempt to retain him on the job. High employee turnover can be costly to any program that attempts to achieve higher productivity. It is important to train the trainers so that they can accomplish what management wishes in a training program.

IMPROVEMENT OF WORK METHODS

The job of making work easier to do in a shorter period of time has been given a number of names, but "work methods improvement" and "work simplification" are the two most commonly used. The study of improving jobs by indicating the proper arrangement of tools, equipment, and materials or by suggesting better work motions is the concern of the industrial engineer. He utilizes human effort and provides methods of working by which motions are made easy and rapid. Energy and time are conserved, and workers thus produce more with greater ease. The industrial engineer also plans rest in order to minimize fatigue.

The first step in improving a job is to take it apart and see how it is done. The industrial engineer identifies those parts of a job which are productive and those in which waste or rest occurs. He studies work methods to see how they may be changed, eliminated, combined, or rearranged to give greater production with less effort. The job is then replanned, avoiding unnecessary rest or waste. Body mechanics and limitations of the body in doing work are considered.

[3]See Standard Brands, *Tested Management Techniques*, "How to Train" and "How to Select Employees."

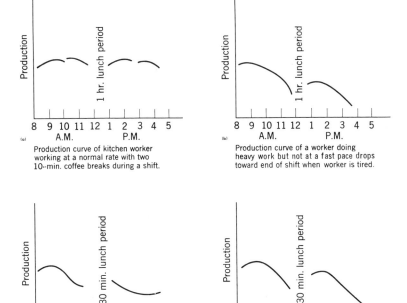

(a) Production curve of kitchen worker working at a normal rate with two 10-min. coffee breaks during a shift.

(b) Production curve of a worker doing heavy work but not at a fast pace drops toward end of shift when worker is tired.

(c) Production curve of a bored worker. Note how, when worker sees end of shift approaching, work production increases.

(d) Production curve of a worker doing heavy work at a fairly rapid pace.

FIG. 2-2 As workers tire, production drops. (a) Production is maintained by coffee breaks in the morning and afternoon. (b) Heavy work causes a significant drop in production as the shift continues. (c) The production curve of a bored worker, indicating mental rather than physical fatigue. (d) Heavy work done at a fairly rapid pace reduces output.

FIG. 2-3 Work smarter, not harder. On the left, the worker uses excess motion in preparing lettuce cups, while on the right the worker reduces effort by planning the work and
sitting down.

Work improvement, however, need not always be a formal job study by an engineer. An alert kitchen supervisor can watch a worker and frequently come up with suggestions for improving the job, especially if he knows some of the basic principles used in work methods improvement. Workers themselves may also note how improvements can be made and change work methods accordingly.

Fatigue

Fatigue is an enemy of production. As a worker tires, his production drops. Rest must be provided on all jobs if workers are to maintain satisfactory production. There are two types of fatigue: physical and mental.

Physical fatigue is that which occurs when muscular exertion causes a person to feel tired. Blood sugar or glucose, the sugar burned in creating energy, is used up in doing work. As its level runs low in the blood stream and metabolic wastes build up in the body, fatigue occurs. Rest rebuilds the supply of glucose and allows the waste metabolic products to be carried away. Eating some sweet food frequently gives a lift because sugars are rapidly absorbed into the blood stream. Coffee acts as a stimulant, causing the liver to free energy-giving compounds into the blood stream. Utilizing productive motions and eliminating waste motions or excessive body exertion will increase production by reducing energy requirements. Avoiding effort that causes a heavy drain of energy is desirable in doing work.

The second type of fatigue with which the industrial engineer deals is that which results from mental factors, or nerve fatigue. A worker, though not physically tired, may feel so. Such tiredness is thought to be a slowing down of nerve impulses, especially between nerve endings. Dislike of a job, noise, poor light, or boredom and other mental factors may cause this type of fatigue.

Rest

Three types of rest must be provided for workers to minimize fatigue. The first type of rest is that which must be given to muscles between work motions to allow a renewal of energy. The heart works continually but rests between beats. If motions are made too rapidly, energy cannot be renewed and the muscles tire. Highest productivity is achieved if an even, smooth, not too rapid pace is established. Rhythmic motions conserve energy. Workers should be encouraged to *work smarter, not harder.* The old adage "Life by the yard is apt to be hard, but life by the inch is more of a cinch" has fruitful meaning in doing work. The old story of the tortoise and the hare also illustrates the benefits of a steady pace, though it need not be overemphasized.

Workers differ as individuals, and work paces should be varied according to the worker and the work. Some workers have excess energy and like to burn some of it up by wasting it. Let them, for restricting them from doing so creates frustrations and mental fatigue. Teaching workers to conserve energy in doing work so that at the end of the day they still have a reserve left will assist in maintaining good production levels. A worker should feel tired during about one fifth of his shift, and most of this tiredness should come at the end of it. Teach workers to treat their energy like their paychecks, spending it carefully so they are not bankrupt before the next one comes along. Plan for rest periods. Studies have shown that if workers are not given rest, they take it anyway, but this rest is only half as beneficial in removing fatigue as authorized rest.

The second type of rest that must be provided workers is breaks, for after several hours of work, a worker's energy reserves become depleted and he needs to slow down. A longer rest period than just momentary pauses between work motions is now required. Short breaks of three to ten minutes after several hours can minimize this fatigue. Getting away from the job for a few minutes also gives a mental lift to the worker. Allowing a worker to go on working after this fatigue sets in and then giving additional rest to overcome the added fatigue is not advisable, for the rest required in proportion to added fatigue increases geometrically. A worker who gets doubly tired will require not twice as much rest when a break is given but perhaps four times as much, or more.

The third type of rest required is rest between shifts to rebuild interest and energy for job performance. Days off or vacations are necessary to achieve good productivity. Working overtime or too long without getting away from the job will cause a productivity drop. During the Battle of Britain in World War II, a 60-hour week was found to produce less than a 48-hour week in spite of high motivation among workers to produce more by working longer hours. Speed-up, working the best workers longer hours than they should, and other factors which may seem desirable may actually lower production.

Time

The standard usually used for measuring productivity is the number of units produced in a given time. Reducing the time required to produce a unit can increase productivity. Industrial engineers try to find ways to combine, rearrange, or eliminate motions in doing a job to reduce production time. They classify motions into finger, hand, arm, and body motions and attempt to accomplish work using the lowest classification of body movement possible. The finger can make a motion twice as fast as the hand, the

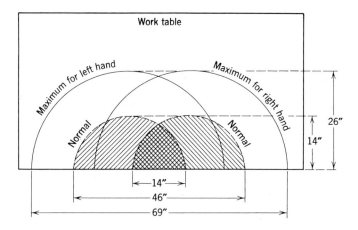

FIG. 2-4 Maximum and normal work areas for a man sitting (10% less for a woman).

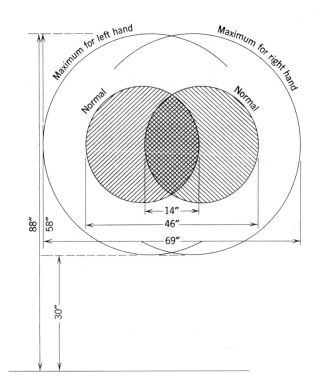

FIG. 2-5 Maximum and normal work areas for a man standing (10% less for a woman).

hand three times as fast as the arm, and the arm six times as fast as the body. Furthermore, the simplest motion is usually the most accurate and the easiest to perform. If workers can be confined to a normal and maximum work area, production will increase. Teach workers to set up their work so that the most frequent motions are made in the normal work area and few—and the least frequent—in the maximum work area (see Figures 2-4 and 2-5).

A understanding by the worker of the flow and nature of the work to be accomplished will assist greatly in increasing productivity. Good planning and organization will govern tool, utensil, and material placement so that the work can be done at desired standards of time and quality. Divide food production into its specific functions and relate these functions to the work centers. When the work related to one work center is completed, move it to the next work center, and to the next, until the job is done. Proper work center planning coupled with proper work planning will assure increased productivity. Many times mobile equipment or other devices can be used so that one work center is changed quickly into another work center without movement of products.

In planning and organizing work for a salad unit, usually three work centers are required: (1) prepreparation, (2) make-up for dressings, gelatin mixtures, and other foods which require mixers, heating units, and so forth, and (3) a final assembly center where the salads are made up. If the vegetable section does the prepreparation, then this center might be eliminated in the pantry. A sandwich unit may require work centers similar to those used for salad, and if volume is light, salads and sandwiches may be prepared in the same work centers. Work centers will usually vary according to whether one or more workers work on products. Assembly line work may speed up some jobs, especially if the work motions are highly repetitive and a large number of units must be produced. Salads, sandwiches, dishwashing tasks, breading, bakery production, and many other jobs lend themselves to assembly production. Moving belts or a moving circular table may be used to assist in such work. If these are mobile, they can be rolled out of the way or used by other sections when not required. Movement speeds should be varied from 8 to 12 feet per minute. Excess speed is not desirable if rhythmic motions by workers are to be obtained.

Much of the work done in quantity food production is not, however, as repetitive as it might be under mass production in a factory. Menu requirements change daily. This makes it difficult to achieve the same degree of productivity as can be achieved when the same work is repeated again and again. Work centers in kitchens must be set up so they can be varied according to the foods produced in them. A cook will make soups, casserole

(a)

(b)

(c)   (d)

FIG. 2-6   Plan work so reach is confined to normal and maximum work areas. (a) Pots and pans unloaded here on this table are easily placed in the dishwashing machine. (b) Equipment for storage placed around this worker makes work easier; dishes are prestacked on worker's right at table and then, when the stack grows to sufficient size, the worker turns and stores. (c) Confining workers in an assembly line system speeds work. (d) Mobile equipment arranged for assembly line production of pies makes it possible to roll and fill a pumpkin pie in 1.1 worker-minutes. (e) The same area shown in (d) is quickly converted into a production line for cutting, rolling, and panning rolls by using mobile equipment. Mobile proofer receives filled trays of rolls.

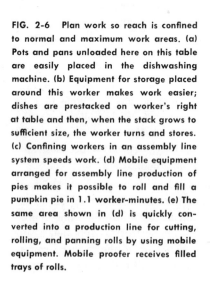

(e)

dishes, roast meats, and other items during the day. Each job has different requirements for materials, equipment, and utensils, and it has not been possible up to now to confine the worker to one area when such a variety of products must be made. Compromises must be made in confining a worker to a work area in food production, but these, if worked out carefully, can reduce travel and motions from those required on ill-planned jobs. Each operation must establish work methods which produce the most efficiency in that particular operation. The same methods may not be applicable or suitable in another operation. The drive-in serving hamburgers, French fries, and shakes will not have the same work methods, layout, and equipment requirements as the hotel serving a dinner trade and banquets and conducting many other food preparation functions.

Motion Economy

The principles of motion economy summarize methods whereby motions in doing work can be most easily and quickly accomplished. Most workers do their work as it comes naturally. This does not necessarily mean that these

FIG. 2-7   Three poses of worker show how work can be confined in a limited area to achieve high production.

(a)   (b)

(c)   (d)

FIG. 2-8   (a) The reach here is awkward and inefficient; the motions lack symmetry and are not made in opposite directions. (b) The change of position shown here corrects the violation of the rules noted in (a). (c) The worker here violates the rule which says, "Use both hands in doing work." (d) The worker has now improved the method of doing work by minimizing the distance of work and using both hands.

motions are not efficient, but it has been found that many workers do use inefficient motions. Training workers to observe the principles of motion economy will yield significant gains in the amount of work done.

Principle

1. Work hands in unison, starting and completing motions at the same time, with neither hand idle except at rest period.

   Example:

   Worker at steam table reaches for soup bowl with left hand while at the same time he reaches for ladle of soup with right hand; worker's hands are positioned in front when at rest.

2. Move arms simultaneously and in opposite and symmetrical directions to give balance and two-handed accomplishment in doing work.

   Example:

   The illustration above also illustrates this principle. Try holding one arm rigidly against your side while moving the other out and in, and note how much easier it is to move out and in with both arms rather than with one only.

3. Use the lowest classification of the body that produces the best results with the least effort and expenditure of time.

   Example:

   Start and stop a machine with the touch of a finger rather than doing the work with an entire hand.

4. Accomplish work with motions easiest for the worker.

   Example:

   Most workers work best with the right hand and arm and with the first and second fingers.

5. Use continuous curved motions with natural rhythm. Make motions ballistic rather than controlled or restricted.

   Example:

   Wash a table top with circular, rhythmic motions. Studies indicate that considerable energy and time are taken in starting and stopping a muscle. Once the inertia of the body is overcome, it is easier and quicker to continue the motion than to stop and start again. Studies also indicate that ballistic (arced) movements are more accurate, easier, and more quickly done than movements made in a straight line.

6. Use momentum or gravity to do work whenever possible and reduce it whenever it must be overcome in doing work.

Principle

   Example:

   Place a swivel faucet above the cook stove so that water may be drop
   delivered into containers. Chop celery on a board near the edge of a sink
   and drop deliver the cut celery into a container in the sink. Use gravity
   rollers to deliver groceries, and some device to stop the items when they
   reach the proper delivery point.

7. Free hands and fingers by using devices, tools, or equipment.

   Example:

   Use a duchess cutter to shape and roll rolls. Use a trip device to turn on
   the coffee urn spigot, freeing both hands of the operator for handling
   cups and saucers.

8. Have tools, utensils, and materials within the normal or maximum reach
   area. Avoid hunt and search.

   Example:

   A roast cook should have his roast pans available within 26 inches. Have
   water, fat, flour, and seasonings within the normal or maximum reach
   area. Provide a landing table with adequate space directly opposite the
   ovens, with knives, boards, and other slicing equipment nearby for
   easy use.

FIG. 2-9   The use of drop delivery in checking red beans speeds the job and makes it
easier to do.

Principle

9. Combine tools and equipment where possible.

    Example:

    Use a spatula which has a serrated edge which can be used for cutting sandwiches as well as spreading them. Utilize attachments to mixers for grinding, slicing, shredding, and so forth.

10. Promote proper motion sequence by good location of tools and materials.

    Example:

    Have bacon, ham, sausage, eggs, and other materials for breakfast arranged on trays on a mobile tiered rack so the breakfast cook can quickly reach to his right for required items as orders come in. In breading items, see that materials for breading — flour, liquid egg mixture, and crumbs — are set in proper order for sequential movement.

11. Provide illumination and placement of work which permit good visual perception. Speed of moving belts and other moving items should not be such as to make movements inaccurate because of excessive speed-up or poor vision.

    Example:

    Set moving belts at a speed from 8 to 12 feet per minute. Provide 50 to 100 foot-candles in areas where fine work, such as canapé preparation or cake decoration, is done.

12. Arrange work heights so they will be most comfortable for the workers. Have workers work seated where work permits.

    Example:

    Where a small hand tool is used, such as a French or paring knife, a pastry tube, or a corer, the work surface should be from two to four inches below the worker's elbow. When a tool serving as an extension of the worker's hand or arm is used, such as a whip or a ladle, have the work surface positioned so the worker can stand erect and place his hands easily and firmly on the flat surface.

13. Provide grasps on tools that require force or must be used for a long time fitted to the hand. The palm of the hand and fingers should be in good contact with the grip.

    Example:

    Look around any kitchen and see how this principle is violated.

14. Position all controls and levers for operation so they can be manipulated most easily and with least change in posture.

    Example:

    Note on your mixers, dishwashing machines, slicers, and other mechani-

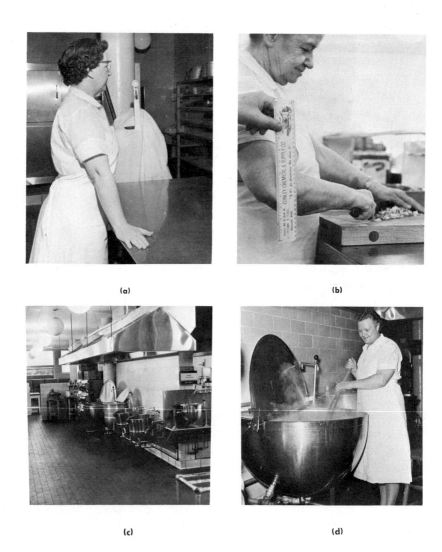

(a)

(b)

(c)

(d)

FIG. 2-10 Proper work heights should be provided workers. (a) When tools such as whips or spoons are used, the table height is correct when the worker can stand erect with the hands flat on the table as shown. (b) In using tools as shown here, have the table height from two to four inches below the worker's elbow. (c) Arrange stock pots so workers can work easily in them. The small trunnion kettles on the right will tilt into containers on a cart. (d) Note that a shallow kettle placed at the correct height makes for easier work.

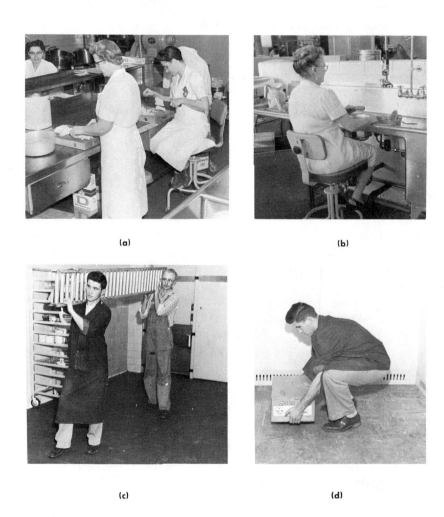

(a) (b)

(c) (d)

FIG. 2-11 Correct use of the body will reduce effort in doing work. (a) The worker on the right, in spite of being seated, is using more effort in doing work than the worker standing on the left. (b) A good chair should be provided workers; note the adjustable seat and back rest. (c) In carrying long objects, as shown here, workers should keep out of step. (d) Lift heavy loads by using the strong leg muscles, not the weaker back muscles.

Principle

cal equipment if this principle is observed. Note how frequently the left hand rather than the right is required to manipulate controls.

15. Minimize disturbing noise and vibration.
    Example:
    A blower fan over the cook's section may be making sufficient noise and vibration to detract from his productivity. Hard surfaces may cause reverberations of sound. Some workers are noisy and may disturb others.

16. **Provide heat and ventilation adequate for the comfort of workers.**
    Example:
    The best temperature for good productivity is between 65° and 75° F. Relative humidities over 65% have been found to lower worker efficiency.

17. Allow appropriate rest periods.
    Example:
    The importance of rest has been discussed.

18. Provide proper training and good personnel relations to give workers the required competence to do the jobs expected of them and the necessary atmosphere and morale to develop effective work methods.
    Example:
    Do you have a training program that is well thought out and achieves results? Do you have a good personnel program that makes employees feel they are a part of the organization and makes them want to promote its interests as well as their own? Do you have a high turnover rate? If so, find out why.

Job Breakdown Techniques

Jobs can be improved only if they are studied and wasteful effort is eliminated. It is oftentimes possible to improve productive effort, too. Taking jobs apart is not difficult. In jobs where analyses are worthwhile, the breakdown into essential parts may be accomplished by various methods. Whatever method is used, every detail must be identified. When this is done, it is surprising to note how wasteful of workers' time and effort some jobs are. In spite of the fact that these jobs may have been performed many times, it is not until they are analyzed that their true nature stands out. Industrial engineers frequently follow a sequence in analyzing jobs and building the new one. The steps may be:

1. Make proper selection of the job.
2. Break down the job in detail.
3. Separate the job into productive, rest, and waste components.

4. Question the essentiality of each component.
5. Rebuild the job, eliminating waste and combining, rearranging, or changing work methods.
6. Evaluate to ascertain if sufficient improvement has been made. Replan if necessary.
7. Apply the new method.
8. Evaluate again and change where necessary.
9. Give sufficient supervision, instruction, and assistance to see that the worker adapts to the change and that desired results are obtained.
10. Remember that there is always a better way, and jobs improved upon can be improved again.

Many times it is best to begin work improvement as an informal program. Where work must be as varied as it is in some kitchen production, this system frequently pays better dividends than introducing the formal study. Work improvement, if thought of as a general philosophy rather than as a strict science, may be more practical and achieve better results. If workers can be taught to *think* work improvement, many natural and completely spontaneous improvements will be introduced by employees themselves. Indoctrinate workers with the idea that there is always a better way to do a job. Small savings in doing work, while not significant in themselves. if added together may make significant savings in a day. Jobs that are improved, that are easier to do, and that result in better quality products quickly win employee approval.

A person need not be trained in work methods improvement study to improve jobs. A beginner should select a job that may be taking too long to do or where a bottleneck in production occurs. Another type of job that is frequently worthwhile for study is one which workers dislike or which is difficult to do. Oftentimes, jobs that require a lot of walking or one with a large number of repetitive hand motions may be attacked with profit. If a large number of items are produced—as in making sandwiches or floured steaks, working on soiled dish table, or dishing up at a steam table—the job may be worthwhile for study.

Remember that every job consists of (1) a *get ready*, or the effort required to set up equipment and tools and obtain materials; (2) a *do*, or the actual production of the item or items; and (3) a *put away* and *clean up*, which must follow the do. It is the *do* that counts, for the *get ready* and the *put away* and *clean up* do not add any value to the product; and the more *do* that can be obtained in proportion to the other steps, the higher will be the productivity of the worker. Study production needs. Could some items on your menu be made in quantity, then frozen or stored under refrigeration, and used later without repeating the required nonproductive processes? If you consistently use a certain number of gallons of salad dressing in a week, could it all be made at one time instead of the number of times it is now made?

In casting about for jobs for study, do not overlook the fact that the amount saved should more than pay for the time spent in study. Ask these questions: What will the effect of the change be on other work? Can it be done practically? What will it cost? Will it result in a sufficiently large saving to warrant installation? Then ask what effect the job change will have upon the worker and other workers in the organization. Employees must go along with the change. They will cooperate and even work to improve their jobs or make suggestions for job improvements if they are allowed to participate in the program and share in its benefits. Workers are usually cooperative if they can see that work can be made easier. Jobs that win employee approval make for satisfied employees, and workers who are satisfied stay on their jobs and produce foods of satisfactory quantity and quality.

The method of study in improving a job will depend upon the job and the detail desired. Jobs which require a large number of repetitive motions

To check productivity, write employees' names on check sheet, go through your operation at different times to determine who is actually doing productive work.

NAME	OBSERVATIONS										TOTAL	%
MARY	√	√	0	0	√	0	0	√	√	0	5	50
JOHN	0	√	0	√	0	0	√	√	0	√	5	50
SUE	0	0	√	0	√	0	√	0	√	0	4	40
TOM	√	0	√	√	0	√	0	0	√	√	6	60
ANN	√	√	√	0	√	0	√	√	0	0	6	60
KATE	0	√	0	√	0	0	√	0	0	0	4	40

FIG. 2-12   This chart shows how the sampling method may be used to estimate worker productivity. At different times observations have been made to determine who is doing productive work; a circle indicates no productive work and a check indicates productive work is being done. Percentage of efficiency is shown on the right.

and in which a large number of units are produced may be broken down into the most minute movements, because small savings will produce significant results. Others need not be studied in as much detail. Simo-studies using slow-motion films are frequently used to study minute movements, while flow process charts, or string or flow charts, are used for the latter.

More and more engineers are using sampling methods for work improvement study. These reduce considerably the amount of detail that must be gathered for analyses. Sampling methods are designed so that a sufficient amount of information is obtained to give the required information. Food service operators may themselves make surveys of their operations and obtain estimates of worker productivity. Figure 2-12 shows a chart compiled in one food service. Using a random method of observation, the manager has shown by a check or a circle whether a worker is engaged in productive work or not. By totaling the percentages of productive work occurring and dividing by the number of employees observed in the study, the percentage of efficiency of the work force can be estimated. In most cases, a satisfactory percentage would be 80%.

The methods for statistical analysis of work methods may be found in more recent texts that deal with work methods improvement.

In making an analysis of any job ask: *What* is the purpose? *What* are the steps? *What* happens? *Why* is the job done? Is it necessary? Could something else be used instead? *When* should it be done? *Who* should do it? (Too many unskilled jobs are performed by skilled personnel paid wages for doing skilled jobs. Search jobs to see if employees are doing work they are capable of performing and commensurate with the wages paid.) *Where* should the work be done? (Should the preparation section prepare the vegetables and fruits used in the pantry, or should the pantry workers prepare their own?) *How* is the work best done? Would changes in layout, equipment, tools, or materials make the job easier and quicker to do?

These *what's*, *why's*, *when's*, *where's*, and *how's* are most important, and asking such questions about a job reveals facts that lead to job improvement. It is often surprising to find out what work is actually being done. Asking *what?* and *why?* may reveal that eggs are hard-cooked and then peeled to obtain chopped eggs for egg salad sandwiches, when the eggs could be cracked into a pan to a depth of about one inch, steamed until hard-cooked, and then chopped, with the elimination of the laborious job of shelling the eggs after they are hard-cooked. The answers to the questions *where?* *when?* and *who?* along with the always recurring *why?* may lead to a combining of operations or motions or the elimination of unnecessary storages and transportations that makes considerable improvement in

FIG. 2-13 These flow process charts (courtesy George Conrade, HRI graduate student, Michigan State University) summarize motions made in doing work in the present and improved job. (a) Original method. (b) Improved method.

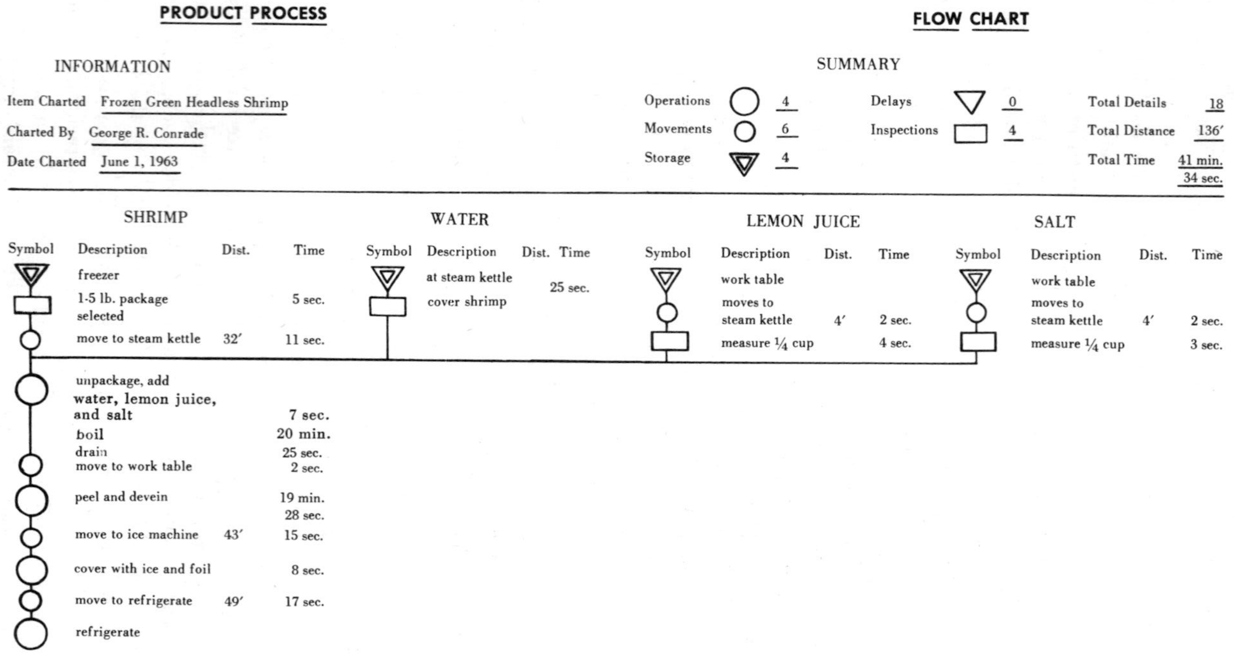

PRODUCT PROCESS

FLOW CHART

INFORMATION

Item Charted   Frozen Green Headless Shrimp

Charted By   George R. Conrade

Date Charted   June 1, 1963

SUMMARY

Operations	4	Delays	0
Movements	6	Inspections	4
Storage	4		

Total Details	18
Total Distance	136'
Total Time	41 min. 34 sec.

SHRIMP

Symbol	Description	Dist.	Time
	freezer		
	1-5 lb. package selected		5 sec.
	move to steam kettle	32'	11 sec.
	unpackage, add water, lemon juice, and salt		7 sec.
	boil		20 min.
	drain		25 sec.
	move to work table		2 sec.
	peel and devein		19 min.
	move to ice machine	43'	28 sec.
	cover with ice and foil		15 sec.
	move to refrigerate	49'	8 sec.
	refrigerate		17 sec.

WATER

Symbol	Description	Dist.	Time
	at steam kettle		
	cover shrimp		25 sec.

LEMON JUICE

Symbol	Description	Dist.	Time
	work table		
	moves to steam kettle	4'	2 sec.
	measure ¼ cup		4 sec.

SALT

Symbol	Description	Dist.	Time
	work table		
	moves to steam kettle	4'	2 sec.
	measure ¼ cup		3 sec.

(a) Original Method

PRODUCT PROCESS

FLOW CHART

INFORMATION

Item Charted	Freeze-Dry Shrimp
Charted By	George R. Conrade
Date Charted	June 1, 1963

SUMMARY

Operations	4	Delays	1
Movements	4	Inspection	4
Storage	4		
		Total Details	17
		Total Distance	147'
		Total Time	23 min. 20 sec.

SHRIMP

Symbol	Description	Distance	Time
	dry storage		
	1 #10 can selected		4 sec.
	moves to can opener	28'	9 sec.
	can opened		18 sec.
	moves to work table	27'	9 sec.
	contents emptied		5 sec.
	water and other ingredients added; contents sit: 20 min., 28 sec.		20 sec.
	drain		8 sec.
	move to ice machine		15 sec.
	covered with ice and foil		8 sec.
	move to refrigerator		17 sec.
	refrigerate		

WATER

Symbol	Desc.	Dist.	Time
	sink at work table		
	measure 3 qts.		25 sec.

LEMON JUICE

Symbol	Description	Dist.	Time
	on work table		
	measure 1/4 cup		11 sec.

SALT

Symbol	Descr.	Dist.	Time
	on work table		
	measure 2 tbls.		19 sec.

Worker Time Summary

	Improved	Original
Selects, opens, and empties can	45 sec.	23 sec.
Selects package and unwraps	55 sec.	36 sec.
Selects and measures ingredients	20 sec.	
Adds ingredients		25 sec.
Drains	8 sec.	
Peels and deveins		19 min., 30 sec.
Completes and places in refrigerator	40 sec.	40 sec.
Total worker time	2 min., 48 sec.	21 min., 34 sec.

(b) Improved Method

the job. If two or more operations can be combined, such as batter-dipping rather than breading, the time and effort required for the combined operation are usually less than those used to perform the former manipulations. Usually one need only observe a cook preparing items for a soup to find out why food services have productivity figures of 45%.

Some of the job breakdown methods that might be used in kitchen study are:

1. *Flow Process Charts*

A flow process chart details work done on a complete job, such as making a pie, preparing a sauce, or making a fondant. The motions studied are gross. Minute motions are not indicated but are included in broad motions such as "travel to sink," "mix," and "pan." Figure 2-14 indicates symbols

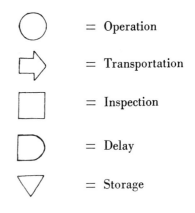

FIG. 2-14   These symbols are used on a
flow process chart to indicate work done.

commonly used in flow process charts. As each motion is made, the engineer records by symbol what has happened. Later he can reconstruct the job, analyze it to improve it, and then create the new job. When he uses the flow process chart, he usually records on the improved job sheet a summary of the number of work motions that occurred in the former and in the improved jobs. This serves as a means of indicating the improvement made.

2. *Travel Study*

Travel on the job is frequently the object of study. There are various methods of doing this. The string or flow chart is oftentimes used. In such a chart, the worker's path is traced on a scale drawing of the work area. The drawing is usually to the scale of one-fourth inch to the foot. Equipment is drawn on the plan as it is on a blueprint. The worker's path is traced and the distance traveled calculated. An improved job is devised and the

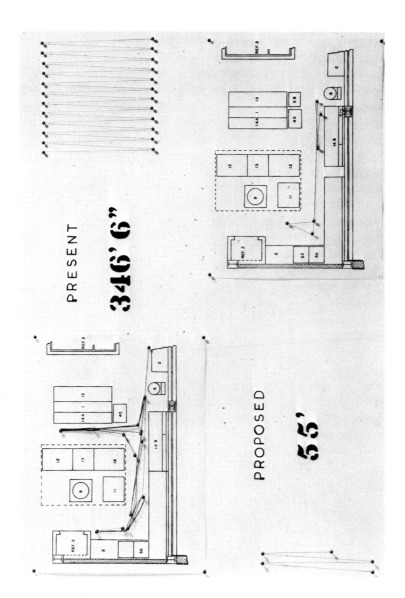

FIG. 2-15 This string chart shows how, by changing a bakeshop layout, travel may be reduced.

FIG. 2-16 (a) Chart of left and right hands doing work as taken from a slow-motion film. (b) The simo-chart made from this record of film analysis.

RECORD OF FILM ANALYSIS

Film Number 52
Date Filmed July 15, 1956
Analysis by LHK
Date July 28, 1956

Operation Trimming lettuce
Operator Hefner
Part Name
Part No.

1 Sheet of 1
Dept H. Economics
16 frames/sec.

Therblig Symbol	Clock Reading	Subtracted Time (winks)	Left Hand Description	Right Hand Description	Therblig Symbol	Clock Reading	Subtracted Time (winks)	Body Member	Therblig Symbol	Clock Reading	Subtracted Time	Notes
TE		16	To bowl of lettuce	Holds knife	H		16					Frame 1
S		19	Selects lettuce leaf	Holds knife	H		19					not shown
TL		18	Carries lettuce leaf	Holds knife	H		18					Frame 2
P		27	Positions leaf for cutting	Holds knife	H		27					Frame 3
H		29	Holds leaf for cutting	Moves knife to cutting position	TL		29					Frame 4
H		210	Holds leaf for cutting	Trims off lettuce cups	U		210					Frames 5-12
G		17	Picks up waste lettuce	Holds knife	H		17					Frame 13
TL		21	Waste to garbage can	Holds knife	H		21					Frame 14
RL		8	Drops waste lettuce	Holds knife	H		8					Frame 15
TE		16	Returns to pick up lettuce cups to deposit in bowl on left	Holds knife	H		16					Frame 16

(a)

SIMO - CHART

Method _____   Film No. _52_____
Operation _Trimming lettuce_____ Operation No. _____
_____ Part No. _____
Part Name _____   Charted by _LHK_____
Operator _Hefner_____   Date charted _July 28, 1956__

Left hand description	Symbol	Time	Total time in sec	Time	Symbol	Right hand description	Clock
To bowl of lettuce	TE	.50	.50	.50	H	Holds knife	
Selects lettuce leaf	S	.60	1.10	.60	H	Holds knife	
Carries lettuce leaf	TL	.60	1.70	.60	H	Holds knife	
Positions leaf for cutting	P	.90	2.60	.90	H	Holds knife	
Holds leaf for cutting	H	.90	3.50	.90	TL	Moves knife to cutting position	
Holds leaf for cutting	H	2.10	5.60	2.10	U	Trims off lettuce cups	
(continued)						(continued)	

(b)

worker's path is again traced. The reduction in distance indicates the savings made.

A string chart is another form of a flow or travel chart. It is made by mounting the scale drawing on stiff paper or cardboard. String is then used to trace the worker's path, winding the string along the worker's path, using brass paper fasteners at each point the worker turns or stops. By straightening the string, the distance the worker travels is easily calculated, since each one-fourth inch equals one foot of travel. Comparison of distances in the former and improved methods is easily made by measuring the string's length in each respective chart. (See Fig. 2-15).

Worker travel may be measured by using a pedometer. Sometimes motion picture cameras are set over a work area with the camera timed so that instead of 16 frames per second, only 1 per second is taken. Then the resulting film is projected at regular speed, giving a quick resume of the travel which the worker did on the job. This makes it possible for one to review the work done in an eight-hour shift in 30 minutes. Industrial engineers call such study of travel *menomotion study*. It is also possible to take on one negative of a picture different positions of a worker doing a job. This will show stroboscopic motion in doing work, and the travel or motions required by the worker can be compared between present and improved jobs. The fixing of the motion is helpful for making detailed analyses.

3. Simo-Charts

The smallest measure of work motion is called a *therblig*. These motions are oftentimes too quickly made to detect easily, so they are usually filmed at

FIG. 2-17 A cyclegraph showing how lights on a worker's hands can be used to study work patterns.

a very fast speed. They are then projected at normal speed, giving the work in slow motion. From such a film, the motions made in fractions of a second can be identified and charted on a simo-chart. The work done by one hand is charted, and then the work done by the other hand. The term "simo-chart" comes from the longer term "simultaneous chart." Frequently a timer or chronometer is set near the worker so that the time taken to execute the therblig is shown on the film. This timer usually has 100 equal divisions on its face, and the hand makes a complete circle 20 times per minute, giving 2,000 divisions passed by the timer hand per minute. One division, or 1/2,000 of a minute, is called a wink, and frequently the time required to complete a therblig is stated in winks.

Therblig	Symbol	Definition
Search	Sh	The eyes or the hand hunts for an object
Select	St	A decision ending with the choice of an object
Inspect	I	Examining and evaluating according to a standard
Transport Empty	TE	Moving the hand toward an object
Grasp	G	Taking hold of an object
Hold	H	A delay in grasp with no movement of the object
Transport Loaded	TL	Moving the object
Release Load	RL	Releasing the object
Position	P	Setting the object into position for use
Pre-position	PP	Setting into position for future operation
Assemble	A	Joining two or more objects together
Disassemble	DA	Separating two or more objects which are joined
Use	U	Manipulating a tool or device to do work
Avoidable Delay	AD	Stopping the operation
Unavoidable Delay	UD	Stopping the operation unavoidably
Plan	Pn	Mental decision on procedure for action
Rest	R	Cessation of work to overcome fatigue

Simo-charts are used to study work motions which are repeated frequently by workers. Small savings are made of perhaps only a part of a second, and yet, because of the number of times the motions are repeated, the savings are significant. Simo-chart study would be worthwhile in food service work only when jobs repeated a great number of times by a worker were studied. A study of the hand-depositing of cookies, cutting foods with a French knife, or hand-paring of potatoes might be worthwhile. The chart will, when completed graphically, portray how a worker uses his hands and fingers in doing work. Factors not evident under normal observation stand out on the simo-chart. The time required to make each motion is shown, and a continuous black line on the chart indicates that the hand is idle. Time lost is easily seen. As in other charts, the present and the improved job can be compared and the improvement evaluated. (See Fig. 2-16).

Another method used by some engineers to study work motions is the cyclegraph. This is made by placing tiny lights on a worker's hands and taking a film as the worker moves his hands. If the filming area is darkened, these lights show up as streaks of light on the picture. The efficiency of the worker's motions can be easily evaluated by study of the path the hands move in when doing the work. When motions are shown to be an established pattern and well-defined in motions that eliminate waste motion, efficiency is increased. Paths of light that show diverse, random motions show waste effort and time. (See Fig. 2-17).

Engineers also improve jobs by introducing better tools or equipment. Frequently they find that jobs can be simplified by the use of different materials, such as a mix for a cake.

Whatever the method and the job, it must be remembered that job improvement deals eventually with individuals, who are not machines and will not respond like machines in doing work. The human factor must be considered. Too frequently a failure to consider the individual, only emphasizing the doing of the work, will lower productivity rather than raise it. Consulting workers during the planning of the job and applying their ideas frequently serves to assure its success.

3 Cleaning and Sanitation

THE PROGRAM

Cleanliness and sanitation should be an integral part of food production, for unless it receives proper emphasis, food standards cannot possibly be high. To produce good food means to make it not only taste and appear good but also be nutritious, clean, and safe to eat. The National Sanitation Foundation has stated: "Sanitation is a way of life. It is the quality of living that is expressed in the clean home, the clean farm, the clean business and industry, the clean neighborhood, the clean community. Being a way of life, it must come from within the people; it is nourished by knowledge and grows as an obligation and is an ideal in human relations." In any food service the standards of cleanliness and sanitation should be emphasized as much as standards of quality and cost.

Clientele demand sanitation and cleanliness in an operation and will refuse to patronize one that does not meet high standards. Not only this, but they also demand neatness and a feeling of order. The operation that presents a tidy parking area, bright, sparkling windows, trim and neat landscaping and a clean, inviting interior wins customers.

All personnel in the operation have the responsibility for seeing that high standards of sanitation and cleanliness exist. Management has the responsibility for seeing that facilities, equipment, and materials are provided, for establishing a program, and for seeing that the program is carried out. Employees have the responsibility for seeing that the work is, done.

The newly established Food Service Sanitation Ordinance and Code of the U. S. Public Health Service establishes minimum standards for a good cleaning and sanitizing program, and local inspectors will cooperate and assist in its establishment. Codes and standards have also been promulgated by the National Sanitation Foundation, the American Hotel

Association, and the National Restaurant Association; and these groups are actively working with local, state, and federal groups to establish desirable and uniform practices.

The Management Job

A staff member of management should bear the responsibility for seeing that a good sanitation program is established and that proper supervision and training are given. Systematic records should be maintained. Standards should be established for all the work. Take care to assign cleaning to workers sufficiently skilled to do the job, but remember that it is not economical to have highly skilled workers spend time in cleaning tasks if this work can be grouped and assigned to lesser but sufficiently skilled employees. Establish standards and methods for keeping work areas tidy during work. Set up procedures for leaving work areas clean at the end of the shift. Establish daily cleaning schedules so that each day the necessary cleaning tasks are done. Weekly jobs, such as cleaning of filters and refrigeration racks, polishing floors, and so forth, should be scheduled for definite days, and checks should be made to see that they are done. Make definite assignments for all cleaning tasks, even those done monthly or even occasionally, such as cleaning of grease traps, removing lint and dirt from ventilators, brushing down motors and condensers, washing windows, cleaning storage areas, and so forth. If a list of jobs to be done is maintained in the supervisor's office and systematically checked off as accomplished, the work will move efficiently. A check list for supervisors to complete, which indicates work done or not done satisfactorily, is useful (see p. 95). A rotating schedule of work may be assigned to workers and they may proceed during the week or month from one job to another according to an assigned cycle. When slack times arrive, assign workers, janitors, or others to occasional cleaning tasks. Some jobs should be done only when conditions indicate, and it may be necessary to hire special workers to do them.

Principles

To establish a good program it is necessary to understand sanitation goals and how they may be accomplished. The aim is to prevent disease, food poisoning, and food spoilage and to prevent off-odors or off-flavors from arising in food or from being transferred to food. In addition, cleaning should be closely associated with the maintenance and care program. A failure to clean may cause equipment not to function properly, and the quality of a product may be affected, not to mention the high maintenance and repair costs incurred. It may also mean that higher operating costs are caused. Dirt on motors or refrigeration equipment may cause breakdown.

Off-flavors or odors may result from a dirty coffee urn or cutting board. Low heat transfer may be brought about by encrusted or baked-on materials on heating elements.

Disease and poison transferred by food to human beings are largely caused by bacteria. Air-borne bacteria may cause contamination, and proper provision to safeguard against this should be taken. Store equipment, dishes, pots and pans, and tools in enclosed areas or upside down. Covers should be provided for food left standing. Unclean or unsanitized equipment may transfer bacteria. Bacteria may be transferred from one person to another by failing to clean and sanitize glasses, dishes, flatware, and utensils properly. Poor procedures for handling food and equipment may cause contamination. Provide clean and sanitized surfaces, equipment, and tools. Flies, roaches, ants, bugs, beetles, moths, weevils, silverfish, and other insects, along with rodents, such as rats and mice, may spread bacteria. Provide a systematic program for eradication of these pests. It has usually been found most satisfactory to retain the services of a professional exterminator for this purpose, since insecticides and poisons may be dangerous in the hands of amateurs. Set up a program also for preventing pests from getting into the building. Check to see that safeguards against their entrance are provided at doors, windows, air vents, and other openings from the outside. Check incoming supplies, and clean up trash and garbage as they accumulate. Do not provide places for these pests to hide and breed.

All foods purchased should come from sources which receive proper inspection by local, state, or federal authorities. Unless milk and other dairy products are properly pasteurized and handled, many diseases may be transmitted by them. Meats and poultry should bear the U.S. stamp "Inspected and Passed." Shellfish should come from beds certified by the U.S. Public Health Service. Watch fruits, vegetables, bakery products, and other foods. See that proper wraps are on them and that all foods are delivered at proper temperatures. Check the premises of purveyors occasionally to see that they are maintained in a condition that meets your standards.

Workers may contaminate food and transfer disease, and all should be required to be checked by public health officials and be given clearance for working with food. Colds and other illnesses may be transferred by workers; workers who are ill should not work with food. Some may also be carriers of disease. They may not be ill themselves, but may carry disease and spread it to others.

Insects may destroy food. Control them by placing tight seals on containers and by using fresh products and proper storage temperatures. In some areas where the temperature level is high, dried fruits, some cereal products, and other items may have to be stored under refrigeration to prevent their infestation by weevils. Good air and light are also effective against food loss from insects.

Salt, sugar, spices, smoke, or substances containing creosote, saltpeter, other curing salts, and other compounds may be used to reduce food spoilage and inhibit growth of deteriorative agents. Some act to destroy bacteria and molds; others, by reducing the quantity of moisture available, as do sugar and salt, may be used to retard food deterioration. A moisture content of 5% or less is usually sufficient to inhibit bacteria and molds. Drying is a means of preservation for this reason. Saline solutions of around 8% are usually sufficient for preservation, especially if temperature and pH are favorable factors, as might occur in pickling. Forty to 50% sugar solutions are usually effective against most bacteria and yeast growth, but some molds grow in solutions containing this ratio of sugar.

Diphtheria, amoebic dysentery, rheumatic fever, trichinosis, scarlet fever, typhoid fever, undulant fever, colds, and many other diseases may be transmitted in food. Most pathogens may be destroyed by moist heat at 145° F for 30 minutes or 160° F for 15 seconds; this treatment is called *pasteurizing*. Some bacteria may be resistant to even higher temperatures for longer periods but these are not usually pathogenic.

Trichinosis is a disease transferred in pork or pork products. Heating fresh pork to 137° F destroys trichinae. Time, however, must be a factor if some temperatures are to be effective. Federal standards require that no cured pork product that might be eaten raw may be sold without being subjected to 160° F. Most fresh pork is cooked to 170° F in quantity cookery. Trichinae may sometimes be transferred from a cutting block to beef and other types of meat.

The most common poison-producing bacteria are *Staphylococcus, Salmonella,* and some dysentery types. From these or from others, such as botulinum, severe illness and even death may result. Ptomaines are not the cause of food poisoning. Illness may be caused by them, but only because of flavor or psychological dislike. Ptomaines are broken-down proteins, and these are not harmful. Many people feel that small game birds should be aged almost to the point of putrefaction, and the flesh contains many ptomaines when ripened to this state. The Chinese have developed a taste for eggs that are quite aged and contain many ptomaines. Some of our cheeses, such as Camembert or Limburger, contain ptomaines and gain some of their characteristic flavor from them.

Staphylococcus bacteria may be either airborne or located in the pus of cuts, sores, or boils of workers. Reassign workers carrying such infections. Once these bacteria are introduced into a food of the proper type, pH, and temperature, they multiply rapidly, producing toxins which cause illness. A person usually becomes ill about four to six hours after consuming the food, but illness may be almost immediate or later than 24 hours. Nausea, vomiting, and diarrhea are symptoms. Even though the food is heated and the bacteria destroyed, the toxin remains and will cause the illness. Another type of poisoning is caused by *Salmonella* bacteria. These must be consumed with the food, for they multiply within the host, creating a toxin that causes severe cramps, diarrhea, and perhaps vomiting. Illness usually occurs from 12 to 24 hours after ingestion of the contaminated food. Heating destroys *Salmonella* and eliminates the danger.

Staphylococcus and *Salmonella* bacteria grow well in foods containing moist carbohydrates and proteins. Cream-filled pastries, meat or fish mixtures, salads, sauces, dressings, broths, stocks, and gravies are all good cultures. Frequently the intestinal tracts of poultry are heavily infested with *Salmonella* and these may easily contaminate other foods used in the kitchen. Watch that one food does not contaminate another. See that tools, tables, utensils, and other equipment are constantly kept clean and sanitary. *Salmonella* are common in eggs, and care must be taken to see that dishes containing uncooked eggs are not handled in such a manner as to favor bacterial development. If processed (dried or frozen) eggs are used, the dishes should be cooked or the processed eggs should be purchased pasteurized. Some food operations cease production of creamed dishes, desserts, or other items which provide good cultures for *Staphylococcus* and *Salmonella* bacteria during warm weather. Many foods should be held in refrigerated cabinets to reduce temperatures below those favorable to the growth of these bacteria.

The temperature range at which bacteria grow best is between 50° and 140° F, and four hours are usually required after innoculation to produce sufficient toxins to cause illness; for *Salmonella* and others that create a toxin within the host, less than four hours may be required. Handle foods as little as possible, for this reduces their chances of contamination. Turkeys steamed and removed from the steamers to cool, put under refrigeration, removed for picking meat from the bones, returned to refrigeration, and later removed for salad or sandwich preparation present a health hazard. The staff member in charge of food production should establish rules and see that they are followed to prevent food poisoning.

Hot foods should be cooled at room temperature to about 140° F; they will cool to this temperature as rapidly as they do under refrigeration. Hot foods should be covered during cooling and then should be moved into refrigeration. To cool foods rapidly, see that good air circulation is given around the sides and under the container. Rapid cooling may be induced by placing the container in a bath of cold running water. Directing air

currents at the product by a fan assists in cooling. The more surface area
exposed in the product, the more rapid the cooling. Thick or solid foods
that retain interior heat for a long time should be spread in shallow pans
for rapid cooling. Three gallons of hot chocolate pudding placed in a thick
crockery container and then into a 40° F walk-in will retain temperature
favorable for bacteria culture for over 24 hours. Establish well-defined procedures for handling and preparing carry-over foods and for length and conditions of storage for all perishable foods.

The acidity or alkalinity (pH) of a food may have much to do with
its susceptibility to bacterial growth and mold or yeast contamination. Salad
dressings, sandwich or salad fillings acidulated with pickles, tomato mixtures,
and other acid foods will resist these growths better than neutral or alkaline foods. Some yeasts grow best in mildly acid foods. Bacteria and molds
will be deterred from growing on meat if the surface is kept acid. Country
hams and ripening meat are frequently wiped with a vinegar-moistened
cloth to reduce mold and bacteria growth. *Clostridium botulinum*, a kind of
bacteria causing violent food poisoning frequently resulting in death, will
not reproduce in an acid medium. Some bacteria and molds grow best at
some pH's and are retarded at others; for this reason, some acid foods,
such as tomatoes, need not be heated to as high a temperature nor for as long
a time to destroy harmful bacteria. If the water in which items are sanitized is
at the proper pH, a lower temperature and shorter time will be required for
proper sanitizing. Some detergents and soaps have compounds added which
indicate by color changes when the pH of the water is not proper for cleaning
and sanitizing. Many detergents and soaps are bacteriastats and deter the
growth of bacteria, molds, and yeasts. Bacteria are not destroyed in freezing
and upon thawing may multiply rapidly. Care should be taken in the handling of these foods. Studies have shown, however, that continued frozen
storage causes bacteria in foods slowly to die off.

Some metals may be poisonous. Copper reacting with an acid may
form a poisonous substance. Lead and cadmium poisoning have been found
in foods, although rarely. Lead may be used in plumbing and cadmium
is used in the manufacture of some metallic pans. Aluminum will not form
a poisonous substance but will discolor acid or alkaline foods and cause
their loss for this reason. Provide secure storage and instructions for the use
of compounds which may cause poisonings, such as lye, trisodium phosphate
(occasionally thought by a worker to be cornmeal), or poisons used for
insect or rodent control. Eliminate materials such as oxalic acid, a bleach
that is poisonous, and use substitutes that are not harmful. As stated previously, hire professional people to free areas of insects and rodents.

Yeasts, molds, and fungi are frequent causes of food spoilage. Yeasts are small plants that cause fermentation. Molds and fungi are low forms of plant life that grow on food, forming hairy-looking round spots. Flavor and color of food are changed by their action. Yeasts require carbohydrates plus moisture and favorable temperature for growth. Many molds can grow at low or high temperatures and on low concentrations of moisture. Some foods are more susceptible to mold growth than others. Some molds may grow in heavy concentrations of sugar or acid; others may prefer protein foods, such as meat, cheese, or eggs. Vigorous treatment may be required to eliminate some types of contamination. *Rope* from bacteria growing in bread is extremely difficult to eradicate. Heat, light, and air may cause food to deteriorate. Rancidity may be the result of oxidation by air, favored by light and elevated temperature. Many foods containing oil, such as coffee, spices, salad dressing, nuts, and cereals, may rapidly develop rancidity. Proper storage, sanitary handling, and freshness of product are recommended for minimizing these types of food spoilage.

Cleaning and Sanitizing

Cleaning

The difference between cleaning and sanitizing should be understood by all personnel. *Clean* indicates the absence of soil. *Sanitary* indicates the absence of harmful bacteria, molds, fungi, or yeast. A clean item will usually, but not necessarily, be sanitary. Items may not be clean but still be sanitary. It is difficult to sanitize an unclean item because of interference of the soil with the sanitizing action. Because soil is a frequent culture for unsanitary elements, it is usually necessary to clean all surfaces thoroughly before they can be sanitized.

Cleaning is accomplished mainly by three factors: (1) water, (2) friction, and (3) a wetting agent, such as a soap or detergent.

1. Water is the most important cleaning agent; the other agents used usually only assist water in accomplishing its task of cleaning. Water acts as a solvent for soil. By moistening or dissolving light soil, it may be possible to remove it with little or no friction or wetting agent. To do a good job of cleaning, the proper type of water must be available. Warm water will moisten or dissolve soil more rapidly than cold. Water at 120° to 160° F is used for dishwashing, with hand-washing temperatures being lower than machine-washing temperatures. Too high a temperature bakes many types of soils onto dishes, making them difficult to remove. Warm water melts grease, facilitating its removal. Where spray or water pressure is used as a flux for soil, the pressure should be between 20 and 30 psi (pounds per square inch). High-pressure motors in pot and pan washers and other cleaning utensils may create much higher water pressures for the removal

of soil; some washers may have such high pressures that wetting agents are unnecessary. Hard water is generally a poorer cleaning agent than neutral or soft water. Hard-water salts precipitate wetting agents, such as soap and some detergents, and make them non-effective against soil. It is necessary under such conditions to add additional wetting agents to make up for the loss. Hard water that dries on glasses, dishes, and utensils will cause spotting. The pH of water is important for cleaning: acid or neutral conditions may not be conducive to the removal of soil. Where items are hand-washed, the pH may have to be held to 8 or 9, but where items are machine-washed an 11 pH may be used. Usually alkaline reactions are desirable in cleaning, for this favors the saponification of fats. The high pressure of steam plus its temperature makes it an excellent medium for removing heavy soil.

2. Friction is effective in loosening soil. This may be accomplished by using scouring compounds, such as cleansers. Brushes, steel wool, or scouring pads are also used. Use care in selecting scouring pads, for broken parts may clog plumbing or get into food. Water under pressure is most frequently used in mechanical equipment for friction.

3. Soaps, synthetic detergents, and similar items are wetting agents; that is, they reduce the surface tension on soil, making it possible for water to attack the soil and moisten or dissolve it more easily. Emulsification of fats by alkalis or other compounds may also occur. Some authorities state that a molecular movement contributed by the wetting agent, called Brownian movement, may aid the cleaning action by forcing off the soil or loosening it from its impacted position. The complete part played by soaps and detergents in cleaning is not yet understood.

Usually about one ounce of wetting agent to three gallons of water is used for washing; for rinsing less should be used. Manufacturers' recommendations should be followed in the use of wetting agents. The type of soil is an important consideration. Stronger wetting agents and greater friction will be required to remove heavy soil or special types of soil, as in pot and pan, floor, or other heavy cleaning. Delicate surfaces may require weaker wetting agents. The glaze on dishes is attacked by soaps and detergents not suited to its composition.

Other factors may determine how items shall be cleaned. The condition of the soil is important, as indicated in the selection of wetting agents. If items are allowed to dry before washing, soil may become more difficult to remove. Sugars and some other compounds will dissolve easily in water, while grease and some others will not. Provide soaking vats to condition items for cleaning, and provide a special container for catching scrapings in pot and pan areas. The soil on pots and pans may need special treatment. A difficult job may be made extremely easy if the factors involved in the pre-cleaning and cleaning are understood. Bleach may be required to remove stains on dishes. Post complete instructions for the operation of equipment and the accomplishment of the cleaning task. Labor and material costs will be lowered and a more satisfactory job will be done.

Sanitizing

Sanitizing may be done by chemicals or temperature. Solutions that contain at least 50 parts per million of chlorine are commonly used in water for the destruction of bacteria. Many other sanitizing jobs require stronger and more effective agents; these should not be used around food, only in rest rooms, floors, and other areas where foods are not present.

Heat will destroy bacteria, especially moist heat. Time and temperature are related in this destruction. Fifteen seconds at 180° F in a dishwasher rinse will destroy most bacteria, but a much longer time will be required to sanitize dishes at 140° F. Usually on hand-washed items a rinse of 180° F for 30 seconds is recommended. Temperatures below 140° F are usually ineffective in destroying bacteria. Hot steam is an excellent bactericide. Ten minutes of boiling is usually required for sterilization. Good sanitizing procedures will destroy most bacteria.

After equipment is sanitized, care should be taken to see that it is not contaminated in handling. Racking inverted glasses and cups and washing them without handling, grasping flatware by the handle in sorting, handling glasses and dishes without touching eating surfaces, and similar measures will prevent contamination. Train employees to handle equipment properly. Provide proper storage spaces with closed doors so that equipment will not be contaminated while standing for service.

Establishing a Program

In any program for cleaning and sanitizing, the human element must receive emphasis. One authority has stated that the problems in this area are 95% human and 5% mechanical. Good training programs must be set up. Schedules should assign jobs to specific employees and set the dates for doing jobs, the time required to do them, and how they are to be done. Employees should understand why things are done. The reasons should be logical. Set up the cleaning and sanitizing requirements by equipment, area, or facility. Each operation will have different needs. For instance, the task of cleaning a potato peeler might be written:

> *POTATO PEELER CLEANING*
>> *Worker Assigned:* *Afternoon vegetable worker.*
>> *Date:* *Daily after work is through.*
>> *Time to Complete:* *22 minutes.*
>> *Job:* *To clean potato peeler so it will be clean and without odor and to prevent clogged drains.*

Steps:

1. *Flush out inside of peeler with water to remove all parings.*
2. *Remove disc and rinse the base thoroughly; wash disc.*
3. *Empty and clean peel trap; flush thoroughly.*
4. *Assemble and open water tap, operating machine for a moment to give it a final rinse; see that all is in working order.*
5. *Wipe outside with damp cloth.*

Or the monthly task of flushing out floor and sink drains might be written in a schedule:

FLUSHING DRAINS

Worker assigned:	*Night janitor.*
Date:	*15th of each month prepare jars; 16th flush drains.*
Time to Complete:	*45 minutes for weighing and filling jars; 25 minutes to flush drains.*
Job:	*To prepare solution and flush drains to destroy bacterial accumulations, free drains of material that might clog them, and keep them free from odor.*

Steps:

1. *Weigh amounts of bionetic powder as indicated, fill gallon jars with lukewarm water, and add correct amount of water. Stir. Let stand 24 hours.*

Amount of Power per Jar	Number of Jars to Prepare	Drains
6 oz	*1*	*Garbage disposal*
2½ oz	*1*	*Pot and pan sinks*
1 lb	*1*	*Vegetable peeler*
5 oz	*1*	*Vegetable sinks*
1½ lb	*2*	*Steam kettle floor drains*
1½ oz	*2*	*Diet kitchen sinks*
9 oz	*2*	*Dishwasher*
1 lb	*3*	*Butcher shop sinks*

2. *On the following night, pour solution into drains, dividing amount equally among drains in the area. Pour all the solution; then return to each area and flush each drain out with one gallon of plain tap water.*

Complete coverage of kitchen and dining areas in scheduling and checking to see that the work is done will establish a very satisfactory program. Remember, however, that no program should be static. Constantly revise and improve, incorporating new methods and new cleaning and sanitizing agents into the tasks.

Establishing Standards and Methods

Tell employees what clean plates and glasses should look like, showing the sparkle and sheen that appear when they are clean. If soaking and some precleaning are required, indicate under what conditions these shall and shall not be done. Explain the part that prerinse plays in cleaning dishes. How should dishes be stacked for washing in a dish machine? Indicate the need to check washing and rinse temperatures frequently. Why is a wetting agent used in the final rinse? Why are post-washing procedures so important after the dishes are clean? Establish methods for varying washing techniques for pots and pans to suit the type of soil. What are the best ways to remove heavy soil? What types of abrasives should be used, and how much? How are pots and pans rinsed and dried properly? How should they be stored? How are floors cleaned and polished? What materials and equipment should be used? What techniques should be used? What care should be given to cleaning equipment? Continue in this manner, detailing each important step and factor so that the employee knows why, how, and when.

The effectiveness of any cleaning and sanitizing program will be affected by six factors:

1. Good cleaning and sanitizing starts on the drawing board when the layout is planned. Proper facilities must be provided. Outlets for water and steam at proper pressures and proper temperatures are required at proper places. Sinks, drains, and other facilities must be located in areas where needed. Floors should be sloped to drains. Floors, walls, and other physical facilities should be planned for easy and good cleaning and sanitizing. Surfaces that are durable, hard, and non-absorbent of soil reduce cleaning costs. Provide proper storage areas for utensils and tools. See that ventilation and light are correct.

2. Selection of easily cleanable equipment and provision of surfaces which make cleaning easy will do much to expedite a program. Mount equipment on walls or make it mobile. Provide access around and under equipment for cleaning. Equipment which can be easily disassembled and taken to a sink for scrubbing and cleaning speeds the task and improves the quality of the job.

3. Select the proper types of cleaning agents and cleaning equipment.

4. Establish a program that meets the needs of the operation.

5. Train and indoctrinate workers so standards are established.

6. Maintain good supervision to see that standards are maintained; change the program as required.

SANITATION FROM CELLAR TO CEILING
a timely check list for food services

CELLAR FLOOR
> Clean and dry
> In good repair; ratproof
> No openings at junction of floor and walls
> Sewer trap covers in place; cleanout pit covered

FOUNDATION WALLS
> Clean and dry
> Whitewashed
> Free from holes and crevices

CELLAR
> Free of rubbish
> Dumbwaiter and elevator shafts and pits clean
> Stored materials neatly arranged away from walls and moved once a month

CEILING OF CELLAR
> Free from cobwebs and dust
> Painted or whitewashed
> Ratproofed around all openings through which pipes pass

REAR YARD
> Free from debris, loose garbage, stagnant water
> No foods exposed
> Garbage receptacles covered

FLOORS
> Smooth, tightly laid and clean
> Drains in good working order
> Graded to drains (if any)
> Free from holes
> No openings at junction of floors and walls

WALLS
> Clean, painted a light color
> Washable; waterproof
> Not broken
> Ratproof; free from holes, cracks and openings around pipes

CEILINGS
> Clean; painted a light color; paint not peeling
> Not broken; smooth
> Ratproof; free from holes, cracks and openings around pipes

WINDOWS AND DOORS

In good repair; clean
Protected against flies
Doors ratproof; $\frac{1}{4}$ inch or less clearance at threshold

LIGHTING AND VENTILATION

Fans, hoods and ducts clean and in good repair
Stoves, ovens, cookers, fryers, etc., provided with hoods properly ventilated to outer air
Exhaust fans adequate, in good order, noiseless
Skylights clean, in good repair, protected against rat invasion
Lighting and ventilation adequate

TOILET COMPARTMENTS

Walls, floors and ceilings clean and in good repair
Properly ventilated and lighted; door self-closing
Seats, bowls and urinals clean; bowls tight at base
Flushes in good repair
Hand basins clean and provided with hot and cold water
Soap and individual towels provided; "wash hands" sign posted

LOCKERS

Clean, in good repair and ratproof; no material or refuse on top
Sufficient number provided; clothing and shoes kept in lockers
Not located in room where food is stored or prepared
Soiled linens, coats and aprons kept in containers
Locker rooms clean, lighted and ventilated

FOOD STORAGE ROOM

Walls, ceilings, floors, shelves, bins and containers clean
Ratproof construction; free from rodent or insect infestation
Adequately lighted and ventilated; not too hot nor damp
Used only for storing foods
Overhead waste and water lines protected against drip
Floor racks removable; at least 10 inches above floor
Foods stored in ratproof, covered metal containers
Bins and containers cleaned before refilling

RAW FOODS

Foods not placed directly on floor
Inspected at least weekly; perishable foods inspected daily
Free from insect infestation, spoilage, contamination
Unwholesome foods segregated, denatured, marked "condemned" and removed promptly

EQUIPMENT

Sanitary construction; readily taken apart for cleaning

In good repair; no open seams, corrosion or defects

No lead or cadmium-plated parts

Dismantled, cleaned and sterilized daily and protected against contamination

Refrigerators clean; equipped with thermometers; temperature not above 50° F.

Drip from ice boxes entering open, trapped, sewer-connected drain

Unused equipment kept clean

Equipment installed so as to facilitate cleaning of surrounding area

Furniture, fixtures and shelving ratproof; free from hollow enclosed bases

WASHING AND STERILIZING FACILITIES

In good working order; plumbing properly installed

Adequate for peak volume

Hot water at not less than 180° F. provided for sanitizing rinse

Sufficient number of wire baskets or trays provided for sanitizing and draining utensils

DISHWASHING MACHINE

Clean; in good working order

Entire surfaces of utensils adequately sprayed

Utensils exposed for sufficient time to washing and sanitizing process

Automatic detergent feeder in good order

Wash water changed frequently

WASHING AND STERILIZING OPERATION

Pots and pans scraped, scoured and cleaned

Eating and drinking utensils thoroughly cleaned and sanitized after each use; scraped, rinsed, then washed in clean hot water (110° to 140° F.) with detergent; sterilized with water at 180° F. or higher; set aside to drain and dry so that towelling is unnecessary

Stored on clean shelves, protected from rodents and insects, dust and splash

GARBAGE RECEPTACLES

Emptied and cleaned daily

Stored away from foods

Adequate number of metal covered garbage cans

Not broken or leaking

Garbage room, if provided, ratproof, clean, free of odors

METHODS AND OPERATION

Foods protected from contamination on counters, show-cases, etc.; no open displays

Perishable foods kept refrigerated between processing operations and prior to serving

Custard filling and custard-filled pastry rapidly chilled and kept refrigerated

Hollandaise sauce not kept more than two hours after manufacture

Pork and pork products thoroughly cooked to prevent trichinosis

No unnecessary human handling of food

No handling of surfaces of eating and drinking utensils which come in contact with the mouth

Poisonous insecticides not carelessly spread where they may contaminate foods or utensils

No evidence of rodent or roach infestation

Use of silver polishes which contain cyanide prohibited

Ice cream scoops kept in cold running water

Milk dispensed from approved dispenser or in single service container

Milk can tags filed and kept for 60 days

Shellfish received from approved sources only

Shellfish tags filed and kept for 60 days

No animals housed

PERSONAL HYGIENE

Hands and fingernails frequently washed, especially before leaving lavatory

Caps or hairnets worn

Clean washable outer garments

No spitting and no smoking

No person at work with any communicable disease, colds, sores or infected wounds

Hands kept away from nose, mouth, skin, hair, etc.

(Courtesy New York Public Health Department)

CHECK LIST FOR NIGHT CLOSING SUPERVISOR

Kitchen

Dish Machine:

Top wiped clean

Sides wiped free of stains

Removable panels on correctly

Floor around and under machine clean and mopped dry

Dish table clean

Trayveyor clean and clean paper in bottom
Supports under trayveyor and dish tables
Dish machine wiped free of soap stains
Doors open on both machines for airing

Truck and carts clean and lined neatly against wall or other storage area.
Grill tops cleaned and heat turned off.
Ovens wiped clean and heat turned off.
Cook's table wiped clean and condiments arranged neatly.
Cook's sink clean and empty.
Steamers turned off and doors left ajar to air out.
Steam jacketed kettles clean.
Pots and pans stacked neatly on pot and pan racks.
Pot and pan sink clean and empty, unless pans requiring soaking.
Reach-in refrigerators wiped off and food arranged neatly and in a sanitary
    manner.
Baker's table wiped clean — condiments arranged neatly — roll divider
    and pie roller clean and covered.
Baker's sink clean and empty.
Salad tables wiped clean — condiments arranged neatly.
Salad sinks clean and empty.
Locker doors closed — uniforms inside — floor clean under lockers.
Floor swept and mopped — corners free of dirt.
White porcelain hand sinks cleaned.
Vegetable Preparation Unit:
    Sack vegetables neatly stacked
    Sinks clean
    Qualheim unit clean and wiped off
    Carts arranged under counter
Walk-ins mopped and arranged neatly.
Walk-in doors wiped off.

Grill Room

Reach-in refrigerator cleaned and food neatly arranged.
All sinks clean and empty.
Stainless steel shelves (on wall) wiped clean and arranged neatly.
Toasters, waffle iron wiped clean.
Sandwich board clean and arranged neatly.
Grill clean and turned off.
Front counter clean and wiped dry — coffee warmers checked.
Front of counter free of stains.
Shelves under counter clean and arranged neatly.

Coffee Maker:
    Wiped clean
    Coffee bowls washed
    Shelves under coffee maker clean and arranged neatly
Fountain:
    Wiped clean
    Syrup rail flushed if needed
    Syrup pumps wiped clean
    Draft arms clean
    Ice cream lids clean on top and under edges
    Front of fountain free from stains
Ice cream freezer washed out—exterior wiped clean.
Condiment table wiped clean.
Tables in grill wiped clean.
Floor behind counter mopped.

Pastry

Counter wiped clean and dry.
Reach-in clean and food arranged neatly.
Condiment table wiped clean.

_____   _____
        Supervisor   Date

Table 3-1. Summary of Factors

Cause or Organism	Incubation Period	Duration of Illness	Symptoms
Staphylococcus Aureus	2-4 hours.	24 to 36 hours.	Vomiting, cramps, abdominal pain, diarrhea, headache, nausea. Sometimes accompanied by fever.
Clostridium Botulinum	18-36 hours. Shortest 4 hours. As long as six days.	70% die in 4-8 days.	Nervous symptoms: diplopia. weakness and paralysis of muscles. Inhibition of body secretions, unable to swallow. Constipation.
Salmonella Typhimurium, etc.	6-12 hours. As long as 72 hours.	1-3 days.	Nausea, vomiting, cramps, diarrhea, fever, headache. prostration.
Typhoid (Eberthella typhosa)	3-28 days.	3-4 months.	Continued fever, skin (rash) eruption, diarrhea, depression, prostration, enlargement of spleen.
Bacillary Dysentery (Shigella)	2-7 days.	Self-limited. Several weeks.	Acute febrile, bloody diarrhea, nausea, prostration.
Amoebic Dysentery (Entamoeba Hystolytica)	10-14 days. Variable months.	Chronic.	Bloody diarrhea, abdominal pains, abcesses in liver, spleen and intestines.
Fluoride	15 minutes to one hour.	Several hours.	Cold sweats, nausea, vomiting, cramps, desire to sleep (Lachrymation).
Cadmium	15 minutes to ½ hour.	Several hours.	Nausea, and violent vomiting.
Antimony	15 minutes to ½ hour.	Several hours.	
Cyanide			Cyanosis, mental confusion, glassy eyes.
Lead	Chronic.		Blue line on gums, cramps in stomach, bowels, and legs, constipation. Wrist drop.
Trichinosis (Trichinella Spiralis)	Primary: 24-72 hours. Secondary: 4-5 days.	As long as a year or more.	Pri: Nausea, vomiting, abdominal pain, diarrhea. Sec: Sub-orbital edema. chest pain, muscular pain, fever.
Wild mushrooms. 1. Inedible. (Boletus) 2. Poisonous. (Amanita)	Several hours. 6-14 hours.	24 hours. Muscarine 15 minutes 3-4 days. followed by death.	1.) Nausea, vomiting. cramps, diarrhea. 2.) Sudden severe abdominal pain, intense thirst, nausea. retching, vomiting, contracted pupils, convulsions, delirium, coma.
Weils Disease (Leptospira Icterohemorrhagica)	5-7 days.	Several months.	Jaundice, muscular pain, fever, spleen and liver enlargement. Constipation.

Foods Implicated	Mode of Transmission	Prevention
Under favorable conditions toxin is formed in many foods — custards, chopped or comminuted foods, chicken salad, fish salad, meat salad, etc., gravies, soups, hollandaise sauce, hash, etc.	Infections in food handlers. Droplet infection from nose or throat.	Sanitation, sterilize, and refrigerate perishable foods. Careful food handling. Healthy food handler. Heating to 190° F. (toxin is heat-resistant).
Foods kept under anaerobic conditions. Prefers protein foods but grows in all common foods. (Canned and improperly processed foods.)	Soil and dirt contaminated foods. 1.) Spores not killed in processing. 2.) Toxin easily destroyed.	Autoclave, under pressure, canned foods of pH over 4.0. Home canned foods, boil for 20 minutes after removal from can. Use of antitoxin proper type soon after attack if infected.
Salads, milk, comminuted foods, custards, soups, gravies, sauces, meats, shellfish. Under favorable conditions.	Fecal contamination of food. Bathing in polluted water. Shellfish from polluted water. Diseased animals. Carriers (Ducks).	Good personal habits of food handlers. Sufficient cooking and refrigeration of perishable foods. Controlled shellfish production.
Shellfish, salads, raw vegetables, milk and milk products, water, soft cheese, fresh cheddar.	Carriers, sewage, polluted water supplies, contact (flies and rodents) through food. Shellfish.	Sanitary water supplies. Proper sewage disposal. Control of known carriers. Shellfish sanitation.
Milk or any food or water may be vehicle.	Carriers, polluted water and milk. Contact.	Personal habits of food-handlers. Sanitary water supplies and sewage disposal. Sanitary plumbing installations.
Water or food may be vehicle, raw vegetables.	Cyst in feces of carriers, through food or polluted water supplies.	Sanitary plumbing and water supplies. Personal habits of food handlers.
Accidental contamination of any food or drink by insecticides.	Insecticides.	Careful use of insecticides.
Acid food or drinks.	Cadmium plated vessels.	Prohibit use of cadmium in manufacture or repair of food utensils.
Acid food or drinks.	Pigments. Chipped enamel lined utensils.	Discard chipped enamelled pots and pans.
Accidental in any food or drink.	Silver polishes. Fumigation.	Prohibit use of silver polishes containing cyanides. Close supervision of fumigators.
Water pipes, acid fruits in contact with lead vessels — Beer — CO^2 — water.	———————	Lead should not be used in any food plant for containers or in repairs of them, or piping or paint.
Pork and pork products.	Poorly cooked pork. Improperly processed pork products.	Eliminate uncooked garbage feeding of swine. Enforce proper processing of pork products. Cook all pork until well done.
Mushrooms picked wild.	Eating wild mushrooms, not knowing identification.	Do not pick wild mushrooms. Use cultivated commercial varieties.
Anything contaminated by the urine of rats with the disease.	By mouth or through skin.	Warfare against rats. Sanitation. Guard foods against contamination. Cooking. Protection of skin.

Taken from the *Sanitation Manual* published by the New York State Restaurant Association, Inc., from a table originally prepared by Joseph Schiftner, former Supervising Health Inspector in charge of Food Poisoning for the New York City Health Department.

Section II

Kitchen Production

4 Pantry Production

THE PANTRY

Pantry production includes the making of salads, appetizers, sandwiches, and other cold items. In some kitchens, the pantry prepares breakfasts. In the continental kitchen cold meat and fish items are prepared in the *garde manger* section, and the *garde manger* chef may be in charge of the pantry as well as of his own section. Some pantries may produce fountain items.

Work in this section is characterized by the production of many small units that require considerable hand labor. These may be of wide variety and require assembly at the last minute to preserve freshness and proper chilling. Garnishing is frequent, requiring skill and time as well as good taste. Workers must be quick and dexterous. They need not have the technical knowledge required in a cook or baker, but they should possess a sense of artistry and proportion in food. The ability to organize work well, to keep a clean work unit, to withstand work pressure, and to maintain an even temperament under pressure are other desirable characteristics. The supervisor and head of this section should have good organizing and supervisory ability. Scheduling should be set so that workers are on the job when work must be done. Workers should be trained for their jobs, be informed of production needs ahead, and be flexible in job requirements.

Materials, tools, and equipment should be placed according to the flow of work and the motions required. A good cutting surface, plenty of work space and sinks, a commodious refrigerated area, and other storage space should be provided. The requirement that many small items be prepared in advance and stored makes it necessary to provide storage for the many dishes and containers required and refrigerated space for them after they are prepared. Good sharp knives and tools should be provided, with good grasps. The French knife, grapefruit knives, paring knives, cheese and egg

101

slicers, forks, and other tools should be convenient to grasp. Small revolving racks, slots, or a magnetic rack may be used for holding these. If the last is used, use two magnets about two inches apart to give secure holding. Portioning equipment is desirable, for in this section, as in no other, actual ingredient cost can be calculated; but portions must be accurate if costs are to be achieved. Scales, slicers, measures, and other tools should be checked frequently to see that they give proper portions quickly and accurately. Post portioning information where workers can see it quickly. Use visual aids to show workers how finished products should appear. To save time in doing work, workers should be trained to obtain exact portions with a spatula or tool, reducing time and effort by using one tool instead of two to do a job;

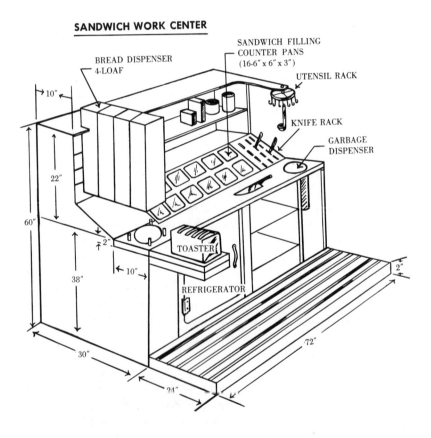

FIG. 4-1 A rough drawing of a work center that might achieve maximum production with minimum utilization of space and worker effort. (Courtesy of HRI student Leonard Z. Eppel)

for instance, one should take a correct portion of filling with a spatula and spread it, instead of using both a scoop and a spatula to do the job.

If a large group of similar items is to be made, repeat one set of motions for the group and then repeat another set until the job is completed. Where orders arrive individually, however, motions must be performed sequentially from start to finish. Thus, in making a large number of cocktails, place all the glasses on a tray, fill all with the cocktail product, cover all with

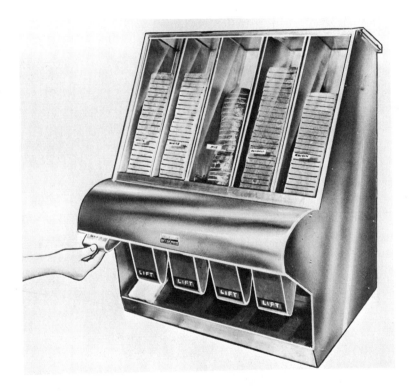

FIG. 4-2   An example of a trip device that could be used to drop deliver bread onto a sandwich table.

sauce, garnish all with parsley, and add lemon slices separately. To make one cocktail, the glass would be secured and the cocktail added, then covered with sauce and garnished. Groups of two or more workers working face to face across a table in assembly line fashion, each doing a restricted group of repetitive motions, may increase production. Moving belts or a moving circular table may be used. A speed of eight feet per minute is adequate for a moving belt, but the speed will depend upon the motions required. Highest productivity is achieved if the pace is steady and even.

In some cases, pantry production may occur in front of customers, as in a fountain lunch or behind a cafeteria counter. Have workers use tongs, forks, or other tools to handle foods. Plastic gloves may be used. High standards of sanitation and neatness are required in such units. Resupply of ingredients in any unit should be quick and easy. A variety and volume of production is required in most units in a minimum amount of space, and menus should be written with the limitations of the unit in mind.

The importance of preparation or "lining up" should be stressed to

FIG. 4-3 See that tools are arranged conveniently for work use, especially in areas where speed is important.

workers. The worker who fails to line up properly usually ends the meal in complete frustration, with much of his defect being imposed on other workers in the form of delay and poor quality products. Freshness is essential, but many foods can be prepared to an advanced stage without loss of quality. Butter or margarine may be softened; fillings may be made ready for spreading; lettuce and salad materials should be washed, crisped, cut, and made ready for immediate use. Slice meat, cheese, tomatoes, and other

FIG. 4-4 Good tools make for good work. Each tool has its correct use. Here are some small tools used in quantity food production.

items, and portion by cross-stacking or by placing scaled amounts on wax paper separators. Purchase prepared items to save time and labor. Management analysis should indicate when labor is saved and quality preserved by such purchases.

Evaluate preparation that requires large amounts of labor, such as fancy sandwiches, complex fillings, radish roses, celery curls, lettuce cups, and so forth. Maximum merchandising through attractiveness of product is essential, but it cannot be achieved at a cost higher than selling price. Simplicity may create more eye appeal than elaborate design or garnish. Good color, form, or other factors may be achieved with a minimum of labor.

FIG. 4-5   A pantry worker assemblies fruit cups for a large banquet. Note how the worker completes a total set of repetitive motions before moving on to another set. This makes for higher productivity. (Courtesy Biltmore Hotel, Los Angeles)

A sprig of mint may do much more for a fruit salad than an elaborately stuffed date. Simply fluting a cucumber or a peeled banana with a fork before slicing may create more interest than cutting into fancy shapes. Eliminating peeling a red apple not only saves time but adds color. By merely using bite-size pieces and lightly tossing them to give a myriad of form and color in a dinner salad, artistic results may be achieved. Avoid what the French call "fatiguing" foods by overworking them. Management may feel that chicken or egg salad sandwiches, coleslaw, Waldorf salad, sliced orange salad, and other such items are low in cost because the ingredients are inexpensive, but time studies show that they are expensive when labor cost is added.

Good merchandising may be assisted by using good arrangement and food combination with attractive service plates or containers. Attractive arrangement of sandwich pieces with a cup of hot soup, a cold jellied consommé served on a bed of ice, or a refreshing salad on a chilled glass plate may be more appealing than far more elaborately decorated food. Cutting a sandwich into varied shapes may add more to its appearance than elaborate

FIG. 4-6 This baked bean and tomato salad is well merchandised because of its fresh and attractive appearance. (Courtesy H. J. Heinz Co.)

garnish. A coquille filled with seafood salad or a fruit salad served in a half cantaloupe may create much appeal. A large sherbet glass may be used for service of a fruit salad. Large bowls or utensils of different sizes and shapes give form and variety to a buffet table. Simplicity coupled with imagination and cleverness may create far more sales in pantry foods than decoration achieved with considerable labor cost.

The production of pantry items may need close co-ordination with the production and service of other foods. Soups should not cool nor malts get thin while the pantry prepares salads or sandwiches to accompany them. A fruit salad plate topped with a refreshing mint sherbet no longer appears refreshing if the pantry has to delay its service because other orders from other units are not ready. The number of orders received and the wide variety of units that must be prepared makes it necessary to give special attention to ways to keep orders in mind and in proper sequence. Pins that can be moved along a rod with the orders on them, a rotating wheel, coding, special order checks, or other devices may be used to achieve this.

Although sanitation has been discussed in the previous chapter, the fact that pantry foods are usually served cold and are of the types that are good cultures for bacteria makes it desirable to give sanitation special emphasis here. Refrigerated units should provide 40° F constant temperature under heavy production use. Only the quantity of food required for a day's production should be made up at one time if that food is perishable, and only what is required for a meal should be removed from the batch. Covers should be provided for fillings when not in use. Foods should set in refrigerated units when they are not on the tables for use. No materials should be allowed to stand over a total of four hours at a temperature over 50° F. Handle foods as little as possible, and keep all utensils, equipment, and storage and work spaces clean. All ingredients should be fresh and in top quality condition. Watch foods that are carried over, for these may quickly spoil and cause trouble.

Sandwiches

A sandwich is bread accompanied by some type of filling. The typical sandwich consists of a filling inside two slices of bread, but sandwiches may be prepared in many other ways. One classification for sandwiches might be:

Hot	Cold
regular	regular
broiled	open-face
grilled	decker types (dagwoods)
deep-fried	rolled or pinwheel
baked	finger, layered, or checkerboard

A regular hot meat sandwich consists of meat, bread, and gravy, and it may be open-face or closed. Gravy may be omitted. Toasted bread may be used for either hot or cold sandwiches. Open-face sandwiches may take the form of small tea sandwiches or canapés.

Sandwiches have good sales appeal and satisfy many food needs. Most sandwiches are used for a light meal, but they may also be used for snacks, desserts, and even for breakfast in such forms as a scrambled egg and bacon sandwich or a toasted marmalade rolled sandwich. A hot sandwich with a vegetable or salad may be a complete meal.

Sandwiches may be made in quantity and held in storage. Some freeze well. Old favorites should be offered frequently on the menu, but good merchandising will require new items offered with the old. A hot creamed chicken sandwich served on toasted cornbread will appeal to shoppers. Unusual fillings, interesting food combinations, service on attractive dishes, or unusual presentation may be used to create sales. Besides variety achieved by fillings and form, the use of different types of breads may give variety.

The Standard

The standard of quality established for a sandwich will depend upon its type. Certainly all of them should be fresh. Fillings should be pleasantly flavored, of a tender texture, and easily eaten. Excess flavor of ingredients, such as sweetness and tartness, and harsh or bland flavors should be avoided. Materials in chopped fillings should be distinct and not messy. If the filling is soft, some crisp material should be included, such as chopped celery, green pepper, lettuce, thinly sliced cucumber, or other such material. The filling should be rich enough to give an appetite-satisfying sandwich. About one-third to one-half of the sandwich's total weight should be filling. The bread should be firm with a close, smooth crumb and of good flavor and moistness. It should be neither stale nor too soft, and the sandwich should be capable of being picked up without bending or losing filling. Bread with excess softeners does not make good sandwiches. Sandwiches should usually be spread with unmelted butter or margarine before filling. Fillings should not hang over the edge of the sandwich. Sandwiches cut raggedly or unevenly or barely holding together are unattractive. Cold sandwiches should be served cold and hot sandwiches hot. Grilled or toasted sandwiches should be warm and possess a crisp, outer crust. Interesting color and design should be sought. Garnishes should be edible and suitable to the sandwich and its filling. Plates or containers should suit the size and type of sandwich.

Ingredients

BREAD

Fresh bread should be used, but the bread should be firm enough to hold in eating and not have a pasty texture. Fresh bread may be stored for immediate use at from 75° to 85° F in a dry place. Store soft-crusted breads in original wraps, but put hard-crusted items in a place where there is free movement of air, without wraps. Hard-crusted breads have a relatively short storage life. Select bread that is proper for the type of filling. Unless production requires a different form, presliced bread should be used. Bread may easily absorb odors; even the odor of cigarettes may be picked up from a worker's hands. A mobile rack or simple drawer is adequate for storage. Clean storage areas daily with a soft, dry brush or with an industrial vacuum cleaner, and scrub and dry once a week. Separate old and new bread supplies each day, and use the old bread for toasting, grilled sandwiches, or French toast. Keep supplies on hand for only a day's production, and re-supply with fresh bread each day. Refrigerating bread causes it to become stale more rapidly. Freezing retards staling. Thaw frozen bread in its wraps. Frozen bread may be spread, filled, and wrapped without harm in the frozen state.

SPREADS

Flavor, richness, or moistness may be factors dictating the choice of a spread. Margarine or butter are the most common spreads used, but mayonnaise, salad dressing, cheese mixtures, peanut butter, jam, jelly or other items may also be used as basic spreads. The danger of soaking is increased when butter or margarine are melted and used; do not blend these items with milk or other moist products for softening, for this too increases chances for soaking. Flavored butter or margarine spreads may be used, and at times their use may eliminate other work motions. The spread should be soft and plastic. Do not allow air to be beaten in when softening spreads.

FILLINGS

The filling gives the sandwich much of its character. Wide variety exists in types of fillings that can be used. Salad fillings containing mayonnaise or salad dressing to bind together chopped vegetables, pickles, chopped fish, meat, cheese, or eggs may be used. A standard ratio for a salad filling would be one part of chopped vegetable and one of pickles to four of meat or other product. Fruit fillings may be used, such as dates and nuts. Mixtures such as banana, bacon, and peanut butter—or combinations with jellies, jams, or other sweet items—are desirable for some types of sandwiches. Many vegetable combinations are possible, including the always popular lettuce and tomato sandwich, or the watercress or cucumber sandwich for a tea.

Mixtures should be soft enough to spread easily and of the proper consistency for good eating, neither too dry nor too moist. Messy fillings should be avoided. Mixed fillings with a fresh and distinct appearance increase sandwich acceptability. All vegetables should be ready for use. Tomatoes, meats, cheese, and other items should be sliced evenly. Meat or cheese slices should be sized to fit the bread. Prepare fillings ahead of use and have them well chilled. Carry-over foods may find good use as sandwich materials, but foods that make inferior fillings should not be used. Limp or greasy bacon or limp, wilted lettuce can ruin an otherwise good sandwich.

GARNISHES

Any garnish used should suit the sandwich in texture, form, color, and flavor. At times garnishes may be substantial in quantity, and it may be questioned whether such accompaniments as a cup of broth, a small coleslaw salad, or a spiced peach half are garnishes. Lettuce, parsley, romaine, radishes, potato chips, shoestring potatoes, nuts, paprika, cheese, tomato catsup, chili sauce, and many other foods may be used as garnishes.

Work Methods

Work centers for sandwiches will differ depending upon whether they are made in batches or to order and whether one or more workers make them. Normally, it takes as much time to line up for sandwich production as it does to make the sandwiches. Workers should be taught to clean up as they go, for clutter can cause confusion, poor quality products, and time loss. Set up containers to match sequences in the flow of work. Keep arrangements the same from day to day so that workers make motions almost automatically. Plan also for use of vertical space to reduce reach. A foot lever may be used to drop bread onto the work board or a moving belt. If both hands can be used simultaneously with hands moving in opposite directions, work will be easier and more will be accomplished. Ballistic motions and

FIG. 4-7 The worker is reaching too far in the making of these baked cranberry and cheese sandwiches. Confine distances of reach to 14 inches, if possible, and never more than 26 inches. (Courtesy American Baking Institute)

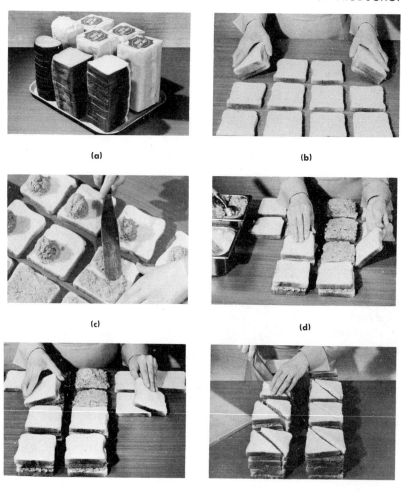

(a)   (b)

(c)   (d)

(e)   (f)

FIG. 4-8   A one-worker method for making sandwiches in quantity. (a) Slit through wrappers in the center and place each half on its open side down on a tray. Remove wrappers
as bread is used. (b) Pick up four slices of bread in each hand and start from center out to
line slices to form four rows on working surface as shown. (c) An efficient spreading
technique. Spread filling with spatula in one motion. With tip of spatula, press filling
lightly, moving from upper right to upper left corner. Complete "S" motion to lower right
and then left portion of slice. (A left-handed person would reverse this procedure.) (d) Using
both hands, cap. (e) An alternate method is shown with the worker topping completed
sandwiches and adding another row of fresh bread, spreading and filling as shown in (c).
This may be repeated and the tier of three sandwiches may be cut at one time as shown
in (f). (Courtesy American Baking Institute)

good rhythm facilitate production. Drive-ins or other operations having high demand for sandwich-type items should design highly efficient work centers. Speed is essential. In one study a worker attained a speed of 44 sandwiches per minute by using a wooden board slightly longer than five slices of bread. Sandwiches were made two high and then cut in half, the board then being placed onto a moving belt for transfer to a mechanical wrapper. Assembly line production may be planned. The American Baking Institute, 400 East Ontario Street, Chicago, can be of assistance in working out methods to give good quality products with low labor requirements.

Fancy Sandwiches and Canapés

Tea or reception sandwiches are small items, usually served assorted and arranged attractively on plates or small trays covered with doilies. They may also accompany other foods. Forms may be closed, open-face, pinwheel, rolled, or other. Occasionally they may be hot. Canapés resemble fancy sandwiches. They are small pieces of bread, toast, wafer, pastry, or other bread product upon which piquant spreads or foods are arranged attractively. The purpose of a canapé is that of an appetizer before a meal, but it may

FIG. 4-9   Bags may be used for wrapping sandwiches and then flip sealed. (Courtesy American Baking Institute)

also be served at receptions or parties as a finger food. While many fancy sandwiches have sweet fillings, these are usually avoided for canapés. Basic butters are used for both fancy sandwiches and canapés (see butters in Chapter 5). Frequently flavorings, pastes, or other finely minced foods are incorporated into the basic butter and spread onto the bread in one motion. The standards of quality for fancy sandwiches and canapés should be very similar to those used to judge the quality of sandwiches. Decoration may be more pronounced and shapes may be more varied.

FIG. 4-10 Automation speeds production. Roast beef is sliced and accurately portioned, then conveyed by belt to a point where it drops onto a buttered bread slice. The second buttered slice is added by a side conveyor and the sandwich is bagged. (Courtesy American Baking Institute)

Many types of breads are used for fancy sandwiches. Besides a variety yeast breads, quick breads—such as date and nut, banana, and fruit— make interesting combinations with cream cheese, fruit fillings, or salad-type fillings. Tiny choux paste puffs, pastry pieces, tarts, or fancy-shaped crusts or crackers may be used to give variety. The bread should be tightly grained and firm. Day-old bread may be desirable. Make fancy sandwiches and canapés as close to time of service as possible. If they must be stored, cover with a moisture-vapor-proof cover and freeze. A moist cloth may be used as a cover if a layer of wax paper separates the sandwiches from the cloth.

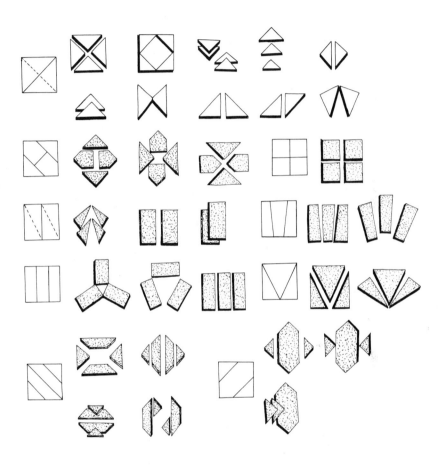

FIG. 4-11 Cut and arrange sandwiches as shown here or in other manners to achieve variety and interest. (Courtesy American Baking Institute)

Keep sandwich sizes small. Oblong canapés should be about 1½ by 3¼ inches, round ones 2 inches in diameter, and oval ones about 2½ inches long and about 1¾ inches wide. If a canapé is to be used as a first course and is the only one served, the size may be larger.

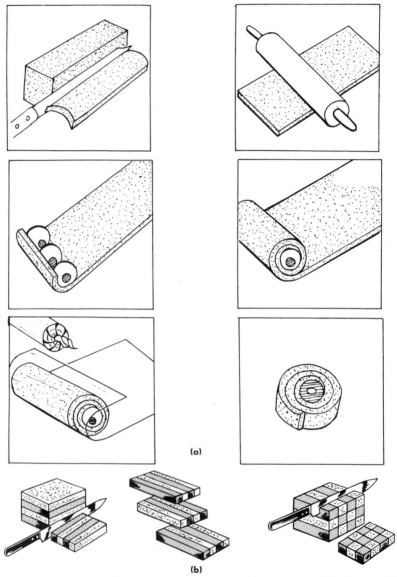

(a)

(b)

FIG. 4-12 The techniques for making some fancy sandwiches are shown: (a) pinwheel, (b) finger or checkerboard, (c) mosaics, (d) envelopes, (e) cornucopias, (f) roll-ups.

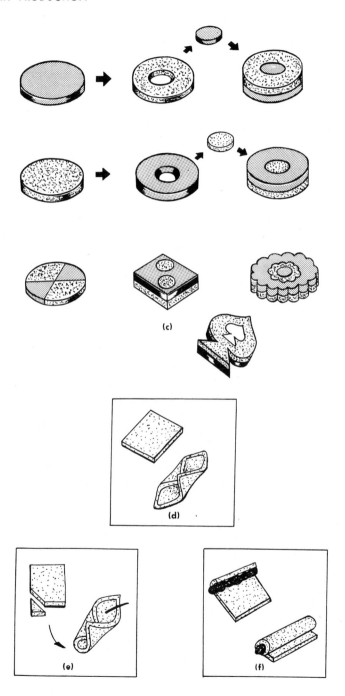

(c)

(d)

(e)   (f)

Canapés are usually made from day-old, unsliced pullman loaves, sliced longitudinally about three-sixteenths of an inch thick. The bread is lightly rolled with a rolling pin to firm it up and then is spread with a basic butter, which may or may not have added seasonings. At times a filling or paste may be used over this. Work the spreads and fillings to the outer edges; then cut the larger slice into desired shapes. The use of pre-shaped items, such as wafers, melba toast, crackers, and pastry pieces, speeds production. Small choux pastes filled with crab meat, chopped ham, cheese, or other preparations may be used. Cheese straws are attractive. Small toasted forms for canapés are available on the market which need only filling with caviar, cheese mixtures, pastes, or other preparations to be ready for service. Decoration of the canapé usually occurs after cutting and shaping. Pastes pressed from pastry tubes, mushrooms, truffles, anchovies, slices of stuffed olives, sardines, caviar, cheese, and other piquant foods may be used for decorating. Overdecoration or too-brilliant colors are undesirable. Neatness, precision, and skillful preparation will give the desired eye and appetite appeal.

Canapés may be spread with tangy fillings, then toasted, broiled, or sautéed and served hot. It should be remembered that seasonings in a hot

FIG. 4-13 Fancy sandwiches arranged for a tea. (Courtesy American Baking Institute)

filling will be more powerful than in the same filling when cold. Less decoration and greater simplicity may be used in the hot canapés.

Hot Sandwiches

To make the typical hot sandwich, use fresh bread. About two ounces of sliced meat makes a good portion. Make it as a regular cold sandwich, omitting the butter or margarine if desired, and cover with about two or three ounces of very hot gravy. The sandwich is better if the meat is hot, too. Serve with mashed potatoes and a vegetable or a salad for a meal.

Grilled sandwiches are best made of one- or two-day-old bread. Select bread that is fairly dry and firm. A grilled sandwich consists of two pieces of bread, each buttered on the outer sides. These sides become crisp and browned during grilling, and the sandwich is served hot. A light weight placed on the sandwich during grilling gives a more rapid and even browning

(a)   (b)

(c)   (d)

FIG. 4-14 Variety in hot sandwiches may be obtained by baking, grilling, or toasting. (a) Baked tacos. (b) Baked egg-dipped marmalade sandwiches getting a final sprinkle of cinnamon before going into a 350° F oven. (c) Baked rolled sandwiches. (d) Preparation for mass toasting. The sandwiches are placed on one greased tray and placed under a broiler and toasted; they are then reversed on another greased tray and the process is completed under the broiler. Toasting may also be accomplished on trays in a very hot oven. (Courtesy American Baking Institute)

and crisping. Fillings of sliced meats, cheese, and ham are most suitable for this type of sandwich.

A toasted sandwich is made of toasted slices of bread. The bread may be toasted under a broiler, on a grill, or in a toaster. Usually the bread is toasted on both sides and then the sandwich is made as for a regular sandwich.

Deep-fried sandwiches are egg-coated and deep-fried. These may be prepared ahead of service and cut into the desired sizes. Upon order, they are then dipped into the egg and fried to order. Do not thin the egg with milk or other liquid. The filling of this sandwich should adhere rather tightly to the bread to aid in holding it in shape in frying. Toothpicks may be used to hold the sandwich together while frying. Sometimes these sandwiches are grilled or baked in a very hot oven on greased pans.

(a)   (b)

(c)   (d)

FIG. 4-15 A breaded fried sandwich gives variety. (a) Dip the sandwich quickly into an egg-milk mixture (six eggs to one pint of milk gives best results, but more eggs to milk may be used). (b) Cover completely in crumbs after draining off excess egg-milk mixture. Use bread crumbs or other crumbs that brown rapidly. (c) Place covered sandwich in frying basket, weight down lightly by covering with another basket or a metal screen, and fry one minute at 375° F. (d) The sandwich is sliced and served.

Cold Sandwich Handling

WRAPPING

Depending upon need, sandwiches may be sent to service wrapped or unwrapped. Vended sandwiches need wrapping. For extended holding in other situations, sandwiches should also be wrapped. Uncut wrapped sandwiches should be clearly labeled. Freezer marker pens write easily on wax paper and many of the plastic wraps. Cut sandwiches may be easily identified if the wrapped cut side is displayed, but even these should be labeled to aid in rapid identification. Use only moisture-vapor-proof wraps. Heat-seal-

FIG. 4-16 Sandwiches may be even desserts. Here a caramel-pecan-covered sandwich, after toasting under a broiler, is covered with a scoop of vanilla ice cream for service. (Courtesy American Baking Institute)

ing of these wraps is recommended. Sandwich bags save labor. Easy sealing is another requirement. If sandwiches are to be heated or frozen in their wraps, the wrap should be suitable for the particular type of treatment. Work out wrapping procedures so the work can be done with a minimum effort and time.

Storing

To hold sandwiches with perishable fillings, store under refrigeration. Refrigeration encourages bread staling, but the danger of deterioration of the filling makes such handling desirable. If the sandwiches are unwrapped, protect in storage from drying out or absorbing odors. Covering with moist cloths is not recommended unless some protecting medium is placed between the cloth and the sandwiches. Place trays or wire baskets of prepared sandwiches in large moisture-vapor-proof wraps, and set these in refrigerated spaces with good air space between baskets or trays. These containers may be set into mobile racks and wheeled into walk-in refrigerators. Maximum storage time should be 12 hours at 40° F. Some sandwiches may be frozen and held for longer periods. The type of filling used will dictate whether freezing is practical. Do not stack wrapped sandwiches more than three high,

(a)   (b)

(c)   (d)

FIG. 4-17   A method of wrapping uncut sandwiches. (a) Place an oblong piece of wrapping paper with the short sides parallel to the counter top. The sandwich is centered so the top and bottom crusts are parallel to the long side of the paper. (b) Bring ends of paper together in a pharmacist's fold. A neat, stay-in edge is formed that keeps air out. (c) Seal by tucking in ends of the paper, folding the top side in first. (d) Fold in the bottom side to form a neat, secure package. (Courtesy American Baking Institute)

(a)

(b)

(c)

(d)

FIG. 4-18   A method for wrapping cut sandwiches. (a) Wrapping paper should be precut to proper size. For cut sandwich, the paper is placed on the working surface so one corner points to the worker. Then the sandwich is transferred, cut side down, onto the center of the crust edges and the paper is turned in from both sides. (c) The sandwich is then laid over on its side and the paper is folded against the crust edges. (d) The excess paper is tucked in securely at the upper edge of the sandwich. Not that all wrapping movments are away from the sandwich maker. (Courtesy American Baking Institute)

nor unwrapped sandwiches more than two high. Sandwiches with moist fillings soak easily when stacked.

Quantities to Use

The quantity of ingredients used for a sandwich will vary according to the size of the sandwich and the type of ingredients. The number of slices obtained from a pound of bread will vary according to the thickness of the loaf, the size of the slice, and the density of the bread. Regular bread sliced one-fourth-inch thick is considered thinly sliced and five-eighths-inch thick thickly sliced. Usually a half to three-eighths-inch slice is used. Quick loaf

bread is usually sliced thinner than this for sandwiches. If a No. 20 scoop
(1½ oz) is used, one quart of filling will be sufficient for 20 sandwiches. One
quart of jelly or jam will spread about 30 sandwiches with two tablespoons
each, while one quart of peanut butter will spread about twice that number
with one tablespoon each. One pound of soft butter or margarine, or one
pint of mayonnaise or salad dressing, will spread about 100 sandwiches,
using one teaspoon per slice. Normally cheese is portioned into ounce slices
about four inches square, and meat into 1½ to 2 ounce slices. Some hot meat
sandwiches may be made with more liberal portions than this. Wieners
usually run around 10 to the pound, and hamburger patties may vary any-
where from 3 to 10 per pound. A de luxe open-face steak sandwich may
require an 8 to 10 ounce steak. All quantities should be carefully calculated
for needs, as stopping during rush hours to prepare additional materials
may seriously hamper efficiency.

Table 4-1

Bread Slices in Standard Loaves

Loaf	Size Loaf (lb)	Slice Thick- ness (in.)	No. Slices (no ends)	Loaf	Size Loaf (lb)	Slice Thick- ness (in.)	No. Slices (no ends)
Regular, white	1¼	⅝	19	Rye, regular	1	⅜	23
Regular, white	1½	⅝	24	Rye, regular	2	⅜	33
Regular, whole wheat	1	⅝	16	Quick bread	1¾	⅜	20
Regular, whole wheat	2	½	28				
Regular, whole wheat	3	½	44				
Regular, whole wheat	3	⅜	56				
Sandwich, white*	2	½	28				
Sandwich, white*	2	⅜	36				
Sandwich, white*	3	½	44				
Sandwich, white*	3	⅜	56				

*4½ inches square

Table 4-2

Yields of Some Common Sandwich Materials

Item	Portion*	Quantity for 100 Sandwiches
Butter or margarine	2 to 3 t	2 to 3 lb
Jelly or jam	2T	3 qt (1 No. 10 can)
Spread-type filling	2½ T	1 gal
Peanut butter	1½ T	2½ qt
Mayonnaise	2 to 3 t	1 to 1½ qt
Lettuce	1 leaf	5 medium heads or 5 to 7½ lb
American cheese	1 to 1¼ oz	6¼ to 8 lb
Meat	1½ to 2 oz	9½ to 12½ lb

*Two slices of bread per portion; rough textured bread will require more spread than
smooth textured bread.

Table 4-3

Amounts Obtained Per Pound of Sandwich Material Used

Ingredient	Quantity per Pound or Other
Bacon, sliced	18 to 25 slices; 2½ c cooked and chopped
Butter or margarine	2 c
Cheese, Swiss or cheddar	16 slices about 4 by 4 inch 3/32 inch thick; 1 qt ground
Cheese, cream or cottage	1 pt
Date and nut filling	1 pt (scant)
Eggs, hard-cooked	10 large eggs, chopped equals 3 c
Fish, flaked	2½ c; each portion about 1½ oz or 2 T
Jelly, jam or preserve	1¾ c
Lettuce	1 medium head yields 16 leaves about ¾ oz each, leaving about 3 to 4 oz of heart
Meat	chicken, sliced 12 to 16 portions, 1½ to 1 oz each; ham, beef, or other 8 to 12 portions 2 to 1½ oz each; ground, cooked meat, 3 c
Olives, drained, chopped	3 c
Peanut butter	1⅞ c
Tomatoes, fresh	18 to 32 slices, 6 to 8 slices per tomato, 3/16 inch thick; a large tomato 5 by 5 size, about 2 to 2½ to the lb will give about the right size slice for a regular sandwich
Vegetables, chopped or diced	Celery, onions, carrots, peppers, etc. 2½ to 3 c

Table 4-4

Sandwich Filling Ingredients and Freezing

These Freeze Well	These Freeze Poorly
Cooked egg yolk	Cooked egg white
Peanut butter	Cream cheese or cottage cheese
Chopped or sliced cooked meats, poultry or fish	Process cheese
Lemon juice or orange juice	Chopped cooked bacon
Butter or margarine	Tomatoes, celery, lettuce, cucumbers, green peppers, radishes, carrots, watercress, onion, cabbage, apples
Dried beef	
Bread and buns	Jelly, jam, or preserves
Baked beans	Mayonnaise or salad dressing
Crushed pineapple or chopped pineapple	Sliced cheese
Roquefort or bleu cheese	Cheese spreads
Milk	Nuts, whole or chopped
Sour cream	Chili sauce or tomato catsup
Applesauce	Whole frankfurters
Horseradish	Honey
	Swiss or cheddar cheese
	Liverwurst
	Olives, sliced or chopped
	Pickles, dill or sweet
	Pimiento
	Prepared mustard
	Sweet relish

Note: Freezing adds nothing to sandwich quality. Thaw under refrigeration 24 hours prior to use; once thawed, sandwiches should be eaten, for palatability is lost on standing. Keep refrigerated until used.

Salads

The definition and classification of salads as they are used in food services is difficult. Originally a salad was a food composed of crisp, leafy greens, but this is not true today, for some salads have no leafy greens or even crisp ingredients in them. Perhaps a salad can best be defined as a combination of ingredients served with a dressing, one of the ingredients usually being a crisp green. A complete salad will usually be composed of an underliner, a body, a dressing, and a garnish, but all except the body may sometimes be omitted. Salads may be classified as hot or cold; according to ingredients, such as vegetable, fruit, gelatin, or meat; or according to their use. In this country salads may accompany meals, may be a complete meal, or may be a snack. A fruit salad is proper served with a wedding breakfast.

The Standard

One requirement of all salads is that they be light and refreshing. A salad should be balanced in flavor, texture, and color with the other foods it accompanies. Color and artistry should be achieved either through a set pattern, through uniformity and symmetry of design, or by careful careless-

FIG. 4-19 This gelatin salad shows a good standard, especially in size of salad to service plate and freshness of appearance. (Courtesy General Foods, Inc.)

ness that leaves no set pattern. Light heaping of different colored greens or fruits and vegetables may give a pleasing pattern. Avoid an overworked appearance. The ingredients in the body should be distinct and not messy, and usually should be bite size. The pieces should be neatly cut, not ragged or misshapen. Bright, clear, fresh colors of vegetables, fruits, or other foods should contribute to the bloom and freshness. Selection of products at proper maturity and quality will do much to give this quality. Good proportion should be observed, with the salad edge about a half inch from the border of the dish. Consider the salad as a picture set in the frame of a plate. Change form and height of ingredients for pattern and to avoid flatness. Vary texture with crisp and soft foods. Cooked fruits and vegetables should not be overly soft. Flavors should be piquant and zestful, not harsh or bland. The dressing should complement the body of the salad and should be more tart and have more flavor than the body. Blending of flavors is desirable. A touch of chervil, mustard greens, a crushed sprig of peppergrass, sorrel,

FIG. 4-20   Fluting of a cucumber to give a simple yet attractive garnish to a salad. (Courtesy General Foods, Inc.)

anise, or basil can add subtle flavor. Nasturtium leaves or tender seeds, capers, and many other herbs are used to give contrasting flavors which add interest.

Ingredients

UNDERLINER

Leafy greens are usually used as underliners, but it is becoming more and more common to omit them and use attractive bowls or dishes. Iceberg, bibb, leaf, cos (romaine), escarole, curly endive, chicory, Whitloof or Belgium endive, dandelion, watercress, spinach, or other crisp, tender, succulent, edible greens are used as underliners. Chopped or sliced greens may also be used. Many times the labor and cost of lettuce cups can be avoided by using leaf lettuce or other greens.

BODY

The main part of the salad is the body, and this may be almost any type of mixture which has a piquant or zestful quality. Good quality products

FIG. 4-21 The design given by simple fluting is attractive, yet simple to do. (Courtesy Fruit Dispatch Co.)

should be used. Meat should be well flavored and tender, and fish is best cooked in a court bouillon before flaking from the bones. Macaroni products should come from good quality semolina pastes, have some slight bite in them, and not be overly soft. The fresher, crisper, and more tender the green used, the better the salad; heavy ribbing, coarse stems, excessively large leaves, and evidence of seeding are indications of age. Wilting also may mean that the green cannot be brought to crispness. Reject those foods which do not meet high quality standards.

GARNISH

The salad garnish should contribute form, color, and texture. It may be composed of some of the ingredients used in the body or may be a complementing food. Simplicity is desirable. A sprinkle of caraway seed over coleslaw, a few chopped cranberries in a Waldorf salad, flakes of green burnet that contribute the subtle flavor of cucumber, a pineapple slice edged with chopped mint, or a crisp food, such as crackers, bread, pastry sticks, toast, cheese straws, or brightly colored gelatin cut into fancy shapes, may add interest. Suit the garnish to the salad and be sure it is edible.

DRESSINGS

There are three basic types of dressings: French, mayonnaise, and boiled or cooked. Each has many variations. Emulsions are formed in the making of salad dressings, although emulsions are common in other food preparation as well.

The emulsion formed in salad dressings is called an oil-in-water emulsion, a combination in which the water forms a continuous network around and separates the tiny globules of oil. There are two parts to an emulsion of this type. One is oil and the other is water or liquid. Oil and water do not join or blend together easily, but if mixed vigorously, the oil can be divided into small globules surrounded by water. The water is in a continuous phase surrounding the oil, which is said to be in a broken phase. A permanent emulsion is one in which the oil remains in a broken phase surrounded by water. If the water and oil separate, forming two separate phases, the emulsion is called unstable. French dressing is usually an unstable emulsion, while mayonnaise and boiled dressings are stable emulsions. Emulsifiers may be used to assist in forming stable emulsions. Some of these are whole egg, egg yolk, starch, agar-agar, tragacanth, hydrophylic colloids of different types, gelatin, casein, starches, gum arabic, pectins, Irish moss, and condensed milk. The type of emulsifier that can be used in foods is regulated by the Food and Drug Administration. Physical means, such as whipping, are used to divide the oil and water. Commercial manufacturers of dressings use high-powered equipment especially designed to homogenize dressings into highly stable compounds. In food services, power mixers are better than hand-whipping because they make a finer and more durable emulsion.

Undermixing or excessive beating of air into an emulsion will cause it to become unstable. The ratios between the two phases must be correct. A mayonnaise will usually be stable if it contains less than 20% liquid. A good commercial mayonnaise may be 50 to 80% oil, 6 to 20% egg yolk, and 12% vinegar, while a normal kitchen-made product may be 65% oil, 20% yolk, and 12% vinegar. Unless special equipment is used, a mayonnaise containing over 15% vinegar will break down. If ingredients are at 60° to 70° F, the formation of a stable emulsion is favored. Freezing destroys some emulsions, but some commercial dressings with extremely high division of oil can be frozen without damage to the emulsion. Excess salt may encourage an emulsion to break by "salting out" the moisture, and for this reason salt is usually added in the making of a dressing with the vinegar or liquid. Heat may cause an emulsion to break, as it sometimes does with gravies and sauces. To reform a broken emulsion, mix well. If this fails, add a bit of liquid or emulsifier to a bowl and then gradually pour in the broken emulsion while beating to reform it.

To make an emulsified salad dressing, add the emulsifier to a bowl. For mayonnaise, this would be egg yolks or whole eggs. Some also add the vinegar and seasonings at this time, claiming that the greater surface area provided by the moisture and seasonings assists in forming the emulsion. Others advise no addition of liquid until a good emulsion is formed; then they recommend that the seasonings with the vinegar be added. Other investigators have reported that if salt and seasonings only are blended with the egg before the addition of oil, these withdraw moisture from the egg, giving it better emulsifying properties. The usual practice is to add only the eggs and begin the emulsion, and then add the vinegar and seasonings after a stable emulsion has been formed.

In making an emulsion, the emulsifier should be in a bowl. This bowl should be small enough to give the agitators a chance to pick up the emulsifier and mix it thoroughly with the oil. Spreading the emulsifier over too wide an area in the bowl may cause an unstable emulsion. Add oil very slowly at the start, mixing well; this seems to favor the formation of a good emulsion. Later, when an emulsion has been formed, oil may be added at a more rapid rate.

The quality of ingredients used to make the salad dressing is important to final quality. Oil is a highly perishable product and should be purchased in one- or five-gallon containers, unless the use is large and a barrel can be used within a week to 10 days. Check all oils before using. Moisture, sunlight, heat, metals, salt, air, and other factors may quickly turn a sweet oil rancid. Only a small quantity of rancid oil is required to turn a good oil bad. Oil spread into a thin film will turn rancid quickly, for the surface area presented gives greater chance for oxidation. Clean oil containers thoroughly, for thin oily surfaces on the sides may quickly grow rancid. Use winterized oil, from which the heavy molecules have been removed so they will not cause solidification in the refrigerator. Corn or cottonseed oil are popular for salad dressing manufacture. Peanut, soy, or other vegetable oils may also be used. Olive oil is desirable for specific dressings and the quality should be of a virgin or sublime oil. Bacon fat, animal fats, butter or margarine may be used for salad dressings. Mineral oil is not considered by medical or federal authorities as an edible salad oil. Good quality, clear, double-strength vinegar should be used for salad dressings. Fruit juices, if used, should be fresh and of high quality. Eggs should be of low bacterial count and of good quality. Spices and seasonings should be fresh and of the sterilized type. Clean utensils and good sanitary practices are required. Mayonnaise and other salad dressings may spoil. They are favorable media for certain bacteria, yeasts, and molds; and if contaminated in manufacture and not given proper storage, they will spoil. The acid in salad dressings will attack metals. Storage should be in enamel or glass-lined containers or in inert metals. Dressings should be stored at from 40° to 50° F.

French dressing is an unstable emulsion formed by adding two parts of oil to one part liquid. The liquid is usually vinegar, lemon juice, or some other acid product. Many ingredients or seasonings may be added for variations, such as honey, chives, Roquefort cheese, poppy seeds, or other items.

Mayonnaise is a permanent emulsion made of whole eggs or egg yolks, oil, vinegar, and seasonings. Sometimes starch pastes are added, but only a small quantity may be added if federal standards for mayonnaise are to be met. Federal standards state that mayonnaise may not contain less than 50% edible oil, and the sum of the percentages of oil and egg must not be less than 78%. A good mayonnaise should be semi-solid and non-flowing (hold its shape), with a good, clear sheen and a yellowish cream color. The texture should be smooth and the flavor sweet, with no trace of rancidity or off-flavor. There should be a distinct tartness to the product.

A cooked or boiled dressing is a mixture of liquids and seasonings thickened with a starch and perhaps with eggs. The liquids may be water, milk, or some acid, such as vinegar or lemon or fruit juices, while the seasonings may be sugar, salt, spices, and other seasoning agents; the starch thickeners may be cornstarch, flour, arrowroot, or other starches. When cooked, the product is a semi-solid paste much like mayonnaise, but it may be slightly thicker, for it is oftentimes blended with other liquids which thin it. Boiled or cooked dressings may have only about 5% oil or fat, but some commercial and other boiled dressings may contain as high as 35% fat. This gives them the consistency and flavor of mayonnaise. Boiled dressings are ex-cellent for potato salads, coleslaw, and many meat and fish salads.

Many variations may be obtained from basic mayonnaise and from boiled dressings. A sour cream dressing may be made from a basic boiled dressing with the addition of sour cream, vinegar, and other seasonings. Russian dressing, tartar sauce, Thousand Island dressing, and some others usually contain around 35% oil. These may be variations of either mayon-naise or boiled dressing.

A marinade is not typically a type of dressing, but it is usually like a French dressing or one of its variations. Use a marinade to build flavor in salad ingredients or other foods by allowing them to soak in the marinade. Tender, succulent greens cannot be marinated. They may be dipped quickly into a marinade and then served at once, but normally vegetables or fruits which do not wilt easily, such as cooked fruits or

FIG. 4-22   For a change, offer a make-your-own vegetable salad on a platter as shown here. (Courtesy H. J. Heinz Co.)

vegetables, firm structured fresh fruits, and vegetables such as cauliflower, carrots, cucumbers, tomatoes, apples, bananas, pears, peaches, and melons may be marinated. The marinade is usually a flavorful product, but it need not have oil in it. It may only be vinegar, seasoned vinegar, or a thin boiled dressing, sour cream dressing, or other liquid to which seasonings have been added. Cooked but still slightly crisp cauliflower, carrots, or julienne beets take on special flavor when marinated in a slightly sweetened vinegar which has just a touch of tarragon added to it. A honey French dressing or a white vinegar sweetened with grenadine will do much to create desirable flavor in a crisp, raw pear slice or grapefruit segments served with halves of Ribier grapes. A marinade used for salads contains an acid, such as wine, vinegar, or fruit juice.

Work Methods in Salad Production

The area in which salads are made should be well arranged. Good landing space is essential, and this should be located close to sinks and refrigerated units. Mixers, hot plates, and other equipment should be convenient for use. Tools, colanders, molds, pans, bowls, and other small equipment should be located in areas of first use. Watch the work flow carefully and plan work accordingly. Where work is repetitive, set up standard pro-

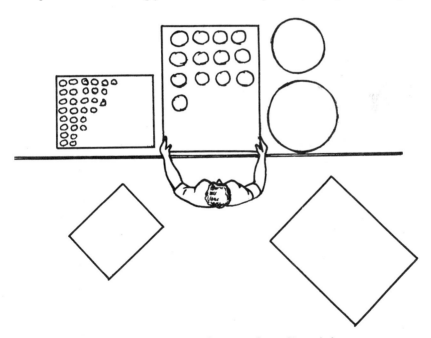

FIG. 4-23 Work center for one worker making salads.

cedures. For best productivity, materials and tools should be gathered together before starting salad assembly. The need for freshness in the salad means that it must be assembled as close to service as possible. Time required to prepare arranged salads will be considerably reduced if proper planning is given their production and the worker knows exactly the arrangement desired. Pictures, patterns, or designs are good in assisting in this. Piece sizes and the number of pieces of different items should be listed. Have the worker repeat the motions the same way each time until they become almost automatic. If workers work in groups, have each do only a few motions and then move products on to the next worker.

An example of good planning and organization in setting up a work schedule for salads might be something like the following, used by one student for planning the production of 100 half-pear (canned) salads rolled in ground cocoa-graham-cracker crumbs, with the hollow center of each pear filled with a creamy cheese rosette:

Equipment Required

100 6 inch salad plates	2 pans for catching juice from pears
7 rack cart or mobile refrigerator to hold 18 x 26 inch trays	1 gallon container for juice
7 18 x 26 inch trays	1 shallow pan for crumbs
Colanders for pears and lettuce	1 large pastry tube with No. 8 star tube

Materials Required	*Portion*	*Requisition from Storeroom*
Half pears, 45 count	½ pear	3 No. 10's, or 2 No. 10's and 1 No. 2½ 10 or 12 count
Leaf lettuce	2 leaves	5 lb EP, 6 lb AP
Cocoa graham crumbs, ground	½ oz	3 lb (4 qt) or 150 crackers
Cream cheese	⅓ oz	2 lb (1 qt)
Evaporated milk		1 14½ oz can to be used for softening cream cheese

The student brought all materials and equipment to the work center. The work was to proceed as follows:

Pre-position the seven trays in front of the worker on the table. Place dishes on one tray in three rows of five, with edges of plates overlapping each other. Place lettuce leaves on each of the 15 plates. Roll pear halves in crumbs and place cavity side up on the leaves. The right hand should pick up the filled pastry tube and, with the left hand guiding it, make 15 rosettes in the pear cavities. Slide the completed tray into the cart at the right and repeat the process. Pass creamy French dressing at service.[1]

Salad greens should be carefully washed in prepreparation to remove dirt and insects. Imperfections should be trimmed away. Headed greens may have their cores broken by a quick twist; then a forceful spray of cold tap water is run into the open heart to loosen the tightly wrapped leaves. If no separation of outer and inner leaves is required, place the heads, open end down, to drain.

Some workers like to take large terry towel sacks, place washed loose greens in these, and whirl them to centrifuge the water from the leaves into the toweling. If the toweling is sufficiently dampened, the greens may be stored for crisping in it. To give good crisping some moisture should remain on the leaves. Air, as it circulates around the leaves, picks up this moisture and encourages crisping. Completely dry leaves will not crisp. Packing in moisture-vapor-proof wraps is satisfactory, provided the greens are not

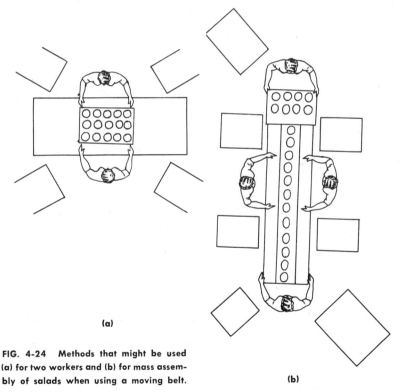

(a)

(b)

FIG. 4-24   Methods that might be used (a) for two workers and (b) for mass assembly of salads when using a moving belt.

[1]This plan of work is taken from a student assignment by Andrew Castle, Montana State University, 1958.

too tightly packed into them. Other workers like to crisp greens by placing them in baskets or colanders and covering them with damp cloths. Others prefer closed, mobile bins. Shaping or cutting of the greens may be done before or after crisping, but if cutting is to be fine, it is best done after crisping. Cutting greens with knives or cutters sometimes bruises them; they are best pulled apart or torn into desired sizes. Too fine a division also bruises them. Cabbage, turnips, carrots, and other crisp vegetables may be grated without loss of texture or quality. A high amount of salt in water, or water quite high in hard-water salts, may wilt greens by withdrawing moisture from them.

Meats, cheese, and eggs should be prepared and made ready for use before they are required. Sometimes all the ingredients for a salad may be combined except the dressing, and this is added last or at service. See that items to be used are ready for use. Leave no work that can be done undone. Stopping to do jobs that should have been done before the peak

FIG. 4-25 To unmold a gelatin salad, dip into hot water and then with a quick rap against the hand allow the salad to drop out. Place it on lettuce leaf. (Courtesy General Foods, Inc.)

of service is the mark of an amateur or inefficient worker. Avoid salting, adding dressing, or other prepreparation procedures that will destroy quality of the salad. Check to see that jobs that must be done considerably in advance of production are done. Molded and frozen salads require pre- preparation 24 hours in advance.

Types of Salads

MOLDED SALADS

Molded salads are made from either plain gelatin or a gelatin dessert. Only high quality gelatin products should be used. Salads lack appeal when the gelatin lacks sparkling, clear color, good setting ability, and a true, pleasing flavor. Gelatin desserts are made from plain gelatin, sugar, flavor- ing, and coloring matter. Plain gelatin may be obtained in sheets or in granulated form. Gelatins may vary in setting strength, but normally a 2% solution will set into a satisfactory gel. This would be one pound of pure gelatin to seven gallons of liquid, or $2\frac{2}{3}$ ounces ($\frac{1}{2}$c) per gallon, for plain gelatin. The proportion of gelatin dessert to liquid is $1\frac{1}{2}$ pounds to the gallon and four ounces ($\frac{1}{2}$c) to the pint of liquid.

Quality of the gelatin is a factor in the strength of gel obtained. Sugar increases the firmness of a gel, while acids decrease it. Foams set by gelatin may require more gelatin than a solid mass. If a mixture contains a large quantity of chopped ingredients, the structure will require more gelatin. Rapid cooling gives a set at a higher temperature and a less firm gel. Cooling slowly to below 100° and then refrigerating at 40° F gives a firm set if the proportion is correct. Setting takes from $1\frac{1}{2}$ to 2 hours and occurs at from 48° to 57 °F. If milk is the liquid, the mass is firmer. Rapid setting can be induced by using from a third to half the required liquid to put the gelatin into solution. When it is completely dissolved, the remaining liquid is added as finely crushed ice. The liquid is then stirred until the ice is melted. Many add crushed ice to the measure and then fill with water to give the desired amount. For almost immediate setting, one fourth of the liquid may be added at boiling temperature and the mixture stirred over low heat until the gelatin is in solution. Fine ice and water are then added to give proper measure, and the mixture is stirred until it sets.

Plain gelatin must be soaked in cold liquid for about five minutes before it is brought into solution. At 100° F gelatin will go slowly into solution but normally 170° F or more is required for the desired speed of dissolving. Uncooked pineapple and figs contain an enzyme which will destroy the set- ting power of gelatin, and these items should be cooked before being used in gelatin mixtures.

Allow a gelatin mixture to begin to set before adding ingredients which should be dispersed throughout the mass. These should be stirred in just as the mixture becomes sirupy. To whip gelatins, the mixture should be sirupy and the bowl may be set into a bed of crushed ice. Mixing should be rapid, and since this action warms the gelatin, the crushed ice bed is usually required. Other items may be folded into the foam after whipping.

Molded salads are colorful and many attractive patterns or designs are easily made in them. A design may be placed on the bottom of a mold and a thin layer of gelatin at the sirupy stage poured in carefully so as

FIG. 4-26   Variety is obtained in a molded salad when whipped and unwhipped gelatin dessert mixtures are combined. (Courtesy H. J. Heinz Co.)

not to disturb the design. After setting, the remaining portion of the gelatin is poured in. Layering of colors also gives striking contrasts. Part solid and part foam mixtures may be used to give variation. Use of different molds and cutting into different shapes will vary the design. A molded salad square composed of a bottom layer of chopped apples in apple gelatin, a center layer of chopped cranberries and orange peel in cherry gelatin, and a top layer of cottage cheese in lime gelatin gives a harlequin effect.

Tossed Salads

To make a tossed salad, assemble all materials in the work center and break into small pieces, dropping the prepared materials into a large container as they accumulate. A large baker's mixing bowl is excellent, for after the materials are ready for tossing, it facilitates light, deft mixing. Store greens in this bowl. It may be placed on a mobile stand and rolled into a walk-in until the salad is to be dished. Cover in storage with a damp cloth or other good cover to prevent drying out. Frequently one or more chapons (pieces of dry bread rubbed heavily with garlic) are added to enhance flavor. A ravigote of chopped herbs may be added. One of the herbs should be related to the onion family. Toasted croutons or croustades may also be added to the tossed greens at service to give the salad added flavor. Dressings, salt, pepper, and other seasonings that destroy texture should be added just before service or by the customer. Chopped egg, sliced salami, or parmesan cheese may be used as a garnish. These are lightly sprinkled over the dished salad. In some operations, the salad is tossed and served at the table. Set-ups for this should be arranged in the pantry so

FIG. 4-27 Fruit and vegetables combine well to make an attractive salad. Note the pleasing affect achieved by the variety and distinctness of shape of lightly tossed ingredients. (Courtesy Fruit Dispatch Co.)

that all materials are available for mixing. A mobile cart may be used. Salad greens should be fairly dry so they will hold the dressing. Excess moisture also dilutes the dressing. It is preferable to add the oil first and toss, and then add the vinegar or acid ingredient. If raw egg is added, this should be done before adding the oil. Toss well, add the oil, toss again, and then add the acid ingredient and herbs last. Blend in croutons that have been toasted in butter and minced or crushed garlic.

FRUIT SALADS

Most fruit salads are quite fragile and therefore are not tossed. To make a fruit salad mixture containing greens, place broken greens on the bottom of a bowl, then sprinkle well-drained fruit, sized as desired, over the greens. Add more greens, then more fruit, until the salad is prepared. The top layer of fruit may be arranged, if desired. Drizzle salad dressing over the layers as they are made, if service is immediate. If not, add at service. The dressing usually is slightly sweet and the body should be heavy enough to permit some dilution with fruit juices on the fruit.

The time required to prepare arranged fruit salads may be reduced by

FIG. 4-28 Neatly cut, fresh appearing items improve salad appearance. A creamy French or honey-orange dressing goes well with such a salad. (Courtesy Fruit Dispatch Co.)

(a)

(b)

FIG. 4-29 Attractive service as well as attractive salads and quality of food makes for high standards. (a) A canned pear on endive, bordered with cream cheese and filled with currant jelly. (b) A fruit-filled melon served with crisp Melba toast. (Courtesy H. J. Heinz Co.)

planning ahead. Work centers and diagrams of the salad should be carefully set up before proceeding. Sometimes it is desirable to send large fruit or other salads to a buffet or table on platters or bowls, and then to dish them at the table. If so, the salads should be prepared with dishing in mind. Plates should be sent for individual dish-up.

FIG. 4-30   Folding fruit and gelatin into a mixture of mayonnaise and whipped cream to make a mousse-like mixture. This may be frozen and served as a frozen salad. Note use of garnish to add appearance. (Courtesy General Foods, Inc.)

FROZEN SALADS

Fruit or vegetables may be used to prepare frozen salads. Most frequently fruit is used. These are made of whole, sliced, cut, or pureed fruits, either raw or cooked. Nuts may be added, as well as some chopped crisp vegetables, for texture. Not all fruits freeze well. Select ingredients for color as well as for flavor. The base for a frozen salad is usually whipped cream or cream or cottage cheese into which fruit and mayonnaise are lightly folded. The salad is usually sweet, but it should have some contrasting tartness to it.

COMPLETE MEAL SALADS

When a salad is to be a complete meal or a major portion of it, the body will usually be quite substantial. Meat, egg, fish, or cheese may be combined with vegetables, legumes, potatoes, macaroni products, and other ingredients. The body of the dressing will also be substantial, and the dressing is usually mixed in with the ingredients.

HOT SALADS

The preparation of some hot salads requires special attention. Service of these must usually be immediate. A wilted lettuce or dandelion salad loses quality rapidly. These are best made individually. Some hot salads hold well, such as celery root, German potato, slaw, and cauliflower. These may be made in larger quantity in pans, either on top of the range or in ovens. Too great a mass, however, made at one time may result in a messy salad. Ingredients for these more durable hot salads are best marinaded for a short time before being blended. Oil or fat from fried bacon, salt pork, or ham is usually blended with hot vinegar or acid liquid at a ratio of about two to one. Frequently the crisp particles of bacon, ham, or salt pork are left in the dressing. Seasonings and a bit of sugar may be added, and some dressings may be thickened slightly with starch. The ingredients may be warmed, the hot dressing added, and the product served. For the more delicate hot salads made from tender greens, place the salad dressing in a pan and over good heat. Bring it to a boil. Add the greens and toss quickly, coating each particle of green. Serve at once. Skill is required to preserve shape and retain texture. A crisp garnish is used, such as croutons, or diced radishes, celery, cucumber, or cabbage may be added at service. Individual skillets, attractive in design and appearance, may be provided and the salad served in them at the table.

Quantities Required

Bulk in relation to weight may vary considerably with different types of salads. From four to six gallons of tossed salad will be required for 100

FIG. 4-31 Convenience foods save many ingredient manipulations. Note the difference in ingredients used to make the same salad dressing. Operators who seek to reduce labor costs frequently find the convensience food reduces these costs while maintaining quality. (Courtesy General Foods Corp.)

portions. Each portion will measure from ⅔ to 1 cup and weigh about 2 to 2½ ounces. It will take 17 pounds of greens AP or 13 pounds EP to produce this quantity, but if trimming loss is high, the AP quantity may be closer to 20 pounds. If heavy materials, such as celery, cucumbers, or tomatoes, are added, the quantity in pounds may be increased. Some garnishes make salads appear larger, and the amount served may be reduced when such garnishes are used. A No. 12 scoop is frequently used to dish a solid type of salad portion, such as fruit or potato. This holds about three ounces rounded and four heaped. About 10 to 12 portions will be obtained per quart of solid salad material. About a third to a half cup of molded or frozen salad is sufficient for a portion. This makes a piece about two inches by two inches and one inch thick, if cut from pans. About three gallons will be required for 100 portions. When the salad becomes a meal in itself, the portion is usually doubled or increased two and a half times. Additional quantities required for salad preparation will be found in the following tables and in the appendix.

Table 4-5

Yields of Some Common Salad Materials

Item	Normal Portion	Yields
Apples, raw, sliced	½ c, 2 oz	2 salads per apple, 113 size (3 to lb AP) 1½ lb AP equals 1 qt sliced
Apples, raw, diced	1/3 c, 2 oz	1 lb unpared yields 4½ c
Apricots, pitted	4 halves	1 22 lb lug yields about 100 salads
Artichoke, globe	one, medium size	Order 60's to 72's per container
Asparagus	3 to 4 stalks	12 to 15 medium stalks per lb
Avocados	½ medium or 3 to 5 slices	16 slices per avocado, medium size (Calavo)
Bananas	¾ banana, split or 1/3 c slices	25 lb AP gives 100 salads
Cabbage, shredded	1/3 c	7 lb EP yields 50 salads
Carrot, grated	3 oz, ½ c	lb AP equals 3⅓ c
Celery, diced	2 oz, ½ c	3 c diced per lb AP
Cheese, sliced	1 oz, 1 slice	6¼ lb for 100
Cherries, pitted	3 oz, ½ c (12 cherries)	20 lb AP for 100 salads
Chicken, diced	2 oz, 1/3 c	12½ lb EP for 100 salads; 30 lb AP ready-to-cook; 40 lb AP dressed
Crab meat	2 oz, 1/3 c	
Cucumbers, sliced	5 slices	6 inch cucumber yields 30 slices
Endive, curly, underliners	1/20 head	
Endive, curly, chopped	⅛ head	
Endive, French (Whitloof)	1½ to 2 oz	Usually one endive split makes a salad
Escarole	1/12 head	
Figs	2 to 3 medium split	6 6-lb boxes, 48 per box, yields 100 salads
Fish, flaked	2 oz, 1/3 c	16 lb cans salmon or 15 18-oz cans tuna for 100 salads
Grapes	½ c	14 lb AP for 100 salads
Grapefruit	5 sections	12 sections per grapefruit; 42 grapefruit for 100
Lettuce, Boston, underliner	⅛ head	
Lettuce, Boston, chopped	¼ head	
Lettuce, iceberg, underliner	1/15 head	Trimmed head usually weighs lb
Lettuce, iceberg, wedge	1/6 head	
Lettuce, leaf, underliner	2 leaves	12 to 15 leaves per bunch
Lettuce, leaf, chopped	¼ bunch	
Lettuce, Romaine, underliner	1/10 head	
Lettuce, Romaine, chopped	⅛ head	
Lobster meat	2 oz, 1/3 c	
Onions, sliced	2 oz, 4 slices	Purchase Bermudas or sweet Spanish; 1 lb AP diced yields about 2½ c
Onions, green, diced		1 lb AP yields 2½ to 3 c
Oranges, sliced	½ orange, 3 slices	6 to 8 slices or 8 to 9 sections per orange

Table 4-5 (continued)

Yields of Some Common Salad Materials

Item	Normal Portion	Yields
Oranges, diced	3 oz, ½ c	8 to 9 doz medium size will yield 100 salads
Pears	½ pear	120 per box
Persimmon	1 whole	8 wedges may also be obtained per persimmon
Pineapple, sliced	2 half slices	100 salads per case of 24 size pineapple (fresh)
Potatoes, new diced	3 oz, ½ c	2 lb AP yields 1 qt diced
Meat, ground	1¾ oz, 1/3 c	
Meat, diced	2 oz, 1/3 c	
Meat, sliced	3 to 4 oz, 2 slices	
Melon, cantaloupe, ring	1 ring	8 rings per melon, 36 to 45 size
Melon, cantaloupe, balls	8 balls	30 to 35 balls per cantaloupe, 36 to 45 size
Salmon (See fish, flaked above)		
Shrimp, small or Pacific	2 oz, 1/3 c	
Shrimp, large, diced	2 oz, 1/3 c	Serve four 25 to 33 per lb shrimp per salad
Tangerine	5 sections	10 sections per tangerine
Tuna (See fish, flaked above)		
Turkey meat	2 oz, 1/3 c	12½ lb net, 25 lb AP dressed, 20 lb AP ready-to-cook
Tomato, slices	3 slices ⅜ in.	about 6 slices per tomato; for 100 salads purchase 17 lb AP
Tomatoes, diced	1¾ oz, 1/3 c	
Watercress	¼ bunch	15 bunches per basket; 1 basket is about 3 lb

Table 4-6

Quantities of Salad Dressing Required

Item	Portion	Yield
Cheese, bleu	1½ T	Use 5 oz bleu cheese per quart dressing
French	1½ T	Use 2¼ qt per 100
Mayonnaise or salad dressing	1½ T	Use 2¼ qt per 100

Table 4-7

Yields and Portions for Some First Course Accompaniments

Item	Portion	Quantity per Pound
Cheese Straws	1 or 2	32
Saltines	1 or 2	130 to 140
Soda, 2 inch square	1 or 2	100
Soda, large	1	50
Toast, Melba	1 or 2	30
Potato chips or shoestring potatoes (See Table 4-9 on garnish yields)		

Appetizers

An appetizer is a small food used to whet the appetite. It may take the form of an hors d'oeuvre, a relish, a canapé, or a cocktail. Appetizers may be served as the first course either at the table or to guests before they are seated. They may also be used as snacks at social gatherings and receptions. When used for the latter purpose, wide variety is characteristic; the appetizers may be passed to guests or guests may go to a buffet to serve themselves or be served there.

Hors d'oeuvres and Canapés

Originally, an hors d'oeuvre was a hot or cold food served immediately after the soup at a formal banquet. Used in this manner, it was a timbale, a creamed dish, or bits of seafood or other food in aspic. The Russians changed the hors d'oeuvre to a food passed to guests as they sipped drinks at social gatherings or before a meal. They called them "flying dishes" because they were passed by hurrying servants, but today a more common name for them is "finger foods." Today an hors d'oeuvre is any small piece of piquant, appetizing food served as an appetizer. A relish is a special type of hors d'oeuvre which is either a crisp fresh vegetable or a pickled item. The term "relish" may also be properly used to indicate pickles, conserves, or sweetened vegetables or fruits served with a meal. A relish on a French menu may be called a *goût piquant*.

Chilled hors d'oeuvres may be celery sticks made into curls, or celery hearts. Raw cauliflower buds are excellent for dipping into tangy mixtures.

FIG. 4-32 An attractive array of appetizers awaiting service. The hors d'oeuvres on picks are placed into a triangle made of pieces of French bread.

Cauliflower or other vegetables partially cooked and marinated in a spicy vinegar make good appetizers. Red or white cabbage sliced thinly, allowed to make a brine for four days in a refrigerator, just brought to a boil in spiced sweet vinegar, and then drained and chilled, is an excellent relish. Tidbits of cheese, smoked oysters or clams, cantaloupe or watermelon pickles, pickled walnuts or mushrooms, as well as the more common pickled items, such as olives plain or stuffed, chow chow, chutney, smoked meats, fish or sausages, thinly sliced meat, cheese, or other foods may be used. Items such as cheese straws, small choux pastes filled with tangy mixtures, fritters, tiny patties, or rissoles may be used. Hor d'oeuvres may be hot, and sometimes a tangy sauce is served with them for dipping. Usually picks or forks are offered with foods that do not lend themselves to picking and eating with the fingers. Oysters broiled in bacon wraps, tiny hot croquettes, hot timbales or mousselines, hot choux pastes or rissoles or patties filled with tangy foods, rolled minced clam pancakes, tiny rolled pancakes filled with sour cream or caviar, deep-fried clams, fried frog legs, mussels, shrimps or other shellfish, snails bordelaise, hot casseroles or golden duck, oyster or clam poulette, tangy deviled lobster, or other hot dishes may be used.

The canapé is another appetizer used as a finger food. Its nature and preparation have been discussed previously under sandwiches.

Simple or high decoration may be desirable. Usually hors d'oeuvres and canapés receive considerable decoration, but at times simplicity may achieve more than high decoration in pleasing effect. Blending of some decorated items with simply decorated ones may give the desired effect. All products should be neat and trim. Good flavor, form, color and texture and bright freshness are essential. Overworked form, color, or design and dried edges or a wilted appearance should be avoided. Good pattern in presenting food in napkins or doilies should be sought. The pattern achieved should be distinct and pleasing. Set up the design ahead; if necessary draw diagrams so workers may achieve a satisfactory pattern. Blend together on one platter or tray different items with varying shapes, heights, colors, and flavors.

If appetizers are to be efficiently produced in quantity, good planning must be done. Many manipulations are required. As in all pantry work, good prepreparation or lining up is necessary. The materials and equipment required should be brought together at one work center so the final assembly can proceed rapidly. It is best to process one kind all at one time and then move on to another type. Make one motion do as much work as possible. It is a waste of time to cut celery into small individual short pieces and then fill each piece with a cheese mixture from a pastry tube. Four long strips of celery can be filled and then cut at one time, reducing handling. When edges or designs are to be placed on items, wait until a large tray or batch is ready

FIG. 4-33 A student fills small cream puff shells with a tangy cheese filling for hot canapés for a cocktail buffet.

and then do the job at one time. Attempt to do as many repetitive motions as possible together and not break them up. Refrigerate a completed batch under moisture-vapor-proof wraps while making other batches. Create another work center for final assembly of the different items. Place onto trays, dishes, or platters, with picks stuck into fruit and vegetables, or use other types of holders. Mass some items, such as stuffed olives or pickles, in a center dish and use individually decorated pieces around this center.

Cocktails

Cocktails may be either alcoholic or non-alcoholic. The former are usually consumed before the guests enter the dining room. Hors d'oeuvres or canapés may be served with cocktails. When this is done, the first course, melon or oysters, may be omitted on a formal dinner. Alcohol in any quantity blunts the appetite. Therefore, aperitifs or wines that have flavor qualities that stimulate the appetite are recommended. These might be vermouth, dry sherry, madeira, Byrrh, or Dubonnet. A fruit punch with or without alcoholic spirits is sometimes used. Cocktails, such as martinis, manhattans, or sweet drinks, such as daiquiris, are apt to deaden the appetite.

Serve the cocktail in its proper glass. Aperitifs should usually be served in two-ounce portions. Recipes for mixed drinks may be obtained from any authoritative bartender's guide; each recipe, except for punches, flips, or drinks commonly served to large gatherings, is for one cocktail. Some common measures are:

Dash	3 drops
Pony	1 fluid ounce or 2 T
Jigger	1 ½ to 2 fluid ounces (3 to 4 T), usually 2 fluid ounces
Part	More or less than a jigger, depending upon individual taste
Split	1 c or ½ pint

A silver or glass shaker or large container is used for mixing cocktails. Cocktails that contain wine as a principal ingredient are stirred with a glass rod or silver spoon. Few of these are shaken. Other types of cocktails are shaken. Cocktails should not be left standing with ice in them. If they must be held, make them, remove the ice, and chill. Cocktails should not be stored in metallic containers, for the flavor of the metal may cause a loss in quality. Serve aperitifs at proper temperature; some should be chilled, while others should be served at room temperature. Service bars should be set up so that the work proceeds rapidly and easily.

Fruit or vegetable juices may be passed to guests in the same manner as alcoholic drinks before a meal. It is usually advisable to include some of these with alcoholic cocktails for guests who do not drink.

First Course Cocktails

Raw oysters or clams on the half shell, or a slice of melon or mango with a wedge of lemon or lime, is frequently used for a first course, especially for a formal meal. Other first courses may be a juice, a fruit or vegetable cup, or a flaked fish or seafood cocktail. It is also proper to serve canapés or hors d'oeuvres as a first course to guests seated at a table. The canapé or hors d'oeuvres are usually more substantial than the finger foods served in the drawing room. It is proper to offer a variety of hors d'oeuvres. Italian antipastos, hot foods in tangy sauce, and other foods may also be passed as a first course. Fruit cups, flaked crab meat, shrimp, lobster, or mixtures of these (other than fruit cups) may be served with a cold sauce over them.

A fruit or vegetable cup should possess attractive colors and be fresh appearing. Colors which contrast pleasantly and are bright, clear, and natural are desirable. Distinctness of form, with pieces in small bite size and of contrasting shape and size, may be used to make a pleasing appearance. Sameness of texture should be avoided. Fresh fruits should be used in season, served in their own juices or in sweetened fruit juice. Canned or cooked dried fruits may be combined with fresh fruits. The fruit cup should not be too sweet; the natural sweetness and acids of the fruit should serve to stimulate the appetite. Contrasts in flavors should be sought if they blend happily. Fruits that tarnish may be dipped into citrus or pineapple juice to keep their colors bright. Usually the liquid on the cocktail is sufficiently acid, however, to prevent this from occurring.

Combinations of fruit juices or combinations of vegetable juices may be used as cocktails to give flavor variety. Colors should be natural, bright, and clear. Carbonized water or sweetened carbonized drinks may be added to fruit juices. Frosted fruit juices may be served; a coarsely frozen frappe is popular, or sherbet or ice may be dished at the last minute into a glass of fruit juice.

Cocktails made of flaked crab or other seafood or fish are popular. Some chopped vegetables, such as celery, cucumber, or other crisp food, may be combined with the main item to give desired crispness, but not to extend or cheapen the cocktail. As in the fruit or vegetable cup, pieces should be of bite size and distinct in form. Color contrasts should be sought; variety and interesting combinations of foods increase appeal. Flavors of blends should be pleasing. A cocktail sauce may be used to give heightened flavor, but the delicate flavor of the basic ingredients should not be destroyed by the sauce. Too much seasoning or too tart a sauce will lower eating pleasure.

Quantities Required

The number of appetizers required in finger foods to be passed may be difficult to determine. The varieties served may govern the quantities required, and the popularity of one type over another may mean it must be produced in greater quantity. The type of function, its length, and other factors will have much to do with the quantity required. Usually, if from three to eight small pieces of food are planned for a social gathering, the quantity is found sufficient. While the range may seem wide, factors specific to the gathering will dictate whether to prepare the minimum or maximum.

Bowls of dips and crisp foods which are easy to replenish may assist in giving flexibility. Some operations plan a run-out time, and toward the end of service have only a few foods remaining, the variety at that time being quite limited.

About 1¼ to 1½ ounces of base material will be required for a meat or fish cocktail, plus about ½ to 1 ounce (1 to 2 T) of sauce. A cocktail glass holds usually about 3 ounces. About eight to ten pounds of crab, lobster or other flaked fish will be required for 100 cocktails. Liquid or solidly packed materials, such as a fruit cup, oysters, or clams, will be required in full 3-ounce (⅓ c) portions, or about 2 to 2¼ gallons (16 to 18 pounds) per 100 portions. Juices are served in about four-ounce portions in special juice glasses. The use of large cocktail glasses with a heavy underline of lettuce, greens, or much chopped celery for fish or seafood cocktails to give the impression of a larger portion is not recommended.

Table 4-8

Appetizer Yields

Item	Portion	Yield
Carrot strips	2 to 3⅛ in. julienne, 3 in. long	90 strips per lb EP
Carrot curls	2 curls	8 per carrot, 6 to 8 carrots per lb EP
Celery curls	1 curl	3½ lb EP or 4½ lb AP yields 100 curls
Clams, Cherrystone	4 clams in shell	300 per bushel
Crab meat	1¼ to 2 oz	8 to 12 cocktails per lb EP
Crab legs	2 to 3 legs	about 18 to 22 dungeness crab legs to the lb
Fruit cocktail	3 oz, 1/3 c	2 1/3 gal for 100 cocktails
Melon cup, balls	9 balls	30 balls per cantaloupe, 36 per crate; 54 per honeydew melon, 8 per crate
Melon cup, diced	3 oz	12 oz per cantaloupe, 36 per crate; 30 oz per honeydew, 8 per crate
Melon, slice		¼ cantaloupe, 45's, 1/6 Persian, 1/8 casaba and 1/6 honeydew
Onions, green	3 whole	Purchase 5 lb AP for 100
Orange cup	1 orange	8 to 9 sections per orange
Orange juice	4 oz	3 32-oz cans frozen concentrated; 11 qts juice from Florida oranges and 9 qts from California per 4/5 bu carton
Oysters, Bluepoint, unshucked	4 oysters	300 cocktails per bushel; serve in shell cocktails
Oysters, Olympia, shucked	1¼ oz	100/per gal
Oysters, small, shucked	2 oz, ¼ c	4 to 5 oysters, 60 per qt
Pineapple cup	3 oz, ½ c	20 oz diced, 24 size pineapple per crate
Punch	3 oz	1 punch cup
Shrimp, small Pacific	1½ oz, 1/3 c	9 lb EP for 100 cocktails
Shrimp, jumbo or large	4 to 5 shrimp	25 to 33 per lb green headless

Table 4-9

Garnish Yields

Item	Portion	Yield
Apples, sliced	2 thin wedges	12 wedges per 113 size apple
Apples, ring	1 ring	5 rings per 113 size apple
Apricots	½ or 1	20 halves or 40 wedges per pound
Avocado	1 slice	30 slices per avocado, 24 per crate size
Banana, split, 1 inch slice	1 or 3 round slices	12 bananas or 2½ c slices per lb AP; 1 banana (3 to lb AP) yields 30 1 inch slices split
Blackberries	3 berries	1 qt yields 100 berries
Blueberries	3 to 5	1 qt (1½ lb) 360 to 800 berries
Cantaloupe	3 balls or small wedges	30 balls or 45 wedges per 45 size per crate
Capers	1 t	10 to 15 capers per t
Carrots (See Table 4-8)		
Celery (See Table 4-8)		
Cheese, shredded, moist	1 T (½ oz)	
Cheese, shredded, dry	1 T (¼ oz)	
Cheese, cream	2 T (1 oz)	for stuffing celery
Cheese, cottage	1 No. 20 scoop,	1½ oz
Cherries, maraschino	½ or 1	640 per gal
Cherries, sweet, fresh	1	40 per lb
Chocolate tidbits	1 T	40 portions per lb
Coconut, long shred	1 T rounded	1 lb equals 6½ c or 60 portions
Currants	3 currants	1 lb equals 150 currants
Dates	1 date	60 dates per lb
Decorettes	1 t	160 portions per lb
Endive, curly	1 leaf	45 per head
Figs	1 fig	48 per box, 6 lb
Grapes	3 grapes	50 grapes per lb, medium size
Grapefruit	1 to 2 sections	12 sections per grapefruit
Kumquats	1 kumquat	1 lb equals 24 kumquats
Lemons, wedge	1/6 to 1/8 lemon	1 doz lemons yield 144 rind twists
Limes, wedge	¼ to 1/6 lime	1 doz limes yield 62 twists or rind
Mint	2 to 3 leaves	300 leaves per bunch
Mushrooms, cap	1 cap	15 to 20 caps per lb AP
Nuts, chopped	1 T	1 lb chopped is 4 c
Nuts, salted for tea	1 T	1 lb nuts is about 4 c; use 3 lb for 100 people
Walnuts, whole	½ walnut	8 oz is 2 c or about 150 halves
Oranges, sections	3	8 to 9 sections per 82 size orange; 1 doz orange rinds yields 164 rind twists
Olives, green	1 or 2	1 qt (1¼ lb) equals 100 extra large
Olives, stuffed, sliced	1 or 2	1 medium size olive yields 6 slices
Olives, ripe	1 or 2	1 qt small size yields 120 olives
Parsley, curly	1 sprig	80 sprigs per bunch
Peach	1 wedge	8 wedges per medium peach
Pear	1 wedge or slice	12 wedges per 5 oz pear
Pepper, ring	1	10 rings per medium size pepper
Pickles, sweet, medium (3 in.)*	½ pickle	24 pickles per qt
Pineapple	1 wedge or 2 to 3 diced pieces	60 wedges or 150 diced pieces per 18 size pineapple
Plums, Santa Rosa	1 medium	70 per till (5 x 5 size)
Pomegranate	5 seeds	25 garnishes per pomegranate
Potato chips or shoestring potatoes	¾ oz	1 c; eight ounces is about 2½ qt
Prunes, dried	1	30 to 40 per lb AP

Table 4-9 (continued)

Garnish Yields

Item	Portion	Yield
Radishes	1 or 2	15 to 20 per bunch; 1 bunch 10 oz; $1\frac{1}{2}$ c topped and tailed equals 8 oz or about 25 radishes
Raspberries	5	1 qt yields 300 berries
Rhubarb	1 or 2 curls	1 lb yields 100 curls
Sardines	1 3 in. long	1 lb yields 48 sardines
Strawberries	1	1 qt yields 60 medium size berries
Tangerines	3 to 4 sections	10 sections per tangerine
Tomatoes	1 wedge	8 wedges per medium tomato
Watercress	1 sprig	30 sprigs per bunch

*Pickles sized per gallon are frequently used: Gherkins 200, pickle rings or slices 400, small sweets (3 in.) 80 to 100, large dills ($4\frac{1}{2}$ in.) 25.

Garnishes

Garniture is a task for every section of the kitchen, but it probably is used more extensively in the pantry and *garde manger* sections than any other. In some kitchens the bakeshop will do much decoration of desserts. In the *garde manger* section it may reach a high peak in the decoration of cold meats, ice carvings, or other pieces which are used to garnish a buffet or table.

Wide variety may be obtained in many hot foods, such as sauces and soups, by using garnishes. Many variations for consommé are achieved by using different garnishes. Similarly, sauces may be changed in nature by the use of garnishes. Elaborate garnishes once practiced in continental cooking are losing favor, and more and more simplicity and goodness in food are receiving emphasis rather than decoration. Some garnishes are traditional. Some may be more accompaniments than garnishes, such as the Yorkshire pudding with roast beef, or sautéed mushroom buttons on a broiled steak. Mushrooms, truffles, diced breast of poultry, salipiçon of meats (a mixture of meats or fish or shellfish with mushrooms cut into pieces $\frac{3}{16}$ to $\frac{1}{4}$ inch and diced), chicken livers, pâté de fois gras, julienne or macedoine (half inch cubes) of cooked vegetables, finely chopped vegetables and seasonings of fine herbs, stuffed vegetables, tiny deep-fried calves' brain or sweetbread pieces, purees of vegetables, small fritters or choux pastes filled with piquant foods, cooked cereals (such as barley), glazes (such as cranberry or brown sugar for ham), milt or roe of fish, tiny sausages or sliced sausages, olives, pickles, cheese, fresh fruits, and a host of other items are used as garnishes. Different types of forcemeat may also be used. A forcemeat is made by pulping raw flesh, adding egg yolks, mixing well, seasoning, and poaching tiny pieces of this mixture in hot broth. If white meat and egg whites are used, the garnish is called not a forcement but a mousseline. A quenelle is a molded forcemeat or mousseline. A godiveau

is a forcemeat made from kidney and suet instead of meat. A meat timbale
is a molded forcemeat larger than a quenelle.

Standard

All garnishes should be edible and should complement the flavor, color,
and texture of the foods they garnish. They may be hot or cold. Good design,
color, and texture contrast should be sought. Excessive pattern, color, or
form should be avoided. Natural colors are desirable, and designs should be
simple. The use of the garnish should dictate its elaborateness. A high degree
of garnish may be required on a wedding cake, *chaud-froid* piece, or pieces
which emphasize an occasion, but simplicity at other times may be far more
appealing. A red strawberry, a few sugar-glazed grapes, or a few pome-
granate seeds will suffice for a fruit salad, while a few capers, a sprig of
chervil, or a cheese wedge may do much for a cold plate. A grilled ripe
tomato slice, a lemon wedge, a broiler-browned spiced pear filled with currant
jelly, or a sprinkle of bright spring vegetables will increase interest by goodness as much as by color or design. Cream of corn soup may be given extra
appeal when garnished with a few croutons of popped corn. None of these
garnishes requires much labor. The cost of labor must be considered in
using garnishes. Too frequently emphasis is given to the garnish rather
than to the quality of the food it accompanies. No garnish should draw attention away from the food it graces. An imitation flower may be used to
decorate a woman's hat, and the hat may be used to decorate the woman,
but when the flower becomes the center of attraction, taking away attention
from both the hat and the woman, an extreme in taste occurs. The greatest
art is simple. Freshness of appearance in the garnish, good taste in color,
and form or texture will be appealing factors. The appearance of overworked
food, dried brown edges, and a wilted condition destroys appeal in spite of
high design and color. The size of the garnish should be related to the size
of the food it garnishes.

Elaborate garnish with *chaud-froid* (sho-frwa) may be desirable. A
chaud-froid is a cooked food, chilled and then covered with a gelatin glaze,
the glaze being usually decorated with pieces of food in it. Two types of
glaze are used: an aspic or clear gelatin mixture seasoned with beef, chicken,
or fish stock; or a *chaud-froid* glaze, made by adding gelatin to a cream sauce
or mayonnaise, mayonnaise being especially desirable for fish items. Designs
made from pieces of pimiento, beets, ripe olives, truffles, cucumbers, green
pepper, chives, leeks, lemon peel, carrots, or other fruits and vegetables are
used. The glaze, when ready to set but still in liquid form, is poured over
the food piece until it is covered. It is then set into a refrigerator to chill,
and after the glaze is set, another layer of glaze is applied until a complete
covering is obtained; this may require from five to eight applications of

the glaze. The design is set into the glaze on the last coating. A light wash of clear aspic may be used to cover the design after it is set into the glaze.

FIG. 4-34   A broken emulsion can be reformed by adding it slowly with good agitation to some unbroken emulsion or liquid, such as vinegar, water, or egg yolks.

FIG. 4-35   Make up and stack filled sandwiches on a cutting board. An electric carving knife is a sharp operator when used to cut stacks of sandwiches. Fast, crumbless, even cutting is done effectively without tilting the knife. Grasp handle of electric knife, position over sandwiches to be cut, start knife, then level and guide it by the handle down through the stacked sandwiches. Release current as soon as stack is cut, repeat until all sandwiches are sliced.

(a)

(b)

(c)

(d)

FIG. 4-36 (a) Variety in salads with different underliners and bodies is shown. Note variation achieved in form and texture by using different types of foods and different cutitng patterns. (b) Good form, texture, and quality are evident in this salid. (c) The method for making
some simple garnishes is shown. (d) The hot salad is oftentimes forgotten but can be tremen-
dously popular on any menu.

5 Stocks, Soups, Sauces, and Gravies

Soups, sauces, and gravies are closely related foods in that they are made from a stock which can be the same for any of them. Their differences frequently are matters of consistency, a few ingredients, or seasonings.

STOCKS

The quality of many foods made in the kitchen is directly related to the quality of the stocks produced there. Stocks are not made; they are

FIG. 5-1 Good stock results when fresh, high-quality ingredients are given proper preparation. Here stocks are shown simmering on top of a range.

built in a painstaking process of blending good ingredients into a flavorful liquid which also possesses good body and color.

A stock is a thin liquid flavored by the soluble substances from meat, poultry, fish, vegetables, and seasonings. The terms *stock*, *broth*, and *bouillon* are not synonymous. A broth is a simple stock served as a soup, with perhaps a few simple ingredients added. A bouillon is a clarified broth with a definite rich beefy flavor. Stocks are used for many foods made in the kitchen other than soups, sauces, and gravies.

Stocks may be concentrated. If a stock is reduced one-fourth its volume, it is called a glaze, and if one-half its volume, it is called a demi-glaze. These glazes are used to enrich soups, sauces, and gravies. Prepared soup bases are being used more and more in kitchens to replace the glazes. A demi-glaze made from meat stock is called *glacé de viande*, from fish stock, *glacé de poisson,* and from chicken stock, *glacé de poulet.* When foods (usually fish or game) are simmered in or steamed over a concentrated stock, the stock is call a *fumet* or *essence.*[1] A rich fish stock used in this manner is more frequently called a *court bouillon.*

Ingredients

Not all products contributing to the flavor of meat have been identified. Meat and bones give stock its primary flavor. Much of this flavor comes from protein substances, non-protein nitrogenous fractions, and fat. The aromatic substances from fat are perhaps most influential, for they give meat its characteristic flavor. Fat also contributes richness to a stock. Flesh from different animals and even parts of the same animal will differ in flavor. The leg and breast of a chicken are different in flavor. Some meats such as turkey or lamb have an astringent and pungent flavor. The meat from pork is acid. Different meats are used in stock for their flavor contributions. Lamb and mutton products give stocks with such distinctive flavor that they have restricted use. Poultry makes good stock, especially older chicken. Turkey gives a rich but somewhat strongly flavored stock. The flavor substances in flesh are more soluble in salted than in unsalted water. Gelatin derived from meat and bones is desirable in a stock to give body. If from one to two ounces of gelatin are extracted with each gallon of stock, the stock will gel. Sometimes gelatin is added to give body and to make a stock gel. The flavor of a stock is modified by soluble substances extracted from vegetables and seasonings. The color is also governed by the color of the ingredients used. The browning of meat, bones, and vegetables gives a dark color and a heightened flavor.

[1]The terms *fumet* and *essence* are also used to indicate the use of concentrated flavors or flavoring items such as "essence of mushroom" or "fumet de concombre."

(a)

(b)

(c)

(d)

FIG. 5-2. (a) Ingredients for making a good stock. (b) A *mirepoix*. (c) Washing the bones for a stock. (d) Steam-jacketed kettles are excellent for making stocks.

The bones for stock are usually well trimmed of meat, cut into three- to four-inch lengths, and split. Knuckle and shank or neck bones are preferred for stock, in that order. If bones are put into a stock pot or steam-jacketed kettle equipped with a spigot, washing them with cold water is facilitated. Young animals' bones and meat are high in natural gelatin. Bones showing rich red centers and good red marrow give a good flavored stock. Bones,

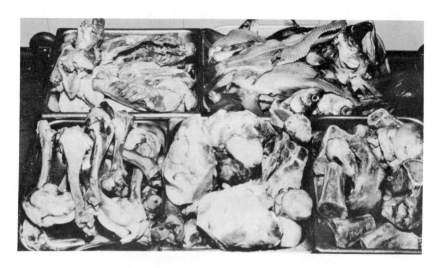

FIG. 5-3 Types of bones frequently used for making stocks: (bottom from right to left) beef, veal, and lamb; (top from right to left) white fleshed fish and chicken.

trimmings, and skin from cured, smoked meats may be used to give specific flavor. Uncured pork bones are used in small amounts with other bones for some stocks.

Meat is usually not washed. The tougher cuts of meat from older animals give a richer flavor and a darker color. Lean meat is preferred. Meat may be diced into one-inch cubes, but if it is to be used for other dishes, it is preferable to leave it in larger chunks so that it may be removed more easily when it is done.

For one gallon of good stock, use four pounds of meat and bones with one pound of mixed vegetables to five quarts of lightly salted water. Other seasonings may be added. For extra-rich stocks, the quantity of meat and bones may be doubled. (Mixed chopped vegetables used are called a *mirepoix*, and mixed seasonings in a cloth bag are called *bouquet garni* or *sachet*.) The water should cover stock materials. Many good stocks result as by-products from steaming or boiling meat or poultry.

Because stocks may later be reduced in volume, seasonings should be light and the *bouquet garni* bag removed after the correct seasoning has been obtained. Many chefs prefer leeks to onions because they give a milder flavor. Vegetables and seasonings are oftentimes added about midway in the cooking to prevent them from giving harsh or bitter flavors to the stock. Some chefs pick out the small round nubs on the tops of whole cloves, feeling that the flavor contributed with this removed is milder.

Procedures

Steam-jacketed kettles are preferred for stock building, but stock kettles are also used for cooking on top of the range. Each should have a spigot from which stock can be withdrawn from the bottom without disturbing solid materials there.

Bones and meat from beef should be simmered for six to ten hours.[2] Meat and bones from young animals and chickens are cooked a shorter time than this and fish is usually not cooked longer than 1½ hours. Flavor in cooking meat develops up to about three or four hours and then declines, but the smooth, mellow flavor in a stock does not develop until gelatin and other compounds are extracted after this. Stocks should be simmered (185° F), not boiled; extended cooking may cause a stock to cloud; hard boiling increases the tendency to cloud. Slightly more flavor is extracted when a stock is started in cold water, but it is doubtful if there is any increase in nutrients.[3] Most meat compounds, soluble only in cold water, coagulate when the water temperature rises, and this coagulated substance is usually skimmed away. A clearer stock is obtained when the start is in hot water. Many chefs recommend blanching the bones and meat first by bringing them quickly to a boil from a cold water start. They then discard this liquor, add more cold water, a bit of salt, vegetables, and seasonings, and then simmer until a good stock is obtained. Chicken stock is milder in flavor when such blanching is done. The stock when done is strained from the bones, meat, and vegetables through several thicknesses of cheese cloth into a stock pot. Cooling should be rapid. The remaining meat on the bones may be trimmed off and used for prepared dishes.

Many kitchens keep a stock pot simmering continually. To do this, fresh bones are added to lightly salted water, and then as clean, edible foods accumulate, such as vegetable trimmings, vegetables left in the steam table at the end of service, liquor from cooked and canned vegetables, bones from roasts and poultry, and other products, they are added. Stock from this pot

[2]Escoffier says "at least 10 to 12 hours of cooking" should occur before the materials "can yield all their soluble properties."
[3]The nutrient value of stocks is small, but meat flavors in stocks whet the appetite and start the flow of gastric juices.

FIG. 5-4   (a) A stock should be simmered, never boiled. The stock on the right has been boiled for a long period, while the sample shown on the left was extracted from the same stock after two hours of slow simmering.

FIG. 5-4   (b) Stocks will gel if they contain about one or more ounces of gelatin per gallon of stock. Gelatin is extracted from bones late in their simmering.

is withdrawn as required, and the amount removed plus evaporative loss is replaced from time to time with fresh water. Once started, stock from such a pot may be used up to four or five days. After this, the stock becomes too weak for use. It may also cloud.

FIG. 5-5 To cool a stock rapidly, cover after placing into a sink. Allow cold water to run slowly into the sink, the overflow going through the overflow outlet. Insert a small object under the pot so the cold water will flow under the bottom.

Stock Care

Stock may sour or spoil quickly, for it is an excellent culture for bacteria. Constant overnight simmering is desirable if the stock is in a steam-jacketed kettle. A stock pot on the range should not be left overnight without being cooled in a running water bath or being placed in a cool, well-ventilated area. Cover finished stock in its container and cool at room temperature until the temperature is around 110° to 120° F. Use a water bath around the stock pot to induce rapid cooling, inserting something under the bottom to allow water circulation there too. Stirring speeds cooling, and giving maximum surface area to stocks also helps. After cooling, place under refrigeration at 35° to 40° F. Fat may be left on the top to congeal and give a protective seal. If stocks are left over four hours between 50° to 140° F, reboil and use or chill. Maximum storage is seven to ten days at 40° F. Reheating, recooling, and returning a stock to refrigeration lower stock quality.

Clarification

Stock may be clarified by two methods. The first is to cool or chill it 24
hours and then decant, pouring the clear stock from the settled products. If
a rich stock will gel in this time, decant just before it gels while it is still in

(a)

(b)

(c)

(d)

FIG. 5-6   (a) Strain stocks through several thicknesses of cheese cloth. Be careful, in
taking the last bit of stock, not to allow flocculent materials to flow off with the stock.
(b) One method of clarifying a stock is to decant after chilling. Here a stock that is about
to gel is being decanted to rid it of flocculent materials that have accumulated on the
bottom. (c) Ingredients used for clarifying a stock. Note the well browned onions added
to increase color and flavor. (d) To allow the raft to act as a filter, break away a small
piece and allow the stock to bubble up and over the raft with a slow roll.

the sirupy stage. The preferred method of clarification is to blend two raw egg whites into one cup of cold water and mix well with 1½ pounds of lean, ground beef. This is added to five quarts of cool rich stock and then heated very slowly to a slow rolling simmer. The mixture should not be disturbed after coagulation of the egg whites and meat begins. Seasonings and chopped vegetables may be added at the same time the meat and egg mixture is blended into the stock. The coagulated mixture will slowly rise to the top, carrying with it much of the flocculent material. This coagulated mass is called the *raft* or *crust*. A small portion of this is broken off so the stock can bubble up through the break, letting the raft act as a filter. After about one hour, the clarified stock is drawn off through a spigot and strained through several thicknesses of cloth. Care must be taken that clouding materials from the bottom of the pot or from the raft are not allowed to run off with the clear stock. This remaining liquid and the raft may be added to a new stock. The yield from five quarts of stock is one gallon of clarified stock.

Types of Stock
Stock is best classified by its color, which is either brown or white. Brown stock is made from well browned beef and veal bones, but sometimes

FIG. 5-7   A brown and a white stock.

browned lamb or mutton bones and flesh are used instead. White stocks are made of unbrowned flesh and bones of meat, fish, or poultry. The type should be suited to the product: beef stock for a bouillon, mutton stock for a Scotch mutton broth, white fish stock for a Normandy sauce, chicken stock for a cocky-leeky soup, brown stock for a bordelaise sauce, and so forth.

Brown Stock

A brown stock results from heavy browning of meat, bones, and vegetables in a hot oven. Some fat is added to assist in browning. Thick slices of onion may be set directly on top of a hot griddle or range top and be heavily

FIG. 5-8   Browning bones, meat, and vegetables to make a brown stock.

browned to give extra-deep color and a richer browned flavor. Salt delays browning and should be added later. Add only in minimum quantity so, in later reduction, excess salt will not be a problem. Tomatoes, tomato puree, or tomato trimmings are oftentimes added.

White Stock

Unbrowned meat, bones, and vegetables are used for a white stock. The finest white stocks are obtained from chicken or veal. Bony chicken carcass parts may be purchased at nominal cost. *Mirepoix, bouquet garni,* and other products added should be light-colored so the color of the stock will not be darkened; some chefs even avoid carrots, while others are not so particular. A white fish stock is made from fish trimmings and bones. White, lean deep-sea fish, such as cod, haddock, whiting, and snapper, or flat-bottom-type fish, such as sole or flounder, should be used; fat fish, such as salmon, sablefish (black cod), and mackerel, give a heavy-flavored and darker colored stock. Seasonings may be slightly more pungent for fish stock. Simmering time should be short, for clouding occurs easily.

Tables 5-1 and 5-2 indicate how stocks are used to derive many different soups and sauces. These tables are not all-inclusive and are simplified; they merely indicate the derivation and wide range of products possible from basic stocks.

SOUPS

Soups at one time were used for a complete meal dish only. Carême, one of the early great chefs, first introduced soup as a beginning course. He felt that light soups, many of which he originated, stimulated the appetite and

Table 5-1
Soups and their Derivation

Meat	Neutral*

BROWN STOCK
Bouillon (beef base)
  French Onion (onions)
  Tomato Bouillon with Rice (tomato ragout and cooked rice)
  Windsor Bouillon (spaetzels of egg, flour, and cream)
Jellied Bouillon
  Avocado Jellied Bouillon (puree of avocado, sour cream garnish)
  Beet Bouillon, Polonaise (minced beets, beet juice, sherry, lemon juice, sour cream garnish)
Consommé
  Argenteuil Consommé (asparagus tip (garnish)
  Vaudoise Consommé (leeks, white turnips, and parsnips julienne)
  Vert-Pré Consommé (tapioca, green peas, string beans, asparagus tips, spinach puree)
Broth
  Beef Broth (rice or macaroni products are usually added)
  Scotch Broth (lamb or mutton stock, pearl barley, diced vegetables)
  Vermicelli Broth (vermicelli)
	TOMATO
	  Cream of Tomato Soup (blend tomato velouté with hot milk or cream)
	  Moute Rouge Soup (carrots, potatoes, marjoram, tarragon)
	  Mongole Soup (equal parts puree of split pea and tomato ragout)
	  Madreilene Soup (consommé in equal parts to tomato and beet juice)
	
	MILK
	Cream Soups[1]
	  Cream of Asparagus (white sauce, asparagus, liason)
	  Cream of Broccoli Soup (white sauce, broccoli, liason)
	  Cream of Spinach Soup (white sauce, spinach, liason)
	Bisques[1]
	  Oyster Bisque (crushed and mashed poached oysters in cream sauce, hot milk)
	  Scallop Bisque (pulp of cooked scallops in cream sauce, hot milk)
	
	*Neutral means that meat is not a product.

[1] A cream or white sauce, a velouté sauce thinned with rich milk or cream, or a bechamel may be used interchangably in making the numerous cream soups.

Table 5-1 (continued)
Soups and their Derivation

Meat

WHITE STOCK[2]
Consommé
  Printanier (spring vegetables)
  Florentine (chopped spinach, almonds)
  Princess (princess royal garnish)
Broths
  Chicken Noodle Soup (noodles)
  Mulligatawny Soup (apples, curry,
    eggplant, cream)
  Chicken Creole (onion, okra, rice,
    tomatoes, celery)
Veloutés (creams)
  Creme of Cressionère (watercress,
    liason)
  Cream of Chicken (diced chicken,
    rice pulp thickening, liason)
  Creme d' Amandine (almond paste,
    almonds, liason)
  Cream of Mushroom (mushroom es-
    sence, liason)
Veloutés. fish (bisques)[1]
  Clam Bisque (chopped clams, clam
    juice, cream finish)
  Lobster Bisque (lobster essence,
    brandy, cream finish)
  Shrimp Bisque (shrimp essence,
    cream, sherry, diced shrimp meat)
Chowders[2]
  Manhattan Clam Chowder (potatoes,
    salt pork, clams, tomatoes, onions,
    celery, green peppers)
  Washington Chowder (salt pork, on-
    ions, potatoes, corn, celery, green
    peppers, tomatoes, milk)
  Okra Chowder (tomatoes, okra, onion,
    parsley, peppers, celery, potatoes)
Purees (cured meat stock may be in-
    cluded)
  Split Pea (split peas)
  Navy Bean (navy beans)
  Potato and Leek (leeks, potatoes)
  Puree of Artichoke (artichoke heart
    puree, starch thickened)

---

[1] A cream or white sauce, a velouté sauce thinned with rich milk or cream, or a bechamel may be used interchangably in making the numerous cream soups.

[2] The stock used may vary. Chicken, beef, or fish stock may be used for the various types of soups, sometimes interchangably, and so exact definition is difficult. A beef bouillon, for instance, may be used for an oxtail, vegetable, or barley soup, and so forth, but a white stock from chickens might do almost as well. Usually fish stocks are used for fish-base soups, such as chowders.

were proper as a first course. Escoffier many years later agreed, quoting the great gastronomist, Grimod de la Reynière, in support of Carême's belief: "Soup is to a dinner what the porch or gateway is to a building . . . it is devised to convey some idea of the whole to which it belongs, or, after the manner of an overture to a light opera, it should divulge what is to be the dominant phrase of the melody throughout." Today light soups are commonly used as a first course, but heavier soups are also still used as complete or nearly complete meals.

The Standard

A soup is a liquid food. Unlike a sauce, it does not complement another food. The standard for the soup will vary according to its type. Hot soups should be served at above 170° F and cold soups at around 40° to 50° F. The quantity in a portion will vary according to the use of the soup. A portion for a first course may be around six ounces (¾ cup), while a more substantial portion is one cup (8 oz). Where the soup is a substantial part of a meal, 10 ounces (1¼ cups) will be served.

The thickness of the soup may vary according to its type and ingredients. Clear soups should resemble thin liquids, but they must possess body and not be thin or watery. A cream soup, bisque, or light puree should delicately coat a spoon, while heavy, thick *paysanne* or country-style soups should build a mound of ingredients when placed in a tureen. Some soups may be almost as thick as stews or ragoûts. Whether a *bouillabaisse* or a gumbo is a stew or a soup has been argued. Hearty or complete-meal soups should be filling and substantial, thick with ingredients; light soups should be thin and delicate, not filling. The form of the ingredients in all soups should be distinct and clear, not mushy or broken, unless the soup is a puree, where usually no evidence of form is desirable.

Flavors should be distinct, mild, pleasant, and characteristic of the type of soup. Seasonings should be delicate, not predominant. Colors should vary according to the ingredients but should be natural and pleasing. Contrasting colors may be desirable, such as in a chicken gumbo, where the red of tomato, green of okra, and white of rice give a pleasing myriad of colors.

A clear soup, such as consommé or bouillon, may show a sheen of tiny, minute globules of fat, but only a trace. Heavier soups may have more fat incorporated in them, but the fat on the surface should appear only as slightly larger dots or globules than those on a consommé or bouillon. Fat should never be apparent in pools or as large, round globules. Clear soups should have bright, sparkling clarity. Season cold soups more highly than hot soups, for chilling reduces the strength of flavors. A puree or cream soup should be free from lumps unless tiny chopped ingredients are incorporated. All particles should be bite size except in special soups, where whole slices of meat, chunks of fish, shellfish in shells, or other products are introduced. A puree should remain in suspension during service. Light purees should be only as heavy as cream soups. Heavy purees and country-style soups, such as old-fashioned bean soup and chowders, may be heavier than this, with ingredients distinct and separate.

The color of a cream soup should be not flat or dead-white but a rich, light cream color. This color may be modified by other ingredients as in a cream of tomato soup. No curdling should be evident, and all thickened soups should be smooth in texture.

FIG. 5-9 A wide variety of soups offered by any operation will increase customer satisfaction. Use soups properly, using thick soups when other foods of the meal are light and thin soups when the foods are quite substantial.

Types of Soups

There is little agreement among authorities on the classification of soups. Consistency or thickness is perhaps as good a method as any other, for this is usually the determining factor in deciding how a soup will be used as a food item. According to this, soups are classified as very thin: broths, consommés, bouillons, turtle, and others; medium or lightly thickened: creams, bisques, and light purees; and thick or heavy: chowders, heavy purees, gumbos, *potages*, country-style soups, and others.

Thin Soups

Most thin soups are clear and derive their consistency from the natural body of the stock and from added ingredients. The best examples are bouillons, consommés, and broths. Bouillon has a distinct beef flavor and a darker color than consommé. It is made from a brown stock and is clarified. Bouillon and consommé are not the same product. A consommé is a clear soup usually made from a combination of two or more kinds of

FIG. 5-10 Ingredients used to make a consommé. Note that clarification by cooking occurs with the making of this type of soup.

meat and bones, one of which is usually veal or chicken. Its delicate flavor should be a blend of seasonings with no one flavor predominating. While it possesses a rich, meaty flavor and is clarified, its flavor, body, and clarity are usually superior to those of a bouillon. The word *consommé* is derived from the word *consummate*, meaning "the finest, the most complete or perfect." Broths are less clear than consommés or bouillons, frequently being clarified by the decanting method. They do not usually possess the depth of flavor of a bouillon or consommé. Some delicate cream soups are classed as thin soups, including milk- or cream-base oyster stew, *vichysoisse*, and other similar soups, as well as light oxtail soup, turtle soup, light puree, or bisque. Thin soups are usually used for the first course of a meal which is quite heavy or formal. Many menu planners use the dictum, "A light soup, a heavy dessert."

Lightly Thickened Soups (Medium)

Some soups derive thickness from their ingredients, such as rice, macaroni, dumplings, or vegetables. Thickness may also be the result of pulped or pureed foods, as well as from thickening agents such as flour, starch, eggs, or panades. Most of these are never as clear nor as delicate as thin soups. They may be introduced as a first course of a light meal or as a main part of a luncheon. A clear broth, abundant but not completely filled

(a)   (b)

FIG. 5-11   (a) The first step in preparing a cream soup is to make a velouté base. Here we see stock being added to a mixture of roux and vegetables in the making of the velouté. (b) Next, after thorough cooking of the velouté mixture, the velouté is blended with good agitation into hot rich milk.

with vegetables, or a moderately thick puree, or an average cream soup may be served with sandwiches or salad for a luncheon. About 10 ounces to one pound of rice, noodles, or other macaroni products are used with every six gallons (100 portions) of soup of this type.

Most lightly thickened cream soups should have the consistency of heavy cream. Stability against curdling is oftentimes a problem in their making. The preferred method is to make a moderately heavy velouté base, add the desired seasoning products in the ratio of one pint of finely minced or pureed foods per gallon of soup, and then thin to desired consistency with hot rich milk or thin cream. Add the velouté mixture to the milk or cream, *not the milk or cream to the velouté base*. The milk or cream mixture is best lightly thickened with starch for soups that curdle easily. Keep the velouté mixture and the thinning agent hot but separate until required, and then blend only the amount that is required for a 20 to 30

FIG. 5-12   Another way to prepare a cream soup is to add a thickened velouté to a thin, hot bechamel or white sauce.

minute serving period. Never mix a new and an old batch together. Excess salt or heat may cause curdling. Some cream soups may be prepared from a velouté base, thinned with milk or cream and then finished with a liaison. A liaison is a mixture of one part egg yolk well blended into three parts of cream.

A fairly stable cream soup may also be made by using a bechamel

(a)

(b)   (c)

FIG. 5-13   (a) The ingredients used for liaison. (b) To use a liaison, blend some of the hot soup mixture into liaison. (c) Next, add liaison to the soup, using good agitation. After liaison is added, the mixture is never heated above 190° F.

sauce, blending in cooked flavoring ingredients, one pint to the gallon of soup, and then thinning to desired consistency with hot milk or light cream.

A third method for making a cream soup is to prepare a white sauce, then blend in cooked foods as required for seasoning, and thin with milk or cream. These soups are the least stable of the three. The student should review the material discussed in Chapter 7 on the preparation of milk products in quantity cookery.

A bisque is a cream soup that has shellfish as its main flavoring ingredient. It is not correct to use the term for other cream soups.

FIG. 5-14   A bisque is a cream soup with a shellfish as the main flavoring ingredient. Here we see a velouté sauce being thinned with a rich fish stock previous to the addition of chopped lobster meat to make a lobster bisque.

A puree soup may gain its thickness in two ways: (1) by using pulp of starchy vegetables, such as beans, lentils, peas, or potatoes, or (2) by using the pulp of succulent vegetables, such as carrots, asparagus, turnips, celery, or green peas, and some starch. A stock containing the flavor of cured meats is oftentimes used for a puree. A *cullis* is a puree soup containing the pulped flesh of meat, poultry, fish, or game. It is thinned to proper consistency with consommé or fish stock, depending on the type. A bit of starch may be used to hold the pulp in suspension. About two pounds of lentils, split peas, or beans or one to two quarts of pureed product will be required per gallon of pureed soup.

Heavy Soups

Thick or heavy soups may be made from clear stock to which vegetables,

FIG. 5-15   Forcing split peas through a china cap with an up and down motion of the ladle to make a puree soup.

rice, macaroni, spaghetti, or other items are added until a heavy consistency is obtained. They are frequently the main course of a meal. Soups such as gumbos, French onion soup, or *bouillabaisse* are in this class. Heavy purees and some fairly thick cream soups may be classified in this group. Heavy purees may be called *potages*.

Most chowders are heavy, thick soups containing chopped onions and other vegetables such as diced potatoes. These may be sautéed lightly in ham or bacon fat or with diced bacon or salt pork. For lenten chowders, butter or margarine is substituted for these fats. A main flavoring ingredient such as clams, corn, mussels, lima beans, or mushrooms is added, and this gives the chowder its specific name. Tomatoes are added to chowders called Coney Island, Manhattan, or Philadelphia. Stock is the base. If milk is the base, tomatoes are not used, and the chowder is called Boston or New England.

Cold Soups

There are a number of cold soups. *Vichysoisse*, cold borsch, jellied consommé, and bouillon are some of the most popular. The Scandinavian people are fond of a cold, slightly sweetened soup which has dried fruits in it. Variation of soups offered on the menu with these types of soups oftentimes brings customer satisfaction.

Accompaniments

Quantities of accompaniments for soups may be found in the chapter on "Pantry Production" in Table 4-7. If garnishes are added to soups and sauces, they are usually cooked separately and added at service. Starchy products should be blanched thoroughly after cooking so their addition will not cloud a soup or sauce. Oftentimes, the garnish or accompaniment used will distinguish soups which in other respects are very much alike (see Table 5-1).

SAUCES AND GRAVIES

A sauce or gravy is usually a richly flavored, thickened stock or liquid used to give moistness, richness, or flavor or otherwise to complement another food. Some sauces or gravies assist in giving color and form to foods. Contrasts in flavor with the food they accompany are sought. A sauce may act as a garnish. The sauce or gravy should never mask or disguise the flavor of the food it accompanies, but rather should heighten it.

The Standard

Sauces or gravies should possess a soft sheen imparted by tiny pinpoint globules of emulsified fat. The texture should be smooth and velvety with

Table 5-2
Sauces and their Derivation

| Meat | Neutral |

Meat

BROWN STOCK

Brown Sauce (Espagnole)
  Bordelaise Sauce (red wine, shallots, beef marrow)
  Chateau Sauce (white wine, shallots, butter)
  Chasseur Sauce (tomato ragoût, fine herbs, mushrooms, white wine)
  Madeira Sauce (Madeira wine)
  Mushroom Sauce (mushrooms, red wine)
  Poivrade Sauce (tarragon vinegar, red wine, tabasco, tomato ragoût)
  Grand Veneur Sauce (game essence, truffles)
  Sauce Diane (whipped cream, truffles, hard-cooked egg)
  Moscovite Sauce (juniper berries, malaga grapes, almonds, raisins)
  Provencale Sauce (tomato ragoût, garlic)
  Robert Sauce (mustard, red wine, shallots, tomato ragout)
  Salmis (currant jelly, mushrooms, port wine)
  Fruit Sauces[2] (sweetened brown sauce)
    Bigarade Sauce (orange juice and peel, lemon juice, brandy)
    Cumberland Sauce (orange and lemon peel and juice, ginger, cayenne, port wine, mustard)
    Brandy Peach Sauce (peach preserves, brandy)
    Pineapple Sauce (pineapple)
    Raisin Sauce (vinegar, raisins)

WHITE STOCK

Velouté Sauce
  Allemande Sauce (egg yolks)
  Poulette Sauce (cream)
    Soubise Sauce (onion puree)
  Supreme Sauce (cream)
  Princes Sauce (mushroom essence, glace de poulet)
  Reine Sauce (almond butter, truffles)
  Vin Blanc Sauce (Fish Velouté)
  Cardinal Sauce (cream, chopped shrimp or lobster meat)

  Flamande Sauce (mussel essence, parsley, mustard, lemon juice)
  Normandy Sauce or Nantua (egg yolks, cream)
    Nantaise Sauce (chopped crayfish, or chopped lobster or chopped shrimp)

Neutral

TOMATO

Tomato Ragoût Sauce[1]
  Creole Sauce (onions, garlic, tomatoes, green peppers)
  Spanish Sauce (onions, celery, okra, mushrooms, garlic, tomatoes, green peppers, stuffed green olives)

MILK (White Sauce)

  Cheese Sauce (cheddar cheese)
  Cream Sauce (cream finish)
  Curry Sauce (curry, apples, onions)
  Egg Sauce (hard-cooked eggs)
  Mornay Sauce (Parmesan cheese)
  Mustard Sauce (prepared mustard)
  Newburg Sauce (sherry wine)

EGG YOLK, VINEGAR AND OIL EMULSIONS

Hollandaise Sauce
  Bernaise Sauce (tarragon vinegar)
  Figaro Sauce (tomato puree, celery)
  Glace Royale Sauce (mousseline sauce, mornay sauce, or cream sauce)
  Grimod Sauce (saffron)
  Maltaise Sauce (orange juice and grated peel)
  Mousseline Sauce (whipped cream)
Mayonnaise
  Chaud-froid Sauce or Mayonnaise Collée (gelatin)
  Imperial Sauce (onion, mushrooms, mustard, pickles, pimiento, cream sauce)
  Ravigote Sauce (shallots, chives, capers, chopped eggs)
  Remoulade Sauce (dill pickles, anchovy, capers, mustard)
  Russian Sauce (chili sauce, chopped pimientos, chives)
  Chiffonade Sauce (chopped eggs, beets)
  Tartar Sauce (dill pickles, onions, parsley)

BUTTERS

Compounded Butters
  Anchovy Butter (anchovy paste)
  Caper Butter (capers)
  Garlic Butter (garlic juice or crushed garlic)
  Lobster (lobster pulp)
Melted Butters
  Clarified Butter (pour melted butter from its curd)
  Noisette Butter (Brown Butter) (brown to hazelnut color)
  Maitre d'hotel Butter (lemon juice, cayenne, parsley)

Table 5-2 (continued)
Sauces and their Derivation

Meat

Bechamel Sauce (chicken or veal stock)[3]
  A la King Sauce (green peppers, mushrooms, pimientos)
  Bretonne Sauce (fish stock, leeks, onions, mushrooms, celery)
  Caper Sauce (capers))
  Dill Sauce (fresh dill)
  Newburg Sauce (sherry wine)

TOMATO

Tomato Ragoût Sauce[1]
  Barbecue Sauce (onions, garlic, sugar, mustard, vinegar, lemon or lime juice, worcestershire, barbecue spice)
  Italian or Spaghetti Sauce (garlic, onions, celery, green peppers, basil, oregano, bay leaf, olive oil)
  Milanaise Sauce (mushrooms, ham, tongue)

Neutral

Caper Butter (capers)
Irish Butter (tomato catsup, nutmeg)
Mustard Butter (dry mustard)
Polonaise Sauce (fine bread crumbs)
Meunière Butter (brown maitre d'hotel butter)
Amandine Butter (sliced almonds, onion juice)
Lemon Bütter (lemon juice)
Noir (black) Butter (brown until very dark)

BREAD SAUCE
  Gooseberry Bread Sauce (gooseberry preserves)
  Horseradish Bread Sauce (horseradish, cream)
  Mustard Bread Sauce (dry mustard)
  Onion Bread Sauce (minced onions or onion puree)

SOUR CREAM SAUCES
  Horseradish Sauce (horseradish)
  Smitane (onions, white wine, lemon juice)

FRENCH DRESSING SAUCES
  Avocado Sauce (avocado, hard-cooked egg yolk, tarragon)
  Cambridge Sauce (hard-cooked egg yolk, anchovy, capers, fine herbs, mustard)
  Chiffonade Sauce (fine herbs, hard-cooked egg, beets)
  Vinaigrette Sauce (capers, pickles, pimiento, mustard, hard-cooked eggs, chervil, tarragon, parsley)

WINE STOCK SAUCES
  Spadoise Sauce (red dry and port wine, bread crumbs, currants, nutmeg)
  Raisin Sauce (Burgundy wine, raisins, currants, mustard, sugar, cloves, nutmeg, cinnamon)
  Port Wine Sauce (Port wine, orange and lemon juice, orange rind, thyme, velouté sauce)

[1]Tomato ragoût sauce may be made from tomato puree which is combined with a meat stock as well as from a stock brought up from the start with tomatoes in it; sauces made with a neutral or meat tomato ragoût are used interchangeably.

[2]Melt several teaspoons of sugar over low heat until it is caramelized; add brown stock and a bit of vinegar and then proceed with the derived sauce.

[3]Variations found in bechamel sauce are applicable also to secondary sauces made from cream sauces; likewise, some sauces made from bechamel or from cream sauce may also be derived from allemande or supreme sauces. A *bechamel maigre* is made from fish stock and can be used for some sauces that otherwise would be made from a fish velouté sauce base.

no lumps, and the flavor should be a delicate blend of a number of flavors with no one flavor predominating. There should be no evidence of uncooked starch, either in taste or texture. Gravies may have the flavor characteristic of the meat drippings from which they are made. The color of a brown sauce should be a rich mahogany brown, modified by the added ingredients. Brown color from prepared browning materials may be used. A white velouté sauce should possess a clear, creamy white color. Butter, margarine, or chicken fat may contribute a part of the creamy color. In a bechamel or a white or a cream sauce, an opaque quality may be evident. A dead, pasty white and lack of sheen indicate a sauce of poor quality.

The consistency of sauces may vary, but pasty, excessively thick sauces are undesirable. Thin sauces should be served over or with foods that need flavor complement but do not need the body of a heavier sauce. Sauces should sometimes be fairly thick, such as hollandaise used over broccoli where some cling is desirable. Meat sauces, such as pan gravy or *au jus* or meat essences, are almost as thin as broths or stock. The clarity of a sauce may vary according to the ingredients used in it, but no sauce should be murky or cloudy. Sauces should have brilliance.

The neutral sauces are made without a meat stock base. They vary considerably in their characteristics and it is difficult to establish a standard for them. Some, like mayonnaise and hollandaise, have a high fat or oil content and thus possess a high sheen; there should be no visible oil and the emulsion formed should be smooth and stable. The color should be a delicate yellow for hollandaise and a yellowish cream for mayonnaise. The consistency or texture of fruit sauces, such as applesauce, cranberry sauce, and gooseberry sauce, should be sufficiently firm to hold a mound and leave little or no seepage of liquid upon standing.

Ingredients

The stock used as the base for sauces should be of top quality. Sometimes stocks are reduced in volume by evaporation before they are used, and wines may be added and also reduced in this process. Frequently shallots rather than onions are used for seasoning because of their more delicate flavor.

Sauces may be finished with a final addition of an ingredient such as cream, butter, a liaison of egg yolks and cream, or wine. After the finishing ingredient is added, the sauce is not boiled but only brought to correct serving temperature. To prevent the formation of a scum, a sauce may be tightly covered while warm, or melted butter may be brushed over the surface or oil paper placed directly upon it. If the sauce stands for a short time, brush with a liquid such as milk, cream, wine, or water.

The thickening agents for sauces are usually flour or cornstarch, but other starch products may also be used. A mixture called a *roux*, half fat and half flour by weight, is the usual thickening agent. The fat is melted,

FIG. 5-16 A finish is an ingredient added at the last moment to complete the flavor. Finishes may be cream, sour cream, wine, butter, or other products. After the finish is added, the item is never boiled.

FIG. 5-17 The main ingredients for making a brown sauce: brown stock, *mirepoix*, *sachet*, and roux.

the flour added, and the mixture cooked about ten minutes until it is quite frothy and leaves the bottom of the pan easily. A roux when properly cooked will have a light hazelnut odor and a slightly gritty texture. Chicken fat is highly prized for roux for a bechamel, velouté, and white or cream sauce. Brown, pale (blond), or white (light) roux are made from well browned, lightly browned, or unbrowned flour. Browning destroys some of the thickening power, a heavily browned flour having about one-third the thickening power of white flour. Dry roux has no fat. It is made by heating a thin layer of flour in an oven until it is slightly gritty. Time and temperature are adjusted to give the proper color. A dry roux can be sifted lightly over items and incorporated, or it can be made into a slurry with liquid and used for thickening. A dry roux is desirable when the fat in a regular roux would give an overly rich product and perhaps a broken emulsion. Some starches or flours are blended with liquid and used as a slurry for thickening. This

(a)   (b)

(c)   (d)

FIG. 5-18 (a) Fat and flour for a roux. (b) Cooking the roux. (c) Unbrowned flour, lightly browned flour, and heavily browned flour in quantities required to give equal thickening to one gallon of stock. (d) A dry roux.

FIG. 5-19 A *beurre manie* is a kneaded mixture of equal parts flour and butter. It is used to give final correct thickness to a sauce or soup.

Table 5-3
Approximate Equivalent Thickening Power of Some Ingredients

Ingredient	Ounces	Cups	Ingredient	Ounces	Cups
Pastry flour	4	1	Tapioca	3½	⅔
Bread flour	5	1¼	Bread crumbs, dry	3½	¾
Cornstarch	2¾	¾	Whole eggs	22	2¾ *
Waxy maize starch	2	⅜	Egg yolks	20	2½ **
*approximately 14 large eggs			**approximately 28 large yolks		

is oftentimes called "whitewash." It is usually less satisfactory than a roux because it gives a less smooth flavor and is apt to have lumps. A *beurre manie* is made of equal parts of butter and flour kneaded together. It is used frequently for giving final correctness to the consistency of a sauce or soup.

Roux can be stirred into a moderately hot liquid or the liquid can be poured into the roux. Some chefs say to use a cold roux with a hot liquid and a hot roux with a cool liquid. Good agitation should occur with a whip as roux is added to a hot liquid. The temperature is then raised to boiling and the mixture cooks for 10 minutes to complete the gelatinizing of the starch cells. Flour, cornstarch, and most other starches start to thicken at around 144° to 162° F and complete their final thickening at around 203° F. A failure to cook such starches completely may give graininess and a raw

(a)

(b)

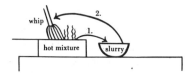

Step 1.   After making a smooth thin paste of
           the starch thickener and liquid, add
           some of the hot mixture to the
           slurry and blend well.

Step 2.   Then add all the warmed slurry to
           the hot mixture, giving good agita-
           tion as it is poured in slowly.

(c)

FIG. 5-20   (a) Roux may be added to a
stock in the manner shown or (b) stock may
be added to a roux in thickening a sauce or
soup. (c) To use a flour or starch and liquid
slurry, first add some of the hot mixture to
the slurry and blend well. Then, with good
agitation, add this mixture to the hot mixture. This method is also used in adding
a liaison to a soup.

starch flavor. Waxy maize starch thickens at around 155° to 167°, and no second thickening occurs. If this type of starch is heated above 195° F a slight thinning occurs.

There are a number of starches on the market and the type used should be suited to the production need. Waxy maize starches are desirable, for instance, for fruit pie fillings. Instant starches are available which thicken in the cold stage. They are little used in sauce cookery, however.

Acid breaks down starch, and for this reason acid ingredients may be withheld from a sauce until cooking is completed. Meat stock and drippings

FIG. 5-21 Acid destroys the thickening power of starch. The sample on the left had the same quantity of starch added as the one on the right, but vinegar was used as the liquid in place of water.

Table 5-4
Proportions of Roux for Soups and Sauces per Gallon of Liquid*

Product	Fat		Flour		Use and Consistency
	oz	cups	oz	cups	
Soups:					
Thin	6	¾	4	1	For light cream soups or other thin soups
Medium	8	1	6	1½	For succulent purees, light chowders, medium creams
Thick	12	1½	10	2½	For heavy, thick soups
Sauces:					
Very thin	6	¾	4	1	Escalloped potatoes; thin, creamy sauces
Thin	8	1	8	2	Thick enough to coat a spoon
Medium	12	1½	12	3	Creamed dishes, newburg or mornay sauce, escalloped dishes and gravies
Heavy	16	2	16	4	Soufflé bases, heavy sauces thinned by the addition of other liquids
Very heavy	20	2½	20	5	For croquettes, cutlets and so forth

*If pale roux, double flour. If brown roux, increase three times; fat may be increased in proportion. If cornstarch, potato starch, or arrowroot is substituted for plain flour, reduce to about three-fourths of flour given here.

are slightly acid, and sauces containing these or other liquids acid in reaction, such as wines, will require more thickening agent than those containing no acid. More starch per gallon of liquid will be required to thicken large batches than smaller batches. This is perhaps because large batches do not rise to as high a temperature as do small batches.

The process that occurs in the gelatinization or swelling of starch is not completely known. We do know that there are about 770 billion starch granules in one pound of cornstarch and that these are insoluble in cold water, but in hot water above certain temperatures they swell and increase in size. When enough are in a solution, the swelled particles crowd one another and cause the product to thicken. Lumping occurs if the starch granules are not separated before swelling occurs. Separation by using fat in a roux is one way to prevent lumping; another is to make a slurry with a liquid and stir this carefully and vigorously into a hot or cold solution, continuously stirring until thickening has occurred. The starch product may also be blended thoroughly with another ingredient, such as sugar, and then blended into the hot liquid, the other ingredient separating the starch granules so they cannot lump.

Starches differ in their thickening power, viscosity, and clarity. Much of the opaqueness or lack of clarity of a sauce thickened with flour is caused by gluten. Flours will differ in clarity and their ability to thicken because they differ in their starch and gluten content. Pastry or cake flours have greater clarity and thickening power than bread flour because they have less gluten and more starch. Bread flour gives a rather stringy quality or cling to a sauce and greater opacity because of its higher gluten content. Sauces thickened with cornstarch are clearer and have less cling than sauces made with flour. Cornstarch gives a thickened mass that breaks rather sharply without the gluey qualities obtained when flour is used. A waxy maize starch paste will be very clear and soft and as thick when hot as it is when cold. It will also freeze without breaking the emulsion. Cream pies, *blanc manges,* and such items are best made with flour, cornstarch, arrowroot, or other root starches, for these require the sheer edge and good form yet delicate softness imparted by these starches. Fruit pies and other products that require a high clarity and soft texture are best made from waxy maize starch. Tapioca, sago, rice, potatoes, rice or potato flour, bread crumbs, egg yolks, and other ingredients are also used for thickening. They will vary in their clarity, viscosity, and thickening power.

Types of Sauces

The wide variety of sauces used in cooking comes from a few basic types. These basic sauces are called *foundation* or *mother sauces,* and the many

FIG. 5-22 Shown here are the amounts of thickening required to give equal thickness to one gallon of stock in order to make a medium thick sauce.

sauces derived from them are called *secondary* or *small sauces*. By making a slight change in ingredients, preparation method, or garnish, many different sauces can be obtained from one basic sauce. A standard portion of sauce or gravy is two ounces, but this may be varied according to the need.

The three basic sauces having meat stock as their base are brown *(espagnole)*, *velouté*, and *bechamel*. A fourth, tomato, may or may not have stock in it, but it usually does. There are a number of basic sauces which do not have meat stock in them and these are called *neutral sauces*. (See Table 5-2.)

Brown Sauce (Espagnole)

Brown stock thickened with a brown roux and seasoned with a *mirepoix*, *bouquet garni*, and perhaps red wine and tomatoes is called a brown sauce or espagnole. It is widely used as a base for sauces for red meat or game.

Velouté Sauce

Velouté is made from plain roux, white stock, and seasonings; a fish velouté, oftentimes called a *sauce vin blanc* or white wine sauce is made from fish stock and dry white wine. A fricassee gravy is actually a velouté. Do not use the term white sauce to indicate a velouté, although this term is heard commonly in kitchens. Reserve the term *white sauce* for a sauce made from milk.

Bechamel Sauce

Bechamel is actually a velouté made from rich veal or chicken stock and then thinned with rich milk or cream. Escoffier says bechamel should be made by cooking veal flesh in milk. After straining, the milk is thickened with a white roux, but few make this sauce in this manner any longer. Bechamel is a delicately flavored sauce used for creamed dishes or for cream sauces. To avoid confusion, this text avoids the term *cream sauce* for a bechamel sauce. Cream sauce in this text means a white sauce in which cream has been incorporated.

Tomato Sauce

A tomato puree, or tomato puree and brown stock seasoned with either vegetables and seasonings, may be called a tomato sauce or tomato ragoût. Tomato should predominate heavily in color and flavor, and the seasonings are usually more pungent than in other meat sauces.

Gravies

When meat drippings are thinned with stock or other liquid and then thickened, they are called gravies. The flavor of the meat drippings should predominate. A pan gravy or an *au jus* is an unthickened gravy. In Southern cookery, sometimes what is termed pan gravy may be a thickened gravy and it frequently contains milk. Meat drippings left after sautéing are called *fond*. *Fond brun* means brown pan drippings. To deglaze or extract a *fond* from a pan, use a process called "swishing and swirling." First, pour off the fat and add stock, wine, or other liquid. Then, over heat, use a fork or a spoon to loosen the encrusted products, bringing them into solution. Use a fairly high heat, adding more liquid if necessary to dissolve the drippings completely. This sauce is frequently poured over the items that were sautéed in the pan.

(a)

(b)

(c)

FIG. 5-23   A process called "swishing and swirling" is used to extract encrusted materials from sauté pans. (a) A stock is added and the encrusted materials are brought into solution. This is then reduced and poured over the sautéed item as a gravy. (b) Some of the fat may be left in the pan and a roux made as shown here. (c) Stock is then added and the mixture cooked about 10 minutes to give a thickened pan gravy.

Milk Base Sauces

Heating milk with a *mirepoix* and a *bouquet garni*, salt, or other season-ing, then straining and thickening with a white roux, produces a white sauce. If cream is added, a secondary sauce is made called cream sauce.

Hollandaise

Egg yolks and butter made into a permanent emulsion with lemon juice or vinegar, made over very hot but not boiling water, produces hollandaise.

FIG. 5-24 A hollandaise sauce is difficult to make and requires painstaking care in the blending of the butter into the egg yolks. Shown here are the ingredients used in the making of a hollandaise. White pepper is in the unmarked container next to the salt.

Mixing must be vigorous and the sauce must not become too warm. Should the emulsion break (curdle), remove from the heat at once, add one or two tablespoons of boiling water to another clean pan, and then slowly reform the broken emulsion in this new pan. Mayonnaise is an emulsion of oil, eggs, lemon or vinegar, and seasonings, but it is not made over hot water. Mayonnaise and hollandaise are basic sauces used to make many secondary sauces.

Bread Sauce

Bread is the thickening agent used for a sauce oftentimes served over vegetables and meats. Many small sauces are made from the basic bread sauce. American bread sauce is made by sautéing minced shallots or onions in butter, adding hot milk, soft bread crumbs, and seasoning, and stirring over low heat. Cream is used to finish the sauce. The English season their sauce with onion juice and omit the shallots or onions. The French substitute white wine and a rich velouté sauce in equal parts instead of using milk and cream.

Butters

Butter sauce or basic butter is made from butter or margarine to which has been added a bit of strained lemon juice and a few grains of cayenne. Margarine containing no lecithin will not brown well. Use butter for sauces that are heated. Compounded butters result when minced or pulped items are added to a softened basic butter. Anchovies, garlic, minced crab, and

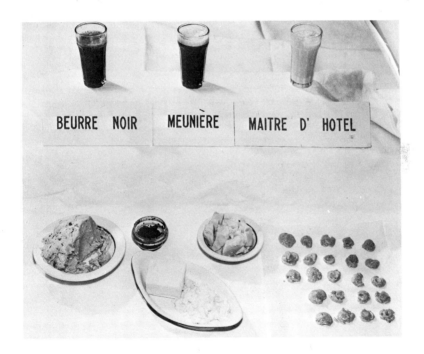

FIG. 5-25 Three of the basic hot butters used in food preparation are shown at the top of this illustration. Some basic butters and their ingredients are shown on the bottom. These are frequently used as spreads for sandwiches or canapés.

other items are used to give such butters distinctive flavor. These are used as spreads for canapés over bread, toast, or crackers. Hot butters are often-times served with meats. A *maitre d'hotel* butter is melted unbrowned basic butter; *meunière* butter is lightly browned basic butter, and if slivered almonds are added to it, it is called almandine sauce. *Meunière* butter, because of its color and aroma, is also known as brown or hazelnut butter or *noisette beurre*. *Maitre d'hotel* and *meunière* butters are frequently served over steaks, chops, or fish. When basic butter is heated to a dark but not burned color, it is called black butter or *beurre noir*. It is served over scrambled eggs or sautéed calves brains.

Miscellaneous Sauces

This text has only discussed some of the broader categories of sauces used, and a complete discussion is beyond its scope. It is felt that if the basic principles and standards presented here are mastered and the range of sauces discussed is offered at high quality, the variety will serve the needs of almost any type of food service. Some sweet-fruit sauces are combinations of the basic sauces with sugar and fruit, such as raisin sauce, pineapple sauce, and other sauces used with meat. Plain fruit sauces, such as apple-sauce and cherry sauce, may be served as sauces and accompaniments. Other sauces may be condiments, such as catsup, horseradish, A-1 and other prepared sauces, which are perhaps not sauces at all. Some sauces, such as mayonnaise and French dressing, are considered salad dressings, but they may be blended with foods and used also as a meat sauce.

FIG. 5-26   Reducing a wine previous to using it as a stock for a sauce.

FIG. 5-27 To prevent a scum forming on a sauce, brush lightly with milk or butter. For short-time holding, a cover may be tightly fitted over the product to prevent the formation of a scum.

6 Beverages

Beverages are often an important accompaniment to a meal or snack, and frequently an operation is judged on the quality of the beverages served. Consumers differ on what makes quality in coffee. In one study 62% said flavor, 24% said strength, and 13% said aroma were the most important quality factors. Consumer preferences may vary. Young people may prefer a milder coffee than older people, and some foreign groups want a coffee more heavily flavored, bodied, and colored than do others. A breakfast cup may be milder than an after-dinner coffee, and the demitasse will be milder than a cup of espresso. By and large, a consistent standard of good coffee as described here will satisfy most people. As exacting care should be taken in the making of tea, cocoa, or other beverages as in making coffee, and the methods for attaining a high standard for all common beverages are discussed in this chapter.

COFFEE

Standard

Coffee should be evaluated on the basis of flavor (taste and aroma) and the physical factors of clarity, color, and body. Judge fresh coffee brewed not over 30 minutes before judging. Add no cream or sugar. Coffee cream may be added last to test the body of the brew.

Evaluate taste on the basis of proper balance of bitterness (astringency), acidity, and sweetness. An excess of any of these or the presence of any off-flavors lowers coffee quality. The taste should be pleasing. Nearly 50 aromatic compounds have been identified in freshly brewed coffee. The aroma of coffee should be fragrant, mellow, heavy, and rich with coffee bouquet. In tasting, swish the brew into the mouth in a spray so the aroma rises into the nostrils, as the mouth identifies the various tastes. Aromas should not be acrid, burnt, rancid, or oily. Off-odors should not be present.

196

Excessive bouquet or fruitiness should not be evident, but some fruitiness associated with aldehydes or other compounds may be present. Taste and aroma should be in balance and sufficiently strong to give a pleasing flavor. Weak coffee is called green or undeveloped. Excess strength is objectionable except in such coffees as Turkish, espresso, or after-dinner coffee. There should be no trace of oiliness. Judging strength of flavor by noting color is not recommended, but many consumers do so.

Clarity is nothing more than clearness of the brew and is directly related to the quantity of insoluble solids. Types of grind affect clarity, and improper handling may cause precipitates to appear, thereby decreasing clarity. Coffee should be bright, clear, and sparkling. A silver spoon lowered nearly to the bottom of the cup should be seen in good coffee. There should be no evidence of floating grounds, flocculent material, cloudiness, dullness, or muddiness. A clarity test may be made by filtering out insoluble material and drying and weighing it, but as yet no standards have been established for this test.

The color of a good brew should be a rich, deep brown. Lightness or paleness of color or a heavy dark brown of almost blackish cast lowers acceptability.

Body of a brew refers to its density, which is directly related to the quantity of coffee solubles present. Soluble compounds in the coffee increase the density of the brew over that of water, and this can be measured by a hydrometer shown in Figure 6-1.[1] Body is noted by a sensation of something more than water in the mouth. Some coffees, such as espresso or demitasse, may possess a heavy body, to the degree that some sensation of thickness or sirupiness is evident. Body should not be contributed by fine grounds or pulverized coffee except in some foreign coffees. If 18 to 22% cream is added, it should not immediately blend, as it would with hot water, but should feather or layer out. If a brew has a good body, some stirring is necessary to make it blend with cream. The milk fat content of the cream has an effect on how it feathers or layers when it is poured in, heavier creams feathering more than lighter ones.

Coffee should be served so it is at 160° F at service.

Principles

The quality of a coffee brew is affected by:

1. The quality and blend of the green beans.
2. Subsequent handling up to roasting.
3. Roasting.

[1]May be purchased from Rascher and Betzold, 730 N. Franklin St., Chicago 10, Illinois.

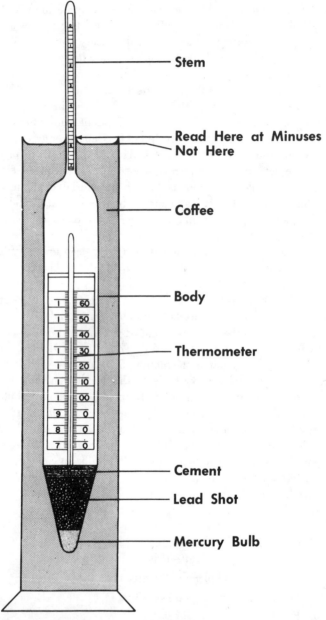

FIG. 6-1   A hydrometer may be used to measure solids in a coffee brew. Have brew at 140° F. A reading of 4.7 to 5.4 indicates solids of 1.15 to 1.35%, the desired range. (Courtesy Coffee Brewing Institute)

4. Grind.

5. Storage after grinding or roasting.

6. Water used for brewing.

7. Equipment used for brewing.

8. Standards of cleanliness in equipment.

9. Methods of brewing.

10. Holding after brewing.

Quality and Blend of Green Beans

The quality of the brew is influenced more by growing conditions than by the variety of plant. Most coffee used in this country comes from the Arabica plant grown at elevations from 3,000 to 5,000 feet in Brazil, Venezuela, Colombia, Mexico, and other Latin American countries. Weather conditions make it difficult to assure consistent standards for coffee in a given area, and blends must be used to obtain standardization. The method of processing used to obtain the green bean from the coffee cherry is important to quality.

Subsequent Handling to Roasting

After harvest and processing, the green beans are bagged and shipped. While they have no true coffee flavor while green, mold, absorption of flavors, or attack by insects may affect quality. A woody flavor is developed if coffee is aged over a year. Green coffee is a commodity purchased on the New York Coffee and Sugar Exchange.

Roasting

Roasting develops flavor. Coffee may be roasted to colors called light, medium, and heavy or dark. Flavor and color of the brew are influenced by the degree of roast, since the intensity of color and flavor increase as the roast is increased. Dark or heavy roasts are used for demitasse, espresso, and Turkish coffees, but for most institutions a medium (mild) roast is preferred. More precision in defining degrees of roast is needed.

Grind

There is little uniformity in grind standards, and more precision is needed here, too. The terms *steel-cut, cornmeal, regular, coarse, percolator, medium, fine, drip, silex, vacuum,* and *pulverized* are interpreted differently by different manufacturers. Grinder settings are not dependable, either, and a percolator grind 6 to 8, urn 4 to 6, drip 3 to 5 and vacuum 1 to 3 will vary depending upon the grinder used. Learning to know the grinds available on the local market will assist in obtaining the correct grind to yield the desired coffee in meeting a standard.

Storage

Coffee quality after roasting and grinding may be influenced considerably by the type of storage given. Storage areas should be dry. As time and temperature of storage increase, flavor loss increases, but the loss is less in the bean than in ground coffee. Ground coffee held three days at room temperature loses 20% of its aroma, and at the end of 20 days it will lose 50%. Staleness also develops rapidly. A ground coffee after five to eight days at room temperature will, because of volatile and staling loss, drop from top quality to fair or poor quality. Plan deliveries so fresh coffee is on hand. Use proper rotation so that oldest stocks are used first. If necessary, grind on the premises to assure freshness. Coffee purchased in the bean can be evaluated by bean appearance. Good quality beans will be plump and full with an even roast. Little or no foreign material should be present. If coffee is stored at from 37° to 44° F, flavor loss over room storage is reduced, and storage at –4° F gives an almost negligible loss. Ground coffee may easily absorb odors and should be stored where this is not possible.

Vacuum-packed coffee is freshly ground and packed under vacuum. Studies have shown that a flavor loss occurs up to a year, and then the loss is stabilized. After sealing, carbon dioxide is released, and this builds up pressures in the cans so the cans may swell. Since the gas is inert, no deterioration occurs. Because of pressures which may develop inside, the size of the can used for vacuum coffee must be restricted.

Water

Ordinary soft water or water of low hardness produces a good brew, but an extremely soft or hard or very alkaline water will not. Waters called permanently hard are usually not harmful to quality. Chlorine, sulfur, ammonia, and other compounds must be in greater concentration than usually found in water to give off-flavors. Detergents, if not properly rinsed from utensils or cups, may give off-flavors. Waters containing over four parts per million (ppm) of iron will give a brew of greenish cast when cream is used. Normally water does not have this high an iron content, but, if it comes from rusty pipes or if other causes increase the iron content, iron can be the cause of trouble.

A high sodium bicarbonate content increases the water flow time through the grounds in brewing. Time of contact may be extended by this factor so that a bitter and harsh brew is obtained. Polyphosphate softeners should be used for water used for coffee brewing, if softening is required. The sodium exchange method (Zeolite) gives bicarbonates if carbonates are present before softening.

Use cold, freshly drawn water and bring rapidly to a boil. Do not use

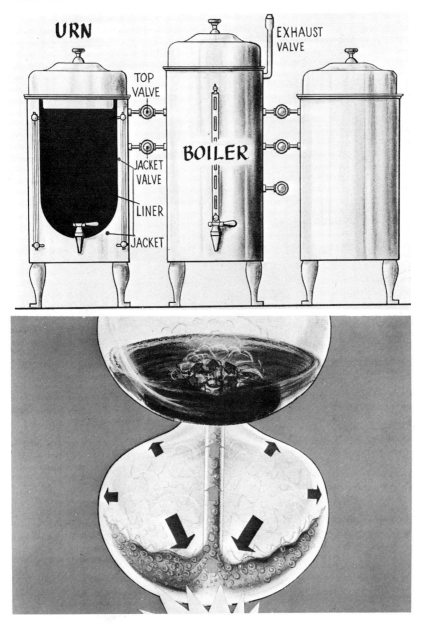

FIG. 6-2 The top picture shows the important sections of an urn battery for making coffee. The bottom figure illustrates how water is forced up through the spout in making vacuum-type coffee. (Courtesy Coffee Brewing Institute)

hot water from the system, for it may be flat and insipid because of the loss of oxygen. Do not use water left in the coffee brewing tanks a long time. The best extraction of coffee flavors occurs if the water is between 195° and 203° F in contact with the grounds. If water is boiling and poured onto the grounds, this temperature is obtained, unless the elevation is so high that the boiling point of the water is low.

Equipment

The proper type of equipment must be available to produce good coffee. The ideal coffee maker "would be one which meets the following specifications: provides essentially *fresh* brew in each cup that is served; meets the general requirements of the establishment in which it is used with respect

FIG. 6-3 A gridded riser, as shown here, keeps the filter bed of coffee more even, thus permitting a more uniform extraction. (Courtesy **Coffee Brewing Institute**)

to cost, size, rates of dispensing and appearance."[2] Coffee-making equipment should be selected for its ease of use as well as its ability to make good coffee. Urns or vacuum coffee makers are mostly used in food services. Never brew less than three-fourths the capacity of any coffee-making equipment. Gang or multiple vacuum coffee makers give flexibility in batch control, fresher coffee, and smaller batch holding, but may increase labor requirements.

Urns are only large-scale versions of small home drip makers. The size of the batch made in urns may be as much as 75 to 125 gallons, and then be dispensed in smaller units. Urns are best used when the demand is heavy. It is better to have two 2½ gallon urns than one five-gallon, or two 60 gallon urns than one 120 gallon, so batches can be staggered and product freshness assured. This also makes it possible to have brew on hand while cleaning and preparing the other urn for a new batch. Urns should be

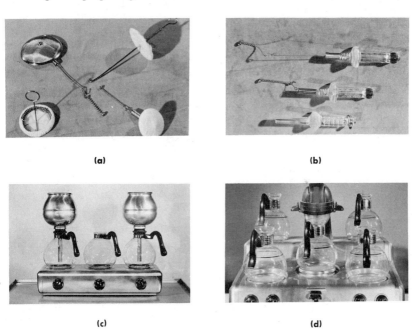

FIG. 6-4 Types of vacuum coffee-brewing equipment. (a) Types of strainer filters. (b) Types of glass filters that require no cloth. (c) Conventional vacuum maker with metal tops. (d) Battery-type brewing equipment; coffee is automatically made in center brewing equipment. (Courtesy Coffee Brewing Institute)

[2]Niven, W., Jr., and B. C. Shaw, "Critical Conditions for Quantity Coffee Brewing," *Coffee and Tea Industries*, 80:44, 75, 76, April, 1957.

designed for quick disassembly, cleaning, and reassembly. The number of parts handled should be reduced to a minimum, and cleaning of parts should be easy and rapid. Spray-head devices should deliver water in the correct time. More and more self-service equipment is being used. Such devices should be safe to use and capable of being easily and quickly replenished with fresh supplies.

The equipment should provide good filtering devices so clear coffee is obtained. The filter should function so that the water runs through neither too fast nor too slow. Paper or cloth filters, if of proper construction and properly used, will give a brew of good clarity. Woven-wire screen filters vary in efficiency, and in some wire filters, particles of fine grounds may catch and become the source of off-flavors. Perforated plates or metal discs with holes are cleaned easily and do not clog as readily as do screen-type filters. These, however, may allow sediment to flow into the brew. Fine grinds of coffee themselves act as filters. Do not repour coffee through grounds to clarify, however. Water should pass through the grounds only once. Clear coffee will hold quality longer than cloudy coffee.

Coffee makers for instant coffee are on the market and make from 300 to 500 cups per hour. To make good instant coffee, the water should be freshly boiled and well agitated after the coffee is added, and the brew should rest two minutes before being served.

Some metals give a metallic flavor to a brew. Color may also change. These reactions are least to greatest with stainless steel, silver, nickel or chrome, copper, aluminum, and tin plate. Glass, porcelain, or similar materials are desirable, but these are easily broken in quantity work. Some metals may be attacked by compounds in the brew.

Cleaning

Deposits from coffee in the equipment rapidly deteriorate and will lower brew quality. Equipment may look clean but actually be dirty, for many coffee deposits are transparent and difficult to see. Thin films of oils rapidly oxidize and give rancid flavors. Select equipment that is easily cleaned and gives minimum surfaces for contact. Do not assign the cleaning job to an untrained employee. Furnish proper cleaning tools, cleaning compounds, and other required material. See that written directions are available. All surfaces coming in contact with coffee should be cleaned thoroughly, but the faucets, glass gages, urn bags, and metal filter baskets are frequently forgotten or poorly cleaned.

Urn Cleaning

Clean the urn immediately after each brewing, using hot water, brushing the sides well, and rinsing until the hot water runs clean and clear.

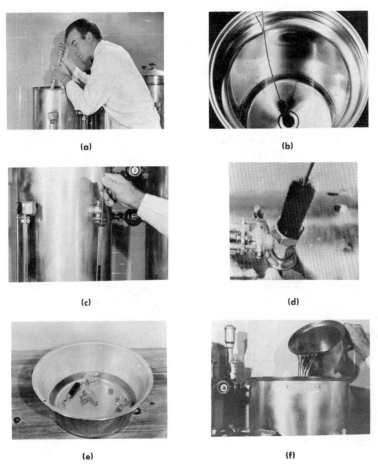

FIG. 6-5 Cleaning the urn. (a) Scrub well with good urn brush. (b) Clean all hard-to-get-at areas well with special brushes. (c) Don't neglect gages. (d) Remove faucets and clean well. (e) Soak and clean parts well. (f) Rinse well before using. (Courtesy Coffee Brewing Institute)

Rinse out the inside of the cover. Unscrew the top of the glass gage, and brush and rinse it well. Remove the clean-out cap at the end of the faucet and scrub the pipe leading from the center of the urn. If the faucet has no caps, take it apart. Scrub the spigot and rinse thoroughly with hot water. Place several gallons of fresh water in the urn. Leave the cover slightly ajar. Empty and rinse the urn before using.

Urns should be given a more thorough cleaning twice a week. To do this, fill the outer jacket three-fourths full of water and turn on the heat. Fill the urn jar three-fourths full of water and add cleaner according to manufacturer's directions. Use a long, thin brush and cleaner on gage glasses, faucet pipes, plugs, and other parts. Use a brush and cleaning solution to clean parts. Take the faucet apart and clean it well. Rinse all parts carefully. Assemble. Scrub and rinse inside the urn three or four times with hot water. Continue until all traces of foreign odor and cleaning solution are removed. Check spray heads to see that all holes are open, using a stiff wire to open them if they are clogged. Leave a few gallons of fresh warm water in the urn with the cover partially open until next use. Using cold water on a hot liner may crack it. Be sure to empty the urn and rinse it before the next use.

Filters, urn bags, and urn baskets should be given good care. A new urn bag or cloth filter should be cleaned thoroughly in 140° F to remove sizing (starch) and other foreign material. Water that is too hot will swell the starch and cause it to stay in the fibers. Afterwards, rinse thoroughly in cold water. Urn bags or cloth filters should be rinsed thoroughly in hot water immediately after each use. Do not use soap, bleaches, or detergents. To prevent urn bags or cloth filters from becoming sour or rancid or picking up food odors, store in a clean container of fresh cold water when not in use. Replace if undesirable odors persist after rinsing. Bags and filters should fit the equipment. Avoid allowing the urn bag to drop into the brew. Use a riser to support the bag. This gives freer drainage through all areas of the grounds, preventing over-extraction in certain areas. Rinse urn baskets after each use and clean thoroughly at the end of each day. Scour with urn cleaner and a stiff brush. Rinse thoroughly to remove traces of cleaner, and dry. Never use steel wool or other abrasive material. Guard against pits and scratches, which catch dirt or coffee deposits. Discard such parts.

Vacuum Equipment

To clean vacuum brewing equipment, after each batch use a good brush that reaches all parts of the top and lower bowl and scrub well. Rinse the bowls, filter parts, and cloths thoroughly. Keep filter cloths in cold water when not in use. Twice a week soak top and bottom parts, filters, strainers, and other parts in cleaner. Scrub and rinse well until all coffee deposits are removed. Rinse with hot water until all traces of cleaner are removed.

Other Equipment

Some operations may make coffee in a drip pot, old-fashioned pot, percolator, or kettle. The drip pot may be cleaned by disassembling and placing it in a kettle large enough to cover all parts with water. Add water and cleaning solution. Soak for 30 minutes. Then scrub and rinse well,

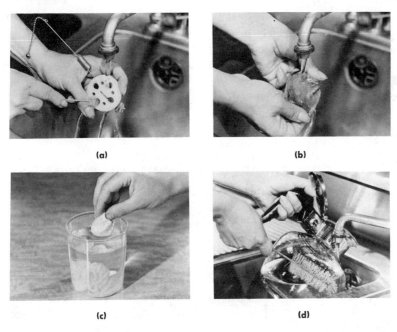

(a)   (b)

(c)   (d)

FIG. 6-6   Cleaning vacuum brewing equipment. (a) Scrub all parts well. (b) Wash filter bags in cold water. (c) Store filter bags in clean, cold water. (d) Wash tops and lower bowls well. (Courtesy Coffee Brewing Institute)

reaching all parts. Other coffee-making equipment may be filled with clear water, to which the cleaner is added, then soaked for 30 minutes and cleaned. Rinse thoroughly to remove foreign odors and cleaning agent.

Procedures

Establish precise brewing procedures. Boiling water will usually give the correct contact temperature unless altitudes are so high that boiling occurs at a temperature below 200° F. Measure both coffee and water accurately. See that good coffee of proper grind, freshly boiled water of the right type, correct contact, and proper equipment that is clean and free from contaminants are used. Give proper brewing, holding, and service instructions.

Coffee is made by hot water extracting certain soluble products from the coffee. The particle size of the grind and the time the water is in contact with the grounds will govern the amount of solubles extracted. The aromatic and milder flavors are extracted first, and the bitter or more pungent flavors last. Too long a contact time encourages overextraction of the latter. The size of the ground will govern contact time: fine or vacuum 2 to 4 minutes, drip or urn 4 to 6 minutes, and regular or percolator 6 to 8 minutes. Higher water temperatures increase the extraction rate. Agitation of the grounds in water lessens the amount of contact time required.

For the best coffee, 18 to 22% of the grounds should be extracted. This is about 2¾ to 3½ ounces of solids per pound of coffee. To obtain this, from 1¾ to 2½ gallons of water should be used per pound of coffee. If

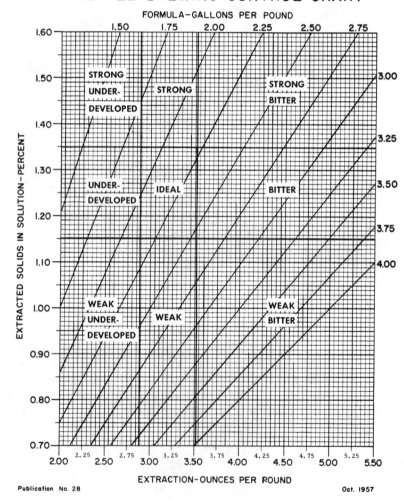

THE COFFEE BREWING INSTITUTE INC.
120 Wall Street, New York 5, N. Y.

COFFEE BREWING CONTROL CHART

FORMULA–GALLONS PER POUND

EXTRACTED SOLIDS IN SOLUTION–PERCENT

EXTRACTION–OUNCES PER POUND

Publication No. 28   Oct. 1957

FIG. 6-7

the water is of the proper condition and if the temperature, contact time, and grind are correct, a brew having from 1.15 to 1.35% total coffee solids will result. If 2 gallons of water are used, approximately 1¾ gallons of brew will be obtained, or forty 5½ ounce cups. The grounds will absorb about one quart of water. If a brew is made using 3 gallons of water to the pound, an extraction of 24% must occur to give a 1.15 to 1.35% coffee-solid content, but the brew may be bitter because of an excessive extraction of solids. Poor coffee may result even if the coffee-water ratio is correct (see Figure 6-7). Excessive contact time, water too hot, too much agitation, or other factors may give over-extraction. Weak coffee may result if these factors are varied inversely. Strong, bitter coffee may result even if more than the correct quantity of water is used, as is indicated by the upper right-hand corner tabulations in Figure 6-7. In addition to the factors mentioned, too small a grind, the wrong blend, bicarbonates, or other factors may cause this. A weak, bitter coffee could be produced under similar incorrect coffee-water ratios if the opposite conditions were true, as shown in the lower right-hand corner of Figure 6-7.

Table 6-1

Proportions for Making Coffee in Quantity

Number of People	Number of Portions (5½ oz each)	Coffee Required (lb)	Water Required (gal)
25	40	1	2
50	80	2	4
75	120	3	6
100	160	4	8
125	200	5	10
150	240	6	12

If coffee *must* be stretched, it is preferable to use a ratio of from 1⅔ to 2 gallons of water to the pound of coffee, give proper contact time, and, after removing the grounds, dilute to desired volume with hot water. While the brew will not be of proper strength, body, or color, it will at least be in somewhat proper balance and not over-extracted, as would be the case if the entire quantity of water were to come in contact with the grounds.

Coffee Making

Accurate ingredient measurement is required if a good quality brew is to be made. Ground coffee may be delivered preweighed in the exact quantities required. Standard measures may be provided, but these should be sized so that only level measure is used. Provide a similar control for

(a)

(b)

(c)

(d)

FIG. 6-8   Preliminary steps in making urn coffee. (a) Fill urn with fresh, cold water. (b) Turn on heat. (c) Use freshly boiled water. (d) Rinse urn well with hot water before using. (Courtesy Coffee Brewing Institute)

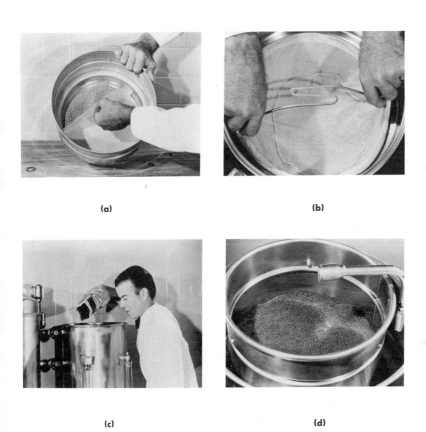

(a)   (b)

(c)   (d)

FIG. 6-9 Making good coffee. Carefully (a) place filter into urn basket or (b) fit clean bag into urn. (c) Pour coffee into filtering devices, spreading evenly. (d) Depth of coffee should be one to two inches. (Courtesy Coffee Brewing Institute)

(a)   (b)

(c)   (d)

FIG. 6-10   Making good coffee. (a) If not self-pouring, run out a gallon of boiling water. (b) Pour over grounds with a steady, circular motion; continue to add water until correct quantity is added. (c) Alternate method is to allow steam pressures in self-pouring types to force hot water over grounds through a nozzle head, measuring water added by water gage. (d) Hold brew at 185° F. (Courtesy Coffee Brewing Institute)

FIG. 6-11 Completing the brewing process. (a) After proper contact time, remove bag. (b) Draw off one gallon of the brew. (c) Pour back, give as much mixing action as possible to give a unified blend removing stratas or layers of different brew densities by the mixing. (d) Check temperature to see that coffee holds at 185° F. (Courtesy Coffee Brewing Institute)

(a)

(b)

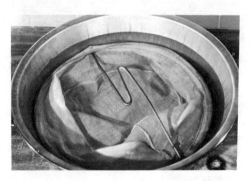

(c)

FIG. 6-12 Finishing the job. (a) Dump grounds immediately after removing them from the urn. (b) Wash bag thoroughly. (c) Soak in cold water. (Courtesy Coffee Brewing Institute)

measuring water. Some equipment indicates water consumption by gage indicator. See that this is accurate.

URN COFFEE

For urn coffee, spread the grounds evenly in a well rinsed bag or basket one to two inches deep. Spray or pour the water over the grounds in a slow, circular motion, wetting all grounds. Remove the grounds after the water has drained through (four to six minutes). Then draw about a gallon of the new brew and dump it into the remaining brew to give a thorough mixing action. This is done to mix fractions of different density which come off at different times in the brewing and which would stay in layers if this mixing did not occur. Keep the cover on as much as possible to prevent heat loss during brewing.

VACUUM COFFEE

To make vacuum coffee, fill the lower bowl with fresh water to the proper level and place it on the heat. If the bowl is unmarked, leave at least one inch at the top for water expansion in heating. Rinse a clean filter cloth in cold water and place it over the filtering device. (Some devices do not require a cloth.) Adjust it into the upper bowl. Add proper quantity of coffee in the upper bowl. When the water boils briskly, set the upper bowl firmly into the lower bowl, twisting slightly to make a tight seal. Allow the steam pressure in the lower bowl to force the boiling water up. Turn down the heat to prevent violent boiling. Stir the water in the upper bowl 30 seconds and allow contact time to be two to four minutes. Remove the heat and allow the brew to filter back. The lowering of the heat will cause the steam to condense and a vacuum to develop which pulls the brew down into the lower bowl. See that the return of the brew into the lower bowl is not prolonged over proper contact time. Some bowls have a steam vent in the side of the tube above the hot water line; with this type of upper bowl, the top may be attached to the lower bowl at the start and this vent left open, to be closed when brisk boiling commences.

MISCELLANEOUS COFFEE-MAKING PROCEDURES

Coffee may be made in some operations in a drip, old-fashioned pot, or in a kettle on the range or in a steam-jacketed kettle. In using these, never boil the coffee; this causes loss of aroma and too great an extraction because of the high temperatures. Use two level tablespoons or ⅜ ounce of coffee per 5½ ounce cup desired.

Drip

1. Bring fresh cold water to rapid boil.
2. Preheat clean pot.

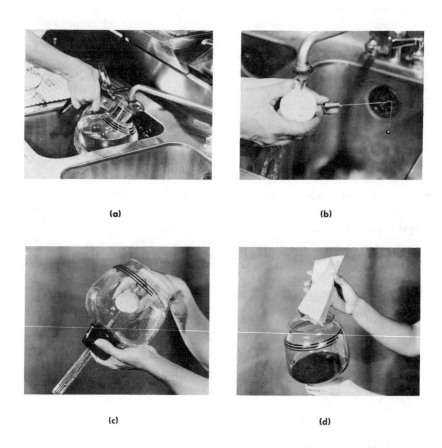

(a)   (b)

(c)   (d)

FIG. 6-13 Preliminary steps in making vacuum-maker coffee. (a) Fill with fresh, cold water. Place bowl over heat. (b) Rinse filter. (c) Place filter in top. (d) Pour measured coffee into top bowl. (Courtesy Coffee Brewing Institute)

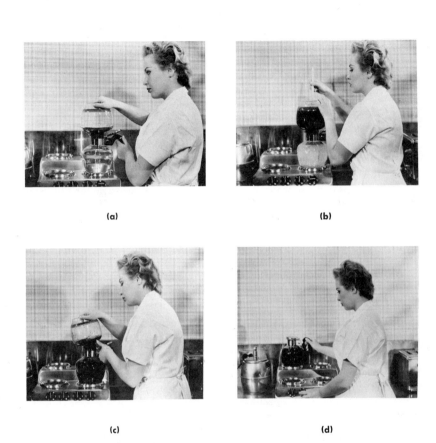

(a)   (b)

(c)   (d)

FIG. 6-14   Making vacuum-maker coffee. (a) When water comes to brisk boil, place top firmly into lower bowl, twisting slightly to give a good, tight fit. (b) Allow water to be forced into top bowl; let remain in top until proper contact time has elapsed. (c) Reduce heat to create vacuum in bottom bowl, pulling the brew down through the filter; when complete, remove upper bowl. (d) Set brew over sufficient heat to hold at 185° F. (Courtesy Coffee Brewing Institute)

3. Place top with correct quantity of coffee in it on lower part. If equipment requires filter, place into position before adding coffee. Pour correct quantity of boiling water into upper container and cover.
4. Correct contact time should be four to six minutes; when water has passed through, remove the upper section and grounds.
5. Stir well to mix strata of different density brew.

Kettle or Steam-Jacketed Kettle

1. Measure correct amount of fresh cold water into clean kettle; put on high heat.
2. Select a clean cloth sack which will be half-filled with dry coffee, allowing for expansion when the coffee becomes wet; space must be provided to allow for free circulation of water. Rinse in warm and then cold water. Squeeze out excess water. Measure coffee into this. Tie the sack so no grounds can escape. Fasten extra cord to kettle handle. Submerge sack in boiling water. Reduce heat.
3. Keep water at low heat, never boiling. Push sack up and down frequently to get proper extraction. Allow contact time of 8 to 10 minutes.
4. When coffee is ready, remove sack, draining well. Serve as soon as possible.

Old-Fashioned Pot

1. Measure correct quantity of fresh cold water into clean pot.
2. Place pot on high heat; when water comes to rolling boil, lower heat, holding water just at the boiling point.
3. Add correct quantity of regular grind coffee and stir. Steep for six to eight minutes.
4. If grounds have not settled at the end of steeping time, a small quantity of cold water may be added, using not more than one cup per pound of coffee.
5. Strain immediately into serving container, removing brew from its grounds.

Iced Coffee

Iced coffee may be made by one of three methods:

1. Extra-strength coffee, using two-thirds the usual amount of water, is made. This is poured over ice cubes to obtain proper strength coffee.
2. Regular-strength coffee may be brewed and frozen into cubes in a non-metallic container. Freeze quickly, for slow freezing may cause the coffee solids to separate from the ice. Then, to make iced coffee, regular coffee is poured over these frozen cubes.

3. Instant coffee can be mixed with a small amount of cold water, and ice cubes and water added to give the proper amount, and the product stirred. Where a large quantity of iced coffee is used, the instant coffee can be premixed, added to a glass containing ice cubes, and cold water added and stirred.

Holding After Brewing

Coffee brew will undergo significant flavor and color changes when held at elevated temperatures over one hour. The best holding temperature is from 185° to 200° F. A maximum of 60 minutes holding is recommended but never over 1½ hours. Excessive grounds or flocculent material will lessen the time the brew can be held. If the temperature is allowed to fluctuate too much during holding, some of the solids may precipitate and make the coffee turbid. Do not cool coffee and then reheat it. Serve coffee so the customer gets it at 160° F or more.

Variety Coffee

Demitasse

Demitasse coffee is made by using about 1½ to 1⅔ gallons of water to the pound of coffee. Any standard equipment may be used. The roast is a dark one but not as dark as those used for foreign types of coffee. It is served in demitasse cups. Sugar, lemon peel, and liquors may be offered with it. A mixed spice of equal parts of cardamon seed, whole cloves, and broken cinnamon stick may be offered, or just cardamon seed. This spice is also served with Italian coffee. Cream may be offered, but this is not considered proper.

Italian

Coffee espresso *(caffe espresso)* or Italian coffee is made with a drip pot, a macchinetta, or an espresso maker. The macchinetta is a drip pot consisting of two cylinders, one of which has a spout. The non-spouted cylinder has a container for coffee fitted at the top. This is equipped with top and bottom sieves. The water is measured into the non-spouted macchinetta cylinder, the sieved container containing coffee is fitted in, and the spouted cylinder is fitted over both, spout down. The cylinder with water and coffee is placed over heat, and when the water is at a full boil, the macchinetta is turned upside down away from the heat, and the water drips down through the grounds. An espresso maker uses steam pressure to force water up and through the grounds much as is done in making vacuum maker coffee. The roast used is quite dark and the grind is fine. About twice the quantity of coffee to water is used as is customary for regular coffee. Service should be in a small (four-ounce) cup or glass with a twist of lemon peel. Sugar may be offered, but never cream. Brandy or other liquors may be offered.

FIG. 6-15 *Café diablo* (coffee made with flaming brandy) can be used to end a fine dinner.

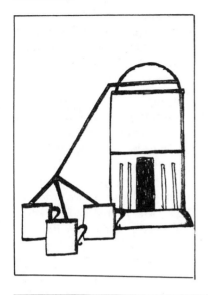

FIG. 6-16 *Espresso* coffee-makers use steam pressure to brew true Italian Espresso coffee. Small electric Espresso machines are available for home use.

The *ibrik* is commonly used in Egypt, Syria, and Turkey. Only the coffee of the Middle East and Near East countries requires boiling.

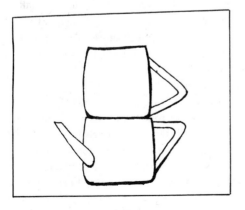

The two-tiered *macchinetta* is the Italian version of our drip coffee-maker. It makes excellent demitasse or Italian coffee.

Caffe cappaccino is Italian coffee blended with an equal quantity of hot milk. The liquids are blended simultaneously by pouring from two pots into one cup. A bit of cinnamon or nutmeg is sprinkled over the top, or whipped cream with a touch of grated orange may be added. The cups used are tall.

Turkish

About twice as much coffee to water is used for Turkish coffee as for regular coffee. The roast is dark and the grind is almost pulverized. The brew is made in a pan with high sides. The special pan used in Turkish areas is called an *ibrik*. Sugar is added with the coffee grounds and cold water. This is then brought to a boil and allowed to froth up three times. This froth should remain on the coffee and is called *face*. After removal from the heat, a few drops of cold water are added to settle the grounds, the face or foam is spooned into tiny, egg-shaped cups, and the brew is poured in. The key to good Turkish coffee is not to "lose face." The flavor is stronger than that of regular coffee brews.

Viennese and French

Viennese coffee is about the strength of demitasse coffee. It may be thinned with hot milk or served plain, but it is always topped with whipped cream *(mit schlagg)*. It may be sweetened. French coffee or *café au lait* is equal quantities of regular-strength coffee and hot milk poured from two different pots into a cup at the same time. It is usually served at breakfast but may be served at other times.

TEA

About 1¾ pounds of tea is consumed per person per year in this country. This is over 34 billion cups of tea every year. Tea is a steeped brew of the leaves of an evergreen bush that grows in tropical climates. Asia and Africa ship most of our tea. Little or no tea is imported from China, and only a small amount of green and oolong tea come from Japan and Formosa.

The quality of the brew will be governed in part by leaf size. Normally, the standard pluck is two leaves and a bud from the tip of a branch. Higher grade teas have fewer leaves than this, lower grades more. As the leaves progress down the branch, the quality of the tea drops. The quality of the brew also depends upon the area of growth, soil, weather, elevation, and the processing given the tea. High-grown tea is the best quality. Tea grown and picked late in the season is frequently poorer in quality than early or mid-season tea. All tea after plucking is withered, rolled, and fired; in addition, some teas are fermented after rolling. Black tea is fully fermented; oolong is partially fermented, and green tea is not fermented. Green tea may be steamed to prevent it from fermenting. To ferment, the tea is spread on trays and allowed to stand in a humid atmosphere for a few hours. Fermentation causes oxidation of some of the tannins, which makes them less soluble. During fermentation some of the essential oils or flavoring constituents change, giving fermented teas their characteristic aroma, taste, heavier body, and darker color. Firing stops fermentation and dries the tea so that it retains quality. Black tea when dry is almost black in color and gives an amber, reddish-copper brew. Oolong and green tea will show the green of chlorophyll. Oolong is slightly darker than green tea. The brew from oolong is a pale yellowish green with a shade of tan, while a brew from green tea is somewhat greener and paler in color.

Since the quality of the brew depends upon rapid extraction, tea manufactures may break up good quality leaves and put them into individual tea bags. To produce a good tea, blends of various teas are required; a tea may be a blend of as many as 30 teas.

Standard

Judge tea by its flavor (aroma and taste), strength, clarity, and color. Unlike coffee, body is not considered. Because of its high tannin content, tea has a slightly bitter taste. Tannin is oxidized in fermentation, so black tea has the least bitterness, oolong next, and green tea the greatest. Some sweetness and acidity may be present. The aroma should be fruity and fragrant. Some aromas may be excessively fruity, and the tea is scored down for this quality. An excess or lack of aroma lowers quality. Like coffee, tea should be swished into the mouth to give taste and aroma at the same time. A tea lacking flavor is called thin or weathery. A tea balanced in flavor is described as brisk, indicating its zestful, stimulating quality. There should be no apparent oiliness. Clarity is essential. Some tea leaves may be apparent if these are not filtered out. Tea made from a tea bag or decanted should contain no evidence of leaf silt. The color should be typical for the type of tea, black tea being coppery red in color.

Principles

The soluble substances in tea are the alkaloid, theine (caffeine), tannins and other astringent compounds, acids, sugars, carbohydrates, some essential oils, and coloring matter. Tannin is more soluble in hot than in cold water, and as the temperature of the water increases, the rate of extraction increases. The best contact time for water and tea is three minutes with the water at around 200° F. Over-contact gives excess tannin extraction with other undesirable compounds. The cooling effect of equipment should be considered in judging water temperature. The essential oils or aromas of tea are highly volatile, especially in brewing, and may be rapidly dissipated in boiling. Because of the high volatility of aromatic fractions, tea should be freshly made for service and not held. Tea will infuse more rapidly in soft or mildly hard waters than in hard, alkaline waters. Clouding may be evident when hard water is used. Hard water produces a dark, dull tea. Tannins may be precipitated by calcium, magnesium, or iron ions in the water as tannates, and sometimes a thin film over the brew indicates that this precipitation has occurred. Flavor may be affected by hard-water salts. A bit of acid, such as lemon juice, will change the pH sufficiently to dissolve tannates, lighten the color, and give a brisker flavor. At times, however, these acids have no effect, as is true even in an acid punch, where clouding may occur if iron tannates form.

The tannin fractions in tea are easily precipitated. Rapid cooling of a tea may induce clouding from tannin precipitation. Tea stored in a refrigerator may cloud, and strong infusions should never be stored in a cold place but should be kept at room temperature. Metals in contact with tea in brewing or service may, as with coffee, give a metallic taste. Glass, earthenware, enameled ware, vitrified china, or stainless steel should be the materials used in making tea equipment.

Procedures

Because tea is most frequently prepared individually for immediate service, techniques recommended for its making in small quantity are applicable in large quantity.

To make tea properly, it is necessary to provide a correct measure for water and tea leaves. One teaspoon of tea is usually sufficient for one cup of strong tea or two cups of milder tea. An individual tea bag holds one teaspoon of tea and there are 18 teaspoons per ounce of tea. Between five and eight ounces will be required to serve tea to 100 people. This will produce four to nearly seven gallons of tea, or from 100 to 150 cups. Tea bags for making larger quantities of tea are frequently packed in ounces. One of these is used to make a gallon of strong tea. Tea may also be measured into a cloth or bag, tied loosely, and steeped in hot water. One level cup of tea (16 T) will make about 50 cups, or a little over two gallons of tea.

The container in which the tea is made should be rinsed with very hot water, the tea added, and boiling water in the correct amount poured over the tea. This is called wet service. It is incorrect to pour water into the container and add the tea, or to serve a tea bag on the side of a cup or pot of hot water. Tea in quantity can be made by bringing the water to a boil in a kettle on the range or in a steam-jacketed kettle. Add the tea. Stir to blend thoroughly and allow to steep for three minutes. Decant from the leaves and serve immediately. Use the right type of water, freshly boiled. Water boiled or kept hot for any period of time is flat. Never boil tea.

Service of hot tea is frequently with lemon only. Occasionally a whole clove may be offered also. Some individuals use sugar with their tea. Cream is said to mask the delicate flavor of tea, while milk allows its subtle flavor to be smoothed out but not lost.

Iced tea is a great favorite. It should be made from a slightly greater proportion of tea to water than regular tea, since dilution by ice may occur. Make the tea in the same manner as regular tea. Use care in steeping, for an excess of tannins may cause clouding when the tea is chilled. Green tea is especially difficult to use for iced tea because of its high tannin content. Certain black teas from India are high in tannins, and these may give difficulty from clouding. Iced tea for quantity service may be made in large batches and held in glass or crockery containers equipped with a spigot. A tall glass may be filled with ice and the brew poured over it. Fresh hot tea may be made and also poured over an ice-filled glass. Because of the high dilution with this method, the tea must be strong. Many operations find instant tea adequate for iced tea. Mint or lemon may be served with iced tea.

The Tea Council recommends the following 1-2-3 method for making iced tea:

For one gallon of iced tea, pour
1 quart of boiling water over
2 ounces of tea; steep six minutes, stir, remove tea and pour into
3 quarts of cold tap water.

For a larger quantity, multiply the 1 qt., 2 oz. and 3 qt. by the number of gallons of iced tea you want. Be sure to use a brewing container of small enough diameter so boiling water completely covers the tea. Finished iced tea can be held for four hours without loss of flavor.

Teas may be blended with fruit juices and other liquids for special occasions. A Russian tea is a sweetened combination of tea and orange, lemon, and pineapple juice, delicately seasoned with cinnamon. Spiced tea is a sweetened mixture of tea delicately seasoned with orange and lemon rind, whole cloves, and cinnamon sticks.

COCOA

Where the service of cocoa is infrequent, it is best to use individual packaged mixes. In quantity service, the use of dry cocoa, sugar, and either liquid or dry milks is recommended.

Standard

A good cup of cocoa or chocolate should have a pleasing appearance. The color should be a light, rich brown and not gray or muddy. A pale weak color is cause for a lowered score. There should be no scum on the surface or mixed in with the cocoa. Foam may be present on the batch from which the cocoa is dispensed, but none should be on the cup unless whipped cream or marshmallow has been added. The flavor should be delicately sweet, with the rich, aromatic, mellow flavor of the cacao bean evident. Richness should be present, especially in chocolate, which will also have a richer color. Flatness or lack of flavor or a scorched or raw flavor is undesirable. The blend of the brew should be uniform. Lowered quality is indicated by poor blending or a large quantity of sediment. Definite wateriness or a sirupy quality is objectionable. There should be more body than in a hot cup of milk. Certain starch fractions in both chocolate or cocoa will cause thickening, but this should be evident as body only in a minor way. Adding starch to give body is not recommended.

Principles

Cocoa and chocolate are the product of the cacao bean. After harvest the long pods containing the beans or fruit are cut open and the seeds removed. These are fermented, a process which develops some flavor, reduces bitterness, and improves color. The seeds are then washed and dried. Roasting occurs next, which further lessens bitter qualities and develops the typical flavor, aroma, and color. The bean is then cracked and the nibs or chocolate are separated from the chaff. The nibs are then ground fine to produce chocolate liquor. Removal of the cacao butter to around 22% fat content and pulverizing produces breakfast cocoa. Regular bitter chocolate contains about 50% cacao butter. Low-fat cocoas contain less than 10% cacao butter, medium from 10 to 22%. Lower-fat cocoas display more starch swelling than high-fat ones. Chocolate will exhibit less thickening. If the richness or fat content of cocoa is not adequate, butter or margarine may be added and beaten into the mixture to give desired richness, but this is difficult to do. Cream may be added to give richness.

Chocolate and cocoa contain starch, protein, fat and fat-like substances, minerals, some tannins, and some color pigments. Caffein and a substance called theobromine, the latter a stimulant and in significantly greater quantities than caffein, are present. Some cocoa or chocolate is given an alkaline treatment during processing to improve flavor, give a darker color, and increase solubility (25% soluble) and digestibility. Cocoa or chocolate treated by this method is called "Dutch." Normal cocoa or chocolate is slightly acid, but Dutch-process cocoas are about neutral. Beverages prepared from chocolate instead of cocoa have a richer flavor and a more velvety taste but are more costly. Substitute two-thirds as much cocoa by weight for unsweetened chocolate. For a pound of chocolate use $10\frac{2}{3}$ ounces cocoa.

Procedures

Cocoa may be made by a sirup method, a dry blend method, or a paste method, or from prepared mixes. Instant dry milks go into solution more easily than regular dry milks. Do not boil cocoas made with dry milk. To make a chocolate instead of cocoa, substitute melted bitter chocolate. A French chocolate is melted chocolate blended with whipped cream and sugar and thinned with hot milk. About one pound of cocoa will be required for five gallons of milk, which will yield about 100 to 120 cups.

Sirup Method
1. Mix dry ingredients (sugar, cocoa, dry milk,* salt) until all lumps are broken.
2. Blend thoroughly with a small quantity of water.
3. Thin with boiling water to desired consistency, or if liquid milks are used, pour into the heated milk and blend thoroughly.
4. Use a whip to produce a foam on the top.

   *Omit if liquid milks are used.

Dry Blend Method
1. Heat milk. Add salt.
2. Blend sugar and cocoa until well mixed and no lumps exist.
3. Pour dry mixture into warm milk, blending well with a whip as it is added.
4. Use a whip to produce a foam on the top.

Paste Method
1. Mix dry ingredients well into cool water until a thin paste is obtained.
2. Heat this until the mixture thickens; thin with water if necessary.
3. Add this to hot milk.
4. Use a whip to produce a foam on the top.

Prepared Mix
1. Add a small quantity of warm water to the cup or container.
2. Add the prepared mix and blend thoroughly to a thin paste.
3. Thin with very hot water or milk.
4. A foam usually forms on this product, preventing the formation of scum.

When milk is heated, even at temperatures below boiling, a thin scum forms on the surface. Covering when heating or beating the milk with a whip reduces scum formation. In making all cocoas or chocolate, the temperature of the mixture should rise to 203° F to gelatinize the starch and make it into a stable product in the solution.

7   Eggs and Dairy Products

Eggs and milk products are often studied together in cookery because they are so closely related as protein foods. The principles and the techniques of cooking used are very similar for both.

EGGS

Eggs find wide use in food services. The menu may feature them as entrees, appetizers, or salads. In food preparation they may be used for thickening or binding agents in custards, pie fillings, or puddings; in meat loaves; and for covering in French toast, breading, or batters. Egg foam is used to incorporate air into sponge cakes, angel cakes, soufflés, and other products. Eggs are excellent emulsifiers, especially the yolks. Eggs' ability to coagulate and give strength to a baked structure gives them utility in baking. They may be used to clarify a consommé or bouillon. The crystalline formations of frozen desserts and candies are stabilized when eggs are an ingredient. Eggs add color, richness, and flavor to foods. They are rich in nutrients, contributing significant quantities of vitamin A, thiamin, riboflavin, niacin, vitamin D, and minerals such as iron and phosphorous; they are complete proteins. They also furnish fat and calories and are easily digested. Good egg cookery is not as simple as it might appear. There are many things to know before good products can be made from eggs, and some of the preparation techniques required are the most exacting and difficult to accomplish in the field of cooking.

Egg Quality

Good egg quality is important to final product quality, especially with break-fast eggs. The position of the yolk, the viscosity and thickness of the white or albumen, the size of the air sac or cell, and the acidity or alkalinity of the egg are indicators of quality. The quality of frozen, freeze-dry, or dried eggs depends upon the quality of the fresh eggs from which they came and the subsequent care given the eggs in processing and storage. A good egg has a well-centered yolk with a firm membrane surrounding it. The white should be firm and viscous. When an opened raw egg of high quality rests on a flat surface, the white should form a rounded mass close to the yolk and have only a small quantity of thin, watery white. The yolk should stand high.

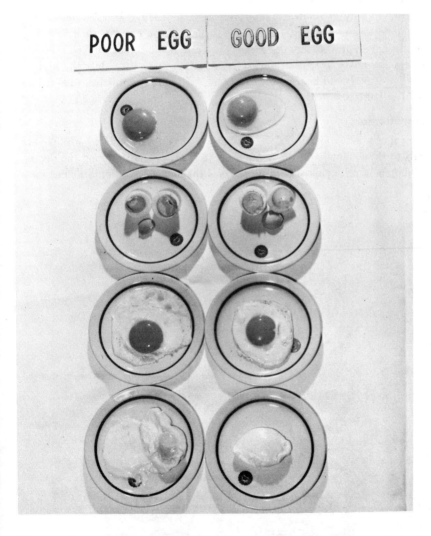

FIG. 7-1   The quality of an egg will affect its usefulness for many purposes in food preparation. Note how egg quality can affect the quality of breakfast eggs.

Up to about three days after laying, the white of an egg is usually opaque or cloudy; after that it becomes clear. Some eggs given good processing immediately after laying, such as an oil dip plus good temperature and humidity control in storage, may retain this opaqueness for a long time. A fresh egg is slightly acid, but as it loses quality, it grows more alkaline. The white becomes thin and the yolk loses its central position; the yolk membrane becomes weak, and the yolk may break when the egg is shelled. Eggs lose quality rapidly at room temperature. A flavor change also develops as an egg deteriorates. Older eggs have a strong flavor or may easily develop strong flavors in cooking. Strong flavors in eggs bake out in baked products unless the flavor is caused by bacteria, yeasts, or molds. Only the highest quality eggs should be used for breakfast eggs, but lower quality eggs can be used in baking.

Egg Standards

A properly soft-cooked egg should have a partially coagulated white. One half to three fourths of the white may be firm, depending upon the degree of doneness. The yolk should be warmed through but be liquid. A medium-

FIG. 7-2   (a) Standards for hard cooked, medium cooked and soft cooked eggs.

FIG. 7-2   (b) Fried eggs country-style, over-easy, and sunnyside up.

cooked egg has the white cooked only to the yolk and the yolk is still liquid. A properly hard-cooked egg has a firm, glossy white and a firmly cooked, mealy yolk that has a bright yellow or orange-yellow color. The yolk should be uniformly coagulated and not surrounded by any darkness. All types of

(a)   (b)

(c)   (d)

FIG. 7-3 (a) Standard for fried egg sunnyside up, (b) country style, (c) poached and (d) scrambled.

eggs cooked in the shell should have a pleasing, delicate flavor. There should be no toughness, rubberiness, crumbliness, stickiness, or other undesirable texture. Eggs which are boiled will have a firmer, tougher white than those cooked at lower temperatures. Hard-cooked eggs to be cut or sliced should be cooked at higher temperatures than breakfast eggs. If this is not done, the eggs are frequently too tender to handle. Eggs cooked in the shell should appear bright and fresh. Colors should be natural and clear. Eggs processed with an oil dip may leave a thin film of oil on the surface of the water. This does not indicate that the eggs are of poor quality but rather that they have had good processing.

A fried egg should have a bright, glossy appearance. It should be compact, much like a poached egg but not quite as bunched up. The white will be more spread out and thinner in depth around the yolk. An egg cooked "sunny-side up" should have a bright yellow, or orange-yellow, well-rounded yolk. If an egg is cooked country-style, "over easy," or hard-cooked, the yolk will be covered with a white film of coagulated white, and the yolk, depending upon the degree of cooking, will be firmer than for sunny-side up eggs. A fried egg should be soft underneath with no hard edges. The egg surface should appear shiny, not dull, wrinkled, porous, or watery. The coagulated areas should be firm, yet tender, not tough or rubbery.

A poached egg should have a bright appearance with a film of coagulated white over a bright yolk. The egg should not be spread out or porous but should be compact, with a clear, bright white that adheres closely to the yolk. Raggedness, wrinkling, dullness, or other undesirable qualities should be avoided.

The standard for a shirred egg is about the same as for a fried egg that has been cooked country-style. It should be bright and not over-cooked or dry at the surface or edge, or have a dark ring around the yolk. Toughness is undesirable.

Scrambled eggs should be bright and clear and possess a soft sheen. The color should be a uniform, pale yellow. There should be no evidence of browning. The egg particles should be small segments, not fine pieces, and they should be moist; not dry, powdery, or watery. Complete coagulation should be avoided, but the eggs should not be runny. They should have tenderness and delicacy of texture. Heavy, compact eggs are undesirable. Avoid a hard layer on the bottom or foaminess on top. A strong flavor or rubberiness indicates overcooking or perhaps poor quality eggs.

A plain, oftentimes called French, omelet should have many of the qualities of scrambled eggs, except that browning may be evident as a delicate, light-tannish browning covering. The omelet may be firmer and have a more continuous mass than is desirable in scrambled eggs. No moist, large segments should be apparent. Moistness, tenderness, and delicacy of flavor should be evident as in the scrambled egg. The folded or rolled shape of the omelet should be even and represent a uniform, well rounded, but not ragged, uneven, or separated mass. A foamy omelet may be served unfolded but it is usually folded in half or rolled. It should be well puffed, of good volume, and well rounded; not fallen or collapsed. It should have a uniform, delicate tan top and a delicate brown bottom. Uneven or pale color or excessive browning are undesirable factors. The texture and consistency should be uniform, well blended, tender, firm, and moist, not tough or dry. There should be no rawness in the center. No unmixed egg white should be apparent. There should be no foaminess on top or toughness caused by solidified products on the bottom. The flavor should be delicate, not pasty, flat, raw, or burned. A foamy omelet depends for its quality upon the light, airy leavening given it by beating of the whites and yolks, and this delicacy of texture should weigh heavily in evaluating this product.

A soufflé should have much of the texture qualities of a foamy omelet. It should be slightly rounded and well puffed, with only a slight cracking evident at the top. The top otherwise should be smooth, slightly shiny, and

(a)   (b)

FIG. 7-4   (a) Standard for a soufflé and (b) foamy omelet ready for service.

not sunken. The color should be an even, delicate brown. No unmixed egg white should be evident.

Baked custard mixtures should be clear, creamy, and shiny. The texture should be smooth; not stiff, tough, rubbery, curdled, or uneven. No wateriness or porosity should be evident. The product should possess a delicate flavor, blended with that of the material used in the custard. An eggy, flat, or tasteless flavor is undesirable. The surface should be shiny and clear and may be lightly touched with a delicate tan.

(a)   (b)

(c)   (d)

FIG. 7-5 (a) An egg just beginning to coagulate; firmness appears as the protein binds in the moisture. (b) An egg custard cooked at the proper temperature on the left and too high a temperature on the right. (c) Using a thermometer to judge the doneness of a stirred custard. (d) The difference in egg tenderness is shown here. Both eggs are cooked to the same doneness, the egg on the left being cooked at 212° F, the one on the right at 185°.

Principles

When subjected to heat above certain temperatures, eggs will coagulate or
become firm. High temperatures toughen eggs and may develop unpleasant
flavors. Low or moderate temperatures are recommended for cooking eggs.
Acids increase the thickening power and lower the temperature of coagulation and also make eggs more tender. Acids help to retard undesirable flavor
development. Whole egg coagulates at about 156° F, yolk at 158° F, and
white at 149° F. Coagulation is not instantaneous at these temperatures but
occurs somewhere around them. Mixing eggs with liquids, sugar, or other
materials raises their coagulation temperature. A custard coagulates at
around 175° to 185° F for this reason.

Coagulation is a physical change caused by heat, but also can be caused
by mechanical action such as beating, by chemical action such as the action
of strong acids or alcohol, or by other means. Raising the temperature slowly
causes coagulation to occur at a slightly lower temperature than when temperatures are raised quickly. Egg protein is fluid because it binds its moisture
in loosely to it when raw, but when it coagulates, the water is bound in
tightly, causing the protein to become firm. If egg protein is diluted with
moisture, high temperatures in cooking will cause the egg to lose much of
this moisture, giving an open, curdled texture to the mass. The protein fractions are now bunched together separate from the moisture. Additional heat
will toughen and harden this curd.[1] This separation or breakdown is called
syneresis. It may be seen in overcooked custards, sour milk, or broken milk
clabber. Overcooked dishes such as rarebit may have a grainy condition
caused by this breakdown.

Coagulation is an endothermic reaction; that is, heat is absorbed in the
process. A custard, therefore, when it is thickening, will not rise in temperature, but when coagulation is complete, the temperature will immediately
rise again. This second rise may be used as an indicator of when to remove
solid and stirred custards from the heat. Curdling will soon follow if the
mixture is allowed to cook after this second rise occurs. Custards usually
break down at around 190° F. Stirring a custard gives a smooth, slightly
thickened liquid, while baking without disturbing gives a smooth, completely thickened solid mass.

Eggs, especially the whites, contain sulfur, and this may combine with
other compounds in cooking to give off-flavors or -colors, especially if the
egg is alkaline in reaction. If the sulfur joins with the iron in the yolk, iron
sulfide is formed. This compound has a strong flavor and a dark greenish

[1]Curdling also occurs with milk. In cheese manufacture, the curd is heated (called
cooking) to give the desired firmness. Some hard cheeses, such as Parmesan, are heated
to temperatures considerably above 100° F to give them a hard, dry texture. The
softer cheeses are cooked at temperatures slightly below 100° F.

color and is found in overcooked eggs. Sulfides form at about 155° F, but the reaction is not great until about 185° F or above, at which time they form rapidly. This development may be retarded by (1) cooking at lower temperatures, (2) using fresh eggs, (3) giving the egg mixture an acid reaction, and (4) shortening cooking time. If possible, eggs should be cooled rapidly after cooking, especially hard-cooked eggs in the shell, for these will develop strong flavors and off-colors if allowed to remain hot after cooking.

Foams

Age and egg quality affect foaming ability and stability. Real fresh eggs may lack good foaming ability, while old eggs of good quality may be more satisfactory. Some age is desirable for the best foaming. Storage eggs or dried or frozen eggs may foam more satisfactorily than fresh shell eggs. Eggs foam best at between 75° and 110° F. The addition of salt seems to aid foam formation. An acid reaction or adding of sugar gives foam stability, and acid, by tenderizing the protein, enables the egg also to extend more easily. One tablespoon of cream of tartar ($\frac{1}{3}$ ounce) to each $1\frac{1}{4}$ pounds of egg is commonly used as the acid. Acid also lightens egg pigments, especially the flavones. When eggs are beaten, the acid and salt are usually added at the start. If sugar is added, it may be added when the eggs become foamy or later. The early addition of sugar buffers the eggs, especially the whites, against overbeating. An egg white cannot be beaten if fat is present, even the smallest quantity. Whites and yolks in shell eggs are separated more easily above 60° F.

The four stages to which egg whites, yolks, or whole eggs are beaten to foams are as follows:

	First Stage	Second Stage	Third Stage	Fourth Stage
Appearance	Liquid but well blended; foam is in large bubbles.	Medium size air cells throughout mass; foam is shiny, moist and fluid; tips fold over into rounded peaks, and liquid separates out in standing.	Stiff foam; small air cells; no longer fluid, especially whites; still moist, smooth, and glossy; points stand when peaked.	Dry, dull, brittle foam; flakes off and can be cut into rigid parts; curds may appear, indicating coagulation; it is difficult to beat whole eggs or yolks to this stage.
Use	Clarifying soups, French toast, coating foods, and for blending into mixtures as liquid.	Sponge or angel cakes, soft meringues, soufflés, foamy omelets.	Cooked frostings, divinity, hard meringues, tortes, sponge cakes.	Has no use in food work; eggs are so over-extended that they will not extend further in baking, causing a failure in the product.

(a)   (b)

(c)   (d)

FIG. 7-6   Stages of foam used in cooking and baking. (a) First stage, from left to right: whites, yolks, whole eggs. (b) Second stage, in the same order. (c) Third stage, in the same order. (d) Fourth stage, egg whites only. These whites have little use in either cooking or baking. Excess beating has destroyed their ability to expand further in cooking.

Recipes should state the stage to which eggs are to be beaten, and at times it may be necessary to indicate whether the top or lower range of the stage is required. Sugar aids in creating a foam because the rough edges carry small particles of air into the foam. The color of eggs lightens as foam increases. The most common fault in the beating of yolks is underbeating. Meringues processed for meringues or angel cakes can be beaten to a stiffer foam than can regular egg whites. Thawed frozen or reliquefied dried eggs should be warmed to around 110° F and beaten by the same techniques used to beat regular eggs. Cook at once to avoid *Salmonella* development.

Techniques of Cooking

Because eggs are oftentimes cooked to order, small quantity techniques may be used for such preparation. The delicate nature and high perishability of quality in breakfast eggs makes it difficult to prepare them in large quantity. Fried, shirred, or scrambled eggs may be cooked almost done, held for a short time, and then finished in a warm oven. Ten minutes in a steam table may destroy the quality of breakfast eggs, especially if they are cooked to doneness and then held.

Cooking in Water
BOILING

Have eggs at room temperature or warm them slightly in lukewarm water before adding them to hot water; if the eggs are cold, they may crack. Times for cooking eggs in the shell are:

	212° F*	190° to 195° F	Steam Pressure, 7 psi
Soft-cooked	3 min	6 min	1 min 25 sec
Medium-cooked	4 min	8 min	
Hard-cooked	12 to 15 min	20 to 25 min	3 min 10 sec

*These times will vary at elevations above 3,000 feet because of the lower temperature of the water at boiling.

Egg boilers are used in many operations, and about four eggs can be cooked at one time in a boiler. To cook eggs in the shell in quantity, place the eggs in a perforated insert and set this into tepid water in a steam-jacketed kettle or a pot that can be quickly brought to boiling. The water should cover the eggs about one inch deep. For breakfast eggs, bring the water to 190° to 195° F. After cooking, plunge the eggs immediately into cold water and send to service. Eggs for slicing or stuffing should be cooked at higher temperatures and cooled in cold water for five to ten minutes. Peel immediately, cracking the shell well; roll to give a good shell break-up. Start at the large end and peel down, using running water if necessary to help loosen the shell from the egg. If hard-cooked eggs are to be chopped, do not boil in the shell, but crack into pans to a depth not over one inch deep, steam or cook hard, and then chop.

CODDLED EGGS

To coddle an egg, have it at room temperature and add boiling water in the ratio of one pint of water to each egg; cover tightly and allow to stand without heat until the desired doneness is attained.

(a)

(b)

(c)

(d)

FIG. 7-7 (a) Coddling eggs. (b) Shelling an egg by starting at the large end and working down, using running water to assist in removing the shell. (c) Dropping eggs toward the side of the pan for poaching them is the approved technique. (d) A properly and an improperly poached egg. Improper cooking is indicated by the rough, spread-out condition of the egg on the right.

(a)   (b)

(c)   (d)

FIG. 7-8   To save time and labor in hard-cooking eggs which must later be chopped, use the method shown here. (a) Brush pan lightly with oil or butter. (b) Crack eggs into bowl and then add to pan. (c) Place into steamer or oven, or otherwise cook firm. (d) Slice as shown or chop. (Courtesy Mrs. Kathryn Flack, Mental Health Hospitals, New York State)

POACHED EGGS

For poaching eggs, have the water from 2 to 2½ inches deep in a 4 inch flat pan, with one tablespoon of salt and two tablespoons of vinegar per gallon of water. Grease the pan lightly before adding the water. The salt and vinegar cause the egg protein to bunch together, retarding spread. Bring to a gentle boil. About 8 to 16 eggs may be poached per gallon of water, and the water can be used for three to four batches before discarding. Crack eggs onto platters and slide the eggs in toward the side of the pan, not in the center; this helps to keep the yolks in the centers of the white. Cook from three to five minutes depending upon desired doneness. Remove with a perforated ladle, slotted spoon, or other utensil which gives good drainage. Eggs may be sent to service, slightly undercooked, in hot, lightly salted water. Eggs poached at too low a temperature may be too tender to handle well in quantity service. Eggs may also be poached in the steam table, starting a few at a time so some are ready to serve while others are on their way to the desired doneness. Eggs may be poached by steam in greased cups.

Cooking with Dry Heat

Eggs are frequently fried to order, even when a large quantity is required. Single or double egg pans are used. Single pans should be four inches in diameter at the bottom, and double pans from six to eight inches. Pans used for egg frying should be conditioned and used only for that purpose. (See method for conditioning pans in the chapter on meat cookery under sautéing.) Clean thoroughly with a soft absorbent cloth or paper; do not wash.

To fry eggs, add fat or butter (the latter is preferred) about $\frac{1}{8}$ inch deep in the pan. Heat to a fairly high temperature and slide the eggs into the fat, immediately reducing the heat to avoid forming a hard surface

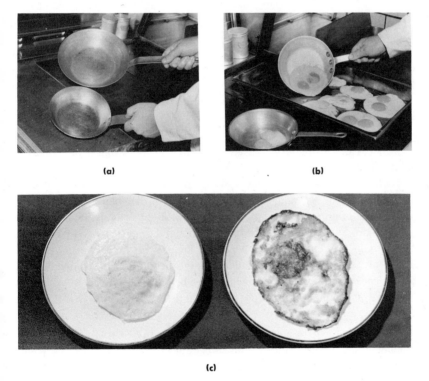

(a)   (b)

(c)

FIG. 7-9   To fry eggs properly: (a) Select the correct-size pan; see that it is well conditioned so the eggs will not stick. (b) Prepare fried eggs in bulk cooking units, as shown, for service elsewhere. Remember that some cooking usually occurs when the eggs are held in the service counter. (c) The underside of a fried egg should be tender, as shown on the left, not crisp and hard, as shown on the right.

under the egg or at the edges. The hot fat helps to prevent spread by coagulating the egg quickly. If desired, the pan may be covered tightly and the egg cooked country-style, a process in which steam from the egg or a bit of water added for steam coats the top of the egg with coagulated white. An egg may also be basted with hot fat and be called country-style. Turning the egg over and cooking is called "over easy."

Eggs may be fried on a well oiled grill. Use plenty of butter or fat on a very clean and carefully conditioned grill set at 300° to 325° F. The eggs produced are not as attractive as those prepared in individual pans, but production is faster. In grilling, keep addition of eggs in the same rotation so they can be removed in the same order. Eggs may be prebroken into a device having a number of cups, which makes it possible to add a number of eggs at one time. For cafeteria service, cook eggs until just set, place in a well buttered pan, cover lightly, and send to finish cooking in a steam table.

For frying in mass quantity, break the eggs onto platters and slide into a 2 to 2½ inch deep fat contained in 4 inch deep flat pans. Have the fat at from 265° to 280° F. Drain these eggs well before sending them to service. Some operations prefer to grease 18 x 26 inch hamburger bun pans, place the egg or eggs in the indented spaces, and then bake them in the oven, a process called ovenizing.

SHIRRED EGGS

Eggs can be shirred or baked either by cooking under a broiler or by baking in an oven. Eggs for shirring are usually placed in well buttered individual cassolettes or shallow baking dishes. Cream or milk is poured over them, seasonings added, and the cassolette or dish placed over low heat for several minutes or until the edges show slight coagulation. The dish is then placed under a broiler or in an oven and the eggs cooked to doneness. The heat in this final cooking should be kept low. Cheese, bacon, chicken livers, or other foods may be added at the beginning of cooking or just before cooking is completed. Sauces may be added to the eggs during the last stage of cooking or just before being sent to service.

SCRAMBLED EGGS

Scrambled eggs are easily prepared in quantity. Usually cream, milk, or some other liquid is added, four ounces per pound of whole eggs. Cooking may be in large greased pans in the oven, under a broiler, in a steam-jacketed kettle, in a *bain marie*, in a steam table, in individual skillets, or in a steamer or double boiler. The heat at the start should be fairly high. Then, it should be lowered rapidly as the eggs coagulate. Lift the eggs carefully from the bottom, allowing the uncooked portions to flow to the bottom and cook. The eggs should be left in about one-fourth-inch segments. Excess stirring divides them too finely. Remove before they are completely cooked and send to service, for holding will give the eggs a chance to firm up. Cooking at too high a heat or holding too long in a steam table will encourage the formation of off-colors and -flavors, and toughness and porosity may also be evident. Whole eggs are sometimes combined with a medium white or cream sauce in the ratio of four or five to one. The eggs are then cooked until just set. These hold longer than regular scrambled eggs, about 30 minutes at about 200° F being possible.

OMELETS

Both plain (French) and foamy omelets are served, but the latter, because of its delicate nature and the skill required in the making, is less

(a)

(b)

(c)

FIG. 7-10 (a) Send scrambled eggs to service with some softness showing in them. (b) On the left are individual molds of spinach timbale, while on the right the egg custard is being poured over bread and shredded, tangy cheese to make a cheese fondue. (c) Eggs being placed into an oven for shirring. The very hot hash has been indented and the eggs dropped into this depression for baking in a moderate oven until the whites are coagulated, but the yolks are still soft. Serve with a bit of brown gravy over each portion.

frequently seen. Either is cooked to order. Plain omelets in quantity may also be baked in large pans, steamed in pans, or cooked in a double boiler, a *bain marie,* or a steam-jacketed kettle. Oven temperatures for baking are around 325° F, and time is about 25 to 30 minutes.

A small plain omelet may be made from one egg, a medium omelet from two, and a large omelet from three. Salt is added to the eggs placed in a bowl, and the eggs are well blended (first stage) by beating with a fork. They should not be frothly. The addition of liquid is not recommended. Use a well conditioned pan covered about ⅛ inch deep with clarified butter, margarine, oil, or fat. Bring to a fairly high temperature. The eggs should bubble as they are poured in. Tilt the pan in all directions to spread the eggs quickly to the outer edges. Then drop the heat and cook at a moderate temperature. Lift cooked portions up carefully so uncooked liquid cooks, but do not break or allow to bunch or form a mass in the center of the pan.

(a)   (b)

(c)   (d)

FIG. 7-11   The making of a plain (French) omelet is shown. (a) Pour the well mixed egg (stage one) into a well-conditioned pan covered about one-eighth inch deep with butter or oil. Have the fat hot so the egg bubbles as it is poured in. Immediately lower the heat. (b) Complete cooking. Fold. (c) Place on a clean plate and shape. (d) Omelets filled with sweet fillings may be dusted with powdered sugar and burned lightly with a hot metal instrument.

When the eggs are set and while the surface is still moist, increase the heat to brown the bottom. To fold or roll, tip the pan to about a 60° angle and shape with a spatula. Before folding, fill with creamed items, chicken livers, chopped bacon or ham, cheese, jelly, preserves, or marmalade. Press the folded edges lightly to seal and then turn and cook for a short time, working to the edge of the pan. Turn onto a plate, shape with a clean cloth or saran wrap, and serve. Omelets with sweetened centers, such as marmalades or preserves, are frequently "burned." This is a process in which the omelet is sprinkled liberally with powdered sugar and a hot metal instrument is used to burn a design onto the omelet.

A foamy omelet is made very much like a plain omelet except that the white and the yolk are separated and each is beaten to a soft foam (stage two). They are then folded carefully together. Fold in well to give thorough incorporation, but handle the mixture delicately. Pour the mixture into a liberally greased pan and bake over heat or in an oven until done at 325° F. The addition of warm water or other liquid in the ratio of one tablespoon of liquid to each egg is recommended, dividing the water half and half between the yolk and the white. Liquids having fat in them, such as milk, should not be used. An acid liquid, such as tomato juice, makes a tender product, or the water can be acidified with lemon juice in the ratio of one part of lemon juice to two parts of water, or a small quantity of cream of tartar may be added during beating. A foamy omelet should be served immediately after preparation. It can be filled before folding and may be scored by burning, as is done for a plain omelet.

SOUFFLÉS

A soufflé is made by blending stage-one egg yolks into a heavily thickened starch base and then folding egg whites at stage two (upper level) into this mixture. The soufflé is then baked at low temperature. Meat, cheese, or other chopped foods may be added. Sweetened soufflés are used for desserts.

With proper techniques, soufflés may be made in quantity. Bake at around 300° F, for at this temperature the soufflé may be baked without placing it in a pan of water. Cooking at low temperature gives a product which will be dry and more stable than when baked at higher temperatures. Baking for a shorter period of time in a 375° F oven in a pan of water also gives a good product. After baking, soufflés and foamy omelets should be left for a short time at the oven entrance with the door open to stabilize. This guards against sudden collapse. As they cool, the volume decreases, but a well-made soufflé will shrink only slightly. Tapioca-thickened soufflés have been found to perform well in quantity service.

FONDUES AND TIMBALES

A fondue is a custard-like product which has bread or bread crumbs in it to give it lightness. It is somewhat like a soufflé when baked, and chicken, cheese, and other chopped items may be added as for a soufflé. The eggs may or may not be stiffly beaten; they usually are not in quantity preparation. A timbale is made from a custard mixture much in the manner of a fondue, but it does not contain any bread or bread crumbs.

Processed Eggs

Frozen or dried eggs are very satisfactory for cooking or baking purposes. Purchase a high quality product, preferably one that is federally inspected. Because of the danger of *Salmonella* poisoning, use processed egg only in products that are cooked. Frozen whole eggs, frozen yolks, and frozen whites are on the market. A sugared yolk is also on the market and contains approximately 10% sugar. Some frozen whole eggs containing added egg yolks are on the market called proprietary eggs. A high quality frozen whole egg is on the market which is of sufficiently high quality to use for omelets, scrambled eggs, French toast, and other breakfast purposes. For the most part, dried and frozen eggs come from eggs that lack sufficiently high quality to sell as breakfast eggs but are satisfactory for the many other quantity food purposes. Store frozen eggs at 0° F or lower.

Thaw frozen eggs under refrigeration. In 30 pound cans it will take two days or more to thaw them at 40° F. Mix well before using to distribute the egg solids evenly. The following are approximate equivalents:

Table 7-1
Frozen and Fresh Egg Equivalents

Type Frozen Egg	Weight (lb)	Volume (pt)	Fresh EP Equivalent (large eggs)* (24 oz to the dozen)
Whole eggs	1	1	9 to 11 whole eggs
Whites	1⅛	1	17 to 19 whites
Yolks	⅞	1	20 to 24 yolks

*Increase approximately 10% in number of medium eggs.

One case (30 dozen) of large eggs will weigh about 45 pounds net and will give about 40 pounds of shelled egg. A 30 pound can will contain about 270 large whole eggs, 670 large yolks, and 435 large whites; 315 medium whole eggs, 760 medium yolks, and 485 medium whites.

Water only is removed in drying eggs, and the method may be spray or tray drying. In measuring the former, use a ratio of 2½ to 2, eggs to water. (The measures given in this text are for spray-dried eggs. See manufacturer's directions to be sure.) Freeze-dried eggs are on the market but have not had extensive use as yet. Dried eggs are on the market as whole-egg solids, egg-white solids, and egg-yolk solids. Eggs are acidulated in processing to make a better product. Dried eggs will keep well in sealed cans if properly stored. Storage under frozen temperatures has been found to retain quality. Shelf storage should be not over 55° F and in a dry place. After opening, the storage temperature should be from 32 to 40° F in a tightly sealed container. Eggs left uncovered absorb moisture and flavors, and if they lump, they are mixed into liquids with difficulty.

If dried eggs are measured, stir lightly with a fork before measuring, but it is preferable to weigh them. When bringing dried eggs to a liquid state, spread them slowly into lukewarm water, stirring constantly with a wire whip, or use a mixer. Let them stand for 5 to 10 minutes, stir again, and use. Do not allow these eggs to stand over 30 minutes at room temperature. Frequently, dried eggs need not be brought back to a liquid state but can be merely incorporated into a mixture with other dry ingredients. The required liquid may be added then with the other liquid ingredients. Table 7-2 gives some equivalents for using dried eggs, but manufacturer's directions, if given, should always be followed:

Table 7-2
Quantities of Dried Eggs Required to Make a Pound Fresh EP Equivalent

Type Egg and Number to Give 1 lb	Quantity for 1 lb Equivalent			
	Dried Egg		Water	
	Ounces	Measure	Ounces	Measure
Whole egg, 9	4½	2 c 2 T	11¼	1 c 7 T
White, 17 to 19	2¼	½ c	13¾	1¾ c
Yolk*, 20 to 24	7¼	1 c	8¾	1 c 1 T
Yolk**, 25 to 27	7½	1 c	8½	1 c 1 T
Yolk***, 16 to 20	6½	1 c	8	1 c

*43% solids   **45% solids   ***Add 1.6 oz of sugar to give yolks with 10% sugar as used in the bakeshop for frozen sugared yolks.

Table 7-3
Miscellaneous Equivalents of Processed and Fresh Eggs Used in Bakeshop Production

Processed Egg	Ratio Egg to Water	Fresh Equivalent EP (large eggs)
No. 10 can (3 lb) dried whole	——	100 whole eggs
1 lb dry whole eggs	——	3½ lb whole eggs
1 lb dry yolks	——	2½ lb yolks
6 oz dry whole and 1⅞ c water	——	1 dozen whole eggs
1 lb dried whole and 2½ pt water	1:2½	3 doz whole eggs (3½ lb)
1 lb dried whites and 6 pt water	1:6	100 whites (7 lb)
1 lb dried yolks and 1¾ c water	8:7	47 yolks (1¾ lb)

Some bakers use dried eggs and water in the ratio by weight of 1 to 2½, yolks 1¼ to 1, and whites 1 to 5. It should be noted that the equivalents between Tables 7-2 and 7-3 for yolks are not quite the same in ratio of yolk to water, bakers preferring to increase slightly the yolk ratio to water.

DAIRY PRODUCTS

Milk is a common fluid in which many food ingredients are suspended or dissolved in cooking. It contributes flavor, color, and richness to many foods, and a number of valuable minerals and vitamins in the diet. Cream is used to give moistness, richness, and smoothness of flavor. Butter and cheese are important for their flavor and nutrient contribution. Cheese is oftentimes combined with other foods, served alone as a snack with crackers, or used as a sandwich filler, a dessert item with crackers and fruit, or a salad ingredient. The use of dry milk is recommended for quantity food production because of its low cost, ease of handling, and lack of perishability.

Standard

The standard applied to foods containing dairy products should be identified with the standard of the particular food, rather than one for the dairy product, for in many foods the identity of the dairy product is lost. Foods high in milk will be significantly modified, however, by the properties of milk. These foods should be smooth and non-curdled in texture, colored considerably by the white color of milk, the yellow color of cheese, or the delicate cream of butter. The flavor should be mild, sweet, and pleasant, as well as rich. Cooking and the addition of other ingredients may modify dairy product flavors to some extent, and this should be considered in evaluating a product.

Types of Dairy Products

A number of milks are used in quantity cooking. Table 7-4 indicates their approximate composition. Creams must contain 18% or more of milk fat. Coffee cream is approximately 18 to 22% milk fat, light whipping cream 30 to 35%, and heavy whipping cream 36 to 40%; half-and-half (not a cream) is about 12% milk fat. Sour cream must be 18% or more milk fat and contain about 0.2% lactic acid.

Table 7-4
Approximate Composition of Milks Used in Cooking

Type Milk	Fat	Non-fat solids	Water	Sucrose
Fresh whole milk	3.5	8.5	88	
Fresh non-fat milk	trace	9	91	
Evaporated whole milk	8	18	74	
Evaporated non-fat milk	trace	20 to 30	80 to 70	
Sweetened condensed whole milk	8	20	30	42
Dry whole milk	27	70	3	
Non-fat dry milk	trace	96	4	

Buttermilk was originally the product remaining after churning in making butter, but today pasteurized milk is soured by special bacteria. This buttermilk should contain not less than 8½% non-fat solids. Some buttermilks may contain small particles of butter, which give a product somewhat like old-fashioned buttermilks. Cultures of *bacterium bulgaricum* are used to sour some buttermilks which are claimed to have therapeutic value.

FIG. 7-12 At the top is shown a clabber of milk set by rennet. This clabber is used to make many of the cheddar-type cheeses, such as the Swiss cheese shown on the right. On the bottom is a curd set by allowing milk to sour. This type of curd is frequently used to make cottage or other milk, non-aged cheeses.

Clabbered milk is milk soured to a solid mass. Sour milk is pasteurized and then soured with lactic-acid-producing bacteria and may be curdled. The equivalent of sour milk can be obtained by adding ¼ cup of vinegar or lemon juice to 1 quart of unsoured milk. Cream may be made into sour cream by using similar proportions. Natural souring of pasteurized products is difficult, since pasteurization destroys the souring bacteria. Attempts to allow pasteurized milks to sour may produce a bitter-tasting product. Yogurt is a semi-solid clabbered milk with a fine, smooth texture. It contains 20% milk solids. Three types of bacteria are used to make it.

Butter is churned from cream and is 80% milk fat. Frequently, butter is clarified by melting it and then removing the unmelted 20%, which is mostly a curd of milk, cream, and salt. Clarified butter is used for frying or for sauce preparation. Margarine is made from vegetable or animal fats and is flavored with dairy products to give it a butter flavor. It too contains 80% fat, the remainder being largely dairy products. Margarine does not foam, as does butter when warmed, nor does it brown as well, unless it has lecithin added to it.

Cheese is a food high in milk fat and milk proteins. Most cheese is made from the curd of milk, but some cheeses may be made partially from whey.

Principles in Cooking Dairy Products

Curdling

At the natural pH of milk, 6.5 to 6.6, the casein, the major protein in milk, is held in stable colloidal suspension. At a pH of 4.6 the casein is very unstable and will curdle or precipitate out of the milk. Evaporated milk is

FIG. 7-13   Many types of cheddar cheese may be used in cooking. Here are a few varieties used to make cheese sauces. (Courtesy American Dairy Association)

more stable against curdling than fresh milk, and dry milk less stable than fresh milk. Curdling is a process in which the casein separates into curds away from the whey. Clabber is a midway process between liquid and curdled milk. It is a soft, shiny, smooth, solid mass of almost custard-like consistency. When a clabber is broken up, curdling occurs. Agitation or heat may break up a clabber. Some compounds such as salts, tannins, or strong food acids may directly curdle milk without producing a clabber, while mild acids, bacteria, or rennet may clabber milk. The acidity of milks may increase in a number of ways. There is a loss of carbon dioxide in standing, which causes increased acidity; bacteria may turn lactose into lactic acid; acid may be introduced in cooking through using lemon juice,

FIG. 7-14 The stability against curdling of different milks used in quantity cookery may vary. On the right is shown fresh milk curdled by vinegar. In the middle is dry milk, also curdled by the same quantity of vinegar, but note that it forms a very fine curd. Dry milk is the least stable of the three milks, curdling most easily. On the left is evaporated milk which, before it would curdle, had to be blended with twice as much vinegar as the other two. Evaporated milk is the most stable of the three against curdling. Its curd is also the tenderest and softest.

vinegar, or fruits and vegetables. Tannins are not acids but act as a denaturing agent, drawing moisture from the milk proteins, thus causing curdling. Cooking salt, curing salts, and salts in foods, such as calcium chloride (used to make canned tomatoes firm), will encourage curdling. Heat makes milk more susceptible to curdling.

Some proteins in milk are coagulated by heat. This can be shown when milk is heated, by the formation of scum on the top or by precipitated material deposited on cooking utensils in which it is cooked. The formation of scum can be avoided by covering tightly during heating, whipping to create a foam on top, or melting fat to cover the surface.

Cream may sometimes curdle when added to coffee, especially if the brew is quite hot or high in acids and tannins. Improper making of coffee may give a brew high in tannins and acids. Adding cream Boston style—that is, pouring cream into a cup before adding the coffee—may reduce the tendency to curdle. Very hard water may also cause cream to curdle. If this is causing curdling, it can be ascertained by adding cream to hot but not boiled water used to make the brew; if the cream curdles, the water is at fault, and softeners should be installed. For the approved type of softeners, see Chapter 6 (on beverages).

Scorching

Milk scorches easily and should be heated over water, in a steam-jacketed kettle, or in a steamer. Prolonged heating below scorching temperatures may darken milk and give it a somewhat caramelized flavor. The milk also becomes flat and less flavorful, probably because of the loss of gas or air.

Homogenization

The fat in milk is held in suspension in small globules by a protein emulsifier which is adsorbed on the surface of the fat. Because this emulsifier has an attraction for milk protein, it holds the fat in suspension. This binding power, however, is not strong, growing less as milk cools. Then the milk fat, being lighter than the milk, rises to the surface where it forms cream. Milk fat is usually separated from milk by centrifugal force.

If the fat globules are very finely divided by a process call homogenization, the milk fat can be put into permanent suspension. This very fine division reduces the upward force or pull of the lighter fat globules so that the protein emulsifier can hold them down in the milk. Homogenized milk performs differently in cooking from regular milk. It can carry less fats in a sauce and gives a somewhat stiffer starch paste than do regular milks. The difference is not great, however, and, under ordinary conditions, little change need be made when using homogenized milk in place of regular milk. Homogenized cream will not whip well. To whip, the fat globules in the cream must bunch together, surrounding tiny air bubbles. Homogenization destroys this ability of the fat globules to bunch together.

FIG. 7-15   To prevent a scum forming on milk solutions, whip as shown on the right to form a foam, or dot heavily with butter as shown on the left.

Pasteurization

Most milk products are pasteurized to eliminate harmful pathogenic bacteria and to assist in giving keeping qualities by destroying enzymes and lactic-acid-producing bacteria. This is done by holding milk either 30 minutes at 143° F or 15 seconds at 160° F. Milk for cheese need not be pasteurized if the cheese is cured for longer than 60 days. Curing over 60 days destroys bacteria much the same as does pasteurization. For making bread, fresh milk is often heated to a higher temperature than for pasteurizing. This destroys thermophilic bacteria. When milk is pasteurized, its coagulation properties are changed, making possible a more tender clabber or custard and a softer, finer curd.

Techniques

Curdling

To avoid curdling, special techniques may be required. If the milk is thickened slightly with starch, the casein and whey are bound to the gelatinized starch, and this retards curdling. The greater the thickening, the less the tendency to curdle. Cooking milk products at low temperatures is also desirable. Restricting salt may delay or avoid curdling. Some authorities recommend the addition of milk in several portions, one at a time, during the cooking of some items, as when cured meat is baked in milk. Canned tomatoes containing calcium chloride should not be used for a dish containing milk, for this salt encourages curdling. Slow introduction into milk of an acid or food containing tannin will reduce curdling. Having both the acid and the milk at the same temperature when combined may retard curdling. Adding bicarbonate of soda or other compounds which give an alkaline reaction will reduce the acidity of a food, but because of the adverse effect of soda on the flavor, color, and vitamin content of many foods, this is usually not recommended.

FIG. 7-16   To prevent escalloped potatoes from curdling, add a moderately heavy cream sauce that has been only lightly salted (shown on the left), or mix dry milk, flour, and seasonings in a bowl with the potatoes, as shown on the right. Put this mixture into a pan, fill the pan to the proper measure with water, and bake. Do not over-season either of these with salt.

Curdling of escalloped potatoes may be lessened by bringing sliced potatoes to boil in unsalted water which barely covers them, removing the potatoes, discarding some of the cooking water, and adding evaporated or dry milk to make up the desired quantity of milk. This milk is then separately made into a lightly salted, thin white sauce and poured over the hot potatoes. They are then baked at 340° F. Another method that works well is to blend dry milk solids, flour, salt, and pepper together thoroughly. Toss well drained raw potato slices into this mixture until well coated and place in baking pans. Then pour hot water until the potatoes are barely covered, add butter or fat, and bake at 340° F until tender.

If a cream soup is made from velouté or bechamel sauce, it will curdle less easily than if made from a white or cream sauce. The method for the preparation of cream soups has been described in Chapter 5. Even tart sauces may be made from milk if proper techniques are used. A cream of horseradish sauce for roast beef can be made by using a heavy velouté sauce, adding horseradish, and blending this warmed mixture with rapid agitation into hot rich or hot evaporated milk. Serve soon after making. Bakery workers sometimes find that the acids in molasses or brown sugar will curdle an item such as butterscotch pudding. If the sweetener is blended with the thickener or added after thickening occurs, curdling will be retarded.

Solutions containing dry milk solids are easily curdled. Syneresis develops easily in custards made from dry milk even though they are properly baked. The portioning of a custard while hot encourages syneresis. A strong custard of 2 to $2\frac{1}{2}$ pounds of eggs per gallon of milk must be made to make a satisfactory custard from dry milk, and savings made by using dry milk over fresh or evaporated milk are lost when this is done. Never boil sauces, soups, or other products made of dry milk. Make dry milk solutions thicker than required, and thin to proper consistency just before service. Salt at the last minute, also. A more stable solution results if dry milk is put into solution the day before it is required. Even making it up 20 minutes ahead of use helps. It is recommended that dry milk solutions be made up with less water than required and the product be thinned just before service with the proper quantity of water. To mix, sift non-instant dry milk over cool water and stir in with good agitation with a wire whip.

Use of Dry Milk

While proportions for the thickening of sauces have been given in Table 5-2, the proportions for a white sauce made from dry milk may differ somewhat from these. Table 7-5 indicates proportions to use in making white sauces in which dry milk is used.

Table 7-5
White Sauce Proportions Using Non-fat Dry Milk
(per 1 gal sauce)

Type Sauce	Water	Non-fat Dry Milk	Butter, Margarine or Fat	Flour*
Thin	$3\frac{1}{2}$ qt	1 lb 6 oz	$6\frac{1}{2}$ oz	4 to 8 oz
Medium	$3\frac{1}{2}$ qt	1 lb 6 oz	$8\frac{1}{4}$ oz	8 to 12 oz
Thick	$3\frac{1}{2}$ qt	1 lb 5 oz	10 oz	1 lb
Very thick	$3\frac{1}{2}$ qt	1 lb 5 oz	$12\frac{1}{2}$ oz	$1\frac{1}{4}$ lb

*Quantity of flour used will depend upon type of flour and thickness desired.

About 13 ounces of non-fat dry milk per gallon of water will give the equivalent of regular non-fat milk, but normally one pound of dry milk is used. Adding five ounces of butter, margarine, or fat makes one gallon of non-fat milk equal to one gallon of whole milk. Increasing milk solids has been found beneficial to quality in some bakery products and frozen desserts. When increased milk solids are added, recipes sometimes require rebalancing. The use of dry milk is also discussed in later chapters in the section on bakeshop production. It is best to weigh dry milk, not measure it.

Table 7-6
Equivalents for 1 Gal Liquid Milk

For 1 gal whole liquid milk use:	For 1 gal non-fat liquid milk use:
18 oz dry whole milk	13 oz dry non-fat milk
7½ lb or 3¾ qt water	7¾ or 3 qt 2½ c water
or	or
13 oz non-fat dry milk	4½ lb non-fat evaporated milk
5 oz melted fat	4¼ lb or 2 qt ½ c water
7½ lb or 3¾ qt water	or
or	3 lb condensed non-fat milk
4¼ lb evaporated whole milk	7 lb or 3½ qt water**
4½ lb or 2¼ qt water	
or	
4 lb condensed whole milk	
6¼ lb or 3¼ qt water*	

*Will also contain 1 lb 10 oz sugar.   **Will also contain 1 lb 5 oz sugar.

Normally one pound of dry milk equals 4 cups, but 5¾ cups of instant dry milk is required to equal one pound. Instant dry milks go into solution much more easily than other types of dry milk. Whenever possible, dry milk is added with sifted dry ingredients and the required liquid added with the regular liquid in the recipe. It is difficult to incorporate dry milk into hot water or liquids.

Foaming

Air can be beaten into milks and creams to make a stable foam. Cream below 30% milkfat content will not produce a stable foam unless special methods and ingredients are used. Whipping cream above 30% usually produces a smooth, thick, glossy mass, rich and pleasant in flavor. In whipping, cream increases in volume two to three times. Recipes usually state whipped cream in unwhipped measure and not in whipped volume. Cream should be used soon after whipping; drainage can be evident even one hour after whipping. To give satisfactory results in whipping cream:

1. Purchase 30 to 40% whipping cream.
2. Age at least 48 hours to give maximum stability and volume.
3. Most cream must be pasteurized to pass milk codes, but pasteurization decreases volume and stability of the foam slightly.

4. Do not purchase homogenized cream, for this greatly reduces volume and stability.
5. To give increased stability, smoothness, and lower drainage, add 1½ ounces of instant non-fat dry milk solids per quart of cream, preferably before aging.
6. 1½ tablespoons of 10% suspension of lime per quart of cream can be used to give increased stability.
7. Have cream at 40° F and utensils cold; use a bowl deep enough for the whipping tool to agitate the cream rapidly into a froth and incorporate air; extended rapid agitation will beat cream to butter.
8. After cream is whipped to desired consistency, add sugar and flavorings, and complete whipping; powdered sugar forms a stiffer foam than granulated sugar.

FIG. 7-17 Four types of foams used in quantity food preparation that are made from dairy products. The hand of the worker is shown using a synthetic whipped cream mixture. On the left is shown whipped cream, in the center whipped evaporated milk, and on the right whipped dry non-fat milk solids.

Cream as low as 18% milk fat may be whipped if all steps except step one are used above. It will, however, have lower volume and stability and higher drainage.

Evaporated milk may be beaten to a foam. It is usually less stable than whipped cream, although the volume increase may be greater. To whip:

1. Scald the milk or place cans in boiling water 5 to 10 minutes.
2. To give better stability, soak ½ teaspoon of gelatin in 2 tablespoons of cold water and add to one pint of hot milk; blend in well.

FIG. 7-18 Excellent products can be made with the whipped topping mixtures now on the market. (Courtesy General Foods)

3. Chill to 40° F.
4. Use bowl deep enough for the whipping tool to rapidly agitate milk to a froth; whip to almost desired consistency.
5. Add 3 tablespoons lemon juice per pint of evaporated milk, sugar, and flavoring; finish whipping.
6. Hold chilled below 50° F.

Either whole or non-fat dry milk solids may be whipped. The foam is smooth and fine with a light, delicate body. The increase in volume is about four times, but the foam is not stable over several hours. Lemon juice and sugar increase stability. Poor-quality dry milk solids will not develop good foams.

1. Use ¾ of a quart of dry milk or 1 quart instant dry milk to 1 quart of ice water.
2. Use bowl deep enough for the whipping tool to agitate milk rapidly into a froth and incorporate air.
3. Beat to a soft peak (about 3 to 4 minutes).

FIG. 7-19 To whip evaporated milk, add a bit of rehydrated gelatin to evaporated milk. Heat the milk slightly to dissolve the gelatin, then chill thoroughly, as shown in the background, in a bowl of ice and whip. Many omit the gelatin; heat in the can, then chill to 32° F and whip.

4. Add 1 cup lemon juice and beat until stiff (about 3 to 4 minutes).
5. Fold in 2 cups sugar and desired flavorings.
6. Keep chilled below 50° F.

An imitation whipped cream is used for toppings for desserts and other foods. This product can be made from a mixture of dry non-fat milk solids, butter, margarine or other fat, sugar, and flavoring. Aerosol-type containers may be purchased for dispensing this product.

Cream

Studies have shown that patrons add cream to their coffee, not by quantity, but until they obtain a desired color. The color of cream in coffee results

FIG. 7-20 Evaporated milk forms a more stable foam if a small quantity of lemon juice is added to it during beating.

largely from fat particles reflecting light. When cream is poured into coffee, a whitening appears. The more plentiful the fat particles, the more color or whiteness is reflected. About one tablespoon or ½ ounce of 18% cream is sufficient for a portion.

Portioning loss in pouring from large to individual portions is approximately 6%. These studies also show that the higher in milk fat the cream, the higher the flavor score for coffee with cream. Homogenized creams give a better flavor to coffee than non-homogenized. Because of these facts, many operations use homogenized coffee creams, regular or heavier, and avoid half and half, since more than twice the quantity of the latter is used by patrons without as rich a flavor yield.

FIG. 7-21   When whipping dry milk, add a bit of lemon juice during the beating. When the milk is whipped, fold in vanilla and powdered sugar.

Cream or sour cream may be used as a finishing agent for sauces and other products. This is a process in which cream is well blended into a product just before service. The product is never boiled after finishing. The cream smooths out flavors, and the product takes on a heightened richness which is not obtained if the cream is added earlier in the preparation.

Cheese

Like eggs and milk, cheese should be cooked at low heat. Ripened cheese has better cooking qualities than medium-cured or unaged cheese; the protein is less rubbery and blends better with mixtures, such as sauces, or other foods. Cheese blends better into sauces at around 125° F than at higher temperatures. A hard, dry cheese blends better if it is grated and moistened with one cup of warm milk to each pound of cheese. In adding cheese to a thickened starch mixture that also requires the addition of eggs, add the eggs first and then the cheese. Cook well, but do not curdle. The egg aids in bringing the cheese into solution in the sauce. If, however, the egg is to be used to make a firm structure by baking, as in the case of a cheese soufflé, this cannot be done. Emulsifiers in processed cheese and cheese foods make these incorporate more easily into sauces and with other foods. Processed cheese is also more stable than regular cheese.

Table 7-7
Conversion of Other Forms of Milk to Approximate Equivalents in Liquid Whole Milk

Liquid whole milk (pound)	Evaporated milk — Milk (14½ oz can)	Evaporated milk — Water (pound)	Dry whole milk — Milk (whole dry) Pound	Dry whole milk — Milk (whole dry) Ounce	Dry whole milk — Water Pound	Dry whole milk — Water Ounce	Dry skim milk — Milk (dry skim) Pound	Dry skim milk — Milk (dry skim) Ounce	Dry skim milk — Butter or shortening Pound	Dry skim milk — Butter or shortening Ounce	Dry skim milk — Water Pound	Dry skim milk — Water Ounce
2.1 (1 qt)	1	1		4	1	12		3		1	1	14
5	2½	2½		10	4	6		7		3	4	6
8.6 (1 gal)	4½	4	1		7			12		4	7	6
10	5½	5	1	3	8	13		14		6	8	12
20	11	10	2	6	17	10	1	12		11	17	9
30	16½	15	3	9	25	7	2	10	1		26	6
40	22	20	4	12	35	4	3	8	1	6	35	2
50	27½	25	5	15	43	1	4	6	1	12	43	14
60	33	30	7	2	51	14	5	5	2	1	52	10
70	38½	35	8	5	60	11	6	3	2	6	61	7
80	44	40	9	12	70	4	7	1	2	12	70	3
90	49½	45	10	14	79	2	8		3	2	78	14
100	55	50	12		88		9		3	8	87	8

8   Vegetable Cookery

Any food service can serve high quality vegetables. A failure to do so means that proper attention is not being given to their production. If quality vegetables and good equipment are used and the correct cooking techniques are applied, good vegetables can be served.

The preparation, cooking, and service must be suited to the type of vegetable; canned, frozen, dried, and fresh vegetables all require their own production methods, and knowing the correct method is one of the first steps toward good vegetable production. Knowing just what is a good vegetable when it is served is one of the best places to start to learn how to produce good vegetables.

Table 8-1
Purchase of Vegetables in Food Services

Vegetable	Purchases by Per Cent*		
	Canned	Frozen	·Fresh
Sweet corn	53.7	22.1	24.2
Green beans	61.5	16.0	22.5
Green peas	53.9	45.2	0.9
Spinach	22.2	45.1	32.7
Broccoli	0.0	85.0	15.0
Carrots	21.8	3.0	74.3
Lima beans	26.0	64.0	10.0
Cauliflower	0.0	67.4	32.6
Leafy greens (kale, collards, turnip greens, etc.)	24.6	23.3	52.1
Asparagus	63.9	35.7	0.4
Mixed	45.5	44.3	10.2
Miscellaneous (brussels sprouts, okra, squash, etc.	9.4	25.1	65.5
Average	31.2	30.4	38.4

*Based on fresh weight equivalent.   (Courtesy USDA)

264

STANDARD

Judge cooked vegetables on the basis of flavor, texture, and appearance. Appearance should include form and color. Correct temperature at service should also be a factor in evaluation. Consider the vegetable in relation to the entree with which it is served. A vegetable is usually not the dominant item in a meal.

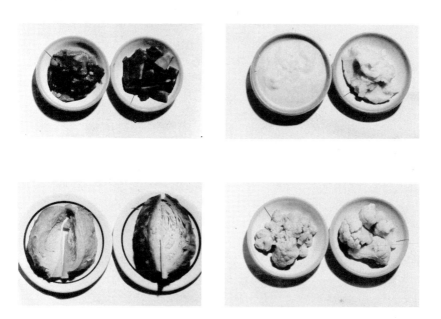

FIG. 8-1 Which vegetable would you select? The portions of the paired vegetable samples on the left lack the form, texture, or color required for best acceptability.

The flavor of the vegetable should be neither bland nor strong, but natural, sweet, and pleasant, without any trace of rawness. Avoid seasonings and sauces which mask natural vegetable flavors. Seek those that give mild contrasts and that blend happily as a light, delicate complement to the vegetable flavor.

Texture may vary according to the type of vegetable. Vegetables with a high moisture content are best in quality if some slight crispness remains when they are served. Cook these to a slight under-doneness, especially if some cooking occurs in holding, which is usually the case. An overly soft, sloughy texture is undesirable. Most starchy root vegetables, legumes, and cereals should be soft throughout. Fried vegetables may be crisp on the outside and soft on the inside. Certain vegetables such as potatoes may be mealy, while others are objectionable with this quality. Excessive wateriness, dryness, softness, crispness, hardness, woodiness, stringiness, or other objectionable texture qualities should be absent.

The vegetable should not be broken or messy. Form should be distinct.

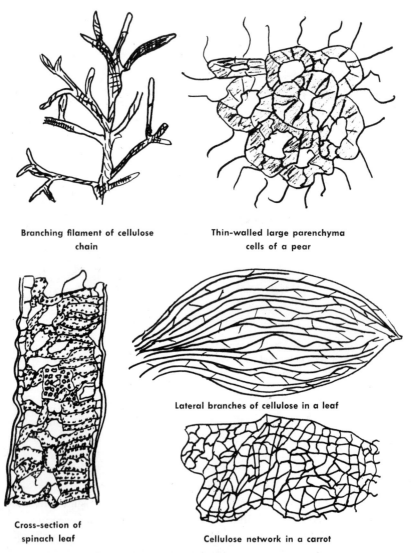

Branching filament of cellulose chain

Thin-walled large parenchyma cells of a pear

Cross-section of spinach leaf

Lateral branches of cellulose in a leaf

Cellulose network in a carrot

FIG. 8-2 Various types of cellulose found in fruits and vegetables. The quantity and type of cellulose varies in different fruits and vegetables, and this variation is an important factor in deciding their toughness or tenderness.

Uniformity is oftentimes desirable. Sheen should be apparent as a part of freshness and in some as a result of frying. When dished, the vegetable should possess a rounded mass and not be flat or runny. Colors should be bright, lively, attractive, clear, and natural; not dull, pale, muddy, or intensified or false. Loss of quality is frequently indicated by loss of color.

PRINCIPLES

Because of their fragility, most vegetables should be cooked in small batches and never held for more than 20 to 30 minutes at serving temperature. Many principles for small-quantity vegetable cookery are applicable in quantity cookery.

The cooking of a vegetable should be suited to its type. There are four types:

1. Vegetables of high moisture with mild flavor: celery, spinach, green peas, string beans, carrots, summer squash.
2. Vegetables of high moisture with strong flavor: members of the cabbage, onion, and turnip families.
3. Moist, starchy vegetables, mainly Irish and sweet potatoes.
4. Dry, starchy vegetables, made up of a diversified group including dry legumes, macaroni products, rice, cereals, and other high-starch items.

FIG. 8-3   Flavor, tenderness, and moisture in the vegetable are the main factors dictating how it shall be cooked. In quantity cookery, vegetables are divided into four groups, and each group is cooked by a method that suits it. Shown are some examples of the four groups. Cabbage, onions, garlic, and shallots belong to the strong-flavored, high-moisture group; broad beans, spinach, and celery belong to the mild-flavored, high-moisture group; potatoes and yams belong to the high-starch, high-moisture group; and noodles, split peas, and macaroni belong to the high-starch, low-moisture group.

Green peas, lima beans, corn, and some other vegetables high in starch could be logically placed in the moist, starchy group, but they are best cooked by methods used for the high-moisture, mild-flavor vegetables.

High-moisture, mild-flavor vegetables are very fragile and require careful handling in all steps of preparation. Most contain from 90 to 95% moisture, and they can, once they have started cooking, supply a large part of the moisture required for cooking. In cooking these vegetables, attention must be given to retaining their delicate flavor, while in cooking of the high-moisture, strong-flavored group, the aim is to reduce flavor. Moist, starchy vegetables have from 70 to 75% moisture and a starch content of 20%. The proper cooking of these vegetables revolves around cooking the starch without losing other qualities. The high-starch, low-moisture group require similar care in the cooking of the starch, but their low moisture content requires that they be cooked in large quantities of water.

To cook a vegetable properly one should understand something about its fiber structure. Two compounds, cellulose and pectin, make up most of the skeletal or woody structure of vegetables. Old vegetables have more of these compounds and young ones less. The amount differs also according to the variety of vegetable. Cooking softens cellulose, and cooking times for vegetables are usually in direct ratio to the quantity of cellulose in them. Old vegetables or vegetables having substantial amounts of cellulose, such as root vegetables, must be cooked longer than young vegetables or those, such as spinach, that contain less cellulose. The stems of broccoli and asparagus must be cooked longer than their tips. Sometimes these vegetables are stood up for a short time in boiling water to precook the stems before cooking the tips. Splitting broccoli stems aids in rapid cooking. Cutting the tender tips from the ends and cooking the latter for a short time before the tips are added is also a recommended practice.

Sugar strengthens cellulose; so does calcium chloride. Calcium chloride may be added to canned vegetables to give them firmness, as in canned tomatoes. Alkalis soften cellulose. In areas where the water is hard, care must be taken to give vegetables minimum cooking so they will retain texture. A bit of cream of tartar, vinegar, lemon juice, or other acid may be used to reduce the alkalinity of such water. Acid, however, may bring about undesirable reactions in the cooking of some vegetables, so care must be taken in its use. An alkaline reaction in cooking favors the softening of dry beans or other legumes, while an acid reaction retards it. Adding tomatoes or other acid foods to these before they are completely cooked may extend their cooking time and these should not be added until the vegetable is cooked tender.

The same vegetable is sometimes quite different in flavor cooked than raw; many people will accept one while rejecting the other because of the

FIG. 8-4 The effects of alkaline, acid, and neutral cooking mediums on vegetables: (1) acid, (2) alkaline, and (3) neutral.

flavor difference caused by cooking. Vegetables are flavored by salty, sweet, bitter, or acid compounds, but their characteristic flavor comes mainly from aromatic esters or essential oils. These esters are volatile; that is, they boil off easily in cooking. To avoid loss of flavor from such vaporization, cooking time may be shortened. Cooking fats or oils absorb these volatile esters, and sometimes about one tablespoon of salad oil per gallon of water is used to capture and hold these flavors in the cooking water. In strongly flavored vegetables it may be desirable to lose some of this flavor, so the cover will be left off to allow these volatile flavors to escape. Most vegetables are acid, and this acid, like the flavor esters, vaporizes easily in cooking. Much of the mustardy, pungent flavor in vegetables of the cabbage, turnip, and onion families comes from a glycoside called sinigrin and from other compounds containing sulfur. These sulfur compounds are usually developed in extended cooking. Acid helps to develop them.

Freshness in a vegetable is an important quality factor. Sugars in vegetables may change to starch rapidly at temperatures above 50° F. Fresh corn, peas, and other fresh vegetables lose sweetness rapidly in moving to market if temperatures are elevated. Loss of vegetable freshness may also be associated with glutamic acid loss. Fresh corn loses 30% of its glutamic acid in 24 hours after harvest, and fresh peas 25%. Refrigeration reduces glutamic acid loss. Dehydration, oxidation, and poor handling can cause a loss of freshness, nutrients, and quality in vegetables.

Appearance is a matter of form and color which prepreparation and cooking can vitally affect. After vegetables come to a boil, reduce the heat so water movement does not break them up. Do not stir or give excessive manipulation. Cooking by methods other than boiling may reduce movement and retain form.

The color in many vegetables may be destroyed, for the acidity or alkalinity of the cooking medium may vitally affect vegetable pigments. Vegetables are classified by color as red, yellow or orange, green, and white. The red vegetable pigments are called *anthocyanins;* the yellow or orange are called *carotenes;* the green pigments are called *chlorophyll,* and the white pigments are called *flavones.* Anthocyanins and flavones are water-soluble; the other two pigments are not.

An acid reaction keeps red pigments red, but an alkaline medium turns them a dirty blue or purple. An alkaline medium may bleach out these pigments. If red cabbage turns green in cooking, it is the result of a combined reaction in which the red pigments have turned blue and the white flavones yellow. A dark discoloration may appear when red cabbage or beets are cut with an iron knife, the iron combining with the anthocyanins to produce a brownish red or muddy color. Cooking some red vegetables in iron pots may cause this color reaction. This reaction may also occur when some punches are made from red fruit juices; iron salts in canned pineapple juice, for instance, may combine with the anthocyanins to produce a murky punch.

FIG. 8-5   If vegetables must be cooked in quantity for service during a meal, avoid holding at high heat. Blanch rapidly in cold water as shown. Spread in pans and hold. Reheat in small quantities in some of the original cooking water.

Carotenes are stable in the normal acid or alkaline mediums used in cooking. Color changes may occur in vegetables containing carotenes, but this is usually caused by a change in the color of flavones in these vegetables, rather than in the carotenes. Oxidation may destroy carotenes, but they are heat-stable. Some members of the carotene family are closely related to vitamin A. Green vegetables also contain significant quantities of the yellow pigments, as well as red vegetables. For instance, lycopene is a carotene found in tomatoes.

Chlorophyll is easily destroyed by heat and by acid, but an alkaline me-

FIG. 8-6 Canned vegetables should generally be brought to a boil and then held at temperatures of around 190° F for 10 minutes; beets and spinach, however, should be held for around 20 minutes at this temperature.

dium tends to preserve it. Carotenes are not affected by acids, as noted, and are not affected by heat. Flavones are white in an acid medium and yellow in an alkaline medium.

The importance of retaining nutrients in prepreparation, cooking, and holding for service should be emphasized. Many times nutrients are concen-

FIG. 8-7 Break mild-flavored, high-moisture frozen vegetables into chunks and drop into boiling salted water. Bring back to a boil and cook rapidly until tender. Do not cook in quantities greater than five pounds.

trated just under the skin of the vegetable, and deep peeling or soaking after peeling may cause large losses. Oxidation or dehydration may cause a loss of nutrients. Small division may increase oxidation loss or increase soaking loss by increasing the surface area. Prepare vegetables in sufficient time to give smooth progress of work from preparation to cooking, but do not prepare too far ahead. Many minerals and vitamins are water-soluble, and heavy loss of these may result in soaking. Soak only a minimum time. Some anti-oxidants into which vegetables can be dipped make it possible to avoid soaking. Salt reduces the loss of ascorbic acid (vitamin C) in soaking. Soda or hard-water salts destroy ascorbic acid and thiamin (vitamin B_1), especially when heat is applied. Copper utensils should never be used, for copper destroys ascorbic acid. Cooking by steaming, baking, sautéing, braising, deep-frying, or broiling may reduce the leaching loss that results from water in boiling. Some vitamins are heat-labile; that is, they are destroyed by heat. The longer the time of cooking or the higher the temperature, the greater is this loss.

It should be recognized that not all preparation or cooking conditions can be correct. Steaming under pressure may be desirable to reduce leaching loss and cooking time, but this may increase nutrient loss because of higher cooking temperatures. Using lots of water gives a milder flavored rutabaga but increases nutrient loss by leaching. Select that method which gives the highest acceptability. Usually this is the one that also gives the highest nutrient values, but it is poor economy to cook vegetables which, while they retain the maximum nutrient value, are left on the plate. If fresh, crisp, young vegetables are purchased at peak condition and given proper handling, storage, and cooking, and if time and conditions are established which retain the quality and nutrients, good quality vegetables of maximum nutrient value will be served in an operation.

PREPREPARATION PROCEDURES

To prepare some vegetables for cooking, procedures such as washing, paring, trimming, cutting or shaping, and soaking may be required. Other vegetables, such as canned or frozen ones, need little preparation. Size vegetables in prepreparation in uniform pieces. Even sizes give evenly cooked vegetables.

Fresh vegetables are living plants, and they continue to live even though they are harvested. Firm, fresh vegetables lose quality rapidly from action of bacteria, molds, yeasts, or enzymes and from chemical changes, surface dehydration, unfavorable storage conditions, improper handling, or allowing too long a period to occur between harvest and use.

Clean vegetables will have less chance to deteriorate. Vigorous scrubbing may be required to produce clean vegetables. Soaking may assist in

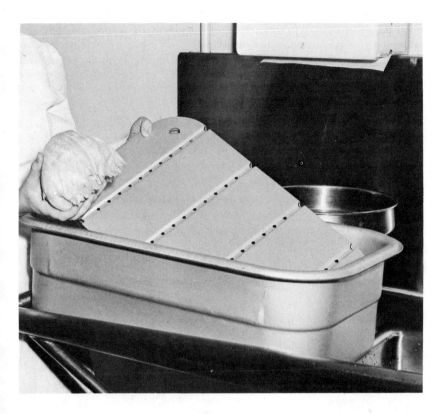

FIG. 8-8 A drain inserted under washed vegetables allows them to drain well. (Courtesy University of Washington, Seattle)

loosening soil, and if the surface is unbroken, leaching loss from such soaking will be small. Adding one tablespoon of salt per gallon of soaking water assists in loosening soil. Some vegetables, such as cauliflower, broccoli, cabbage, and brussels sprouts, may contain tiny mites. Soaking one-half hour in cold, salted water will encourage these to leave the vegetable. When vegetables are being rid of soil, lift them out of the water; do not run the water from the vegetables unless they are being washed in a colander or other perforated container.

Attention to edible loss is needed. Waste is inedible food, but much edible food can be lost in vegetable preparation if workers are careless. Many times freshening vegetables in cold or iced water may reduce waste. Vegetables or parts of vegetables that are not suitable for cooking for service may be utilized in stocks or soups, as seasonings for roasts, and so forth.

Bruised parts of young leaves may be trimmed away and the remainder used for salad greens. Woody stalks and stems or parts that would not be attractive in service may be cooked and pulped for use in cream soups, purees, or other dishes. Using proper tools and observing proper peeling times will reduce loss from waste.

Potatoes

To serve good potatoes, purchase the right kind. Potatoes high in starch are good for baking, while moist and waxy potatoes are preferred for salads, hash browns, and creamed, boiled, or steamed potatoes. Potatoes having a specific gravity of 1.08 or better (17% or more of starch) are high in starch, while those of 1.07 or less (13% or less of starch) are moist and waxy. If potatoes sink in a solution of 20 ounces of salt to one gallon of room temperature water, they have a specific gravity of 1.08 or more; and if they float in a solution of $14\frac{1}{2}$ ounces of salt per gallon of room temperature water, they are 1.07 or less in specific gravity. Mature potatoes are mealier and dryer than new potatoes.

Select evenly sized, smooth potatoes; machine paring losses are high

FIG. 8-9   High-starch, high-moisture vegetables are good products when they are partially steamed and then finished by baking. The washed yams shown here being placed into the steaming tray will receive this treatment.

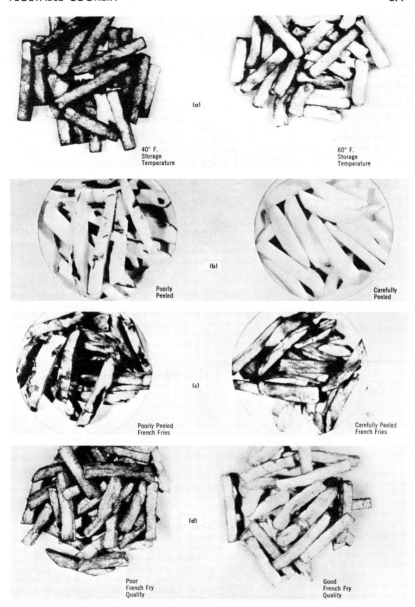

40° F.
Storage
Temperature

60° F.
Storage
Temperature

(a)

Poorly
Peeled

Carefully
Peeled

(b)

Poorly Peeled
French Fries

Carefully Peeled
French Fries

(c)

Poor
French Fry
Quality

Good
French Fry
Quality

(d)

FIG. 8-10 Select a potato that has received the right kind of treatment for French frying. (a) The potatoes stored at 40° F have too high a sugar content for good frying. Hold at least three weeks above 50° F to condition potatoes for French frying. (b) Prepare potatoes properly. (c) The potatoes shown in (b) have been fried. Note how preparation affects quality. (d) For good quality French fries, select the proper potato.

if potatoes of different sizes or crooked or nobby potatoes are used. A uniform size gives uniform doneness. Studies at Michigan State University have indicated that the savings will repay the labor cost of separating potatoes into small, medium, and large sizes. The large potatoes can be used for baking and French frying.

Potatoes for French frying should be high in starch and low in sugar. Potatoes high in sugar darken in frying and may show streaks because of excessive caramelization on the surface. Potatoes stored below 50° F develop a high sugar content, and three weeks above 50° F is required to condition them properly for cooking. Sprouting potatoes are high in sugar. Frozen potatoes will show dark streaks after deep frying. Select firm, crisp potatoes. Flabby, soft potatoes will not perform well in frying. To crisp potatoes, cut into proper shapes, drop into cold water, and place under refrigeration. Soak only as long as necessary to crisp. The claim that soaking removes excess starch and thereby reduces the tendency of potatoes to stick together in cooking has not been verified. Soaking may be required to give potato chips an even color. See that potatoes have all peel and blemishes removed after paring. Mold spots show as dark spots on the final product. Spoiled sections give off-flavors. Knobby, crooked potatoes do not give uniform pieces. A lack of uniformity will result in differences in doneness. Appearance may also be lowered. Potatoes, after being cut into proper shapes for deep-frying, should be dipped into a bleach solution, drained, placed into pans, containers, or polyethylene bags, and stored at 32 to 40° F until required. Prepare only that quantity required for a 24-hour operating period.

Shape French-fried potatoes about 3 to 4 inches long and $\frac{3}{8}$ to $\frac{1}{2}$ inch thick. Shoestrings are about $\frac{1}{4}$ to $\frac{1}{8}$ inch thick, while juliennes are closer to $\frac{1}{4}$ inch thick. The length of both should be around 2 to $2\frac{1}{2}$ inches. Shoestrings are cooked to a crisp stage, while juliennes are not. If a medium-size potato (five ounces pared) is cut into quarters longitudinally, the proper size for long branch potatoes is obtained. Because of their greater size, long branch potatoes should be deep-fried at a slightly lower temperature than the smaller sizes. Long branch potatoes may also be partially cooked in fat and then finished in the oven. Potato chips are sliced about 1/16 inch thick and allowed to soak about an hour in very cold water. Wafered or waffle potatoes are made by a device that cuts across the width of the whole pared potato to give a round slice with tiny waffled holes in it. Parisienne ball potatoes are cut from raw, pared potatoes with a round melon-ball cutter. Souffléd potatoes are made by cutting crisp potatoes into slices about $2\frac{1}{2}$ inches long, $1\frac{1}{4}$ inches wide, and $\frac{1}{8}$ to $\frac{3}{16}$ inch thick. For souffléd potatoes use only good quality, mature potatoes, high in starch; have all pieces even and of the same size. Crisp in ice water 30 minutes. Potatoes for browning (rissolé) are usually selected one potato to a portion, about five ounces pared. Rounding may be accomplished in a potato peeler.

Table 8-2

Vegetable	Preparation Procedures
Asparagus	Cut or break off tough or woody portion at or approximately ½ inch above white portion. Scrub well; remove lower scales, as dirt or grit may be under them. The lower portions may be scraped. Clean and rinse thoroughly. Tips may be cut from ends. Toughest ends may be set aside for pureeing for soup.
Beans, snap	Use only young, tender beans which snap readily when bent to a 45° angle. Cut into 1 inch sections or French by cutting lengthwise into strips. Rinse thoroughly. Beans cook more readily if cut lengthwise or at an angle instead of crosswise.
Beans, lima	Purchase fresh shelled beans or frozen beans. Cook frozen beans, and rinse fresh beans thoroughly and drain.
Beets	Leave uncut 1 inch of stem and all of root. Trim and wash, scrubbing if necessary to remove soil. Boil or steam. Beets may be machine-peeled and cooked, but a heavy loss of red pigment occurs when this is done.
Broccoli	Wash well and cut off tough ends of the stalks. Remove tough outer leaves. Clean and rinse thoroughly. Split ends of thick stalks, or cut ends from tops. Cut into 2 inch by ½ inch wide strips and cook, adding tops after 5 minutes of boiling.
Brussels sprouts	Trim yellowed or coarse outer leaves. Soak in salted water ½ hour, clean, and rinse.
Cabbage	Strip off wilted outer leaves, remove core, rinse thoroughly, and cut into sections or shred. For sectioning, coring is often omitted.
Carrots	Remove tops if present. Pare in peeler. Less flavor loss occurs in cooking if carrots are sliced lengthwise, since this avoids cutting across the fibrovascular structure (juice-retaining fibers.) Very young carrots may be cooked by first scrubbing and then cooking, removing skins after cooking. Cool by plunging into cold water and remove skins while warm and wet.
Corn-on-the-cob	Strip the husks and remove silk. Trim any inedible portions. Keep cold.
Onions, dry	Trim. Peel outer skins with paring knife. Rinse. Chop, slice, or prepare as required.
Parsnips	Peel. Trim and rinse. Slice lengthwise to avoid cutting fibrovascular bundles and increased flavor loss in cooking.
Peas, green	Shell. Rinse in colander in cold water. Purchase and cook frozen.
Potatoes, Irish	Scrub well for baking, pare for others. Steam for mashing, hash browns, etc. Cooking in skins and then paring gives a darker potato and higher labor costs.
Potatoes, sweet	Best cooked in skins and then pared, but may be machine-pared if uniform in size and not long and thin. Machine-paring loss may be high with some shapes. Wash before cooking in skins.
Rutabaga or Turnip	Pare in peeler. Trim and rinse thoroughly. Slice into slices ½ inch thick or dice into ½ inch cubes.
Spinach	Remove tough stems, wilted leaves, and roots. Wash in large quantity of water, lifting spinach up and down to loosen dirt. Lift spinach from water and drain well. Continue washing until no evidence of soil or grit shows. The water clinging to the leaves of fresh spinach may be sufficient to cook it in a steam-jacketed kettle.
Squash, summer	Trim ends. Rinse. Cut into slices approximately ¼ inch thick or into bite-size pieces.
Squash, winter	Cut into pieces of convenient size. Remove seeds and fiber. Steam. Remove peel. Complete by mashing or baking or as required. For baking, squash may be portioned before steaming.

Note: Vegetables that must be held for long periods before cooking should be, after prepreparation, placed into containers or polyethylene bags and held under refrigeration.

Dried Vegetables

Most dried, dehydrated, or freeze-dried vegetables will require some soaking before they can be cooked. Weigh rather than measure to obtain quantities required. Many of these vegetables should be soaked in cool or lukewarm water, then salted with about three tablespoons to the gallon of water. Never use hot water for soaking unless the manufacturer recommends it. Soaking is usually 20 to 30 minutes. High-moisture vegetables require about two gallons of soaking water per pound, and one gallon per pound for starchy vegetables, such as potatoes, rutabagas, and turnips. Few vegetables will return to their original EP equivalent in soaking. Soaking overnight increases their volume. However, cooking assists in rehydrating them so that the final yield is the approximate equivalent of fresh vegetables. Manufacturers' recommendations should be checked and followed in using this type of vegetable.

COOKING

The fragile quality of many vegetables makes it necessary to set up continuous batch-cooking procedures to have high quality vegetables during the entire

FIG. 8-11   Mild-flavor, high-moisture vegetables may be steamed if they are not packed too deep into pans.

period of service. With proper planning, labor requirements need not be increased by batch cooking. No special equipment is required, but high-speed cookers make batch cooking faster and easier and produce better quality items. Tilt-model steam-jacketed kettles, one quart to four gallon size, are well suited to batch cookery. Sometimes these may be placed directly behind service areas so that transport can be shortened. If they are equipped with perforated bottoms and stainless steel inserts, the vegetables can be cooked in them and removed easily in one motion. Regular or high-pressure steamers also may be used. A timer on these, set automatically, exhausts steam and opens the door, guarding against overcooking. Vegetables may remain a few minutes in the open chamber without serious loss of quality.

Production schedules should list the meal, the vegetable, the quantity to prepare in a batch, the total quantity required, the time required for cooking each batch, and the service area to which the vegetable will be sent (if several exist). Time should be allowed for loading into pans and cooking equipment, removing, and getting the vegetables to service. Experience will indicate proper timing. Some use the rule that a new batch is started when half of the preceding batch has been served. The cook in charge should be responsible for checking and adjusting times if conditions vary from those set up in production schedules. Dividing the vegetables into the proper individual batch sizes before cooking begins is sometimes helpful but not always possible. The vegetables should be cooked only to tenderness. A slight crispness may be desirable. Such vegetables are brighter in color, have more flavor, and are more nutritious. Test for doneness of large vegetables, such as beets, parsnips, or potatoes, by piercing them with the tip of a sharp paring knife or a long, thin-tined fork. Smaller vegetables may be pressed between the thumb and forefinger or pressed against the side of the container with a spoon. Of course, the best test is tasting. Never mix cooked batches. Serve out all of one batch before another batch is placed into the serving counter unless the vegetable in the counter is not acceptable.

Cooking Procedures

The method of cooking will depend upon the type of vegetable, although many perform well under a number of different cooking procedures. Canned vegetables are already cooked and require only seasoning and heating in about half of their own liquor above 190° F for 10 minutes. Reheat spinach and beets 20 to 30 minutes. This should be done just before service, for they will lose quality if prepared too far in advance.

Careless preparation of canned vegetables has undoubtedly caused much of the criticism directed at institutionally prepared vegetables. Adequate preparation can do much to make these vegetables popular. String beans delicately seasoned with crisp browned bacon bits, canned peas delicately

Table 8-3
Cooking Times and Quantities Required in Vegetable Preparation

Vegetable	Boiling*	Steaming** Free Vent	Steaming** 15 lb psi	Steaming** 5 lb psi	Baking	Approx. Min. Prep. Time 100 Portions	Quantity per 100 — 3 oz Portions AP (lb)	EP (lb)
Artichoke, French, whole, fresh	30 to 45	35	10 to 12	20 to 25	30 to 60	30	56	8⅓ doz
Artichoke, Jerusalem, whole	25 to 35					40	25	18
Asparagus, whole or butts, fresh	9 to 15	10 to 16	1 to 1½	8 to 10		85	38	25
Asparagus, tips, fresh***	7 to 9	8 to 12	½ to 1½	6 to 8			20	20
Beans, lima, green, fresh	15 to 25	20 to 30	1 to 2	10 to 15		120	48	20
Beans, lima, green, frozen	6 to 12	8 to 15	1 to 1½	8 to 12			20	20
Beans, lima, dry	60 to 150	60 to 150	15 to 25	20 to 30			6	6
Beans, snap, cut, fresh	15 to 25	20 to 30	2 to 3½	20 to 30		60	24	20
Beans, snap, Frenched, fresh	10 to 20	15 to 25	1 to 2½	18 to 25		75	24	20
Beans, snap, frozen, cut	8 to 10		2 to 3½	15 to 20			20	20
Beans, snap, frozen, Frenched	5 to 10		1 to 2	12 to 18			20	20
Beans, dry, navy or kidney	60 to 150	60 to 150	20 to 35	25 to 35			5½ to 6	5½ to 6
Beets, new, whole, medium, fresh	30 to 45	40 to 60	5 to 10	40 to 50	40 to 60	15	25****	20
Beets, old, whole, medium, fresh	45 to 90	50 to 90	10 to 18	60 to 75	50 to 75	15	26****	20
Broccoli, cut or split, fresh	7 to 12	12 to 18	1 to 3	7 to 10			35	22
Broccoli, cut or split, frozen	5 to 8	10 to 15	1 to 2	4 to 6			20	20
Brussels sprouts, whole, fresh	10 to 15	10 to 20	1½ to 3	10 to 12		30	24	20
Brussels sprouts, whole, frozen	4 to 9	8 to 15	1 to 3	8 to 10			20	20
Cabbage, shredded, fresh	6 to 10	6 to 10	½ to 1½	5 to 10			25	20
Cabbage, quartered, fresh	8 to 15	15	1½ to 3	8 to 12			25	20
Carrots, whole, fresh	15 to 25	20 to 30	2 to 5	15 to 20	35 to 45	30	26****	20
Carrots, sliced, fresh	10 to 20	15 to 25	1½ to 4	12 to 15	30 to 40		26****	20
Carrots, sliced, frozen	10 to 25	15 to 25	1½ to 4	10 to 12			20	20
Cauliflower, whole, fresh	10 to 25	15 to 25	10	15			50 to 60	26
Cauliflower, broken up	8 to 12	8 to 12	2 to 3	8 to 10			50 to 60	26
Cauliflower, frozen	4 to 8	6 to 10	1½ to 2½	6 to 8			20	20
Celery, cut up, fresh	6 to 15	8 to 20	2 to 3	10 to 12			27	20
Corn-on-the-cob*, fresh	5 to 15	10 to 15	3 to 4	8 to 10	30 (in husks)	30	50 to 75	8⅓ doz
Corn-on-the-cob, frozen	5 to 8	8 to 12	2 to 3	6 to 8			8⅓ doz	8⅓ doz
Corn, kernel, frozen	2 to 3		½ to 1	2 to 3			20	20
Eggplant, sliced	10 to 18	10 to 20					26	20

Greens		(Greens in quantity are difficult to steam because of packing.)						
Beets, greens only, fresh	3 to 10						33	20
Beets, frozen	3 to 10						20	20
Chard, fresh	8 to 15						27	20
Dandelion, fresh	10 to 20						35	20
Kale, fresh	10 to 20						27	20
Mustard, fresh	20 to 30						32	20
Mustard, frozen	8 to 15						20	20
Turnip, fresh	10 to 30						27	20
Kohlrabi, sliced	15 to 20	25	4 to 5	15 to 25			35	21
Mixed vegetables, frozen	10 to 20	15 to 25	1 to 2	8 to 15			20	20
Okra, sliced, fresh	10 to 20	20	2 to 4	10 to 18			23	18
Onions, small, whole or cut	15 to 25	25 to 35	3 to 5	15 to 20	50 to 60		25	22
Onions, large, whole	30 to 35	35 to 40	5 to 8	25 to 30	30 to 45		25	22
Parsnips, whole, fresh	20 to 40	30 to 45	8 to 10	15 to 20			24	21
Parsnips, quartered, fresh	15 to 30	25 to 40	4 to 8	12 to 18			24	20
Peas, green, fresh	6 to 8	10	1	4 to 5			53	20
Peas, green, frozen	4 to 7	8	1	3 to 4			20	20
Peas, dry, split	90 to 120					100	5	6¼ gal soup
Potatoes, Irish, whole, fresh	25 to 40	30 to 45	9 to 15	20 to 25	45 to 60		39	28
Potatoes, Irish, quartered, fresh	20 to 25	30 to 40	4 to 12	18 to 22			39	28
Potatles, Irish, diced, fresh	10 to 15		5	10			39	28
Potatoes, sweet, whole, fresh	25 to 35	30 to 35	5 to 8	20 to 25	30 to 45		35	26
Potatoes, sweet, quartered, fresh	15 to 25	25 to 30	6				35	26
Rutabagas, diced ½ in, fresh	20 to 30	35 to 40	5 to 8	15 to 25			32	28
Rutabagas, sliced ½ in, fresh	15 to 25	25 to 35	4 to 7	15 to 20		20	32	28
Spinach, fresh	3 to 10	5 to 12					31	26
Spinach, frozen	1 to 4	2 to 6					20	20
Squash, hubbard, pieces	20 to 30	25 to 40	6 to 12	15 to 20	40 to 60		46	32
Squash, summer, sliced	10 to 15	15 to 20	1½ to 3	8 to 12	30		24	20
Tomatoes, fresh	7 to 15		1½ to 3	5	15 to 20		23	22
Turnips, whole, fresh	20 to 30		8 to 10	10 to 15			25****	22
Turnips, fresh, sliced or diced	15 to 20	20 to 25	1½ to 2	10			25****	22

*Time is calculated from time water comes to boil after vegetable has been added; corn on the cob is sometimes placed into cold water and brought to a boil and then sent to service.

**Increase free vent times at higher altitudes. Steam time will depend upon type of pan; fill solid pans less full; solid pans increase steaming time over perforated pans; thaw frozen corn on the cob before cooking it.

***Reduce times slightly for frozen tips.

****topped

flavored with mint leaves, succulent kernel corn bright in contrast with bits of sautéed pimiento and green pepper, sautéed sauerkraut flavored mildly with juniper berries or caraway seed, and a flavor blend of suc-cotash garnished with a sprinkling of crisp bacon cracklings over it are some of the dishes that can be served to make canned vegetables attractive. Use a light hand with seasonings.

The drained weight of many canned vegetables will be 60 to 65% of the total can contents. A No. 10 can gives 20 to 25 three-ounce portions of drained vegetables, such as string beans, kernel corn, beets, and so forth, but 35 three-ounce portions of a vegetable all of which is served, such as cream-style corn, tomatoes, and succotash.

Most frozen vegetables can be cooked without defrosting. Simply break up the blocks into small chunks before cooking. Corn-on-the-cob and some leafy green vegetables may perform better if thawed. Most frozen vegetables to be steamed are best thawed. Overlong defrosting impairs the flavor and texture of frozen vegetables. The time of cooking frozen vegetables will be shorter than that of fresh vegetables, for blanching in their processing before freezing partially cooks them. Dehydro-frozen vegetables have about 50% of their moisture removed in processing. This water must be replaced in cooking, so the quantity of water used compared with that used for frozen vegetables will be greater. Follow manufacturer's instructions for cooking. Less salt is required for frozen and canned vegetables, for salt has been added in their processing. The time for cooking dehydrated or freeze-dry vegetables is also slightly less than for fresh vegetables. Buttered vegetables should receive about ½ cup of butter or margarine, and creamed vegeta-bles 1 to 1½ quarts of cream sauce per 5 pounds of cooked vegetables. Fats melted with seasonings or spices give more subtle and delicate flavors than when these are added separately.

Vegetables are cooked by boiling, steaming, baking or oven-braising, deep-frying, grilling or sautéing, oven-roasting, and broiling. Cooking tech-niques should be based on whether vegetables are mild flavored or strong flavored, of the high-moisture type or the moist dry starchy type.

Boiling
MILD-FLAVORED VEGETABLES

Boil mild-flavored vegetables by placing them directly in boiling salted water using ¾ gallon of water, three tablespoons of salt, and two tablespoons of salad oil per five pounds EP (25 three-ounce portions). About half a cup of sugar may be added, if desired. A perforated inset assists in rapid addition and removal. Use only enough water to cover. After adding the vegetables, bring the water to a reboil as quickly as possible. Steam-jacketed kettles do this more quickly than pots on the range. Cover, if neces-sary, to speed time to bring back to a boil, but *remove cover immediately after boiling starts,* and leave it off for about three to five minutes to allow the volatile acids to escape. Then cover and cook only to doneness. Send immediately to service. If the vegetables *must* be cooked ahead, plunge them into cold water until chilled. Then drain them and spread in shallow pans. If the vegetables are leafy greens, drain well, press out excess water, and place in about one-pound mounds in the pan. Cover pans and store under refrigeration. Investigation has shown that this method gives better color, texture, and flavor than holding vegetables hot over an extended time. If this procedure is used, save some of the cooking water. To reheat, bring some of the cooking water to a boil, add the vegetables, and heat. Then send to service.

STRONG FLAVORED VEGETABLES

The strongly flavored, high-moisture vegetable family is best cooked by boiling. Its abundant flavor makes it desirable to obtain as much dilution of the flavor as possible. Batch cooking—or cooking, blanching, and then reheating, as described above—is recommended. Avoid any holding at high heat. The onion group may be strongly flavored with sinigrin or sulfur products, especially if cooked at high temperatures, while the cabbage and turnip groups tend to develop strong sulfur products with long cooking. Factors to observe in cooking these vegetables are:

1. Controlling cooking time. The cabbage and turnip groups are best cooked for a short time. Add to rapidly boiling, salted water. Onions, leeks, garlic, and others are best cooked for a long time at low heat; the longer cooking allows sinigrin to escape as a volatile substance. Add these to dressings and other dishes early, not late, in the cooking process so the time of cooking is extended.

2. Cooking uncovered. The vegetables may be covered when added to boiling water, but *remove the cover as soon as boiling starts,* and leave the cover off. Acids develop sinigrin. Leaving the cover off during boiling allows the escape of both the acids and sinigrin.

3. Small division. Cutting into small pieces gives greater surface area. This permits strong flavors to be more easily dissolved into the cooking water. If vegetables of the onion family are finely minced or their juice only is used, which gives wide dispersion of the flavors, sufficient surface area will be obtained to rapidly dissipate the volatile sinigrin. Fine division makes it possible to cook these items a shorter time. Sautéing or cooking small pieces of these vegetables before adding them to a dish helps to dissipate their strong flavor before adding them to other foods.

4. Cooking in a large quantity of water.	This permits greater dilution of the strong flavors. Use 1¼ gallons of water and 3 tablespoons of salt per 5 pounds EP of vegetable; this gives 25 three-ounce portions.
5. Using young vegetables.	Old vegetables contain more sinigrin than young ones.
6. Short time storage.	Storage develops sinigrin; old cabbage, onions, etc. are stronger in flavor than young ones.

MOIST STARCHY VEGETABLES

Moist starchy vegetables, such as potatoes, are best steamed. If boiled, they should be dropped into boiling salted water, about one-fourth cup of salt to the gallon of water. Cover and bring to a boil as rapidly as possible. Leave the cover on and gently boil until tender. Hard boiling will break up the vegetables.

DRY STARCHY VEGETABLES

Legumes

Dry starchy vegetables, such as dried beans, should be sorted and washed well, drained, and covered with water to soak for two to six hours. This soaking may be done in a steam-jacketed kettle if it is not required for other cooking. (There is some question whether quality is improved and cooking time materially reduced if lentils or split peas are soaked before cooking.) Add about 1½ gallons of water and ¼ cup of salt for every 5 pounds of dried vegetables, using approximately 11 pounds of dry vegetables for 100 six-ounce portions. After soaking, bring to a boil, cover, and cook gently until they are tender when pressed with a spoon on the side of the kettle or between the fingers. Breaking of the skin indicates doneness and perhaps overdoneness. Add no acid until the vegetable is cooked. Cooking time will vary from one to three hours. Some lima beans and split peas may cook in less than one hour.

Macaroni Products and Rice

Macaroni products and rice are cooked by adding them slowly to rapidly boiling salted water, stirring while adding. Use one gallon of water and two tablespoons of salt per pound of product. Leave the kettle covered until boiling begins; then uncover and boil gently until tender. If the product sticks to the bottom or together, stir gently or loosen with a long-handled fork. A small quantity of salad oil mixed into rice before cooking helps to prevent the grains from sticking together. (Sometimes, for added flavor, rice is lightly sautéed in oil and then boiled in salted water.) Test for doneness by pressing a grain with a fork or spoon against the side of the kettle or between the fingers. If it breaks easily and cleanly, it is done. Do not over-cook. Drain

FIG. 8-12 Pared Irish potatoes are shown being boiled on top of the range. Use plenty of water for high-starch, high-moisture products when cooking in this manner. Steaming is also an excellent method for preparing these vegetables. The yams shown in the foreground have been cooked by steaming.

water through a spigot. Blanch immediately in cold water. When cold, drain thoroughly. Refrigerate until needed. Macaroni products should not be over-cooked. They should still have some chew or resistance to the bite, called in cooking "*al dente.*" Rice should be tender but not excessively soft.

FIG. 8-13 Carefully sort dry legumes to eliminate dirt, small stones, and other undesirable materials.

Another method used to cook these dry starchy foods is to add them slowly to boiling salted water, using three quarts of water and two tablespoons of salt per pound of product. Stir slowly as boiling continues for about two minutes. Then remove the kettle from the direct heat, or, if a steam-jacketed kettle is used, turn off the heat. Cover at once and lét stand 10 minutes or until the product is tender. Drain and blanch in cold water. Heavy, thick-walled macaroni products cannot be cooked by this method.

Rice may also be cooked in a manner used by the Orientals. The quantity of water used is only that required to cook the rice. If cooked on top of the range, use a heavy kettle. Wash the rice thoroughly several times, each time in fresh water, to remove excess starch. Oil added in the ratio of two tablespoons per pound of rice helps to separate the grains in cooking. Add water, using 1¾ quarts of water and two tablespoons of salt per pound of rice. Cover the kettle tightly and bring to a boil. Set off at low heat and cook slowly. During the last period, the rice should be uncovered so that it steams dry, leaving the grains light and separate. If the rice absorbs all the water but is still dry and hard, add more water. Too much water will give an overcooked, over-soft rice. This same method may be used in a steam-jacketed kettle with the same proportions and methods, except cook slowly approxi-

(a)   (b)

(c)

FIG. 8-14 (a) Add rice to rapidly boiling salted water. (b) When tender, blanch in cold water. (c) The beginning and end of the method used by Oriental cooks to prepare rice. In the background, cold, salted water is being poured over well-washed rice previous to its being cooked in this manner.

mately 40 minutes covered and leave uncovered during the last 10 minutes of cooking. Stirring may be necessary with this method for the first two minutes of boiling, but it should not be stirred after that.

Yields often vary in cooking starchy dry vegetables because of cooking time or other factors. Normally, however, the cooked yields are:

1 lb rice	3 to 4 lb (1½ to 1¾ qt)
1 lb macaroni or spaghetti, etc.	4 lb (2¼ to 2½ qt)
1 lb noodles	3 lb (2 qt)

For 100 five-ounce portions, use eight pounds of rice or noodles and ten pounds of macaroni or spaghetti.

(a)   (b)

(c)   (d)

FIG. 8-15 To cook dry cereals, measure out the proper amount of water and salt for the cereal to be used. Bring water to a boil. (a) Add cereal, giving good agitation as it is stirred into the hot water. (b) Stir until some thickening is apparent. Then reduce the heat to a simmer and cook covered until the cereal has reached the desired consistency and the raw starch taste has disappeared. (c) Then serve. (d) A well cooked product such as this breakfast cereal will bring highest customer satisfaction. (Courtesy Quaker Oats Company)

Breakfast Cereals

Add breakfast cereals to boiling salted water. Fine cereals that might lump may be mixed with a part of the water and blended as a slurry. Coarser cereals may be added slowly. Give good stirring with any type of addition and continue until some thickening is apparent. Then reduce heat to simmering and cook covered until the cereal has reached the desired consistency and the raw taste of starch has disappeared. The more stirring given after thickening occurs, the more slick and pasty will be the cereal. Minimum stirring is therefore recommended after thickening occurs. For 100 five-ounce portions, use 4 gallons of water and $\frac{1}{4}$ to $\frac{1}{3}$ cup of salt and 4 pounds of fine grained cereal, such as cornmeal, grits, or farina, or 5 pounds of coarser cereal, such as oatmeal or cracked wheat. For best quality, cook as close to service as possible.

Steaming

Many vegetables steam well, but some few do not. Normally, if cooking directions indicate that the vegetable should be immersed in water in a pan for steaming, the vegetable does not respond as well to steaming as to boiling. Frequently, frozen vegetables should be thawed before they are steamed, especially leafy greens and corn-on-the-cob.

Steam provides efficient heat because it is hotter than water. One Btu (British thermal unit) is required to raise 1 lb of water 1° F, and to change this pound of water at 212° F to steam at 212° F takes another 970 Btu's. This same steam under 15 lbs pressure raises to 250° F. The heat in the steam plus the heat it absorbs in vaporizing from a liquid makes steam much hotter than water. This is why cooking times are shorter when steam is used, especially steam under pressure. Steam is moist and does not dry products out, and, unlike water, it will leach away few nutrients. Table 8-4 gives the temperatures of steam at various pressures. Additional information on heat values will be found in Tables 15-2 and 15-12a in the Appendix.

Table 8-4
Temperatures of Steam at Various Pressures

Pounds Pressure	°F	Pounds Pressure	°F	Pounds Pressure	°F	Pounds Pressure	°F
0	212	8	235	25	267	45	292
2	218	10	240	30	274	50	298
4	224	15	250	35	281		
6	230	20	259	40	287		

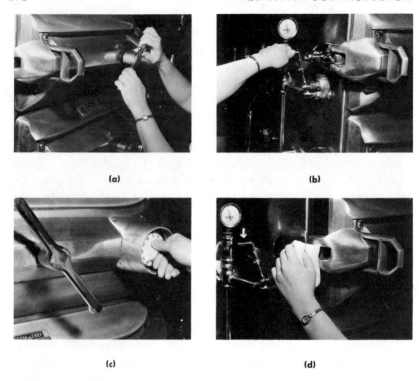

(a)   (b)

(c)   (d)

FIG. 8-16   The method used to operate a large steamer is shown. (a) Place item to be
steamed in a proper type of container in proper depth and place in the steam chamber.
Set the safety catch shown on the left and tighten the door with the lever as shown. (b)
Pull the lever forward, allowing the steam to enter into the chamber. (c) When the air is
exhausted and the pressure of steam closes the solenoid valve, set the timer. (d) When the
product is cooked, push back the steam-close-off lever to shut off the steam, loosen the
lever, and then release the safety catch and withdraw the product.

Small high-pressure units are often used for batch cooking, but large
compartment steamers holding one bushel (60 pounds) of potatoes are commonly used for large quantity cookery. The compartments in the latter are
tiered and a number of pans may be placed inside. Most vegetables are
cooked in perforated pans so steam can circulate freely around them. When
steam is turned on for cooking, air is exhausted from the chamber. Then an
automatic exhaust closes and steam pressure is built up. Steam which comes
in direct contact with food should not be recirculated, since off-flavors may
come from it. After cooking is completed, exhaust the steam carefully.
Novices frequently exhaust the pressure so rapidly that the quick release
of pressure forces liquids from the pans or pops peas from their skins.

FIG. 8-17 Small high-pressure steamers, like the one shown here, can cook many vegetables in a matter of a few minutes. Using one or several of these, it is possible to process vegetables continuously in small batches and send them to service at peak quality.

Table 8-5
Recommended Steaming Practices for Quantity Vegetable Cookery

Vegetable	Recommended Procedure
Asparagus	Lay flat in counter pans, 2 inches deep; add small quantity of warm salted water.* Steam until stalks are tender. If desired, cut off tips, sizing end pieces to equal length of tips. Steam ends 1 minute, add tips, and steam until tips and ends are soft and done.
Beans, dry	Soak 2 to 6 hours. Cover with salted water in solid basket and steam until skins just crack.
Beans, lima, fresh	Place in solid basket to a depth of not more than 3 inches. Add small quantity of salted water.* Steam until tender.
Beans, snap	Place in flat, perforated basket up to 2½ inches deep. Steam until tender. For large quantities, place in tall, narrow, solid basket half full with small quantity of salted water.* Avoid overcrowding. Steam until tender.
Beets	Top only. Steam in perforated basket. Cool and remove skins after steaming.
Broccoli	Lay flat in counter pans with enough warm salted water* to cover stalks. Steam only until tender. Split heavy or thick stalks. Avoid overcooking because of loss of color.
Brussels sprouts	Place in counter pan about 1 inch or single layer deep. To shorten cooking time, stem ends may be split slightly.

Table 8-5 (continued)
Recommended Steaming Practices for Quantity Vegetable Cookery

Vegetable	Recommended Procedure
Cabbage	Place in flat, solid basket half filled with small quantity of warm salted water.*
Carrots	Steam in perforated basket half full.
Cauliflower	Steam in flat, perforated basket, one-fourth full. Should be tender when cooked, with stems having waxy appearance, but should possess firm texture, maintaining original form characteristics.
Cereals	For each 4 pounds of the flaked or coarse type, use 4 gallons water and ¼ cup salt. Bring water to boil and add cereal. Stir to blend thoroughly. Use 5 pounds of fine granular cereal to 4 gallons water and ⅓ cup salt. Steam until done.
Corn-on-the-cob	Thaw frozen corn-on-the-cob before steaming. Place about 25 ears per perforated basket. Steam. Doneness is indicated when kernels are pierced with fork and no milk comes out.
Corn, kernel	Place in counter pan with small quantity of warm salted water.*
Dumplings	Drop on greased baking pans separated sufficiently to allow for expansion. Steam for 15 minutes.
Macaroni products	Bring salted water* to boil in solid basket. Add macaroni product, 1 pound to each gallon of water, stirring to separate for 2 minutes. Steam for 12 to 15 minutes.
Onion, dry	Steam mild onions in perforated basket, third full. Strong, old onions should be steamed in solid basket with small quantity of warm salted water.*
Parsnips	Place in perforated basket, one-fourth full; steam only until tender.
Peas, green	Place in counter pans without water to a depth of not over 2 inches. If necessary, midway through cooking, pressure may be released and peas stirred.
Potatoes, Irish	Steam in perforated basket, three-fourths full. May be partially steamed in skins and baked. Steaming French fries to a partially done stage is also satisfactory.
Potatoes, sweet	Steam in perforated basket, three-fourths full, with skins on. Cool and peel. May also be partially steamed and then baked.
Rice	Wash rice well. Use approximately 2 quarts salted water* to every quart of washed rice. Bring this water to boil in solid basket. Add rice, stirring to separate, for 2 minutes. Cook until tender. Rinse with hot water and steam without water until grains are tender and separated.
Rutabaga	Steam in perforated basket, half full. Old rutabagas should be steamed in solid basket covered with warm salted water.*
Spinach	Steam in small quantity until almost cooked in solid basket containing some warm salted water.* Remove and stir. Complete cooking. Heat in spinach just before doneness may be used to complete cooking without further heat.
Squash, summer	Steam in perforated basket until soft. Do not place more than 2 inches deep.
Squash, winter	Place in perforated basket, half full, and steam.
Turnips	Place in perforated basket, half full, packed loosely. Place old turnips in solid basket with some salted water* and steam.

*Where salted water is required, use 2½ to 2 T salt per gallon of water.

Baking

Baking of vegetables is usually considered roasting in an oven with dry heat. The moist starchy vegetables, such as Irish and sweet potatoes and some of the winter squash bake well. A few high-moisture vegetables, such as tomatoes, may be baked. Quite frequently, baking may be a dual process

(a)   (b)

FIG. 8-18   (a) To bake potatoes, arrange on the tray as shown here and brush lightly
with grease. (b) When the potatoes are done, serve at once. Open the potato immediately
upon coming from the oven, pushing in the ends to give free release of steam; this steam
would otherwise make the potato soggy.

whereby vegetables are first boiled or steamed to partial doneness and then
are finished in the oven. This method is satisfactory for reducing cooking
time and is excellent for sweet potatoes and winter squash, but Irish potatoes
usually have better quality if they are baked without such precooking.
Combination dishes with vegetables may be baked, such as turnip soufflé,
spinach timbale, and corn pudding.

Baked beans, *au gratin* potatoes, escalloped tomatoes or potatoes, zucchini in tomato sauce, glazed onions, and carrots are baked by braising;
that is, they are cooked under moist heat and sometimes under cover. At
times, vegetables may be baked in a covered roaster with meat, meat juices,
sauces, or other products.

FIG. 8-19 Three types of baked products. At the top are the traditional escalloped potatoes. In the middle are bananas baked for service with grilled lamb chops. The thick tomato slices have been topped with a spinach soufflé and baked to give a very colorful, pleasantly flavored product.

Deep-Frying

Vegetables may be deep-fried, a process which imparts a nutty flavor and a crisp outer texture to the item. Potatoes are most often deep-fried, but many other vegetables perform satisfactorily. Some are fried with no coating,

Table 8-6
Deep-Fat Frying of Vegetables

Vegetable	Quantity per 100 Portions (lb EP)	Temperature of Fat (°F)	Frying Time (min)	Procedure
Asparagus	24	360	1 to 3	Boil almost done; cool; dip into batter and fry until golden brown.
Carrots or Parsnips	24	360	3 to 5	Boil or steam almost done; cut lengthwise into quarters; batter or bread and fry.
Cauliflower	20	360	1 to 3	Partially steam or boil. Bread or batter and fry.
Corn-on-the-cob	100 ears	350	3 to 5	Husk ears and remove silk; fry in fat, turning frequently. If frozen corn is used, be sure it is thawed before use; frozen corn is not as satisfactory as fresh.
Cucumbers	35	360	3 to 5	Wash only. Cut into quarters and cut these quarters lengthwise into halves. Batter or bread.
Dill pickles	50 pickles	350	3 to 5	Split pickles in half lengthwise. Batter or bread. (Excellent with boiled beef, corned beef, ham, or pastrami.)
Eggplant	16	370	5 to 8	Do not pare. Cut into slices ½ inch thick or cut into ½ inch strips. Soak in salted water, ¼ cup salt per gallon for 1 hour. Batter or bread and fry.
Onions	16	375	2 to 3	Cut peeled onions into rings ½ inch thick. Separate into individual rings. Dip into evaporated milk and then into flour and continue until well coated, or dip into batter.
Potatoes, Irish (*rissolé*)	24	360	5 to 8	Steam or boil until almost done, if desired. Brown in fat. Finish baking in oven. If not partially cooked before browning, extend baking time.
Potatoes, Irish (French fried)	24			See discussion below.
Potatoes, sweet	24	360	5 to 8	Parboil or steam ¼ inch sticks or slices. Then deep-fry.
Squash, winter	24	360	5 to 8	Parboil or steam pieces ½ inch thick. Then deep-fry.
Tomatoes	20	360	2 to 4	Slice ½ inch thick and dip into batter or bread.
Zucchini	16	360	3 to 5	Dip into batter or bread.

such as potatoes or corn-on-the-cob. Others may be breaded or dipped in batter. Some vegetables may be partially cooked by boiling or steaming and then be finished in deep fat. Many different types of vegetable fritters may be prepared.

POTATOES

Dry all potatoes well before deep-frying. Two methods of frying French-fried, long branch, julienne, or shoestring potatoes may be used:

1. If orders are spasmodic and demand is not heavy, use the one-operation method. This is cooking the potatoes at about 375° F until done, about 7 minutes for potatoes ½ inch thick.

2. The two-operation method is used where volume is high and a large quantity of potatoes must be produced in a short time. In this method, the potatoes are blanched in fat at about 375° F until tender but no coloring shows. These may then be stored under refrigeration for several days, or they may be frozen and held longer. After blanching, the potatoes are ready for service by cooking in 350 to 380° F fat for about two minutes. If the potatoes are at room temperature or if they are slightly warmed in an oven, browning time is reduced. Commercially blanched frozen potatoes are commonly used in many food services and now outrank frozen peas in quantity of frozen vegetables marketed. Potatoes may also be blanched one to two minutes under seven to 10 pounds of steam and then fried.

Potatoes which are smaller than ½ inch thick may be fried at 360 to 380° F for four to six minutes to give a crisp, appetizing potato that still has a soft center. If a crisp potato is desired, as in a shoestring, the potatoes should be fried at a temperature of 335 to 340° F for about six to nine minutes or until golden brown in color. They should be crisp at this point, but if all the moisture is not driven off, remove from the fat and raise the temperature to 375° F and crisp for a few seconds. This potato will keep for a week in crisp condition if it is not salted and if held in a cool place in an airtight covered container.

Soufflé potatoes are difficult to make. After soaking raw, cut potatoes, dry well and cook four to five minutes in 275° F fat. Allow the potatoes to be free in the frying fat. When tender but not browned, drain on absorbent or brown paper. Chill at least five minutes. Raise the temperature of the fat to 400 or 425° F (this requires a good fat), place a few of the potatoes in a basket, and lower quickly into the fat. When the potatoes puff, are crisp outside, and have a golden-brown color, remove, drain, and serve at once. Sweet potatoes are sometimes souffléd in this manner, too.

Grilling

Sautéing (pan-frying) of cooked or raw vegetables is common, especially where short orders are served. Hash browns, lyonnaise, and many

FIG. 8-20 Many vegetables deep-fry well. At the lower right are the traditional onion rings. Breaded cauliflower is just above them, while to the left are breaded egg plant sticks. Note how the operator uses care in dropping in the items. The basket is kept above the fat level until filled to the desired degree and then carefully lowered into the fat.

other potato dishes may be sautéed on a griddle. Some other vegetables may also be sautéed. Mushrooms, string beans and bacon, breaded tomato slices, onions, parsnips, squash, shredded cabbage, and other vegetables may be attractively and appetizingly prepared by sautéing.

(a)

(b)

FIG. 8-21   Potatoes may be (a) grilled or (b) ovenized.

Pan-braising may also be done in a pan, steam-jacketed kettle, or oven. Shredded, diced, or thinly sliced vegetables high in moisture may be placed into a skillet with one tablespoon of oil, butter, or margarine, one teaspoon of salt, and two tablespoons of water per quart of vegetables. The pan or container is covered tightly and allowed to steam or braise. The vegetables are occasionally stirred. This method usually results in a well flavored vegetable, but the labor cost is high and production time may be longer than in boiling.

Oven Roasting

Oven roasting is often called *ovenizing*. It produces results very similar to sautéing, but different equipment is used. In using this method, vegetables are placed in well greased pans and then into a hot oven, when they are fried,

FIG. 8-22 Some vegetables broil well. Here a parboiled slice of eggplant is shown after being spread with a thin coat of mayonnaise and almost completely cooked under the broiler, after which a tomato slice and mushroom cap have been placed on top of it and the cooking completed under the broiler.

with frequent stirring. Ovenizing may also be similar to braising. Some vegetables may be parboiled or steamed and then finished by cooking with fat in heavy roasting pans in an oven. Rissolé potatoes are frequently parboiled or steamed, browned in deep fat, and then ovenized or baked.

Broiling

Broiling may be used to produce some excellent vegetables. Raw tomato slices broil well if cut about one inch thick, brushed with oil, and placed on a broiler grid about four inches from the flame. They are turned only once. Unpeeled eggplant may be sliced one-half to one inch thick, soaked in salt water for an hour, parboiled, and then spread with mayonnaise on top and broiled. Other items may be partially parboiled or steamed and broiled, such as mushrooms, zucchini, onion slices, carrots, and parsnips. Some vegetables may be boiled or steamed, given a rich coating or glaze in the oven, and then finished off or browned under a broiler. Menu designations may indicate that these are broiled vegetables, but actually they are braised and then given a last-minute finish under the broiler.

STUFFINGS OR DRESSINGS

While bread dressings and other stuffings are not vegetables, they are frequently served as a moist starchy or cereal product with meat, so perhaps their inclusion with vegetables is logical. A dressing—or, as it is called in the Continental kitchen, a panade—has many variations. The type served should be carefully selected to blend with the dish or meat with which it is served; complementary flavor contrasts should be sought. Strong meats should have mild dressings and rich meats lean dressings. Dry dressings may be desirable if a moist, rich sauce or gravy is served with the meat. A moist dressing is desirable if the meat is dry. Portion size varies, depending upon the type of food it accompanies. With a two- to three-ounce portion of roast or poultry, four ounces of moist dressing is adequate, and about two ounces of dressing is sufficient for stuffing a pork chop or a heavier portion of meat. Use three, four and five pounds of stuffing respectively for a 10, 15, and over 15 pound bird, ready-to-cook weight. On the average, allow one cup or eight ounces for every pound of dressed bird and 1¼ cups or 10 ounces for every pound of ready-to-cook bird.

Of all dressings, perhaps bread dressing is the most popular. Rice and other cereal products are also used, however. Various ingredients may be added to dressings, such as almond, chestnut, apple, cranberry, crabmeat, shrimp, oysters, giblets, and sausage. With 12 pounds of dressing use three cups of chopped or sliced almonds or chestnuts, or one quart of chopped apples, or one quart of ground cranberries with one-fourth cup of sugar (omitting onion and poultry seasonings) ; or use one pound of either crab or shrimp meat or one quart of oysters with two eggs; or use one quart of cooked, chopped giblets or two pounds of sausage.

Refrigerate dressings immediately after preparation unless they are to be baked at once. At no time, before or after baking, allow dressings to stand between 40 and 140° F for over four hours. Dressings for stuffing into birds should be thoroughly chilled when placed in the birds, and the birds should be baked at once. Remove dressings from cooked birds before refrigerating. It is usually desirable in quantity cookery to bake dressings separately in pans and then dish with the meat or poultry at service. Hot dressings should be spread in shallow pans to cool before being stored under refrigeration. After cooling, cover. Reheat dressings under steam pressure or in an oven until they are well above 180° F. Do not fill pans more than two inches deep.

Table 8-7
Bread Stuffing Guide

Stuffing Ingredients	Poultry Weight (ready-to-cook)				
	4 lbs	6 lbs	10 lbs	12 lbs	20 lbs
Shortening	¼ cup	⅓ cup	½ cup	⅔ cup	1 cup
Chopped onion	½ cup	⅔ cup	1 cup	1⅓ cups	2 cups
Chopped celery	½ cup	⅔ cup	1 cup	1⅓ cups	2 cups
Fresh enriched bread: ½ inch cubes or number of ⅝ inch slices	6 cups or 6	9 cups or 9	15 cups or 15	1⅛ gal or 18	1⅞ gal or 30
Salt	⅔ t	1 t	1½ t	2 t	1 T
Pepper	dash	⅛ t	¼ t	¼ t	½ t
Poultry seasoning	1⅓ t	2 t	1 T	1⅓ T	2 T
Water	⅓ cup	⅔ cup	1 cup	1⅓ cups	2 cups
Average number cups of stuffing	4	6	10	12	20

(Courtesy American Institute of Baking)

Dumplings, hot biscuits, or pastry may be used also as meat accompaniments similar to the manner in which dressings are used. The making of these products is discussed under Section III of this book.

(a)

(b)

(c)

(d)

(e)

FIG. 8-23   Good dressings are often important to meat quality. (a) To make a moistened dressing, wet the cubed bread or bread in pieces, soak well, and then press out excess moisture with the palms of the hands as shown. (b) For a dry dressing, use firm but fresh bread as shown here. (c) To either the moistened or dry bread, add sautéed vegetables, salt, and seasonings. Mix well. (d) Spread into baking pan. A plastic glove averts handling the material with the bare hands. (e) Dressings are highly perishable. Never allow to stand at room temperature. Cover with a moisture-vapor-proof cover as shown and store under refrigeration.

9   Meat, Fish, and Poultry

Meat is usually the main item of a meal, and its selection frequently dictates the other foods that are served with the meal. Good meat will be served only if good meat is purchased and proper preparation procedures are followed. Brillat-Savarin once said, "Good roast cooks are born, not made"; but today we know that good cooking techniques can be learned. As Escoffier said, a good meat cook can be developed with "application, observation, care, and a little aptitude."

    The flesh of animals, poultry, and fish are very much alike; and the principles dealing with their cooking are therefore very similar. In the discussion of principles that follows, the flesh from these three are treated as one. Only in the latter part of the chapter, under specific techniques for cooking, are the directions for cooking each discussed separately.

PRINCIPLES

To cook meat properly one must understand something about its composition and structure and how it reacts to various cooking and handling procedures.

Composition

Meat is about 25% solids and 75% moisture. Of these solids, four fifths are protein and the other fifth are fat, fat-like compounds, ash, and other substances. Meat contains glucose or the precursor of glucose, glycogen, a product related to starch; even though this is small in quantity, it is quite important in the color and flavor developed in browning. The flesh contains most of the protein, moisture, ash, vitamins, and other compounds.

    There are two main groups of meat proteins, one type being found in the connective tissues and the other in the meat fibers. Most of the meat proteins are soluble in cold water; heat coagulates a large share of these, making them insoluble. Fat is found in three areas: emulsified in fiber

306

liquids, as marbling, and as finish. As an animal fattens, fat as finish forms first around the vital organs and then over the interior and exterior surfaces of the body. As fattening continues, this finish spreads over the body, and the quantity of marbling in the flesh and emulsified fat in the fiber juices increases. Young animals have less fat than older ones, but animals of very advanced age often lack fat. The moisture in fat may vary from 15 to 50%. For this reason, fat can prevent meat from drying out in cooking. Roasts are cooked fat side up and poultry with its fat back up so that moisture from the fat will run down and keep the meat moist. Meat may also be larded, or pieces of fatty tissue may be laid over it to give it moisture in cooking. Marbling in meat contributes to tenderness by separating meat tissues. Fat is also quite soft when hot.

Structure

Lean meat is made up of tube-like rods or fibers tapered on both ends. They measure in diameter from 1/200 to 1/1100 inch and may be up to two inches long. These fibers can be seen as strings or shreds when well done chicken breast, boiled short ribs of beef, or other meat is pulled apart. A meat fiber is actually a cell with many nuclei. The cell is filled with a liquid containing proteins, emulsified fat, fat-like substances, minerals, vitamins, and other compounds. The fibers are bound together by connective tissue in bundles like straws in a broom. This tissue spreads like a network around the fibers, holding them in place. Tendrils of connective tissue may even enter into the fibers. A heavier mass of connective tissue surrounds each bundle of fibers, binding these bundles together to make a muscle. At the end of each muscle, long ends of the connective tissue join to form a tendinous mass attached to a bone.

The size of the muscle fibers has much to do with the grain or texture of the meat. Fine fibers give a fine, smooth texture and a tenderer meat. Buyers, in selecting meat, look for a velvety, smooth, soft surface indicating fine grain. This surface should also have a soft, moist sheen and show marbling. Young animals have finer fibers than older ones. Males castrated when young and females will have finer-grained flesh than mature males or stags. The strength of the outer sheath or membrane of the fiber also affects the tenderness of the meat. Muscles that are exercised considerably develop stronger fiber sheaths and more connective tissue than those receiving less exercise. The feed, care, and breed of an animal may also affect the fiber quality. Tenderness may be an inherited factor, but it varies considerably among animals of the same kind or breed.

The types and quantities of connective tissue found in meat are also factors which influence tenderness. There are two kinds of connective tissue:

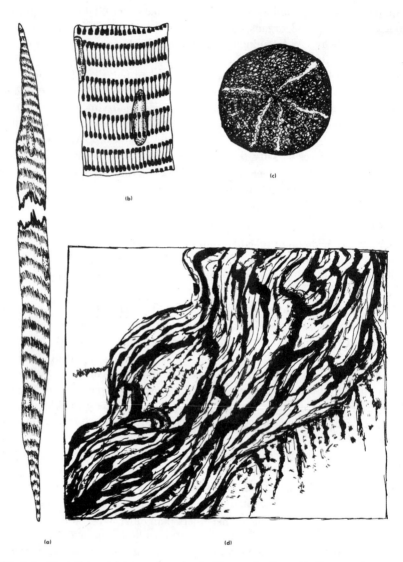

FIG. 9-1   Meat fibers. (a) Long, tapered, tube-like muscle fiber. (b) Close-up of section.
(c) Cross-section of fiber. (d) Dark areas show connective tissue in a meat tissue.

white (collagen) and yellow (elastin). Collagen can be changed into gelatin
and water by moist heat. The time of cooking and the amount of collagen
and its thickness affect the speed and amount of breakdown; acid speeds the
change, but in normal cooking, the acid in foods used is not strong enough,

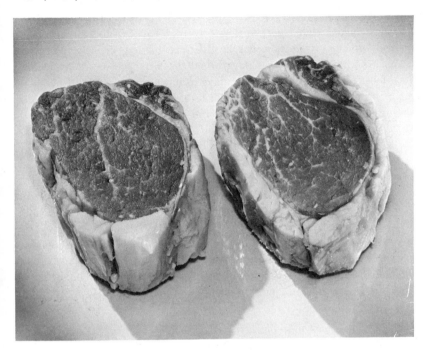

FIG. 9-2 Well marbled tenderloin steaks. Note the sheen and the soft silky texture indicating fine fiber structure in the muscle. (Courtesy Armour & Co.)

or the pieces of meat are not small enough, or the time of cooking is too short to make much difference. When meat is marinated with an acid such as vinegar, tenderization as well as increased moistness is evident after cooking. Elastin is not changed materially by cooking and must be broken up to make it tender. Meat containing a substantial quantity of elastin is tenderized by mechanical treatment such as grinding, pounding, or cubing.

As an animal ages, its flesh toughens. Some increase in connective tissue may cause this, but it is more probable that the type of the connective tissue changes as an animal grows older. Usually muscles receiving a large amount of exercise will contain higher quantities of connective tissue, especially elastin, than those exercised less.

Meat can be tenderized by solutions containing proteolytic enzymes which digest connective tissue. Injection of a tenderizer just before slaughter, providing wide distribution before death through the capillary system, gives improved tenderization over the older method of coating or spraying the meat with a tenderizer after slaughter.

Ripening

If meat is cooked while rigor mortis is present, the meat is tough. Such meat is called "green." Rigor is a muscle stiffening that appears after death but disappears after three or four days, when the meat becomes more tender. Since most meat takes about seven days to move through marketing channels to institutions, few operations will be troubled with green meat. Pork develops little rigor. Chickens develop and lose it quickly.

Ripening or aging is the holding of meat at temperatures between 35° and 40° F under controlled humidity. Beef, lamb, and mutton are usually aged, but pork and veal seldom are. An increase in flavor, tenderness, and moistness results from aging. This is brought about by enzymatic actions and increased acidity in the meat. After 21 days, meat ages little. A good fat coverage is required to age meat properly. This protects lean meat from mold and bacterial attack, surface darkening, and drying out. Molds and bacteria grow with some difficulty in the fat but more easily in flesh. Aging, because of a loss in weight, cost of storage and refrigeration, tie-up of money, and trim, increases cost. Game is frequently aged, and this aging, as in the case of game birds, may proceed almost to the point of putrefaction.

Cooking

Heat coagulates meat proteins at from 165 to 175° F. Coagulation changes the color and flavor of meat and gives it firmness. Just before coagulation occurs, denaturation or loss of moisture occurs at about 140° F. Shrinkage loss varies in cooking according to cut, type of meat, amount of fat, and other factors, but the most influential factor is the temperature of cooking, low temperature giving a lower loss. Minimum shrinkage in cooking might be considered: beef rib rare 10%, medium 15%, well done 25%; baked ham 15%; fresh pork loin 40%; leg of lamb 25%; and leg of veal 30%. That high heat "seals the pores" of meat and thereby reduces shrinkage has not been proven. Rather, cooking at a high temperature increases shrinkage. Searing at a high temperature and then cooking at a low temperature increases shrinkage over cooking at a constant low temperature, but it may be done anyway to develop a caramelized outer surface and to improve aroma. A constant low temperature in cooking saves labor and fuel and reduces spattering and burning. Salt delays browning, and since the penetration of salt in cooking is small, from a half to a quarter of an inch, it is frequently omitted until just before serving the meat. Excess cooking of meat may dry it out and toughen it. Check all procedures carefully and ascertain which method of cooking gives the best quality and least shrinkage.

Color

The red color of raw meat is from myoglobin pigments and some red blood corpuscles remaining in the meat. Acid darkens myoglobin. Ripening meat increases acidity, making it dark. Intensity of redness is governed by the quantity of myoglobin present. Milk fed hogs, calves, or chickens are apt to be anemic, and for this reason they have a light-colored flesh that lacks myoglobin. Fish flesh has little myoglobin. Oxygen with myoglobin forms oxymyoglobin, a bright red pigment. Heat turns myoglobin to hematin, a gray or grayish-brown substance. Cured meats are red after cooking because the myoglobin combines with the nitrogen of the curing salts to form nitroso-myoglobin, a pigment stable under heat. It is possible for hamburger or pieces of meat to pick up traces of curing salts from meat blocks or cutting equipment, and this may cause these meats to have a red color after cooking. It is probable that dehydrated onions, dried in inert nitrogen gas, causes a red, uncooked appearance in a meat such as meat loaf. Sometimes ground meat patties, presalted and frozen, show a red color after cooking. The reason for this is not known, but meat processors advise that the patties should not be salted if they are to be frozen and held.

Flavor

There is much conjecture on how cooked meat derives its flavor. At one time nitrogenous and non-nitrogenous extractives or waste metabolic products were thought to be the primary factor. It is now thought that while a part of the flavor is contributed by these and by sweet, salt, acid, and bitter compounds, a major portion of flavor is derived from volatile esters in fat. Flavor is also developed by cooking. The flavor developed by caramelization of carbohydrates has already been mentioned. Amino acids may also break down into flavorful products; free fatty acids and carbonyl fractions increase and may be the cause of the rich aroma of cooking meat. Flavor develops in cooking up to three hours and then declines.

There is a correlation between the breed and diet of the animal and the flavor of its flesh. A milk mash diet for chickens gives a milder-flavored flesh than that of barnyard fowl. Cattle fattened on distiller's mash have a sharply acid, ferment-flavored meat. Good care and environment give mild-flavored flesh, while animals that must withstand the rigors of climate and are poorly fed and housed will have a strongly flavored flesh. The marine diet and iodine content of fish are the basic factors behind their flavor. Sex and age affect flavor. The meat of males, unless castrated when young, is stronger than that of females, and the flesh of young animals is milder than that of older animals. Meat after cooking has a characteristic sulfurous flavor which varies in intensity according to the kind of animal, its diet, degree of cooking, and other factors. Even different muscles of the same animal may differ in flavor, as can be noted between the leg and breast of a chicken. Poultry is especially acid and astringent in flavor; turkey has an almost pungent flavor. Pork is sweeter but more acid and sulfurous than beef. Lamb and mutton with a pH of 7.0 are more alkaline than beef or pork with a pH of 6.0 and have a strong flavor associated with the odors of caproic, caprylic, and pelargonic compounds. The flavor of meat may be heightened by the use of hydrolyzed proteins such as monosodium glutamate (MSG) or related compounds. When MSG is used alone, the flavor is not that of meat; but when combined with meat flavors, the meat flavor is heightened.

Doneness

Meat is cooked to make it more palatable and perhaps more digestible. When development of tenderness is an objective, moist heat must be supplied for this to occur. Overcooking with dry heat may toughen flesh. High-temperature cooking is more apt to toughen meat than low-temperature cooking. High temperatures or extended cooking toughens many shellfish, poultry, and other flesh foods. Cooked to the same internal muscle temperature, simmered fowl is tenderer than fowl cooked under high steam pressure.

Doneness in meats cooked by dry heat can be judged by outside and inside appearance, but the surest way is by thermometer. An exception is small pieces of meat, such as chops or steaks. There are six stages of doneness in quantity food service, and these are defined as follows:

Very rare	The meat has only a thin portion of cooked meat around the edge; red, almost bloody juices, exude from the meat. Under pressure of the finger, the meat is soft and jelly-like inside.
Rare	The raw portion is thinner and the meat around it is now pink; there is a good brown outer surface. The meat has a full, plump appearance and still feels somewhat soft to pressure. The juices are red but not bloody.
Medium rare	The interior is a rich pink. The meat is still plump and the juices are pink. The depth of the gray outer surface has increased and the firmness to touch is more apparent.
Medium	The color of the interior is a modified rose. Pink juices are apparent but the quantity is less plentiful. The exterior is well browned and the surface does not appear as plump or full. When pressed, there is a definite resistance.
Medium well	The pink color has completely disappeared. Juiciness is still evident, but the juices are clear or gray, not pink. There is no longer a plump appearance, and the meat is firm to touch.

Well   The meat is completely gray inside. Little or no juice
              appears. The meat has a hard, flinty touch and a
              shrunken appearance. The surface is browned and dry.

Temperatures indicating doneness are:

Beef	*Rare 140° F, medium 160° F, and well 170° F*
Lamb	*Medium 165° F, well 175° F*
Pork, fresh	*Well 165° to 175° F (always cook pork well; note that temperatures recommended for doneness in pork have been lowered)*
Pork, cured	*Well 155° F*
Poultry	*Well 180° F, medium 165° F*
Veal	*Well 170° F*

Aged beef at 140° F may appear medium rather than rare because ripened
meat loses color rapidly in cooking. Large pieces of meat increase internal
temperature after cooking, and items such as rib roasts that are required
rare or medium should be cooked from 15 to 25° F lower than required
at service. Time varies for doneness. If meat is at room temperature, it
will cook more rapidly than chilled meat, and times for cooking frozen meat
are two to three times those of refrigerated meat. As cooking temperature
is increased, time is decreased. High cooking temperatures increase shrink-

FIG. 9-3 Fine quality is indicated in this roast beef. The moist, shiny surface, glistening
fat, and fine texture indicate fine eating quality. (Courtesy Armour & Co.)

age and reduce appearance, juiciness, tenderness, and flavor. Usually the larger the cut, the longer the cooking time; but a flat roast or a piece of meat with a large surface area will cook in less time than a more solid or compact piece of equal weight. Boned meats take a longer time to cook than their unboned counterparts. Fat meat may require a longer cooking time because fat may act as an insulator against heat penetration. Cooking meat in aluminum foil increases shrinkage and cooking time; there is also a loss of flavor. To cook meat by the pound, calculate time by the piece and not the entire pan contents; e.g., a roast pan containing six seven-pound roasts should be timed for seven pounds, not for 42 pounds.

STANDARDS

It is difficult to give one standard for cooked meat because of the wide variety of meats and the many ways of cooking them. All meat should be of good flavor and pleasing appearance. Drippings should be rich and juicy. The meat should be moist, not dry or crumbly, and have a degree of firmness consistent with its doneness. It should be tender and not pulpy, stringy, or excessively soft, greasy, or oily. The color should be natural to the meat, cooking, and degree of doneness. There should be no burned portions or any burned taste. Roasts should be well browned. Veal roasts should have a reddish brown, and roast pork a uniformly rich brown surface. The skin of roasted poultry and the outer surface of lamb and pork roasts should be crisp, not dry or tough. Sliced meat should be firm, juicy, and tender and hold its shape. Broiled exteriors should be evenly browned, juicy, and glossy in appearance. Broiled bacon should be crisp but not brittle, with crispness dictated by personal preference. Browned meats should have a rich brown color with a well-developed flavor and aroma. Braised meat when done should be tender and juicy, not stringy, and should hold its shape and not fall apart. There should be a rich gloss from the drippings or gravy over the surface of the meat, and pieces should be uniform, even, symmetrical, and attractive. Unbrowned meats lack the color and the characteristic flavor developed by browning, but otherwise they have qualities similar to browned braised meat. Standards for poultry, fish, and shellfish are somewhat different from those given here for meat.

Deep fried or sautéed products should have a crisp, deep golden, brown surface and possess a sweet, nutty flavor. They should have a soft, rich glaze or sheen. These properties may be varied by the frying fat used, for some give more crispness and a deeper color than others. Covered fried products should have crusts which adhere tightly and are tender, even, and not too thick. The product should not be grease-soaked, and the inside should be moist, hot, succulent, and completely cooked. Outer crusts or surfaces should be tender; edges should not be overcooked. Evaluate fried foods on the basis of appearance, golden-brown surface, and uniformity of color and shape; texture should be crisp, tender, and light; flavor should be true, pleasing, and appetizing.

· TECHNIQUES

The tenderness of the meat will largely dictate how it should be cooked. Usually tender cuts are cooked by dry heat, while tough cuts are cooked by moist heat. Some tough cuts may be treated mechanically or with tenderizers to make them tender, and then they may be cooked by dry-heat methods. The cooking of frozen meat is discussed later.

Dry heat methods of cooking meat are:

1. Broiling, pan broiling, or griddle broiling.
2. Roasting or baking.
3. Barbecueing.
4. Sautéing, pan-frying or grilling.
5. Deep-frying.
6. Ovenizing.

Moist heat methods of cooking meat are:

1. Braising (pot-roasting, fricasseeing, casseroling, swissing, or stewing).
2. Simmering (poaching and stewing; few meats, if any, are boiled).
3. Steaming.
4. Blanching.

Dry-Heat Cooking

Work Areas

A considerable portion of the production time in any food operation is spent in the preparation and cooking of meats. Maximum efficiency and quality should be achieved by planning work and layouts properly. Broiling, sautéing, and deep-frying require fast and heavy production. Equipment should be carefully related to flow of work, with proper working space and landing areas provided. Small tools and materials, such as tongs, forks, knives, salt, pepper, oil, oil mop, and cloths, should be located within easy reach and with the required work motions in mind. Provide refrigerated storage for perishable foods within the work area. Procedures and work schedules for each area should be well worked out and the workers trained to follow them.

Heavy-duty broilers with adjustable grids are required. Clean these grids after each day's use or more often if required. Use a stiff wire brush, removing encrusted materials, and then wipe clean with an oil-dipped cloth. Wipe grease away from surfaces frequently and never let grease remain collected in pans. At intervals, remove grids, soak or boil them in a strong cleaning solution, and scrub them well. Rinse and dry. Steam cleaning is also good. Grids, like griddles and sauté pans, require conditioning to prevent them from sticking. Before using a grid, brush it lightly with oil. Grids that are too hot or cold will cause products to stick to them.

A griddle should also be of heavy-duty type; have a good back splash,

FIG. 9-4   A heavy-duty broiler such as this is required to serve good quality broiled products in food service operations. (Courtesy Vulcan Hart)

oil-catching depressions on three sides, and an oil outlet for overflow; be made of good heat-conducting, durable metal; and give even heat. Thermostatic controls should give temperatures to 500° F, not more than 10° F plus or minus desired temperature. Rapid input of heat must occur so the shock of cold foods does not drop grill temperatures. Griddles should be made so they can be easily cleaned.

To prevent griddles and sauté pans from sticking and to give them a fast, workable surface, condition them by placing salt and a high quality fat or oil on the surface. Bring these to a smoking temperature. Then scour the surface with the salt, using a cloth rolled into a pad, pumice, or soapstone for scouring. Wipe clean with a dry cloth or soft paper. Repeat until a smooth, non-sticking surface is obtained. After each meal or day's work, polish thoroughly with salt and oil, using pumice or soapstone until the pan or griddle shines. Cool slowly. Then wipe clean with a soft, absorbent cloth. Never wash or allow water to remove this conditioned finish. If the surface is lost, recondition. Keep sauté pans in which moist items are cooked separate from those for plain sautéing. Salting foods in the pan or on the griddle breaks down fats, resulting in gummy deposits forming on the surface. Salt meats only after removal from pans for this reason.

(a)   (b)

FIG. 9-5   (a) Conditioning a pan by scouring with pumice, salt, and oil over heat.   (b) Conditioning a grill in a similar manner, using a special holding device for the pumice stone.

The deep-frying and sauté work areas should be planned so the worker can work easily around the equipment. Provide space for holding foods before and after cooking. Have these areas free of traffic; provide good footing and unobstructed vision. Most operations today use rapid-recovery, thermostatically controlled fryers heated by gas or electricity. Thermostats in these should be durable and accurate. Set up adequate filtering facilities for the fat. Provide in the work center a thermometer, tongs, a long-handled fork, and perhaps a skimmer.

An unclean fryer or basket will encourage fat breakdown and give poor quality foods. Gums or resins formed around heating elements can cause heat loss and inaccurate temperature control. Clean fryers thoroughly at least once a week. Scrub the kettle with a stiff brush, using hot water and a good cleaning detergent. Some frying basins, after they are drained of fat, can be taken to the pot sink for cleaning. Do not use abrasive materials on elements. Clean daily around fryers and griddles where grease can accumulate. Provide automatic closing devices on ventilating systems so drafts may be closed off quickly in case of fire. Fire caused by fat or oil should be smothered with a blanket or carbon dioxide gas, not drenched with water. Carbon tetrachloride may break down at high temperatures and give off a toxic gas. Hot fat can cause severe burns. If a fryer has much encrusted material on it, empty and then fill with water, using two ounces of good detergent per gallon of water. Bring to a boil, boiling 15 to 20

FIG. 9-6   The mobile table and rack made it quick and easy for the roast cook to move items to and from the roast ovens. Providing supplemental equipment such as this can do much to increase worker productivity and quality of product.

minutes. Drain. Repeat until the kettle is clean. Rinse with clean water and then rinse again with one cup of vinegar added to each gallon of water.

Plan the roasting section so there is space for pans awaiting loading and for pans to cool after roasting. Provide a convenient area for slicing and working. Twelve-inch-high deck ovens may be required if heavy ribs and turkeys are to be roasted. Small revolving ovens may take less space and make work easier than deck ovens. If possible, the roasting center should have its own ovens, and these should be used only for cooking meats.

Broiling

Any method of cooking by radiant heat is called *broiling. Grilling* at one time meant broiling, but the term is now used to indicate sautéing or frying on a griddle top. The common heat sources for broiling are charcoal, gas, and electricity. Radiant heat from these may be reflected toward the meat from below, from the side, or from above. Some gas broilers heat ceramic tiles, which in turn reflect radiant heat. Temperatures of cooking should be slightly higher than those used for roasting. To estimate temperatures, hold the hand at the cooking level. If the hand can be held there only two seconds, it is a fast fire (350 to 400° F); three seconds, a medium fire (300 to 350° F); and four seconds, a slow fire (275 to 300° F). Good ventilation should be provided to remove smoke and fumes. Drafts should

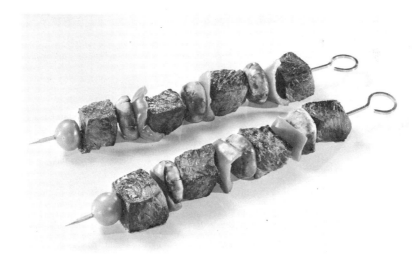

FIG. 9-7   Small items such as this shish-kebab should be broiled at higher temperatures, by placing them closer to the broiler than larger items. (Courtesy Armour & Co.)

not bother workers or cool the foods. Good draft must be provided for a charcoal fire so it can obtain oxygen to burn.[1]

The broiling temperature should be governed by the cut, type of meat, and size of the piece. Meat of lower fat content or small pieces are cooked

FIG. 9-8   A tenderloin butt broiled and then planked. After being placed under the broiler, it is sent to service.

[1]Use hardwood kindling to start a charcoal fire, or soak the charcoal in a can for several hours in lighter fluid or wood alcohol. Fit the can with a tight lid and keep away from fire. Or, about half a cup of alcohol or lighter fluid may be poured on a small mound of charcoal and, after standing two minutes, they may be lighted. Do not use an excess so that fluid runs from the charcoal and starts a dangerous fire. Do not use kerosene or other fuel oils, tar, or creosote products, for these give off-flavors to broiled items. Special gas or electric lighters can be used.

   Once a good fire is started, pile charcoal on the lighted pieces, and when a bed of coals is obtained, spread with a fire pick and cover with more charcoal. Use charcoal from hard wood, not soft woods, for the latter may give resinous flavors to foods. Build a bed of glowing coals two to three inches deep, depending upon the heat intensity desired. Have the bed of coals larger than the grid area used for broiling and have the coals even except for outer edges, where greater heat will be required because of air cooling the coals at this spot. Some broiler men adjust thickness of coals to give different broiling temperatures. Most, however, vary the grid distance from the coals. Allow heat to build up to about 350° F at grid level, or adjust electricity or gas so the heat is correct. A charcoal fire takes about 45 minutes to come to correct heat. Heat heavy-duty broilers in advance, for time is required to bring to proper temperature. In a charcoal broiler, when the coals are glowing and show white ash, the fire is ready.

(a) (b)

(c) (d)

FIG. 9-9 (a) To sauté or broil a strip steak, cut lightly into the edge to prevent curling. (b) Next, dip into oil. (c) Place on a preheated broiler grid, judging the proper distance from the heat by thickness of steak and type of steak. (d) A thick ham steak broils well. Here, after a slight broil, the ham steak is being covered with a mixture of prepared mustard, ground cloves, and brown sugar for finishing under the broiler.

Table 9-1

Cuts of Meat and Recommended Methods of Cooking*

ROASTING

BEEF	LAMB	FRESH PORK	SMOKED PORK	VEAL	VARIETY MEATS
Rib	Leg	Ham (leg)	Ham	Leg (round)	Liver
Sirloin butt	Loin	Loin	Picnic	Loin	
Loin strip	Rack	Boston butt	Shoulder butt	Rib	
Tenderloin	Rolled shoulder	Picnic	Canadian-style bacon	Rolled shoulder	
Rump butt*	Cushion shoulder	Rolled shoulder	Loaf (ground ham)	Loaf (ground veal)	
Round*	Loaf (ground lamb)	Cushion shoulder			
Inside (top) round*		Spareribs			
Outside (bottom) round*					
Knuckle (tip)*					
Inside chuck*					
Shoulder clod*					
Loaf (ground beef)					

BROILING, GRIDDLE-BROILING, OR PAN-BROILING

BEEF	LAMB	FRESH PORK	SMOKED PORK	VEAL	VARIETY MEATS
Rib steak	Shoulder chops	Fresh pork is not broiled or griddle-broiled.	Sliced ham	Veal is not broiled unless it is fairly mature and well-fatted, and then only loin chops or steaks.	Sliced veal or lamb liver
Club steak	Rib chops		Sliced bacon		Lamb kidneys
T-bone steak	Loin chops		Sliced Canadian-style bacon		Brains
Porterhouse steak	Leg steaks		Shoulder butt		Sweetbreads
Sirloin steak (cut from loin strip)	Lamb patties (ground lamb)				
Butt steak					
Tip steak (knuckle)					
Inside chuck steak*					
Top round steak*					
Beef patties (hamburger)					
Flank*					

*Usually only prime to choice quality in these should be cooked in this manner.

BRAISING

Beef	Lamb	Pork	Veal	Variety Meats
Chuck (all cuts)	Breast	Chops	Breast	Heart, all kinds
Brisket	Neck	Loin	Chops	Liver
Plate	Shank	Rib	Loin	Beef
Flank	Shoulder	Shoulder	Rib	Pork
Neck		Feet	Shoulder	Kidneys
Outside (bottom) round		Hocks	Cutlets (leg)	Tripe
Heel of round		Spareribs	Neck	
Rump butt		Fresh ham steaks	Shoulder	
Shank		Tenderloin	Shank	
Short ribs				
Skirt steak				
Ox tails (joints)				

SIMMERING

Beef	Lamb	Pork	Veal	Variety Meats
Fresh	Neck	Spareribs	Neck	Kidney
Chuck (all cuts)	Breast	Backbones	Shank	Heart
Rump butt	Flank	Pigs feet	Breast	Tongue
Shank	Shanks	Hocks	Flank	For pre-cooking:
Heel of round	(Large cuts of lamb are usually not cooked in water)	Ham	(Large cuts of veal are usually not cooked in water.)	Brains
Brisket		Shoulder		Sweetbreads
Plate		Picnic		
Flank		Shoulder butt		
Short ribs		Hocks		
Corned				
Brisket				
Rump				
Plate				
Round				

(Adapted from *Cooking Meat in Quantity*, National Livestock and Meat Board)

at higher temperatures. Thin pork chops or steaks, bacon, and other thin items are cooked within two to three inches of the heat, while thick turkey breasts, chateaubriands, and other pieces may be cooked eight inches or more from it. Some larger pieces may be scored to aid heat penetration. Too high a temperature develops a hard, dry crust on the surface; this insulates the interior of the meat from the heat, resulting in a charred outside and an undercooked inside. Excessively thick pieces may be broiled five to eight minutes on each side and then completed in a 350° F oven.

Broiled meat, poultry, or fish may be served planked. The item is broiled nearly to desired doneness and placed in the center of a heated oak plank about two inches thick; a border of duchess potatoes is piped around the edge; the open spaces are filled with various cooked vegetables; the whole is garnished with broiled mushrooms or other items; and the entire plank is placed into a hot oven or under a broiler to brown. It is sent to service after being drizzled liberally with melted butter.

Small pieces of meat, extremely tender flesh such as fish, or breaded foods which might stick to a grid or break in turning may be placed into a double grid that folds like an old-fashioned toaster. Oil this double grid well before using.

Most foods to be broiled are first dipped into vegetable oil, then held over the oil pan for a moment to drain, and then placed onto the grid. Steaks, chops, chickens, and other items that broil well are dipped into oil, placed directly on the grid, pressed gently onto the grid to give good contact, and cooked to half-doneness (100° F interior for rare to medium and 135° F for medium to well done). They are then turned and seasoned with salt (salting earlier retards browning). For large pieces, four turns may be required, and salting is not done until the third and fourth turns. Items turned only once show single grid marks (////), while those turned

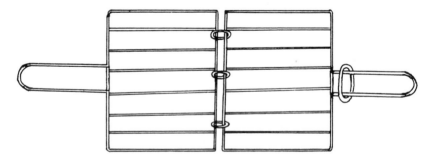

FIG. 9-10   A double grid used to hold fish and other items under the broiler; such a device makes it possible to turn these items without breaking them.

twice show crisscross grid marks (XXXX). This criss-crossing is achieved by making a 90° angle turn on successive turns. Press the meat gently onto the grid each time it is turned. Edges of some foods may have to be scored (cut) to prevent curling. Meats, poultry, and fish of low fat content are difficult to broil satisfactorily, but if dipped in flour and then in oil and placed in a double grid which holds them firmly in place, they may be slow-broiled. Basting these with oil while broiling assists in producing a more satisfactory product.

Do not allow drippings to flame. If this happens, a sooty smoke and off-flavors will contaminate the meat. Grease fires may also start. To control such flames, have at hand a bottle of cold water with a perforated top, a

FIG. 9-11 Grid markings on these steaks indicate they have been turned only once in broiling. (Courtesy Armour & Co.)

syringe of cold water, or a small container of cold water containing chipped ice. Vertical spits before a vertical heat source should revolve up and over toward the worker. This assists in keeping drip away from the fire, provided the speed is sufficient to carry the melted fat up and over. A shallow pan placed under the spit in front of the fire can catch this drip. Send all broiled meats to service as soon as they are done.

When many items must be broiled at one time, such as for a banquet, have the broiler at the correct temperature but place the grid closer to the

FIG. 9-12 The pan-broiling of fatty foods, such as sausages, requires that the fat be poured off as it accumulates; otherwise, sautéing is the result. However, for a less fat item, pan-broiling is satisfactory without pouring-off, as seen with the tenderloin steaks.

Table 9-2

Time-Table for Broiling

Cut	Approximate Thickness	Approximate Rare	Cooking Time (minutes) Medium	Well-done
Broiler (Charcoal, Gas or Electric)*				
Rib, club, T-bone, porterhouse,	1 in	15	20	30
tenderloin or individual serv-	1½ in	25	35	
ings of sirloin beef steak	2 in	35	50	
Sirloin beef steak (whole steak)	1 in	20 to 30	30 to 40	
	1½ in	30 to 40	40 to 50	
	2 in	40 to 55	50 to 65	
Ground beef patties	1 in (4 oz)	15	20	
Shoulder, rib, loin and sirloin	1 in		12 to 15	16 to 18
lamb chops or steaks	1½ in		17 to 20	
	2 in		20 to 25	25 to 30
Ground lamb patties	1 in (4 oz)		16 to 18	
Smoked ham slice	½ in			10 to 12
	1 in			16 to 20
Bacon, Griddle or Pan Broiling				4 to 5
Individual servings of beef steaks	¾ in	4	8	12
	1 in	6	10	15
	1½ in	10 to 12	15 to 18	20
Ground beef patties	¾ in	4 to 5	8 to 10	12
	1 in (4 oz)	6 to 8	10 to 12	15
Lamb chops	1 in		10	15
	1½ in		15	20 to 25
Ground lamb patties	¾ in		10	12 to 15
	1 in (4 oz)		10 to 15	15 to 20
Smoked ham slice	½ in			6 to 10
Bacon				2 to 3

*There are automatic speed broilers which cook both sides of the meat at once and may, therefore, decrease the time to half or even a third of that given for broilers heating only from one side.

Courtesy, National Livestock and Meat Board.

heat than normal. Broil the items only to proper color. Remove, cool, place in pans, and at the required time finish in a 350 to 400° F oven. To pre-pare lobsters in this manner, broil to desired color, then set them in pans, and place a weight on the tails to prevent them from turning up and charring in the oven.

Pan-broil in a fairly heavy skillet. Select a pan suited to the quantity to be cooked so the drippings will not burn. Rub the bottom lightly with fat. Preheat. Cook the meat on one side and then on the other; turn as often as necessary to insure even cooking. Pour the fat off as it gathers; do not cover the pan or add water. Broiling on a griddle may be accomplished in a manner similar to pan-broiling. It is used for heavy production. Pan-broil only meats that are high in fat. Both pan- and griddle-broiling give products resembling sautéed foods rather than broiled ones.

Table 9-3

Time and Temperatures for Roasting Meats

Cut	Approx. Wt. of Single Roast	No. of Roasts in Oven	Approx. Total Wt. of Roasts in Oven	Oven Temperature (F)	Interior Temperature of Roast When Removed from Oven (F)	Minutes per lb Based on One Roast	Minutes per lb Based on Total Wt. of Roasts in Oven	Approx. Total Time Roasting
	lb		lb					
BEEF								
Standing rib (7-rib)	20 to 25	1		250°	125° (rare) / 140° (medium) / 150° (well)	13 / 15 / 17		4½ hr / 5 hr / 6 hr
Standing rib (7-rib)	23	1		300°	125° (rare) / 140° (medium) / 150° (well)	11 / 12 / 13		4 hr / 4½ hr / 5 hr
Rolled rib (7-rib)	16 to 18	1		250°	150° (well)	26		7 to 8 hr
Rolled rib (7-rib)	17	1		300°	150° (well)	24		6 hr
Standing rib (7-rib)		2	56	300°	140° (medium) / 160° (well)		6 / 7 to 8	6 hr / 7 hr
Chuck rib	5 to 8	1		300°	150° to 170°	25 to 30		2½ to 4 hr
Rump	5 to 7	1		300°	150° to 170°	25 to 30		2½ to 3½ hr
Round (rump and shank off)	50	1		250°	140° (medium) / 154° (well)	12 / 14		10 hr / 11 to 12 hr
LAMB								
Leg	6 to 7	2	16	300°	180°		15	4 hr
Cushion shoulder (with stuffing)	4½ to 5½	1		300°	180°	30 to 35		2 to 3 hr

Cut	Weight (lb)			Oven temp.	Interior temp.	Min. per lb.	Servings	Total time
Rolled shoulder	3 to 4	1		300°	180°	40 to 45	10	2½ to 3 hr
Rolled shoulder		5	29	300°	180°			5 hr
Square cut shoulder		8	40	300°	180°		7	4 to 5 hr
FRESH PORK								
Loin (bone in)	12 to 15	1		300°	185°	16		3 to 4 hr
Loin (bone in)	11 to 15	1		350°	185°	15 to 18	14	3 to 3½ hr
Rolled loin (two halves tied together)		3	21	300°	185°			5 hr
Rolled loin (two halves tied together)		3	23	350°	185°		11	4 hr
Half loin (bone in)		6	33	300°	185°		11	6 hr
Half loin (bone in)		6	33	350°	185°		8	4½ hr
Center cut loin	3 to 4	1		350°	185°	35 to 40		2 to 2½ hr
End cut loin	3 to 4	1		350°	185°	45 to 50		2½ to 3 hr
Shoulder	12 to 14	1		350°	185°	30 to 35		6½ hr
Cushion shoulder (with stuffing)	4 to 6	1		350°	185°	35 to 40	9	3 to 3½ hr
Cushion shoulder (with stuffing)		3	30	350°	185°			4½ to 5 hr
Rolled shoulder	4 to 6	1		350°	185°	35 to 40		3 to 3½ hr
Boston Butt	4 to 6	1		350°	185°	45 to 50		3½ to 4½ hr
Ham (leg)	15	1		300°	185°	30		8 hr
Ham (leg)	10 to 12	1		350°	185°	30 to 35		6 hr
Ham (leg)		3	34	300°	185°		10 to 12	6 to 7 hr
Ham (leg)		3	38	350°	185°		10	6 to 6½ hr
Ham (leg) boned, split, and tied in two rolls	10 to 12	1		350°	185°	30 to 35		5 to 7 hr

Cut	Weight (lb)	No.		Oven temp.	Interior temp.	Min. per lb.		Time
Ham (leg) boned, split, and tied in two rolls	10	1		350°	185°	20 to 25		4 to 5 hr
SMOKED PORK								
Whole ham	10 to 14	1		300°	160°	15 to 18		3 to 3½ hr
Half ham	6 to 10	1		300°	160°	20		2 to 3½ hr
Ham, sweet pickled	16	1		350°	170°	15		4 hr
Shoulder butt	2 to 4	1		300°	170°	30 to 35		1 to 2 hr
Picnic	3 to 10	1		300°	170°	30 to 35		2 to 5 hr
Canadian-style bacon (casing on)	7	1		350°	160°	10 to 12		1 to 1½ hr
Canadian-style bacon (casing on)		3	19	300°	160°		5	1½ to 2 hr
VEAL								
Leg	7 to 8	1		300°	170°	25		3 to 3½ hr
Leg	16	1		300°	170°	22		6 hr
Leg	23	1		300°	170°	18 to 20		7 to 7½ hr
Loin	4½ to 5	1		300°	170°	30 to 35		2½ to 3 hr
Rack (4 to 6 ribs)	2½ to 3	1		300°	170°	30 to 35		1½ hr
Shoulder	7	1		300°	170°	25		3 hr
Shoulder	12 to 13	1		300°	170°	25		5 to 5½ hr
Cushion shoulder (with stuffing)	9 to 10	1		300°	170°	30 to 35		5 to 5½ hr
Cushion shoulder (with stuffing)		3	24	300°	170°		10 to 12	4 to 5 hr
Rolled shoulder	5	1		300°	170°	40 to 45		3½ to 4 hr
Rolled shoulder		3	20	300°	170°		14	5 hr
Rolled shoulder	9 to 10	1		300°	170°	35 to 40		6 to 7 hr
Round (rump and shank off)	20	1		300°	170°	20		6½ hr

Roasting

The pan used for roasting should be of heavy material, of the correct size, and deep enough to permit turning the meat without spilling juices and fat. The meat should cover the pan bottom and not leave space for drippings to burn. Sometimes a trivet or perforated underliner is placed on the bottom so that the meat does not rest in its own juices and fat. Omit the trivet for some meats, such as leg of veal, where it is desirable to turn the meat in its own juices as it roasts. Some chefs add roughly chopped vegetables at the start of roasting. Salt is not added until browning is completed. Never pierce the lean flesh in turning a roast or broiled item, but insert the fork in the fatty tissues or merely roll with a fork. Use no liquid and do not cover, except for fish and a few other items that may require it. Place meat fat side up. Meat which lacks fatty tissue may have to be basted, larded, or covered with fatty tissue.

If a thermometer is used, select the smallest piece of meat in the lot and insert the thermometer in the center of its largest muscle. When the proper internal temperature is reached, the thermometer is removed and

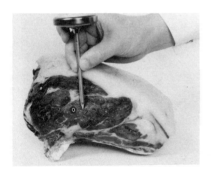

(a)   (b)

FIG. 9-13   (a) Insert a thermometer into a roast in the deepest part of the muscle. Measure the distance, as shown here, so as to place the thermometer tip at the proper location. (b) Checking roasted meats for interior temperatures.

inserted similarly into the next smallest piece until it is done, and then into the next smallest piece, and so on, until the batch is done. To roast meat, place it in a preheated 300° F oven and maintain this temperature throughout the roasting period, or preheat to 475° F and sear until well browned; then drop the temperature quickly to 300° F and complete roasting. To minimize drying, roast small pieces at higher temperatures. *En papillote* means wrapped in paper and roasted; this is most frequently done with fish or chicken. Cured meats may require some soaking or parboiling before roasting. Follow the manufacturer's directions for such items. Do not sear cured ham.

If thermometers are not available, test doneness of roasted meat with the thumb or forefinger. Experience is required to do this, and even the experts are sometimes fooled. Allow a roast to stand from half an hour to one hour before carving. Remember, internal temperatures will rise 15° to 25° F as a roast stands. If a roast is held in a steam table, leave the cover open and reduce heat so the roast will not cook there.

To carve, cut against the grain of the meat in thin slices. Serve at once on a hot plate. Machine-slicing gives, on the average, more portions per pound than hand-slicing.

FIG. 9-14   Slice meat across the grain, as shown in the carving of this rolled shoulder of lamb. (Courtesy Armour & Co.)

FIG. 9-15 Temperature control is necessary if meats are to be properly roasted. Two identical roasts are shown, one roasted at a proper oven temperature and the other at a temperature much too high. The amount of drippings obtained from the meat roasted at too high a temperature far exceeds that of the meat roasted at the correct temperature.

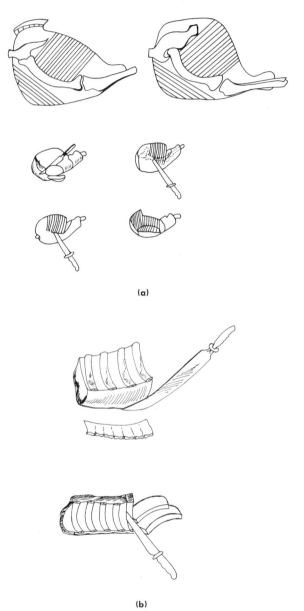

(a)

(b)

FIG. 9-16   (a) The carving of a leg of lamb is shown by the diagram on the left; the method for carving a ham or leg of pork is shown on the right. (b) The proper method to carve any rib section is to remove the chine bone first, as shown in the upper part of this illustration, and then to carve down through the ribs, as shown in the bottom part.

Barbecueing²

Broiled or roasted meats basted with a tangy sauce—and meats cooked on a spit or rotisserie before an open fire or cooked in a covered pit—are called barbecued. All are served with a tangy barbecue sauce.

Sautéing

Any method of cooking meat in a thin layer of fat is called sautéing or frying. A frying pan or a griddle is used. To pan-fry, select a low-edged heavy skillet or frying pan made of good heat-conducting metal. Three types of pan are used. One is straight-edged with no handle. Another is straight-edged with a handle. Either is used when foaming is a problem or when foods must be sautéed, covered, and cooked. The slanted type with a handle is the most frequently used for sautéing, however, since this pan is easy to get into with a spatula. Fit the pan to the quantity to be fried. Some pans used for batch frying may be 12 to 14 inches or even larger in diameter. The smaller or thinner the item to be sautéed, the more rapid should be its cooking. Have the fat hot when the food is placed onto the griddle or into the pan, sliding it easily into the fat to prevent splashing. Cook approximately to half-done and turn. Add fat as required.

Thick foods may be sautéed or grilled, then finished in an oven or covered in a pan and cooked over low heat to tenderize. Some added moisture

---

²To build a barbecue pit, dig a pit 4½ feet deep and 3 feet wide. Vary the length to suit the numbers to be served. It is better to have three 16 foot pits than one 50 foot pit for 3000 people. Select soil that is firm, will not crumble easily, and will give good straight sides. Locate in a well drained area so that if it rains, the pits will not flood. Pile dirt three feet from the pit. Select ash, birch, apple, or other hard wood cut into about two-foot lengths and about an arm thick. Pile it six feet from the pit. For each pit have two spades, a shovel, a rake, a hoe, and a five-tined fork. Dump close to each pit about a yard of fine, dry sand or washed pea gravel. For every two feet of pit length have one two-inch pipe six feet long and enough corrugated tin or aluminum roofing to cover the pit.
Size boned meat in solid chunks in six- or seven-pound pieces. Season with salt and pepper, and put each piece in a double stockinette. Then wrap in aluminum foil or in parchment paper and tie with a string. Start the pit fire three to five hours before the meat goes into it. Stir frequently to induce good burning. When only glowing embers remain, about six to 24 inches deep, use a rake to remove the unburned wood. Then cover the embers with a thin layer of sand or gravel. Lower the meat carefully onto this bed, allowing space between pieces, and have no piece touch the side of the pit. Lay pipes across the pit two feet apart and cover with corrugated roofing extending it from one to 1½ feet over the sides of the pit on all sides. Cover tightly with 10 to 12 inches of dirt, sealing in the entire top. If any steam escapes, seal in the spot. Allow the meat eight hours to cook.
For each six feet of pit have two people to slice for serving. Give each a slicing knife, a cutting board, and a table. Slice and set meat onto trays. Cover thinly sliced hot meat generously with hot barbecue sauce and serve. Slice some ahead. Best speed is achieved if foods are dispensed by servers rather than allowing self-service. Provide coffee and self-service items twenty feet away from the main serving tables. If there are young people, reduce coffee and provide half-pint cartons of milk or bottles of pop. Plan for heating water for coffee and barbecue sauce. Plan for paper supplies required. By allowing additional pit, potatoes wrapped in aluminum foil may be roasted.

FIG. 9-17 The incorrect way to dry-roast a tender piece of beef is shown. Instead, turn the fat side up. Some roasts that lack fat may be barded—that is, strips of fat may be placed over them to give moisture in baking. Select the right-size pan for roasting. Fill the pan without crowding the roasts. Also, use a trivet so that the roasts will not rest on the bottom of the pan and will keep out of the drippings.

(a)   (b)

(c)   (d)

(e)   (f)

FIG. 9-18   (a) Barbecue pits constructed for permanent use. Heavy, quarter-inch iron plates are used instead of corrugated materials. No pipes need be placed over the pits to hold up this type of cover. (b) Putting the meat into double stockinettes. The meat for this barbecue was the inside rounds of elk. (c) Wrapping the elk in foil previous to placing it in the pits. Heavy wet cloths may also be used. (d) Crowds gather as the fires burn through the night to provide a deep bed of hot coals. (e) Knocking down the coals with a cover of pea gravel. The meat is placed on top of this cover. (f) Placing the elk on the bed of gravel about 12 hours before serving time.

FIG. 9-19 Types of sauté pans that can be used in quantity foods. The deep, straight-sided pan is used when frying fat may boil up. The straight-sided black iron pan (center) is good for frying items which must be covered later. The two aluminum pans have sloped sides, which makes it easier for the worker to work on the product during frying. Aluminum is an excellent heat conductor.

Table 9-4
Quantities for a Barbecue

Items Required	Numbers to Be Served							
	100	300	500	750	1000	1500	2000	3000
Meat, boned, lb	75	200	350	500	650	1000	1300	1600
Salad Materials								
Lettuce, lb AP	25	75	125	180	250	400	500	750
Fresh tomatoes, lb AP	6	18	30	45	75	100	150	200
French dressing, gal	1	1½	2¼	3	4	5¼	7½	11
Vinegar, gal	¼	½	1	1½	2	2	3	4
Salt, lb	2	3	4	6	7½	10	15	20
Black pepper, lb	1	1	2	2	3	3	6	9
Coffee, lb*	2½	7	12	17	25	37	50	75
Cream, qt	2	5	8	12	16	24	32	48
Sugar, cube, lb	2	3½	5	8	10	15	20	30
Pickles, dill, gal	1	3	5	8	10	15	20	30
Buns, flat type, each	200	600	1000	1500	2000	3000	4000	6000
Cupcakes	100	300	500	750	1000	1500	2000	3000
Butter, lb	4	8	10	13	18	25	36	48
Barbecue Sauce, gal	1	3	5	7	10	15	20	30
Potatoes, 6 oz each	100	300	500	750	1000	1500	2000	3000
Length of pit, feet	4	6	8	13	16	25	30	50
Wood, hard, lb	1200	1800	2400	3600	4000	7500	9000	15000

*Substitute instant coffee 1¼ ounces per gallon of boiling water.

(Source: American Lamb Council)

(a)

FIG. 9-20 (a) Sautéing lamb chops on a griddle. Note the small quantity of fat used with these chops. Their natural fat content provides all the fat required for their cooking. (Courtesy National Livestock and Meat Board) (b) Frequently items are sautéed in pans as shown here. This makes it possible to fry in a larger quantity of fat. These cube steaks will later be tenderized by braising in the oven.

(b)

upon covering may be required if this is done. When large quantities of foods are sautéed, prepare in this manner. Recrisping is possible just before service by uncovering and drying the items out in a hot oven. Fish is frequently salted five to 10 minutes before it is sautéed. Sometimes fish is marinated five minutes in lemon juice, worcestershire sauce, and salt and pepper, and then sautéed. Sautéed fish may be called pan-fried or *a la meunière*. If the latter, *meunière* butter is poured over the fish just before service. The making of pan gravy for sautéed items has been described in Chapter 4.

If breaded or batter-covered foods or eggs are grilled, allow three to four ounces of oil per square foot of griddle; if the foods are not covered with batter or breading, use two to three ounces. Spread the oil lightly over the surface. Some chefs spread oil with an oil mop around the edges of the food during frying. Oil gives rapid heat conduction from the griddle to the food. Supply oil according to the fat content of the product. Bacon, unbreaded pork chops, and other fatty items will not require much oil.

Table 9-5

Recommended Quantities of Fat for Sautéing

Pan Size (diameter in inches)	Uncovered Foods	Breaded or Batter-Covered Foods
8	3 T	⅓ c
9	¼ c	⅓ c
10	⅓ c	½ c
12	½ c	⅔ c

Temperatures Recommended for Pan Sautéing and Grilling

Food Item	Temperature ° F	Approximate Cooking Time in Minutes
Griddle cakes	350-360	3 to 4
Eggs, fried	325	3 to 4
Bacon, ham, or sausages	325	4 to 5 (thick portions more)
Steak, ½ in. thick	340	10 to 15 (well done)
Steak, 1 in. thick	330	10 to 15 (medium)
Steak, over 1 in. thick	320	10 to 15 (rare)
Pork or veal cutlets	300-325	6 to 8
Small fish or fillets	350	10 to 15
Small steaks or chops	340	10 to 15

Deep-Frying

Cooking foods in fat deep enough to cover them is called deep-frying. They are usually popular menu items. To achieve consistently satisfactory results, proper frying procedures must be used, and a knowledge of some of the properties of oils or fats is helpful in obtaining desired results.

Table 9-6

Problem, Causes, and Corrections in Pan and Griddle Sautéing

Problem	Cause	Correction
Food sticks	1. Not enough fat	Use more fat or oil
	2. Food too cold	Thaw or warm food slightly
	3. Surface needs conditioning	Condition with fat as directed above
	4. Surface too hot or cold	Adjust temperature
Food burns	1. Surface too hot	Adjust heat.
Food doesn't brown	1. Surface too cold	Adjust heat.
Spattering	1. Moist foods added to too hot fat	Drain moist foods thoroughly; reduce cooking temperature.
Foods not crisp	1. Food too cold	Warm food
	2. Insufficient fat	Add more fat
	3. Too low cooking temperature	Adjust heat

(Adapted from Procter and Gamble, *Proper Frying*)

There is little chemical difference between a fat and an oil. Physically there is more, for at room temperature a fat is solid and an oil is liquid. Some oils become solid when refrigerated.

Fats and oils are triglycerides or esters formed when three fatty acids combine with a glycerol radical as follows:

```
    H
H   C————————C–C–C–C–C–C–C–C–C–C–C–C–C–C–C  (etc.)
H   C————————C–C–C–C–C–C–C–C–C–C–C–C–C–C–C  (etc.)
H   C————————C–C–C–C–C–C–C–C–C–C–C–C–C–C–C  (etc.)
    H
glycerol                    three fatty acid chains
radical
```

In a good fat, the three fatty acids are long carbon chains. One of the carbon chains may appear as follows

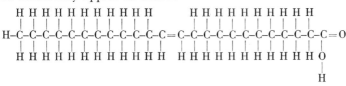

It will be noted that some carbons in this chain are joined in four different

places, thus, $-\overset{|}{\underset{|}{C}}-$, while one carbon in the center of the chain is joined $-\overset{|}{C}=$.

The latter has one less H or hydrogen attached to it. The first carbon is said to be attached to the chain in a *single* or *saturated* bond, while the latter is said to be attached by a *double* or *unsaturated* bond.[3] When fats or oils are hydrogenated, they are treated so as to break this double bond and add the missing hydrogen to the carbon, thus making a single or saturated bond at this point. Double bonds are weak points in a chain, for it is there that fats break up in deep-fat frying or where fats will add oxygen to become rancid. When a fat breaks down into a chain of seven or less carbons, it has a very disagreeable flavor.

When a fat or oil is hydrogenated, it becomes more firm. (It may also be dehydrogenated to make it softer or more plastic.) Fats containing long carbon chains tend to be more firm than fats containing short ones. By varying the length of the carbon chains or by varying their degree of saturation, many different types of fats can be manufactured for general use, for deep-frying, or for baking use. Shortenings should be selected for their specific uses. Manufacturers may add anti-oxidants to fats to retard oxidation

---

[3]Animal fats are more saturated than vegetable, poultry, or fish fats. A polyunsaturated fat is one with two or more unsaturated bonds. Fish and some vegetable oils are polyunsaturated.

or rancidity, or may add silicon or other compounds to give them greater stability in frying. Emulsifiers, usually monoglycerides or diglycerides, may be added to some fats to make them better for baking use. While free fatty acids in a fat increase its shortening power, a factor desirable in making pie crust, manufacturers remove these in a frying fat, for free fatty acids cause the fats to break down more quickly when heated.

Fats and oils must receive proper treatment in quantity food preparation. High temperatures and exposure to air or light speed oxidation. A large surface area exposed to air will also increase rancidity development. Metals such as copper, brass, or iron encourage breakdown, and copper is twenty times worse than iron. Curing salts, cooking salts, and other compounds speed breakdown. For this reason, salty foods fried in fat or foods salted over frying fat will encourage the fat breakdown. Poultry, pork, and some fish fats grow rancid more quickly than beef or lamb fats. Mixtures of fats or oils grow rancid more quickly than do individual fats.

Some fats may develop off-flavors by losing oxygen, a process called *reversion*. It is first detected as a beany flavor, then as a metallic one, and finally as a fishy flavor. Potato chips with a noticeable fishy flavor may be fried not in fish oil, as is suspected, but in soybean oil, which reverts easily unless especially treated. Salting favors reversion. Enzymes called *lipases* may develop off-flavors in fats, a phenomenon sometimes seen in butter or cheese made from unpasteurized milk or cream. Molds may grow in fats that are high in moisture. When fats are heated, broken-down fat products may join together in a process called polymerization. The products formed are waxes, resins, or gums and may be seen as gummy substances on griddles, deep-fat frying kettles, and broilers. Many polymers give off-flavors to fats.

Animal fats (such as butter, lard, chicken fat, and suet) and vegetable oils (such as olive oil) contain fairly large quantities of free fatty acids. This makes them poor frying fats, for they lower the smoking temperature and encourage breakdown. If foods high in free fatty acids, such as pork, mackerel, and bacon, are fried in a good fat, they lose some of their free fatty acids into the frying fat and speed its breakdown.

Other factors that cause frying fats to break down are: (1) high cooking temperatures, (2) moisture, (3) flour, crumbs, or other free food particles in the fat, (4) emulsifiers added to give improved baking quality to bakeshop shortenings, and (5) too large a surface area in relation to the mass of fat used (fat breaks down more quickly in a shallow frying pan than does the same amount of fat in a smaller, deeper pan). To obtain the best results in deep-fat frying or sautéing, select a frying fat designed for this use. Give fats proper care, and use proper frying techniques.

(a)   (b)

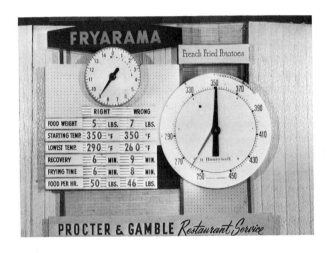

(c)

FIG. 9-21   Overloading a fryer can produce a poor product as well as reduce production. (a) Frying baskets filled properly. (b) Frying baskets filled improperly. (c) This
picture shows the results of the right and wrong ways of frying potatoes. Note how a seven-
pound load dropped the frying temperature to $260°$ F, giving poor frying temperature,
compared with 290° F resulting when only five pounds were fried. Time for frying the
correct amount was six minutes, compared with eight minutes when the fryer was over-
loaded. At this rate, 50 pounds of potatoes could be fried per hour, giving a good quality
product, compared with only 46 pounds of a poorer quality product. (Courtesy Procter &
Gamble)

If a solid fat is used for frying, pack it around the heating elements of the fryer, and set the fryer at 200° F. Allow the fat to melt and flow around the elements. Do not underfill or overfill. Refill as the level of fat falls in frying. If the quantities to be fried vary, install several small fryers rather than one large one, so that during periods of low demand, only one needs to be operated. Since breaded foods cause fats to break down more quickly, some operators reserve one kettle of a group for frying such foods.

To heat a fat for frying, raise the temperature slowly, but not above 400° F. When heated to too high a temperature, fat smokes, giving off a thin, bluish-white vapor. This first trace of smoke is said to be the *smoking point* and indicates that the fat is breaking down. A good deep-frying fat, when fresh, should not smoke below 450° F. The smoke contains acrolein, which has a sharp, pungent, acrid odor, irritating to the eyes and mucous membranes. When fat breaks down from heat, off-flavors from rancidity, reversion, polymerization, and short-chain fats may occur. The free fatty acid content also increases, which in turn speeds the fat breakdown even more.

Select the correct frying temperature. Too cold a fat gives a poor color to the fat and a greasy, soggy product. Too high a temperature burns the food and overbrowns it without properly cooking the food inside. Use food pieces of the same size and kind so as to obtain uniform cooking and browning. Avoid filling the basket too full, for frying too much food at one time lowers the temperature excessively. Some foods, such as breaded foods, should be in single layers in the basket, and they should not touch. Foods at room temperature speed frying, for cold foods chill the fat. Fry at the proper temperature—and use a thermometer to check the temperature, even though the fryer has a thermostat.

To start frying, lower the basket carefully into the fat, and avoid spillover from boiling up. Shake the basket occasionally to prevent the pieces from sticking together. The fat should cover the food. Fry until golden brown in color. Lift the basket and drain well. Spill into a pan, or place on absorbent brown paper, and salt. Serve fried foods hot.

Strain the frying fats frequently to remove sediment, filtering them at around 200° F. Handle carefully. Use several thicknesses of cheesecloth, a special filter bag, or a special filtering machine. If sediment still remains when the fat is below 200° F, sprinkle lightly with water. Allow the water to carry fine particles of burned material to the bottom. Pour or siphon the clear fat from this water sludge. If a solid fat is used, it may be allowed to solidify; then the sludge is easily removed. Any undesirable portions may be cut from this solid chunk.

Keep frying kettles and equipment used in frying clean. Clean the fryer regularly, and boil it out thoroughly at least once a week with a detergent compound especially designed for this. After the detergent has cleaned the kettle, rinse thoroughly; then fill the fry kettle with clear water and bring the water to a boil at least twice. A little vinegar in the last rinse water will neutralize any alkalinity left from the detergent. Dry thoroughly before adding fat. If fat breaks down quickly, check to see whether wire baskets, thermostats, or other parts contain exposed copper or brass.

FIG. 9-22 Good equipment properly maintained is necessary if good results are to be obtained in deep-fat frying.

FIG. 9-23   Breaded foods contaminate a frying fat quickly. Strain often to remove crumbs. Also, shake off excess crumbs before adding food to fat.

(a)   (b)

FIG. 9-24   (a) If solid fat is used, set the fryer at low heat and allow the fat to melt completely before raising the heat. (b) Fryers left in this condition soon contain poor frying fat. Sediment and crumbs are frequently significant factors in contributing to fat breakdown.

The old-fashioned frying kettle is seldom used, but if it is, select one with straight or almost straight sides to minimize boiling over. It should be large enough to permit bubbling up after the food is added. Fill with fat or oil to about half full. Use a basket fitted to the kettle. If of heavy-gage material with good heat conductivity, the kettle will perform more satisfactorily. The amount of fat to surface area should be large. See that the bottom of the kettle is flat so heating is even. If the kettle is used over a gas burner, do not allow the flame to rise around the sides and set fire to the grease.

Fat and oil are highly combustible, and grease fires can be very dangerous. Handle fats with care. Never overheat; never allow fats or oils to come into contact with open flames or materials at high temperatures. Lower wet foods into fryers with care. Never leave a fryer or pan of grease unattended

FIG. 9-25 A good quality frying fat is being used to fry potatoes. Note bubbling of the fat rather than foaming. Note also that the potatoes are not over-crowded in the basket. (Courtesy Procter & Gamble)

over heat. Keep handles of sauté pans or other utensils containing deep fat turned inward except when in use.

If the frying fat receives proper care in deep-frying, it will never have to be discarded; only filtering will be necessary. Good management in deep-frying will keep the volume of food produced high enough to use up the fat in the kettle before it deteriorates. Fresh fat is added as fried foods absorb the old fat. Replacement of fat in this manner is called turnover. Minimum turnover each day should be 15 to 20% of the total fat in the kettle. Ten pounds of potatoes absorb one pound of fat in frying. Batter-covered or breaded foods absorb two ounces more per ten pounds fried. Keep volume of food used to fat in the fryer at the proper ratio. Size fryers to production need. Fryers that cook a large quantity of food efficiently will give proper turnover. If a small ratio of food to fat is used, the turnover rate will drop below that desired. About $1\frac{1}{2}$ to 2 times the weight of the fat in the fryer can be fried in food in an hour. The ratio of food to fat cooked in a fryer will be about 1:10 in the old-fashioned kettle and 1:5 to 1:8 in the newer types; in the latter, potatoes may be 1:6. Overloading a fryer may drop the temperature to such a point that excessive grease absorption occurs. This results in a high fat loss and grease-soaked foods. Greasy foods result when poor equipment, poor frying fat, or poor frying techniques are used. The type and condition of the food fried will also be a factor in grease absorption. Further discussion of factors influencing grease absorption in frying foods will be found in the chapter on desserts.

Correct prepreparation of the foods is an important factor in producing good quality deep-fried products. This may be simple for some foods, but for others considerable treatment may be required before the foods are ready for frying.

Breading, batter-dipping, or wrapping in dough may be preliminary treatments. Such coatings contribute flavor, color, and texture and preserve shape. They may also act as protective coatings. Not all foods are suitable for covering and frying. The product must cook inside while the outer covering cooks. Some foods may be cooked by other means before or after deep-frying.

The quantity of coating used will vary with the size of the product, the thickness of the coating, and the surface area. Excessive cover to extend a product is not to be condoned. Heavy covers are apt to be tough and dark and will separate easily from the product. Small items, such as shrimp, fish sticks, and oysters, should have a ratio of cover to product of not more than 1:2, while larger products, such as veal cutlets and croquettes, usually have a ratio of not more than 1:3 or 1:4. On the average, 100 pounds of batter or crumbs will cover 200 to 400 pounds of food. Chicken and other simi-

larly lightly breaded items should not increase in weight more than 10 to
15%. Dough-wrapped products should be in the dough-to-product ratio
of 1:1 or 1½:1. High-moisture foods require a heavier and tighter cover
than foods with a lower moisture content. Firmness of the food is a factor,
firmer foods requiring less cover. Covering foods may require considerable
labor, and good work centers and good production techniques should be
planned.

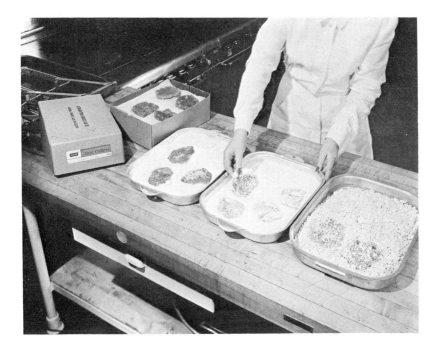

FIG. 9-26   The proper method to bread a product is shown; flour first, then egg wash, and
finally crumbs. (Courtesy Armour & Co.)

Breading is one of the most common coatings used for foods. There
are usually three steps: flouring, moistening, and crumbing. Paprika for
color and seasonings for flavor may be added to the flour. The flour absorbs
the moistening agent used in the second step, thus setting up a good base for
the adherence of the crumbs added in the last step. Milk, water, or other
liquids, or a liquid combined with egg, or egg alone is used for moistening.
Moisteners containing milk give a less crisp crust than those made from
water or eggs. Moisteners form the strongest to the least strong cover in the

Table 9-7

Deep-Frying Temperatures and Times[1]

Type of Food	Frying Temperature ° F	Frying Time (minutes)
Potatoes:		
One operation, ½ in. cut	350	7
One operation, ⅜ in. cut	350	6
One operation, ¼ in. cut	350	5
One operation, ⅛ in. cut	360	4
One operation, ⅛ in. cut completely crisp	330	6 to 9
Two operation, ½ in. cut to ⅜ in. cut		
Blanch	350	4
Brown	350	3
Two operation, ¼ in. cut		
Blanch	350	2½
Brown	350	2½
Two operation, ⅛ in. cut		
Blanch	360	2½
Brown	360	2½
Frozen, blanched, ⅜ in. cut	350	2
Seafoods:		
Frozen breaded shrimp	350	4
Fresh breaded shrimp	350	3
Frozen fish fillets	350	4
Fresh fish fillets	350	3
Breaded clams	350	1
Breaded oysters	350	3 to 5
Fresh breaded scallops	350	4
Frozen fish sticks	350	4
Abalone, breaded	375	2 to 3
Sliced fish, breaded	350	6 to 8
Chicken: (1½ to 2 lb, sectioned)		
Raw	325	12 to 15
Steamed 20 min, then breaded	350	3 to 4
Miscellaneous:		
Breaded veal cutlets	350	3 to 4
Breaded onion rings	350	3
Croquettes, meat	350	3 to 4
Precooked cauliflower, breaded	350	3
Eggplant, breaded, raw	350	3
Tamale sticks, breaded	350	3
French-toasted sandwiches	350	1 to 2
Yeast-raised doughnuts	350	1 to 3
Hand-cut cake doughnuts	350	1 to 3
Glazed cinnamon apple rings	300	3 to 5
Corn-on-the-cob	300	3
Fritters	350	3
Turnovers, meat	350	5 to 7

(Adapted from Procter and Gamble, *Deep Frying Pointers*)

Note: The potato ratio should be 1:6 in the new type of fast-recovery kettles and 1:8 in the old type of kettles. If smaller loads of potatoes are used, use slightly lower temperatures.

[1] See also Table 8-6 for deep-frying of vegetables.

following order: eggs, eggs and liquid, evaporated milk, other liquids. The crumbs used may be cracker, bread, other cereals, or prepared mixes. The particle size should be even; sift if necessary to give uniformity. The finer the crumbs, the firmer will be the coating. Products should be placed on a rack and allowed to dry after breading. If placed in pans, sprinkle a few crumbs on the pan bottoms first to avoid bottom soaking. them to avoid bottom soaking.

Breadings are modified to suit the type of food. Veal cutlets, oysters, tomatoes, eggplant, croquettes, partially cooked cauliflower, and other products having some firmness may be breaded in a standard manner. Some products such as onion rings and oily fish and some vegetables high in moisture may be best dipped into flour in the third step and not into crumbs. This gives less grease absorption than crumbs and a product similar to one that has been batter-dipped. Some meat and fish may be only covered with flour,

Table 9-8
Problems, Causes, and Corrections in Deep-Frying

Problem	Causes	Corrections
Objectional smoke	1. Temperature too high. 2. Failure to strain fat frequently. 3. Old fat.	Use lower temperature; strain fat and store in cool place after use. Set up filtering schedule; check fat turnover.
Fat bubbles over	1. Too much fat in kettle. 2. Too much food in kettle. 3. Excessive moisture in food.	Check fill of deep kettle; add smaller quantities to be fried in basket; drain batter-dipped or egg-and-crumbed foods dry potatoes thoroughly.
Foods not crisp	1. Frying temperature too low.	Use high temperature for frying; use frying thermometer or check temperature with bread cube.
Strong flavor and color	1. Old fat or deteriorated fat. 2. Wrong fat for frying.	Keep used fat in cool place; select proper type of frying fat; strain after use; if too many strongly flavored foods must be fried in fat, discard after use.
Excessive foaming	1. Failure to strain fat. 2. Deteriorated fat. 3. Extremely cold foods added to hot fat. 4. Too much egg and crumb or batter. 5. Frying temperature too low.	Strain fat before storing in cool place; do not take foods direct from refrigerator to kettle; drain batter-dipped or egg-and-crumbed foods; use correct temperature for frying; use thermometer or check temperature with bread cube; discard deteriorated fat.

(Adapted from Procter and Gamble, *Proper Frying*)

FIG. 9-27   Flouring for sautéing is accomplished as shown here. These liver slices will be ovenized after fat has been drizzled over the slices. An oven at about 375° F is used. (Courtesy Armour & Co.)

a process called *flouring*, and the method of frying may then be sautéing or grilling rather than deep-frying.

Check the accuracy of thermostats on deep-fryers by using a thermometer. If thermometers are not available, use the bread-cube test. A one-inch cube of soft bread will become a delicate brown in 1 minute 15 seconds in fat at 350 to 360° F, 1 minute at 360 to 370° F, 40 seconds at 375 to 385° F, and 20 seconds at 385 to 400° F. Escoffier says fat "is moderately hot when, after a sprig of parsley or a crust of bread is thrown into it, it begins to bubble immediately; it is hot if it crackles when a slightly moist object is dropped into it; it is very hot when it gives off a thin white smoke perceptible to the smell."

Do not allow loose crumbs or batter to drop into the fryer. Before adding a breaded object, shake it free of crumbs; allow batter-dipped items to drain well before dropping them into the fat. Many breaded items may be placed in baskets and then lowered into the fat, but the basket should be lowered and batter-dipped items dropped into the fat. This keeps them from sticking to the basket. Keep moisture content of foods to be fried

FIG. 9-28 Two shapes used for deep-fried turnovers. (Courtesy Procter & Gamble)

(a)

(b)

FIG. 9-29   (a) These apple-stuffed pork chops have been ovenized. (Courtesy Processed
Apples Institute) (b) The liver shown being floured in Figure 9-27 is shown here after
ovenizing. (Courtesy Armour & Co.)

as low as possible. Fry at the correct temperature. Too low a frying temperature causes grease-soaking and a loosened cover. Excess temperatures leave foods uncooked in the centers. Do not crowd foods in frying baskets so that unevenness of cooking and coloring result and sticking together will be avoided. Add about one pound of covered food for each six or seven pounds of fat in the kettle. Upon completion of frying, lift the basket and give it a shake to remove excess fat, but do not shake it hard enough to break the covering. Then turn the food onto a flat, warm surface. Salt, if desired. These items will usually hold crispness about five minutes. If necessary to hold longer, keep in a warm, dry place. If frozen breaded products are to be deep-fried, allow them to stand a short time at room temperature to partially thaw, and then deep-fry as for any other breaded product.

Ovenizing

The term *ovenizing* is a coined term used to describe a process in which meats are baked by being placed on well greased baking sheets or pans and then put into an oven so that they fry or sauté. Breaded veal cutlets and other flesh foods requiring a high amount of fat for frying in this manner may have fat drizzled over them in addition to the pan greasing. In total, the quantity of fat required is less than that required for sautéing. Oven temperatures are usually from 325 to 425° F. Smaller foods are ovenized at higher temperatures than larger foods. Ovenizing may be used to process a larger quantity of foods for service than can be prepared by pan-sautéing or grilling.

Moist Heat Cooking

Braising

Meat cooked in its own juices or in a bit of added moisture is called braised meat. Stewing, pot roasting, fricasseeing, and swissing are forms of braising. If stewing or simmering differs in any respect from other braising, it is that a larger quantity of moisture is used. Many meats are braised in covered pots called braisers or casseroles, which have straight sides about six to eight inches high; but when large quantities must be prepared, roasting pans and the oven, large pots, or steam-jacketed kettles are used. Marinating may occur before braising, such as the several-day marinade used for *sauerbraten*. Lean meat may be blended with some fat meat to give it moistness, or it may be larded. Browning may or may not occur. If unbrowned, the braised item is called "blond" or "white," such as a blond or white stew or fricassee. Braised meats are usually served with vegetables. If served without vegetables in an earthenware casserole, the correct menu term is *en casserole*; if with vegetables, the proper term is *en cocotte*. *Jugged* means

Table 9-9

Timetable for Braising

Cut	Average Weight or Thicknes	Approximate Cooking Time
Pot roast	3 to 5 lb	3 to 4 hr
Pot roast	5 to 15 lb	3 to 5 hr
Swiss steak	1 to 2½ in.	2 to 3 hr
Round steak or flank steak	½ in. (pounded)	45 min to 1 hr
Stuffed steak	½ to ¾ in	1½ hr
Short ribs	Pieces 2 x 2 x 2 in.	1½ to 2 hr
Fricassee	1 to 2 in. pieces	2 to 3 hr
Beef birds	½ x 2 x 4 in.	1½ to 2 hr
Stuffed lamb breast	2 to 3 lb	1½ to 2 hr
Rolled lamb breast	1½ to 2 lb	1½ to 2 hr
Lamb shanks	½ lb each	1 to 1½ hr
Lamb neck slices	½ to ¾ in.	1 to 1½ hr
Lamb riblets	¾ x 2½ x 3 in.	2 to 2½ hr
Pork chops or steaks	¾ to 1 in.	45 min to 1 hr
Spareribs	2 to 3 lb	1½ hr
Stuffed veal breast	3 to 4 lb	1½ to 2 hr
Rolled veal breast	2 to 3 lb	2 to 3 hr
Veal cutlets	½ x 3 x 5½ in.	45 min to 1 hr
Veal steaks or chops	½ to ¾ in.	45 min to 1 hr
Veal birds	½ x 2 x 4 in.	45 min to 1 hr

(Courtesy National Livestock and Meat Board)

Table 9-10

(Large Cuts and Stews)

Cut	Average Size or Average Weight	Approximate Cooking Time	
		Min per lb	Total hr
Fresh beef	4 to 8 lb	40 to 50	3 to 4
Corned beef	6 to 8 lb	40 to 50	4 to 6
Fresh pork	Weight desired	30	
Smoked whole ham	12 to 16 lb	18 to 20	4 to 5
Smoked half ham	6 to 8 lb	25	2½ to 3½
Smoked picnic	4 to 8 lb	35 to 45	3 to 4½
Stew, lamb or veal	1 to 2 in. cubes		1½ to 2
Stew, beef	1 to 2 in. cubes		2 to 3

(Courtesy National Livestock and Meat Board)

braised, as in "jugged hare." To *poëler* means to brown the meat well and then braise it in its own juices while basting with butter; temperatures of cooking are high, and the process is partly roasting, partly sautéing, and partly braising.

The size of braised meat may vary, as in pot roasts, swiss steak, or one-inch cubes of stew meat. Poultry is portioned so it can be served as cooked.

(a) (b)

FIG. 9-30 (a) Chicken may be placed on large baking sheets after being seasoned and sprinkled with paprika, and ovenized. This method of baking is also called "banquet style" preparation. (b) The chicken after ovenizing. (Courtesy Procter & Gamble)

FIG. 9-31 Vegetables are being added to the browned meat prior to finishing by braising. The gravy is thickened just before service. (Courtesy Armour & Co.)

(a)

(b)

FIG. 9-32 (a) Pot roasts or stews may be satisfactorily browned in a steam-jacketed kettle, as shown here. (b) Some flesh foods may be toughened by too long cooking or too high a cooking temperature, such as the oysters being boiled here. The best method for moist-cooking such foods is to poach lightly.

Oftentimes, before braising, the meat is floured, especially if browning is to occur. The meat should fill the pan or container well so it builds up moisture around the meat in cooking. Browning may be accomplished over direct heat, in an oven, or in a steam-jacketed kettle. Add enough fat to cover the bottom of a pan about ⅛ to ¼ inch, bring to about 350° F, and add the floured pieces of meat. When the meat is richly browned, add moisture, such as water, stock, milk, tomato juice, wine, or sour cream, or cover tightly and allow the meat to build up its own moisture. Diced or minced vegetables may be added for flavoring during the browning. After browning, the meat is simmered slowly until quite tender. If vegetables are served with the meat, they are usually added late in cooking so they will be unbroken and bright at service, or they may be cooked separately in stock and added with the meat at service. When the meat is tender, the cover may be removed and the liquid reduced until the stock is at the desired consistency. If necessary, the meat may be removed, the sauce thickened, and the meat returned to the gravy.

FIG. 9-33   Tough cuts may be made into a quality item by simmering. This brisket of beef has tenderness and flavor because of its proper preparation. (Courtesy Armour & Co.)

Meats and poultry in quantity are best braised in a shallow steam-jacketed kettle. The kettle should be heated, cover down, with steam on full. Then, with some melted fat added, drop in even-sized pieces of meat. Pot roasts should be evenly sized between five and 10 pounds. Next, turn the meat 15 to 25 minutes until all sides are well browned. Do not cover, and keep the steam on full. After browning, add a small quantity of liquid, cover, reduce the steam, and simmer. When done, remove the meat and make a gravy with the liquid.

Only firm-fleshed fish are braised. A straight-sided braising pan is used. Live, firm, fleshed fish may be stunned, scored (or crimped), dressed, and then soaked for a short time in cold water. This process toughens the flesh enough so that braising is possible.[4] Fat fish should be used; lean fish gives a dry product. Fish is usually skinned and left in fairly large pieces for braising. Liquids used for braising may be court bouillon or white wine. If the fish is browned and a brown roux is used, red wine may be used. Because of the short cooking time required, the cover may be off or loosely fitted so evaporation occurs to give a stock of proper flavor and body. A *matelote* is fish braised with vegetables, a sort of stew with thickened gravy. A *bouillabaisse* is also a fish stew but contains such a quantity of thin stock that it is oftentimes called a soup.

Simmering

Cooking meats in a large quantity of water or other liquid may be called poaching, boiling, stewing, or simmering. Few flesh foods should be boiled. To simmer, bring the water to a boil, add the product, and immediately drop the temperature to 185 to 250° F. Added flavor is gained if stocks or rich broths are used instead of water. Poultry should be simmered at around 190° F. Meats may be marinated, prebrowned in fat, and then simmered. Avoid heavy seasoning, since the stock may be reduced for other use. A fork may be inserted a half inch into the meat and twisted to see if it is tender. Small pieces of meat will be tender to the fork. Do not overcook and cause the meat to be dry and in shreds. As meat cooks, skim as often as necessary.

Vegetables are often boiled separately in stock and served with the meat. Time their cooking so they are done only at the time required. If cooked with the meat, add them about 30 minutes before serving time. Cabbage and some other vegetables that cook more quickly may be added even later than this. Meat may be sliced ahead of service and kept warm in some of the stock. Meat, fish, and poultry that are to be cooled and held should be cooled in their own stock or in cold water and then refrigerated.

[4]Cutting beef immediately after slaughter toughens it; crimping may cause the same reaction. See Belle Lowe, *Experimental Foods*, John Wiley & Sons, Inc., New York, p. 226.

The process of simmering fish is called poaching. A special pan equipped with a removable perforated bottom, called a trivet, is used so the fish can be lifted out without breaking. If this equipment is not available, use a shallow pan. Fish may be poached in the oven, on top of the range, in steamers, or in other equipment. To poach, before adding liquid to the pan, set the fish flat on the greased surface. Do not allow pieces to touch; a whole fish should fit freely in the pan. Use a good fish stock, salted water, court bouillon, wine, or other liquid. Mild-flavored fish may be cooked in a liquid of one-fourth milk and the remainder water. Large pieces of fish are best started in cold liquid; a hot liquid may encourage breaking up. If the fish is large, it may be scored deeply to aid in quick cooking. Strongly flavored fish are

| (a) | (b) |

FIG. 9-34 (a) Two items, tongue and hearts, which respond well to moist long-time cooking are shown being prepared for simmering. (b) Brisket also is excellent prepared in this manner. (Courtesy Armour & Co.)

also best started in a cold liquid. If small pieces are poached, set these into boiling liquid and immediately reduce the heat and simmer for about eight minutes. Some white-fleshed fish may be baked in milk in the oven. Fish cooked in liquids that do not contain milk are often served with a bit of rich court bouillon poured over them. For *garde manger* work, allow the fish to chill thoroughly in the stock before handling. Live fish may be killed, dressed, and immediately poached; this is a method called *au bleu* in the Continental kitchen.

Steaming

Meats, fish, or poultry may be steamed over rich stock, a process called free vent steaming, or they may be cooked in pressure steam chambers.

Pressure steaming reduces cooking time. Many meats may be given preliminary treatment, such as prebrowning, in an oven, for sautéing or broiling and then be finished in a steam chamber. Times must be accurately gaged to prevent overcooking in pressure steaming.

Blanching

Dropping into boiling water and removing or simmering to partial doneness is called blanching. Some presoaking in cold salted water may be a preliminary treatment. Blanching makes it possible to remove undesirable portions or to firm the product for handling. After blanching, the item is removed and plunged into cold water. Blanching is more a prepreparation treatment than cooking. Sweetbreads or brains may be blanched in slightly acidulated water to keep them white, and then chilled. The membranes are removed and cooking is then completed by another method.

Frozen Meat

Frozen meats may be cooked by the same methods as those used for nonfrozen meats. Better flavor and higher nutrient values are obtained if meat is cooked from the frozen or partially frozen state rather than from the

FIG. 9-35 Many meats can be prepared in the frozen or partially frozen state. Here we see partially thawed liver slices being separated for flouring. (Courtesy Armour & Co.)

completely thawed state. If completely thawed, procedures and times are the same as for regular meats. Meats that need shaping, grinding, or breading before cooking are thawed and then prepared as required.

Hard-frozen roasts require approximately one to three times as much

Table 9-11

Refrigerator Storage Time Chart

Refrigerator Temperature 36° to 40° F

MEAT (loosely covered)	Limit of Days for Maximum Quality
BEEF	
Standing Rib Roast	5 to 8 days
Steaks	3 to 5 days
Pot Roasts	5 to 6 days
Stew Meat	2 days
Ground Beef	2 days
Liver (sliced)	2 days
Heart	2 days
PORK	
Roasts	5 to 6 days
Chops	3 days
Spareribs	3 days
Pork Sausage	2 to 3 days
CURED AND SMOKED MEATS	
Hams, Picnics—	
whole or half	7 days
slices	3 days
Bacon	5 to 7 days
Dried Beef	10 to 12 days
Corned Beef	5 to 7 days
Tongue	6 to 7 days
LAMB	
Roasts	5 days
Chops	3 days
Heart	2 days
Liver (sliced)	2 days
VEAL	
Roasts	5 to 6 days
Chops	4 days
Liver (sliced)	2 days
Sweetbreads (cooked)	2 days
COOKED MEATS	
Home-cooked Meats	4 days
Hams, Picnics	7 days
Franks	4 to 5 days
Meat Loaves (sliced)	3 to 4 days
Luncheon Meats (sliced)	3 days
Bologna Loaves (unsliced)	4 to 6 days
Dry and Semi-dry Sausage (uncut)	2 to 3 weeks
Liver Sausage (sliced)	2 to 3 days
Liver Sausage (uncut)	4 to 6 days
POULTRY	
Chickens (drawn, whole)	2 days
Chickens (cut-up)	2 days
Turkeys (drawn)	2 days
Ducklings (drawn, whole)	2 days
Cooked Poultry	3 to 4 days

(Courtesy Swift & Co.)

roasting time per pound as refrigerated meats. Prepare frozen meats for roasting in the same way used for other meats. Place fat side up into a pan and then into a 325° F oven, and cook until thawed. At this time, the thermometer may be inserted into the meat. Then roast from 300° F to 350° F. Thin frozen steaks will require only slightly longer broiling or pan broiling time than regular steaks, but thicker steaks will require one to

Table 9-12

Freezer Storage Time Chart

Freezer Temperature 0° F or Colder

Meat in Freezer Wrapping	Limit of Time for Maximum Quality
Beef (steaks, roast)	6 to 8 months
Lamb	6 to 7 months
Veal	3 to 4 months
Pork (fresh)	3 to 4 months
Variety Meats	3 to 4 months
Chicken (ready to cook)	6 to 7 months
Turkey (ready to cook)	6 to 7 months
Ground Beef	3 to 4 months
Cooked Meats	3 to 4 months
Cooked Chicken	2 to 3 months
Cooked Turkey	2 to 3 months
Smoked Ham*	Not over 2 months
Sausage (fresh), Franks, Bologna*	Do not freeze
Sliced Bacon*	Do not freeze

*Cured and smoked meats, as well as salted meats, deteriorate rapidly in flavor when frozen.   (Courtesy Swift & Co.)

Table 9-13

Frozen Meat Cookery

Cut of Meat	Approx. Wt. of Cut	Cooking Temp. F	Cooking Time	Cooking Method
Swiss Steak	6 oz	360°	3 hr	Flour and brown; braise
Beef Rib Roast*	10 lb	300°	2½ hr	Roast
Beef Pot Roast*	10 lb		4½ to 5 hr	Braise
Luncheon Steak	5 oz	350°	5 to 7 min	Sauté or grill frozen
Hamburger Patties	3 oz	350°	3 to 4 min	Sauté or grill frozen
Beef Liver	5 oz	325°	8 to 10 min	Sauté or grill frozen
Grill Steaks	4 oz	350°	3½ to 5 min	Sauté or grill frozen
Cube Steaks	4 oz	350°	5 to 7 min	Sauté or grill frozen
Breaded Cutlets	3 to 4 oz	350°	4 to 6 min	Sauté or deep-fry
Lamb Loin Chops	5 oz	400°	8½ to 12 min	Grill or broil 5 in. from heat
Lamb Leg Roast*	7½ lb	325°	4½ hr	Roast; baste
Pork Chops	4 to 5 oz	400°	22 to 26 min	Grill or broil 6 in. from heat
Pork Loin Roast*	8 lb	300°	2½ to 3 hr	Roast; baste
Veal Leg Roast*	7 to 8 lb	300°	4 to 4½ hr	Roast; baste
Chicken Thigh	3 to 5 oz	325°	12 to 14 min	Deep-fry
Chicken Drumstick	2 to 3 oz	325°	12 to 14 min	Deep-fry
Chicken Breast	4 to 5 oz	325°	12 to 14 min	Deep-fry or sauté
Pot Pie	9 oz	425°	40 min	Bake frozen
Pot Pie	14 oz	425°	45 to 50 min	Bake frozen
Sausage, Brown-n-Serve	30 per lb	350°	3 to 4 min	Grill or sauté

Broiled Steaks, Frozen

Thickness (inches)	Doneness	Average Cooking Time (Minutes)	(Seconds)	Heat Control Setting	Distance from Heat (inches)
		(Electric Broiler)			
½	Rare	4	0	High	4
½	Medium	6	30	High	4
¾	Rare	6	30	High	5
¾	Medium	8	0	Medium	5
1	Rare	12	0	Medium	5
1	Medium	13	30	Medium	5
1¼	Rare	22	30	Medium	6
1¼	Medium	24	30	Medium	6
		(Gas Broiler)			
½	Rare	3	10	High	2
½	Medium	4	10	High	2
¾	Rare	5	30	High	3
¾	Medium	6	30	High	4
1	Rare	10	30	High	5½
1	Medium	11	30	High	5½
1¼	Rare	14	30	High	7¼
1¼	Medium	17	0	High	7¼

Note: Steaks 1½ inches thick or more should be partially thawed or thawed before broiling.   (Adapted from tables of Swift & Co.)

two times as much time. Place thin or medium frozen steaks four inches from the broiler heat and larger steaks farther away, about eight to 12 inches. Reduce heat and thaw. Place meats for pan-broiling in a pan or on a griddle at a slightly lower temperature than required for non-frozen meat, and cook until thawed. Then, broiling, pan-broiling, or grilling may proceed as for regular steaks. Sautéing may be preferred to pan-broiling because the steaks thaw more quickly. Sauté or grill frozen meats at lower than normal temperatures until thawed. To speed thawing place a cover over the pan or over the item on the grill or partially cook in 325° deep fat. To sauté or grill frozen breaded items, partially thaw before cooking. Braising small pieces of frozen meats takes only slightly longer than for unfrozen, but larger pieces take much longer. Brown while frozen. If the frozen pieces can be separated, they may be dredged with flour first, or they may have to be thawed first. The procedure is then the same as for regular meat. Simmering frozen meat in water differs in no way from handling unfrozen meat.

To thaw meat, leave it wrapped under refrigeration. Usually refrigerator thawing takes 1½ hours per pound in a piece, and thawing at room temperature about one hour per pound. If the meat is placed in front of an electric fan, it may be thawed in less time. Meat, if in waterproof wraps, may be placed under cool, running water. Do not thaw unwrapped meat in this manner. Time of thawing in water is approximately one hour to the pound.

Because of time required in equipment, it may not be possible to cook meats in the frozen state. Partial thawing reduces cooking time. For best results, it is recommended that this be done rather than attempt complete thawing.

BREAKFAST MEATS

Fast service is required at breakfast time. Customers are usually in a hurry and dislike waiting. Meats take time to cook, and for this reason some precooking is advised. Corn beef hash, steamed salt mackerel, finnan haddie, and other meats need prepreparation. Hash may be shaped ahead and browned so it needs only reheating. The mackerel and finnan haddie may be partially poached and left in hot water so they can be cooked in a few minutes. Thin ham slices are grilled rapidly to order, but thick ham slices may be cut into four-ounce portions, grilled, and placed in a steam table in a small amount of stock or water. Bacon may be placed on 18 by 26 inch baking sheets or wire racks and partially cooked in an oven; the grease is then poured off and the bacon stacked in a shallow pan. It then takes only a few minutes on the grill to crisp it. Some place a weight on the bacon

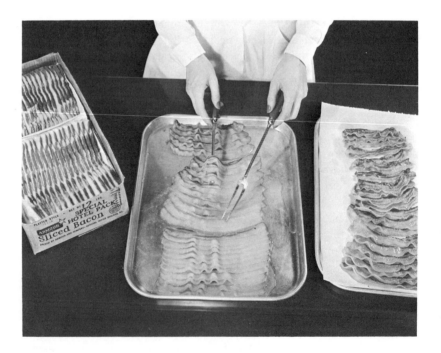

FIG. 9-36 Turning bacon onto a tray during oven-baking. Cooked bacon is shown on the right, draining on absorbent paper. (Courtesy Armour & Co.)

when grilling so it holds its shape. Sausages or sausage patties may be parboiled or steamed. Parboiling is usually from a cold-water start. Remove and hold, and then, as orders arrive, brown on the griddle. Some fry sausages and then hold a small quantity in the steam table. If necessary, they can be given a quick sauté before serving. Brown'n-serve sausages require three to four minutes browning under a broiler or on top of a griddle. About two minutes in deep fat will cook sausages, but the contamination of fat from the free fatty acids in the sausage will be so great that this method is not recommended.

POULTRY COOKERY

The flesh of poultry is much like meat, and methods of cooking it are much the same. Raw poultry is a highly perishable product; freshness is essential to a good quality cooked product. Fresh poultry should be delivered chilled and held at 34° F (40° F is too high). Storage time should not be more than four days. Hold frozen poultry at 0° F or lower. At 10° F frozen chicken will hold quality for eight months, while at 20° F, for only two to four months. Most frozen poultry must be defrosted to prepare it for cooking. To thaw, place in a 40° F refrigerated area. At this temperature chickens will thaw in one to two days, and larger birds will thaw in two to four days. Poultry may be left in its original moisture-vapor-proof wraps and defrosted under cool, running water; this takes one to two hours for chickens and two to six hours for turkeys. Directing fan-driven air on the birds reduces thawing time. To speed thawing, as soon as the legs are pliable, remove giblets and neck and spread the legs and wings. For more rapid

(a)   (b)

FIG. 9-37 Two chicken items prepared by sautéing and then finished by braising in the oven. (Courtesy Ocoma Company)

thawing, cut-up poultry may be separated at the crinkly thawed stage. Wash thawed poultry in cold water, drain, and then prepare for cooking. Never refreeze.

Cooking procedures for poultry are the same as those used for meat. Low-temperature roasting (250° F) gives less shrinkage and a moister and better-appearing product. Old birds are cooked by moist heat, while young birds may be cooked by dry heat. The larger the turkey, the greater the net yield of meat to bone. Turkeys at 18 pounds or above have about 9% skeletal structure to total dressed weight, regardless of size. The abdominal cavities of birds 20 to 30 pounds are about the same size. Most poultry is cooked well done, except some few, such as duck. Small birds, such as pigeons, squabs, quail, and game ducks, may be best cooked at temperatures of around 400° F rather than at lower temperatures. This reduces drying out during cooking. Rabbits are cooked in the same manner as poultry. Cooked poultry meat and its stock are highly perishable. Cool quickly to 140° F, then refrigerate. Use within 24 hours. Cover well to prevent drying out.

Roasting

Do not truss the legs or wings of large birds for roasting. Brush with fat, and season inside and out. Paprika may be added on the outside to aid in browning. Place in pans. Have pans full, but do not allow birds to touch. Large birds should be breast side down on a perforated bottom. Small birds may be breast up and covered with bacon, salt pork, or other fatty tissues, or covered with a cloth soaked in oil. Fat birds, such as geese and ducks, may be left breast side up and need no basting during roasting. Pour the fat from the birds as it accumulates. Sometimes ducks and geese are steamed almost to doneness and then finished by roasting. This method gives a less fatty flesh.

Place small birds in a preheated 325° oven and large ones in a 250° F oven, or in a 225° F oven if they can be roasted overnight or for long periods of time. When almost done, turn large birds breast side up and complete roasting, basting if necessary. Large birds at this point may have the legs broken away from the side. This gives a more rapid heat penetration into the thigh area. Large birds may be split in half lengthwise and roasted, or the breasts, legs, and wings may be roasted separately and the bony parts used for stock. Simmer giblets 1½ to 2½ hours for proper doneness.

Doneness of poultry may be indicated by a 180° F temperature in the center of the thigh or breast, or when the meat on the thigh or breast feels soft, or the leg joint gives readily, or a fork inserted into the shoulder muscle of the wing twists out easily. Some chefs like to roast large, tender birds

FIG. 9-38 Small poultry items should be roasted quickly and served at once. Here we see hot *sous cloche* bells being placed over small squabs prior to service.

slightly under-done, cool, and slice—and then, for service, to warm the slices in a rich stock. Banquet birds may be roasted slightly under-done, cooled, and sliced. The slices are then placed over mounds of dressing, dark meat first, finished with broad slices of white meat. Cover with a moist cloth and refrigerate. Just before service, cover and heat in an oven or steam chest; serve one mound per plate and cover with *very* hot gravy.

Table 9-14
Timetable for Roasting Poultry in a 325° F Oven

Ready-to-Cook Weight in lb	Approximate Minutes per lb	Total (hr)	Ready-to-Cook Weight in lb	Approximate Minutes per lb	Total (hr)
1⅓ to 2½	30 to 40	1 to 1¾	6 to 8	30 to 40	3½ to 4
2½ to 3½	30 to 40	1½ to 2½	8 to 10*	25 to 30	3 to 3½
3½ to 4¾	30 to 40	2 to 3	10 to 14*	18 to 20	3½ to 4
4¾ to 6	30 to 40	3 to 3½	14 to 18*	15 to 18	4 to 4½
			20 to 30*	12 to 15	5 to 6

*unstuffed

Cooked yields are oftentimes difficult to estimate. Normally 50% of the dressed weight of turkeys is obtained as clear meat and 25 to 35% of chickens. Geese and ducks are lower in yields.

Table 9-15
Portions from Various Size Turkeys

Dressed Weight (lb)	Loss to Ready-to-Cook	Ready-to-Cook Weight (lb)	Sliceable Meat Cooked (lb)	Number of Portions		
				2 oz	3 oz	4 oz
12 to 14	15%	10 to 12	4½	36	22	12
14 to 16	15%	12 to 14	4½	42	26	15
16 to 18	15%	14 to 16	6	48	30	18
18 to 20	15%	16 to 17	6⅔	54	32	20
20 to 22	15%	17 to 18	7⅓	59	37	23
22 to 24	15%	18 to 20	8	64	40	25
30 to 35	13%	26 to 30	13½	108	67	40

Poaching

Poaching poultry in place of roasting, especially large birds, increases yield, moistness, flavor, and tenderness. Cooking time will be reduced about half over roasting, and less cooking space will be required. More attractive and uniform portions may be obtained, for much of the meat can be sliced on a slicer. For this, bone the bird completely or purchase boned parts. Use the carcass, wing tips, neck, and other bony parts for the stock pot; picked cooked meat from these can be used in made-up dishes. Arrange the legs and thighs on the bottom, skin side down, then the breasts, in a stock pot, roasting pan, or steam-jacketed kettle. Cover with hot, salted water, using one tablespoon of salt and one teaspoon of white pepper for every six pounds of bird. Simmer at low heat or bake in a 330° F oven about 2 to 2½ hours or until fork-tender. Remove from the heat and cool rapidly in the stock or plunge into cold water. Place in a refrigerator and chill. Then slice. Use meat and stock within three days.

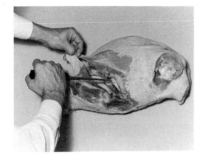

(a)

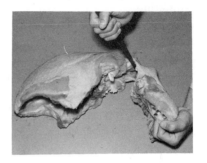

(b)

(c)

(d)

(e)

FIG. 9-39 Select young tender toms for boning and poaching. (a) After cutting away the leg and wing closely from the carcass, being sure to remove the "oyster" with the leg, cut through as shown, and (b) break and cut away the back parts. (c) Cut flesh from the breast bone. The natural filet may be separated from the remaining breast meat by lifting it out with the fingers, starting at the arrow. (d) The poaching parts are shown here, while the simmering parts for stock are shown in (e).

Simmering

Whole birds or parts of birds may be placed in stock kettles or steam-jacketed kettles and covered with one gallon of stock or water seasoned with one tablespoon of salt for every five pounds of poultry. Vegetables and seasonings may be added. Bring to a boil, reduce the heat to a simmer, cover, skim, and add water as required until the birds are tender. Cool in the stock or in cold water.

(a)   (b)

FIG. 9-40   (a) Precooked and prebrowned items such as this chicken may speed service, for only a short frying period is required to have it ready for the customer. (Courtesy Swift & Company) (b) Pan-frying chicken after it has been batter-dipped. (Courtesy Procter & Gamble)

(a)   (b)

FIG. 9-41   (a) Chicken fricassee and dumplings, such as shown here, are a favorite dish. (Courtesy Armour & Co.) (b) Deep-dish chicken apple pie made from picked chicken meat. (Courtesy Processed Apples Institute)

Steaming

Older birds for picked cooked meat may be cooked to a tender stage quickly by pressure steaming. This gives a light-colored meat and requires from a third to half as long as simmering. A small quantity of water is added to the pan or container in which the birds are placed, and the pan is placed in the steamer. High pressure may toughen birds more than simmering. Overcooking is a danger, and times must be watched.

Braising

Poultry may be braised in a manner similar to that described for meats. Fricasseed or stewed poultry is braised poultry.

FISH COOKERY

Fish is a low-priced food and, if properly prepared, can vie in quality with the finest meat or poultry as an entree for a meal. The flesh of fish is similar to meat and poultry except that it contains little connective tissue, and almost

FIG. 9-42 Good merchandising of seafoods is an excellent means of raising check averages and of pleasing patrons. (Courtesy Institutions Magazine)

any method of cooking will cook it to desirable tenderness. Fish should be cooked well done, except for a few items, such as mollusks, which may even be eaten raw. One of the most common mistakes in fish cookery is overcooking. When cooked to proper doneness, fish should flake easily and be moist. Overcooked fish will break up easily, and the meat will be dry, pulpy, and tough.

The fat content of fish varies from 1 to 20%. Marbling and finish are not found in fish as in meats; the fat is spread somewhat as an oil throughout the meat. In meats, the type and quantity of connective tissue are significant factors in dictating the type of cooking. In fish flesh it is the fat content that dictates the cookery. Fat fish are usually moist, and this makes them suitable for baking, broiling, or simmering (poaching). Lean fish, such as flounder, halibut, and cod, sauté well, and sauces which add moisture may make the service of poached lean fish feasible. Both lean and fat fish deep-fry well, as a rule, though lean fish breaded or batter-dipped are more

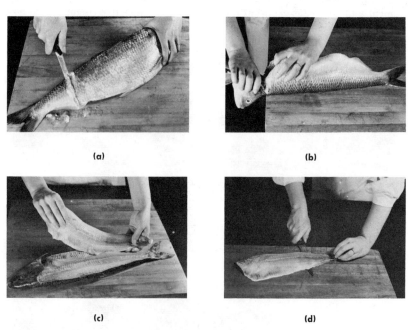

(a)   (b)

(c)   (d)

FIG. 9-43 Preparing fish fillets. (a) Whole or round fish are scaled, except for trout and those that may be skinned, such as bullfish. (b) The head may be cut or broken off as shown, or left on to assist in holding in boning. Cut the fish open next on the under side and remove entrails. Wash well. (c) Lay the fish flat on a cutting board and take hold of the tail. Then cut about a half inch from the tail, slanting down to the bone, and then set the flattened knife forward, obtaining a strip as shown here. (d) Remove the skin by using the knife as shown. (Courtesy U.S. Department of Interior)

suitable for this treatment than fat fish. Lean fish may be baked, if basted or covered with fatty tissues. Baking quickly helps to keep lean fish moist. Most fish, fat or lean, are accompanied by sauces such as hollandaise, lemon butter, Bercy, Normandy, or Mornay sauce.

Fish, if properly selected for good quality and correctly cooked, should not have a strong fishy flavor. While the flavor of cod, mackerel, herring and others may be more abundant than that of other fish, the flavor should never be objectionable. These fish with more abundant flavor may be cooked in such a way that some flavor is lost or modified.

Fish is usually baked covered. It is sautéed in more fat than meat or poultry, especially in the case of lean fish. Do not attempt to broil lean fish; this treatment gives a dry, pulpy product lacking color and flavor. It is also apt to curl under the broiler. Steam fish in a cloth to hold its shape, or steam it on an oiled trivet.

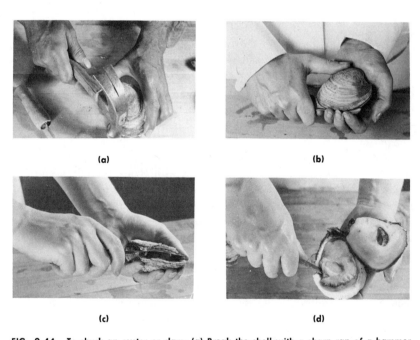

(a)   (b)

(c)   (d)

FIG. 9-44 To shuck an oyster or clam: (a) Break the shell with a sharp rap of a hammer. This is called "billing." Bill at the thin shell area. (b) Hold the oyster or clam with the hinge part of the shell at the palm, as shown, or flat on a cutting board, and insert tip of knife where the shell was broken. (c) After insertion of the knive, twist it slightly to open the shell and then run the knife in and up close to the top, cutting through the adductor muscle that joins the clam or oyster to the shell. (d) Cut the adductor muscle attached to the lower shell. The clam or oyster is now ready to be served on the half shell or removed from the shell for other preparation. (Courtesy U.S. Department of Interior)

Shellfish, if cooked at too high a temperature or too long, become tough and rubbery. Simmering at 190° F is preferred to boiling. Studies have indicated that live shellfish, placed in 140° F water, are stunned and expire rapidly. Cooking shellfish in 190° F salted water (lobsters 205° F) is recommended rather than boiling. This gives a more flavorful and tenderer product.

Green shrimp may be purchased with heads on or headless, and fresh or frozen. Cooked shrimp may also be purchased in the same forms on some markets. To peel a raw shrimp, make a shallow cut along the back and peel. The sand vein is removed and the shrimp washed. It is then ready for cooking. Peeled raw shrimp may be butterflied by splitting through to the tail. Cooked shrimp in the shell may be peeled, deveined, and washed. To cook shrimp, use a half cup of salt and one gallon of water for every five pounds of raw headless shrimp AP. Yield from headless green shrimp after cooking, peeling, and deveining is 50%. Raw headless shrimp, shelled and deveined, are on the market (PDQ). Cooked yield is 55% AP.

Wash clams or oysters thoroughly before steaming. To rid clams of sand, add one-third cup of salt per gallon of water and soak for 15 to 20 minutes. Wash. Repeat until clams are sand-free. Salt water must be used, for clams will not become sand-free in fresh water. Some cooks also add a bit of cornmeal and allow the clams to remain overnight under refrigeration.

To steam clams, use three-fourths of a pound, or six to eight clams, per person. Place clams in a container with a perforated bottom containing one cup of water per pound of clams. Steam five to 10 minutes or until partially opened. Serve on a plate or dish with clam nectar in a cup and a side dish of melted butter. Clams or oysters may be roasted by placing them in a baking pan and roasting 15 minutes at 450° or until they are open. Oysters and clams may be baked or barbecued in the half shell. Where a large quantity of clams or oysters are to be shucked, mechanical shuckers are used.

Lobster tails should be poached about five minutes and then split for broiling. This gives a tender and moister product than broiling alone. The time for broiling, using this method, is about five to six minutes. To reduce curling of the tail, thaw and split, or remove the thin undershell and bend back firmly to break the connective tissue that causes curling.

FIG. 9-45   Fish or shellfish may be prepared a variety of ways. The lobster tail shown at the top right is cooked as described in the text, except that the tail meat is removed whole and broiled, instead of being split and broiled. Pan-sautéing or deep-frying a lean fish such as a sand dab gives a good product. Steaming of clams only until the shells open also gives an excellent item. Light poaching of a fish in court bouillon, as shown at the lower right, is also an excellent method of preparation.

(a)

(b)

(c)

FIG. 9-46   To obtain crab meat from cooked crabs: (a) Break off the large claws, pull off the top shell, and break off legs. (b) Remove gills and internal material by scraping and washing. (c) Slice the top right side of the inner skeleton by starting at the top. Remove the meat and repeat slice on left side, removing meat. Crack claws and remove meat. (Courtesy U.S. Department of Interior)

(a)

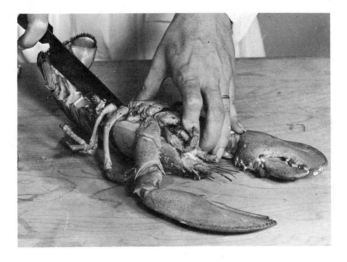

(b)

FIG. 9-47   (a) To cook a live lobster, plunge it head first into water at about 150° F. Bring to a simmering temperature of about 205° F and cook about 20 to 25 minutes. (b) To split, lay lobster on its back and cut through to shell. Remove stomach back of the head and the intestinal vein which runs from the stomach to the end of the tail, but do not discard the green liver or coral roe. Many people like them. Claws may be cracked before it is sent from the kitchen.

FIG. 9-48   To have clams or oysters sand- or silt-free, first wash carefully in a strainer, then soak in salt water.

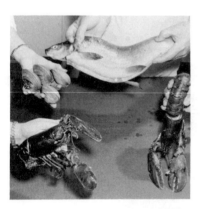
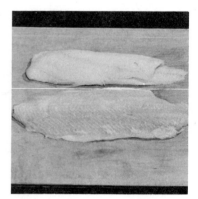

FIG. 9-49   Freshness in fish or shellfish is essential if good quality products are to be served. Clams should be tightly closed, indicating they are alive. A lobster should have bright eyes, twitching antennae, claws held up, and tail curled under, not hanging down as shown on the right. A fish should have firm flesh, tightly adhering scales, and bright eyes—factors lacking in the fish shown here. To insure quality products, select the correct method of cooking for the type of fish used. The fat whitefish fillet shown at the bottom broils or bakes well, while the lean cod fillet above it will not perform adequately with such treatment.

Section III

Bakeshop Production

10   Bakery Ingredients

Perhaps no other area in food production requires as high a degree of technical knowledge and skill as the bakeshop. Most bakery products are made of very similar ingredients; but with slight variations in their proportions, manner of preparation, or baking, the final products will differ greatly. Success and failure may be a matter of slight detail, and a knowledge of the properties bakery ingredients exhibit under various conditions is essential if successful baking is to be done. A brief discussion of the properties of flour, shortening, leavening agents, and spices and seasonings is therefore appropriate. The properties of eggs and liquids have been mentioned previously under eggs and dairy products, and sugar is discussed later in the chapter on cakes.

FLOUR

Flour has been defined as a finely ground wheat or other cereal, but some finely ground products used as flours are not cereals, such as flours from potatoes, almonds, filberts, soy beans, and tapioca. Some ground cereals are not fine enough to qualify as flours but are instead meals, such as cornmeal or oatmeal, although they act as flours. Perhaps it would be best to define flour for our purposes here as a ground starch-like product used to furnish structure and body to bakery products.

Wheat Flour

Wheat flour is our most important flour used in baking. Rye, buckwheat, rice, corn, barley, and oat flours are also used, but in much lesser quantities, and because they lack good baking qualities, they are frequently mixed with wheat flour. The type of wheat flour used will vary according to the baking properties required, and the kind of wheat and method of manufacture decide these properties. Flours from different wheats may be blended to give a desired flour.

383

The average wheat flour consists of 63 to 73% starch, 7 to 14% protein, 1 to 2% fat, 0.4% ash or minerals, 1 to 2% sugar, and 11 to 13% moisture. Variations in the quantity of starch, protein, or ash will make a great difference in the baking properties exhibited.

Soft or winter wheat produces a soft, velvety, powdery flour, with more starch and less protein than hard or spring wheat. A good flour from soft wheat possesses a clear, white color. Soft flours are used for pastry, many quick breads, and cakes and cookies. A good hard-wheat flour will be slightly creamy in color and will have a rough texture and a high protein content. Hard-wheat flours are used for making yeast breads and a few pastry products.

The quantity and quality of protein in the flour influence its structure-building properties. Breads, puff paste, eclair pastes, and some other items require strong structures, while cakes, cookies, and muffins must possess less structural strength in order to be tender. Flour made from hard wheat is frequently called "strong" because of its ability to form a strong structure, while soft-wheat flours are called "weak" flours because they produce a tenderer, more delicate structure. When a soft flour is called "strong," the term does not mean that it makes a strong structure but rather that the flour has the strength in a batter to carry high ratios of sugar, fats, and other ingredients.

The best wheat flours are called *patents* and the poorest *clears*. A flour called *middlings* is a flour between patents and clears in quality. A straight flour is all the flour that is taken from the wheat kernel. Whole wheat or graham flour is straight flour containing some bran. High quality patents are required to make good flours from either hard or soft wheat. Whole wheat flour will not form as strong a structure as white flour because the bran and clears reduce the amount and quality of gluten. A good patent white flour may have to be added to a whole wheat flour to give it better structure-making properties.

Six proteins are found in flour, the most important and by far the greatest in quantity being gliadin and glutenin, which together, when the flour is moistened, form an elastic, tenuous product called gluten. Gluten forms the framework for structural strength in the baked product. It has the ability to absorb approximately 200% of its weight in moisture, and when completely hydrated it makes a pliable, elastic, viscous mass which extends in thin strands as a network throughout a batter or dough. When gluten coagulates in baking, it becomes firm and thus forms a solidified, continuous mesh which gives strength. Fat, sugar, starch, and other ingredients interfere with the formation of gluten. Salt strengthens gluten, while sugar peptizes or tenderizes it. Fat acts as a lubricant and prevents gluten particles from joining, thus making a product tender. Alkalis weaken gluten,

FIG. 10-1 Note how a slurry made from bread flour has more stringy qualities than a slurry made from cake flour. The higher gluten content of the bread flour is the factor causing this phenomenon, while the lower gluten and higher starch contents of the cake flour are responsible for the qualities displayed here.

while acid ingredients make it more pliable and extensible. Too much liquid in a batter cause the gluten to become over-extended and unable to form a strong network. To perform properly, gluten must form a sufficiently strong network to retain leavening gases and hold other ingredients in suspension in the batter or dough. That is the reason why even delicate cake flours must contain some gluten.

The bleaching and aging of the flour will affect its baking quality. A flour which is not aged at least three to six weeks is called "green" and is apt to be bucky, or rigid and inflexible, in its baking performance. The texture of products made from it will be tough. Bread made from green flour may have odd humps on the top or may break or tear due to the failure of the gluten to gain proper elasticity. Flour can also be over-aged, and when this occurs, it will lack extensibility and give poor volume. Rye flours should not be aged.

Moisture is necesary to develop gluten, and a dough or batter must be worked or manipulated to bring the moistened gluten particles together to form a gluten network. This is why mixing or kneading is desired in some bakery work and avoided in others. When gluten is cold or not completely hydrated, it cannot form a strong structure, but when conditions are favorable, such as when it is warm and given proper moisture, it develops rapidly.

(a)

(b)

FIG. 10-2   Three gluten balls showing the approximate gluten content of (left to right) cake, pastry, and bread flours. (Courtesy Wheat Flour Institute) (b) The development of the gluten in the dough is shown in these baking powder biscuits. Note the tiny strands and the layering of the dough which occurred because of gluten development. As gas pressures pushed the dough up in baking, these strands and layering of the dough became evident. (Courtesy General Foods)

especially when the dough or batter is manipulated. Keeping a muffin batter cool and a pie dough cold retards gluten formation.

Gluten development can be demonstrated by mixing a hard-wheat flour into a stiff dough and kneading it for about ten minutes. After a rest of approximately 20 to 30 minutes—a process called conditioning, which allows the gluten to hydrate completely—the starch is carefully washed out under running water, and a yellowish viscous and elastic mass remains. This is crude gluten. If this gluten is formed into a ball and placed in a 375° to 400° F oven, the steam in baking will swell this mass into a large hollow sphere.

A good hard or soft flour should absorb from 60 to 65% of its own weight in moisture and still make a firm, pliable dough. Soft flours will usually absorb slightly less moisture than hard flours. The ability to absorb water is one criterion used to judge flour quality. A flour able to bind a high amount of water gives a moist product which performs well in mixing and baking and which has good keeping qualities. If a hard flour fails to absorb a good quantity of water, this is an indication of a weak gluten. This failure in a soft flour indicates poor ability to produce a stable batter. Some sugars and acids used in cooking increase gluten's ability to absorb moisture. As fermentation proceeds in a yeast dough, acidity increases, and this causes increased moisture absorption. Thus a yeast dough may be slightly sticky on make-up but it will later become firm and pliable because of increased moisture absorption. Salt reduces moisture absorption and will raise the coagulation temperature of the gluten.

Baking firms a batter or dough by gelatinizing the starch and coagulating the gluten. The starch in flour absorbs water only when quite hot, beginning gelatinization at around 144° F and ending at around 203° F. At approximately 165° F gluten coagulates and becomes firm. Other ingredients in a batter or dough, such as eggs, may also coagulate and become firm. Some moisture, from 8 to 16%, is lost by evaporation, and this assists in giving firmness. It is important that the proper expansion or leavening occur before the product firms. A highly complex balance must take place between the action of leavening agents, moisture, and structure-forming ingredients and the introduction of heat.

The ash content of flour is important to quality in baked goods. If ash is above 0.5%, the flour will not perform properly, especially in yeast products. The size and uniformity of the grind are also important to product quality. Flour granules that are too large will not absorb the quantity of liquid required nor give the flour the capacity to carry the amounts of sugar, shortening, and other ingredients needed. A loaf of bread from too coarsely ground flour will be heavy and will shape up with difficulty. Too fine a grind gives a pasty, tightly grained product which bakers say "has not been allowed to breathe." If flours are too finely ground, they absorb too much water. Proper granule size gives products with uniform cell structure, good oven spring, maximum volume, and good texture. Hard-wheat flour, if too fine, ferments too rapidly and has excessive starch swell in baking. Unevenness of grind gives large particles, which have slow moisture absorption and low stabilizing ability, while the small granules have excessive moisture absorption and excessive stabilizing power.

Flours should be stored at around 70° F in a dry place where there are no odors. Give good ventilation. It is usually recommended that flour not be stacked more than eight bags high. Flour is usually purchased by the barrel. A barrel is 196 pounds and represents two 98-pound or four 49-pound bags. Some cake flours are sold in 100-pound bag lots.

Bread or Hard-Wheat Flour

Hard wheat with good strong gluten is selected to make the best short patent bread flour. The gluten should be capable of development and retention of strength under kneading, fermenting, and other treatment. Good bread flour should contain 65 to 70% starch, 1 to 2% fat, 10 to 12% protein of high quality, 1 to 2% sugar, 0.4% ash, and 11 to 13% moisture. It should be enriched with iron, thiamin, niacin, calcium, and vitamin D. The flour should absorb a high quality of moisture and make a dough which is elastic, pliable, and soft. A sufficient viscosity, elasticity, and tenacity is required after mixing to give the dough good spring in rising and to hold in the gas pressures. Too great a viscosity or tenacity, however, gives a bucky, unyielding dough that breaks or humps in baking. A good flour will not become slack under fermentation.

Soft-Wheat Flour

The best pastry and cake flours are made from the first patents of good soft wheat. Careful selection of the wheat must occur for delicate cake flours. Cake flour contains approximately 7 to 8½% protein. The batters become pasty when there is less protein, and the structure of the product lacks volume and quality. The flour should have the ability to absorb a high quantity of liquid and blend well with varying proportions of fat, sugar, and eggs to make a stable batter. A cake low in moisture absorption and low in stability cannot support the quantity of liquid and richness required to make cakes or other pastries. Pastry flours contain more and stronger gluten than cake flours and are used for quick breads, pie dough, and other products requiring stronger structure than cakes. The protein content is around 8 to 10%. This flour may have a fairly high amount of gluten, but because the gluten is not strong, the flour will be suitable for pastry work. Pastry flour is usually used for general cooking as well as for specialized use in the bake shop.

If *necessary*, strong flour can be used for cake or pastry work. Adding 2½ ounces of cornstarch to every 14 ounces of bread flour for every pound of cake flour required will give a fairly satisfactory flour. Usually the ratio of shortening is also increased in the recipe to help counteract the stronger gluten of the bread flour. All-purpose flour is suitable for cake, pastry, or bread, but is not especially adapted to the specific needs of quantity food production and so is not generally used in food services.

SHORTENINGS

Wide use is made of shortenings because they impart specific physical properties to bakery goods. Shortenings used in the bakeshop may be butter or margarine, animal fats, hydrogenated vegetable or hydrogenated animal fats or oils, or blended compounds of vegetable and animal fats. The shortening used should be flavorless and colorless unless it is butter or margarine or a fat used for its flavor contribution. A butter flavoring may be used to give a butter flavor. Shortenings for bakery products should possess good shortening power and high stability.

Fats are used to give tenderness to bakery goods. When shortening surrounds gluten, it acts to separate it, giving a tender product. Fats also give softness to the crumb. Because of its lubricating qualities fat gives "slip" to a batter or dough, and this slippage is important in obtaining proper leavening and movement in baking. A product lacking this mobility as it rises may not develop properly.

Fats shorten or give good tenderization if they contain fatty acids or if they have good spread in a batter or dough. Many animal fats are high in free fatty acids but do not possess good plasticity and therefore are not suitable for pie doughs. Suets and tallows are too brittle. Some animal fats, such as lard or curd-free and washed butter or margarine, give short pie crusts. An excess of free fatty acids may give fats too much shortening power. Some hydrogenated shortenings and lard are processed to give them plasticity or spread for pastry work. Soft fats such as those found in poultry or oils give good shortening power, since they spread well, but they blend so easily with flour that it is difficult to make other than mealy pie crusts from them.

Plastic fats cream well and incorporate air, which increases the volume, texture, and lightness of a product. Fats give sheen or gloss to the crust and crumb. If a protective coating is placed around moistened ingredients, moisture loss is delayed. Excessive fat gives a greasy crumb or oiliness to a product. Cakes possessing excess fat will fall and cookies will crumble. Volume will be lost if fats exceed correct proportions. Too little fat gives a tough, hard, dry product. Fats that are too hard or fats that lack plasticity will not give optimum results because they fail to mix well with other ingredients. Temperatures of mixing are important in establishing the plasticity of some fats. Conditioning is recommended at the proper temperature for at least 24 hours in advance of use.

Emulsifiers may be added to shortenings to make them cream better and spread more easily throughout the batter. This contributes to better volume and also gives a smoother, finer texture and thinner cell walls to the crumb. Cakes made with plasticized and emulsified fats can hold more liquid and sugar. Emulsifiers reduce the tendency of cake batters to curdle, reduce batter viscosity, and increase batter smoothness. When emulsified fats are used, simplified methods of mixing are possible which will reduce production time.

LEAVENING AGENTS

Leavening is the aeration of a product that occurs during mixing and baking. A leavening agent develops texture, shape, and volume and may also make other beneficial contributions, such as increasing the spread or reducing the viscosity of the batter or dough. It may also darken pigments and tenderize or toughen proteins.

Air, steam, chemicals, and yeast are used as leavening agents. Leavening is seldom the result of one leavening agent working alone, but is a combination of two or more working together. The amount of leavening contributed by each will vary. A cake made by the conventional creaming method will obtain one-third of its leavening each from steam, air, and baking powder. A popover will get most of its leavening from steam.

The type and quantity of leavening required will vary with the type of product; the amount and method of creaming, mixing, or beating ;the type and quality of ingredients used; the sequence of ingredient addition; the altitude; and the technique of the operator. To properly leaven a product, leavening pressures must be retained until the structure is set by baking. Firmness of the structure after baking should be sufficient to hold shape and retain the desirable eating qualities developed. Excess shrinkage after removal from the oven is frequently caused by a lack of structural strength to support the volume obtained. Over-development of gluten in mixing may restrict movement of leavening gases, and misshapen products with poor texture and volume may result. Tunnels develop in baked goods because the unbaked structure is so strong that gases cannot spread throughout the dough. The gases gather and force their way upward, making the typical up-and-down vents called tunnels.

While only a small quantity of leavening may be used in proportion to other ingredients, its influence on quality is so great that exact measurement is necessary. Insufficient leavening yields poor volume and color, a heavy, close grain, and a coarse crust. Excess leavening will give a rough, loose, uneven grain and a crumbly, hard, dry texture which lacks smoothness and flavor; over-expansion of cellular walls may proceeds to the point that the development caused by the gas cannot be supported and the product falls. The quantity of leavening used must be related to the loss of gas occurring in mixing, benching, and baking. A batter which is quite fluid or soft will have more gas leakage than one that is less fluid, and therefore it requires more leavening.

The size of the cell or grain developed in leavening is also important. A large cell is desirable in a cream puff or popover, while fine cells are desirable in most cakes or similar products. The structural strength developed in a product must be related to the size of the cell wall. A cream puff or popover must have a strong structure on the outside to support the large cells developed. A tenderer structure will support the fine texture which occurs in a cake. Too fine a cell gives a compact, heavy product.

The speed at which a leavening agent works must be controlled. Usually the more rapid the development of the leavening in baking, the more quickly the structural walls must be set. Most of the leavening action from chemical leaveners should be obtained during baking and only a small amount during mixing or benching. Temperature and time in baking should permit freedom of movement in the batter until maximum volume from the leavening agent is obtained, at which time the structure should be set; no leavening should occur after the product has set. A cake with an overly dark crust and a cracked high center indicates that the outside area was set before completion of leavening in the interior. A pie crust or cracker baked at too low a temperature will set before steam can develop between layers of the dough, and lightness and flakiness will be lost. Products such as popovers and eclair pastes should have only the outside portion lightly set at the time steam develops in the interior. If more than this is set, the product will not rise.

Air

When fats, eggs, and sugar are creamed, air is incorporated, giving an increase in volume and a light creamy texture to the mixture. If this air is retained after baking, a porous texture is obtained. Pound cakes or cookies may be leavened almost completely by this method. The air in the foam of eggs leavens angel and sponge cakes, meringues, and many other products. Air may be incorporated also in sifting flour, in the beating of a batter, or in the manipulation of a dough. After air is once incorporated, care must be taken in handling to see that it is retained. Air expands about one-third in volume in baking. The ratio of leavening contributed by air will depend upon the quantity of air incorporated, the subsequent treatment of the product, and the kind and amount of leavening contributed by other ingredients.

Steam

When water changes into steam, it increases in volume 1600 times, making steam an effective leavening agent. Popovers, cream puffs, crackers, and pie crust depend almost solely upon steam as their leavening agent. The steam developed by one quart of liquid in a batter or dough is usually considered sufficient to leaven one pound of flour in a dough.

Chemical Leavening Agents

Soda, baking powder, and baking ammonia are chemical leavening agents. Baking ammonia has limited use. To give equal leavening, $\frac{1}{4}$ ounce of soda, one ounce of double-acting baking powder, and two ounces of single-acting baking powder would be required to leaven one pound of flour. Chemical leaveners should be finely divided. Mixing of the leavening agent into a batter or dough should be thorough to give even leavening and a fine grain. Coarsely ground leavening agents will give grainy, open products. The finer the grind, the smaller the quantity of leavener required.

SODA

Sodium bicarbonate or soda is finely ground today, but formerly it was not, and this is the reason why so many recipes today still recommend that the soda be placed in solution in a liquid before it is added to a product. When soda is mixed with hot water, there is a large loss of gas and a possibility of introducing an excessive alkaline reaction into the product.

Heat alone will cause moistened soda to free carbon dioxide gas. An acid reactor with soda causes this gas to develop at a cold stage. Usually both heat and an acid reactor are used. When acid is not present to balance the soda or when soda is in excess of the acid present, the leavened product will have an alkaline reaction. This may or may not be desirable. Color pigments of cocoa and chocolate are reddened, and molasses, spices, fruits, nuts, vegetables, and some other foods are darkened when the reaction is alkaline. Longer standing of chocolate cakes before baking gives a higher development of red color if they are alkaline in reaction. The flavone pigments in flour and other products turn yellow in an alkaline medium, while anthocyanin pigments turn blue or purple.

In many products, acids are used to neutralize soda completely, and if additional leavening is required, soda is not added; instead, baking powder is used. An alkaline reaction softens gluten and toughens eggs. Gingerbreads may sink in the middle because of excessive tenderization from soda. This may be counteracted to some extent by increasing the mixing action. The residue remaining after soda has reacted by heat alone is sodium carbonate, a soapy, bitter-flavored substance, and this flavor is often objectionable. Some acid reactors leave a tasteless residue. Sour milk with soda leaves a tasteless sodium lactate.

Frequently, the quantity of soda required is guided more by the quantity

FIG. 10-3 An acidified water has been poured into baking soda in the glass on the left, and neutral water has been poured into baking soda in the glass on the right. Pouring boiling water and cold water into these same types of samples brought about the same reactions.

of acid reactor present than by the quantity of flour to be leavened. Liquids such as honey, molasses, sour milk, buttermilk, fruit juices, and vinegar are used as acid reactors. Ingredients such as chocolate, cocoa, spices, nuts, and fruits are also sufficiently acid to be utilized at least in part as acid reactors. Cream of tartar is often used as an acid with soda. Table 10-1 gives the approximate quantity of acid required to react with soda, but it is difficult to establish exact proportions, since the acidity of these liquids varies.

Table 10-1
Approximate Balanced Reactions Between Liquids and Soda in Food Preparation

Liquid	Weight	Measure	Soda Required for Complete Reaction Weight	Measure
Sour milk or buttermilk	8.3 lb	1 gal	¼ oz	2⅔ T
Molasses	11.5 lb	1 gal	1¾ oz	3 to 4 T
Sorghum	11.3 lb	1 gal	1 oz	2¼ T
Honey	11.3 lb	1 gal	½ to 1 oz	1 to 2¼ T
Vinegar, 40 to 50 grain	3 oz	⅓ c	1¼ oz	2⅔ T
Orange juice	4 oz	½ c	1¼ oz	2⅔ T
Cream of tartar	5 oz	1 c	2 oz	4½ T

BAKING POWDER

The most widely used chemical leavening agent is baking powder. This is usually bicarbonate of soda and an acid reactor blended together to give a product which "yields not less than 12% available carbon dioxide. . . . The acid reaction materials may be tartaric acid or its salt, compounds of aluminum or acid salts of phosphoric acid, or any combination in substantial proportion of the foregoing."[1] Starch is used as a diluent of the baking powder to give the standard 12% yield. The starch also acts as a drying agent, preventing caking of the powder. Manufacturers also produce baking powders having 17% carbon dioxide yield for quantity food production.

Certain baking powders evolve gas immediately upon coming in contact with moisture without the application of heat. These are called single-acting baking powders, because complete reaction can occur in one stage when cold. Double-acting baking powders evolve from one-fifth to one-third of their gas in the cold stage, but heat is required to evolve the remainder. A

FIG. 10-4   Reaction rates of powders to cold water: (left) tartrate baking powder, (center) sodium acid pyrophosphate baking powder, and (right) sodium acid phosphate and mono-calcium phosphate baking powder.

[1]USDA. Food and Drug Insecticide Administration, SRA, FD 2, Revised 4, 1933, p. 20.

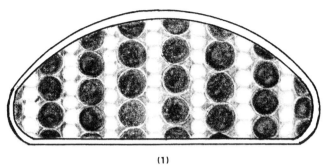

(1)

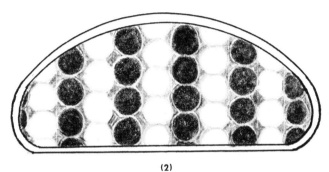

(2)

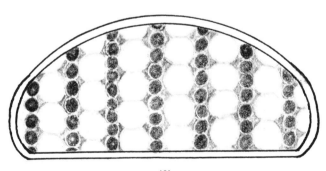

(3)

FIG. 10-5 Reactions of ingredients in a baking powder. Dark spots show reaction in the cold stage and white spots show reaction in the warm stage.

double-acting power has an acid reactor which reacts when cold and another which reacts when heat is applied. Baking powders made of tartaric acid ($H_2C_4H_4O_6$), or monocalcium phosphate ($CaH_4(PO_4)_2.H_2O$), or monosodium phosphate (NaH_2PO_4) are single-acting. Tartaric acid and soda, when placed in water, reacts completely in two minutes. Monosodium phosphate and soda react almost as rapidly, but monocalcium phosphate takes a bit longer. A baking powder containing sodium acid pyrophosphate, ($NaH_2P_2O_7$) releases gas slowly in the cold stage but more rapidly when heat is applied. Sodium acid phosphate and monocalcium phosphate are used to make one popular type of double-acting baking powder. Sodium aluminum sulfate (SAS) [$Na_2SO_4.Al_2(SO_4)_3$] baking powder, another popular baking powder in food services, reacts even more slowly than a sodium acid pyrophosphate baking powder. While sodium acid pyrophosphate and SAS baking powders are called double-acting, they are actually single-acting, but the action is slow when cold and fast when hot, giving a type of double action. One truly double-acting baking powder used widely in quantity production contains calcium acid phosphate to react when cold, and sodium pyrophosphate or sodium aluminum phosphate to react when heat is applied. Calcium lactate is added to these ingredients to control the action.

High loss of gas before baking can occur in using single-acting baking powder. For this reason mixing procedures may call for the addition during the later stages of mixing. More single-acting baking powder is required to give the same quantity of leavening action, and from one to two ounces of single-acting powder is usually used per pound of flour, compared with one-half to one ounce for double-acting baking powders. While a small amount of gas development is desirable in mixing, in panning, and on the bench, the amount should be limited to that required to give good mixing and handling properties. Because an excess of certain baking powders may give undesirable flavor, only the minimum quantity required to give proper leavening should be used. Tartaric acid baking powders leave no aftertaste, but because of their single action, they are not used much in quantity food work. Double-acting baking powders of the types that react either slowly or in two distinct stages are best suited for quantity work. Good tolerance, both in mixing and in benching, is necessary in a baking powder used in the bakeshop, for times and conditions may not always be optimum in quantity work.

BAKING AMMONIA

Ammonium carbonate [$(NH_4)HCO_3.NH_4NH_2CO_2$] or baking ammonia, is sometimes used as a leavening agent. In the presence of moisture and subjected to heat, it will change to carbon dioxide, ammonia gas, and

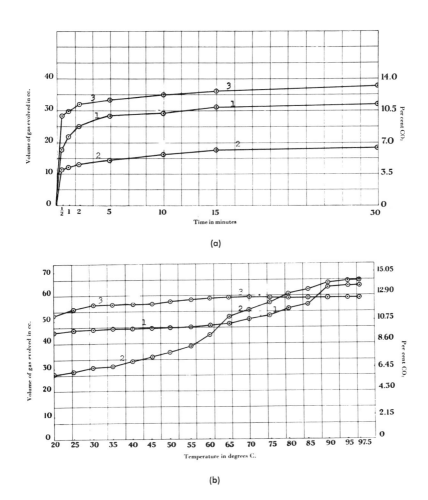

(a)

(b)

FIG. 10-6 This drawing indicates the reaction rates that occur in batters containing baking powder (a) in the cold stage and (b) in the hot stage. Baking powders are (1) pyrophosphate, (2) calcium-acid-phosphate (SAS), and (3) tartrate.

water. If the reaction is complete, there is little or no aftertaste. If used in thick products, aftertaste may result, so it is usually used in thin products such as cookies, choux pastes, and so forth. It gives a rapid expansion, and this is desirable to give spread to cookies and a rapid rise to choux pastes. Baking ammonia rather than baking soda should be used to give spread to cookies. Most recipes for machine-deposit cookies call for a part of the leavening agent to be baking ammonia. If a recipe using only soda or baking powder for leavening is to be changed so as to use ammonia in order to give spread, omit approximately one-half the required chemical leavening agent. If the leavening agent is baking powder, replace 40% of the omitted weight with baking ammonia; and if soda, replace with 80% of the omitted weight of the soda.

FLAVORINGS AND SPICES

Cocoa and chocolate are used in bakery goods to give flavor, richness, and color. Chocolate is pure chocolate liquor containing not less than 50% cacao butter and not more than 7% crude fiber. Unsweetened chocolate contains 8 to 16% starch, approximately 30% total carbohydrate, 14% protein, and around 52% cacao butter. Cocoa is ground chocolate after about half or more of the cacao butter has been removed. Breakfast cocoa must contain not less than 22% cacao butter, but other cocoas may contain as little as 8%. Cocoa contains approximately 38% total carbohydrate, 20% protein, and 10 to 20% starch. Because of the starch content in cocoa and chocolate, some thickening occurs when they are moistened and heated. In some instances, this starch must be considered as a part of the flour used. There is little difference between richness contributed by shortening or cacao butter, and if a product low in cacao butter is used, the difference may be made up in added shortening. Cocoa or chocolate turn reddish in color under an alkaline reaction.

Spices should be of highest quality. Keep inventories low, for quality is lost as time is extended. Spices will darken in an alkaline medium.

The quality used for flavoring or seasoning should be the highest that can be purchased. While the quantity used is small, the flavor contribution is considerable. Some flavors bake out. Select flavorings that are especially prepared by reliable manufacturers for bakery product use. Freshness is an essential factor. Flavorings used in the bakeshop will be extracts which are natural esters or essential oils, or imitation products dissolved in alcohol or sometimes in water or other solvents. Others may be emulsions, which are essential oils placed into solution with the aid of gums or other emulsifiers so that the natural or imitation flavoring will be brought into the product. In many cases the natural oil gives the finest and truest flavor, but in many others it will be found that the chemist has been able to create an imitation which will be retained in the product and not bake out as the true flavor might.

11 Breads

Most food services will purchase their loaf bread, but those wishing to obtain high customer satisfaction will make their own rolls and other small hot breads. These may be yeast breads or quick breads.

YEAST BREADS

Standards

The factors judged in evaluating the quality of yeast breads are volume, color of crust, symmetry of form, evenness of bake, character of crust, break (shred), grain, color of crumb, texture, and flavor. Different breads and rolls have different characteristics, and these must be considered in the evaluation.

Size compared with weight is the basis for judging volume; normally, bread should occupy 125 to 155 cubic inches per pound. Too brown a crust, as well as spotting or unevenness of color, will detract from the score. An even, rich golden-brown color or bloom is sought. Evenness of shape, proportional balance, and the absence of any deformity of shape are considered under symmetry or form. A product which has an even bake will have a uniform appearance and will be uniformly browned on the sides, ends, and bottom, with no excessive browning. Tenderness, moderate thickness, and uniformity are desirable characteristics of the crust. Certain products such as hard rolls or French breads may have thick and crisp crusts. Break or shred is judged from the condition of the loaf between the areas at the top of and above the pan. An even break should appear in this area, with an evenly shredded appearance. A ragged, open break is undesirable. Small yeast rolls will not have a break or shred.

The character of the grain or the internal appearance is judged on the basis of size, shape, evenness of distribution, and porosity of the cellular structure. Even-sized and evenly spaced cells are sought. A slice of bread or

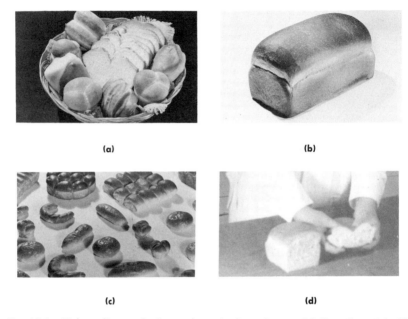

(a)   (b)

(c)   (d)

Fig. 11-1 High quality standards are shown in these pictures. (a) Hot rolls and freshly
sliced bread served in a basket invite consumption. (Courtesy Armour & Co.) (b) A fine
standard for a loaf of bread. (c) A few of the lean type of rolls possible from one yeast
dough. (d) Good bread, when squeezed as shown, should spring back into almost the
original shape.

roll held at a 45° angle toward the floor in good light should have a creamy
white interior with a soft sheen. A gray color or unevenness of color is undesirable. Most judges determine texture by rubbing the tips of the fingers
or the side of the check against the cut surface. Velvetiness, softness, and
elasticity are desirable. Any harshness or graininess will detract from the
score. A judge may roll a bit of bread into a ball between his fingers to
test texture. Moistness and softness with some resilience is evidence of
quality. Doughy, crumbly, or lumpy bread with a hard, flinty texture is
undesirable. Taste to evaluate texture. A good loaf after cooling, when
pressed down or squeezed, should spring back to nearly its original shape.
Flavor is judged by aroma and taste. The bread should have a fresh, sweet
odor with no trace of sourness or off-odor. The taste should be sweet, wheaty,
and not too salty.

Types of Bread

White bread is made from white wheat flour of high gluten content.
No flour over the 3% of the total may be added other than white wheat

flour if the bread is to be called white. The procedures discussed in this text are normally those used for white bread. Where they must be varied for other types, this will be indicated.

Whole wheat (graham) bread is made from 40 to 60% whole wheat flour and 60 to 40% white flour. The dough is handled very much like that of white bread, except that mixing may be less and it may be taken to the bench before it has reached a full rise, frequently referred to as "taking it to the bench young." The grain of the bread will be slightly heavier and the volume will be less than that of white bread.

About 20% rye flour is used with white flour for regular rye bread, but some rye breads may contain as much as 50% or more of rye flour. Rye flour lacks good gluten and the grain of such bread will usually be heavy. When mixing the dough, use less liquid and mix the dough less; overmixing gives a loss of volume, holes in the crumb, and split sides. The loaf may even burst because of overextension of the weak rye gluten. Yeast

FIG. 11-2 The popular pizza is made from a very lean type of yeast dough. This has been baked in a very hot oven in which cornmeal has been sprinkled on the bottom shelf so the pizza could be baked directly upon a hot surface, giving it a crisp crust.

may be increased 1% and a shorter fermentation given than that given wheat breads. Shortening and sugar are kept at minimal levels. Proofing time is also shorter, 30 to 35 minutes being desirable. Rye loaves are usually *docked* at make-up or just before baking; this is done by making four slashes across the top of the loaf about a fourth of an inch deep. Steam is used in the oven for the first 10 minutes of baking. Gas pressures may cause the bread to burst in baking if docking and steam are not used. If steam is not available, cold water may be brushed over the bread just before it goes into the oven and again when the bread has completely risen in the oven. Some bakers use a wash for this purpose, made by boiling 2 to 2½ ounces of cornstarch in one quart of water.

Hard, French, Italian, or hearth breads require a crisp crust. They are made from a lean formula with very little sugar and sometimes no shortening. The breads are frequently docked and steam is used to give good crisp crust. Braided breads are not docked. These breads are often baked in ovens or hearths on hot bricks. Simulated conditions may be used, such as sprinkling cornmeal on pans to prevent sticking and using regular ovens. Hard breads should not touch in baking.

FIG. 11-3 Two workers making dinner rolls. The baker on the left scales the dough, turns, and walks to the duchess cutter on the right, and then gives the other baker the rolls for panning. After pans are filled, she turns and places rolls into proofer on her right. Arrangement of a scaling center next to the cutter would eliminate travel of the first worker.

Sweet doughs are used for rich dinner rolls, baba rums, breakfast breads, and coffee cakes. Some sweet doughs may be as rich as cakes. A rolled-in sweet dough or Danish pastry has shortening rolled in as is done for puff paste. Usually a rolled-in dough is one that has been taken to the bench young and had the shortening rolled in, while a Danish pastry is one given a short rest to loosen up a bit after benching, after which the shortening is rolled in and the dough allowed to rest about 45 minutes before make-up. Margarine or special shortenings are used for rolling in, using about two to four ounces per pound of dough. A less sweet dough may be used for dinner rolls. Rich doughs retard or freeze better than non-rich doughs.

Soy flour may be added to some breads to give increased protein content. When it is used, the bread has a deep creamy, almost yellow color. Corn flour, potato flour, raisins, or nuts may be used for variety breads.

Ingredients

Yeast doughs are made from flour, fat, liquid, yeast, and salt. Richer doughs contain sugar, eggs, and flavorings. There are two basic doughs—the bread, or lean; and the sweet, or rich. Many variations are found between them. Ingredient proportions are usually stated in percentages, related to flour as 100%. Normally, ingredients will be found to vary within the following ranges:

	Lean	Rich*
Flour, bread	100%	65 to 100%
Flour, cake		0 to 35%
Sugar, granulated	2 to 3%	6 to 25%
Shortening	1 to 12%	8 to 40%
Eggs, whole		10 to 45%
Yeast, compressed	2 to 3%	2 to 8%
Liquid	58 to 60%	40 to 60%
Milk, non-fat, dry	0 to 6%	3 to 8%
Salt	1 to 2½%	1½ to 2½%
Spices		¼ to ½%
Flavoring		¼ to ½%
Conditioner	¼ to ½%	¼ to ½%

*For a rolled-in dough, use margarine or other shortening 20 to 50% of the flour for rolling in.

Good quality flours must be used. All yeast breads will require some bread flour, and this should come from good quality hard wheat. Enriched flours should be used, or enrichening pellets should be added to the dough during mixing.

Salt will contribute flavor, assist in developing fine cellular structure, strengthen the gluten, retard moisture absorption by the flour, and give whiteness to the crumb. Breads made from graham or rye flours or those high in milk and shortening require more salt. Salt controls yeast growth, especially that of wild yeasts. If rapid fermentation is desired, from ½ to 1% of salt is used; greater amounts slow it down. Where temperatures

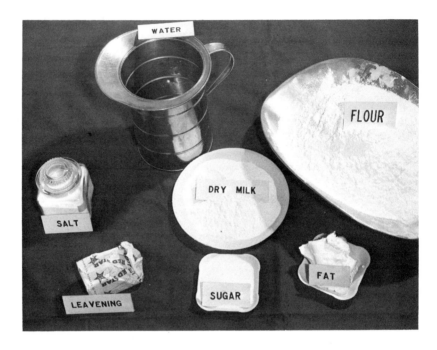

FIG. 11-4 Basic ingredients for a bread dough. Milk and sugar could be omitted and a bread dough would still result. Richer doughs have eggs added and higher percentages of fat and sugar.

are high and cannot be controlled, salt is helpful in controlling the fermentation rate. Salt is never mixed directly with the yeast. It is added to the sponge doughs in the second mixing. Low-sodium breads should be made with calcium salt.

The quantity of liquid used will also assist in controlling fermentation; a slack dough ferments faster than a firmer one. Liquid is also used to establish the correct temperature for fermentation. To obtain the correct temperature after mixing:

1. Take the temperature of the flour; add the temperature of the room and the expected rise in temperature from mixing friction (about 10° to 15° F). For instance, if these are respectively 65°, 70°, and 10° F, the total will be 145° F.

2. Multiply the temperature you want your dough to be for fermentation by 3, and subtract from the result the sum obtained above. This gives the correct temperature of the liquid to use for mixing. For instance, if the desired temperature is 75° F, the calculation will be $3 \times 75° = 225° - 145° = 80°$ F for the water temperature.

Occasionally, it is necessary to use ice in place of water to obtain the correct temperature.

Certain minerals in hard water may be helpful because they strengthen gluten, but an excess may toughen it so it will not ripen properly in fermentation. A strong alkaline reaction weakens gluten. Some hard-water salts retard enzymatic action and cause a weak fermentation. If the water is acid, fermentation may be too rapid. Mineral yeast foods, called conditioners, are used to balance water so it is suitable for good growth of the yeast. A conditioner will reduce fermentation time and losses and give a softer, drier dough with a strengthened gluten, suitable for use in machine production. Greater volume, better uniformity of product, and improved keeping qualities are obtained, as well as improved oven spring, color, grain, and smoothness of crumb. Because diastatic and maltase activity is favored, crust bloom is improved. Conditioners depress the action of wild yeast. Conditioners are added with the liquid in straight doughs and with the second flour in a sponge.

The right quantity of moisture is important to final product quality. If an insufficient amount of liquid is added, the dough will not develop proper elasticity, tenacity, and viscosity and will not handle well in mixing, kneading, and shaping. Straight doughs take up more moisture than sponges. If the absorption rate of the flour used is not known, add flour to the liquid, stopping when the dough is at proper consistency.

In quantity work, non-fat dry milk and water are used. Added shortening can replace the missing milk fat in the amount of $4\frac{1}{2}$ ounces of fat per gallon of liquid used. Milk improves flavor, nutrient value, keeping quality, and crust color and softens the cellular structure. It depresses bread volume but contributes strength to the flour proteins. Fermentation is retarded and stabilized by the buffering action of milk. The color of the crumb is more creamy when milk is used. Usually milk is omitted from hard-crust breads, for milk tends to give a softer crust. Up to 6% milk solids may be used in lean doughs, and rich doughs may contain up to 8%. Excess milk solids may give a sticky dough; this condition is frequently noted in mixing but usually disappears during fermentation. Dry milk should be sifted in with the flour.

Sugars give flavor, improve crust color, and furnish food for yeast growth. From 2 to 10% sugar is used in lean doughs, and rich doughs may have up to 25%. Above 10%, yeast growth is slowed; more yeast is added to such doughs to counteract this. The milk sugar, lactose, cannot be used by yeast, but lactose gives good crust color.

Emulsifying agents may be added to increase the tenderizing action of shortening. These may be lecithin, monoglycerides, or diglycerides. In addition, these emulsifiers retard staling and tend to keep bread moist and soft. Excess quantities of emulsifiers are harmful to bread quality. Lard may be used as the shortening for bread.

Cultured yeasts are used for bread. Yeast is a one-celled plant which grows by feeding upon glucose. A yeast stock can be made by allowing wild yeast from the air to start in a culture such as potato water or other moist product containing sugar or starch, but breads made from such yeast usually lack quality. Old bread dough may be added to new bread dough for yeast culture if yeast is not available.

Yeast grows best between 78 and 90° F; growth is slowed above 98° F, and yeast is destroyed at temperatures above 140° F. Moisture must be present in liberal quantities for proper growth. Salt or other chlorides retard yeast activity, while sulfates and phosphates promote it; phosphates are essential for yeast nutrition. The amount of yeast used in warm weather will be less than that used during cold weather.

Compressed and active dry yeast are the most commonly used yeasts. Keep compressed yeast at 45° F. Freezing may affect some of the compressed yeast's activity, but if not frozen for over 30 days and if thawed at 40° F

FIG. 11-5 The three types of yeast. Top, compressed. **Right, dry active granule. Left, old-fashioned cake. The last is seldom used.**

(a)

(b)

(c)

FIG. 11-6   (a) Condition dry active yeast in water at about 110° F — no higher — and condition compressed yeast in water at around 100° F. (b) The effect of too warm a temperature, salt, and 100° F water with a bit of sugar are shown on yeast growth. (c) When using compressed yeast, sprinkle into warm water as shown. To use dry active yeast, sift over the warm water. Let both stand about three minutes before stirring.

and slightly more is used, good results will be obtained. Compressed yeast contains approximately 70% moisture. Active dry yeast is the equal of compressed yeast. It is shaped into small pellets, dried, and packed in hermetically sealed cans. Freezing does not harm it. It contains approximately 8% moisture. One pound of active dry yeast equals 2½ pounds of compressed yeast. Crumble compressed or sprinkle dry active yeast into water; allow to stand for three to four minutes and then stir. The water should be a part of the total water used. Weigh, do not measure yeast.

Table 11-1
Ratios for Using Compressed and Dry Yeasts

Compressed Yeast	Active Dry Yeast	Water* Weight**	Approximate Measure
1 oz	½ oz	2 oz	¼ c
2 oz	¾ oz	3 oz	½ c
4 oz	1½ oz	6 oz	1 c
8 oz	3¼ oz	13 oz	1 pt
12 oz	4¾ oz	1 lb 3 oz	1¼ pt
1 lb	6½ oz	1 lb 10 oz	1¾ pt
2 lb	12¾ oz	3 lb 3 oz	1 qt 1¼ pt
3 lb	1 lb 3¼ oz	4 lb 14 oz	2 qt 1 pt
4 lb	1 lb 9½ oz	6 lb 6 oz	3 qt 1 c
5 lb	2 lb	8 lb	4 qt

*Water temperatures should be 90° to 100° F for compressed yeast and 5° to 10° F higher for dry active yeast.
**Corrected to nearest ¼ oz.

Mold inhibitors and moisteners are oftentimes added to doughs to reduce mold growths and to assist in giving moistness to bread. Poor sanitation or improper cooling will favor mold contamination. Mold develops rapidly above 80° F, and refrigeration or freezing may be required to inhibit its development even though refrigeration increases staling. Proper handling of breads, thorough baking, and the use of a mold inhibitor such as sodium or calcium propionate will reduce the danger of mold and rope. The latter is caused by a bacteria called *bacillus mesentericus*, which digests the crumb of bread into a sticky, pasty mass that has a dark color and an odor similar to that of an over-ripe cantaloupe. When the crumb is pressed together and pulled apart, it will stretch into silky threads. These bacteria grow best at temperatures between 90° and 95° F. Control is obtained by good sanitation, the introduction of an acid into the dough, or the use of conditioners. Once a bakeshop is infected with rope, all floors and equipment must be thoroughly cleaned. Heavy steam cleaning—or washing equipment with a solution of vinegar—destroys the bacteria. Good bread has a pH of from 5.5 to 5; a pH of 4.6 kills rope. A pint of vinegar, 40 to 45 grain, for every 100 pounds of flour—or the use of an inhibitor, 2½ to 3½ ounces or 4 to 5 ounces per 100 pounds of white or dark flour used, respectively—will usually control rope.

Mixes

Bread and roll mixes may be used. These contain all ingredients except water and yeast. Once they are mixed, handling is the same as for regular breads. The quantity of rolls made from varying quantities of mix are approximately by the straight-dough method are:

Yield	Pounds of Mix					
	4 lb	6 lb	8 lb	10 lb	12 lb	16 lb
1 oz rolls	75	115	150	190	225	300
1¼ oz rolls	65	100	130	160	200	250

Procedures
The steps required and their approximate times in making yeast breads by the straight dough method are

1.	Weighing and mixing.	12 min
2.	Fermentation.	45 min to 1 hr
3.	Punching.	3 min
4.	Benching and resting.	10 to 15 min
5.	Make-up.	20 min
6.	Proofing.	15 to 30 min
7.	Baking.	1 hr loaf; 20 min rolls
8.	Cooling.	
9.	Storing.	

Total time for producing a loaf of bread or a batch of rolls may be from two to four hours, but the actual production time for one worker by hand should be about 45 minutes for 100 portions or 11 pounds of dough.

Weighing and Mixing

Use standardized recipes. Weighing should be accurate. It is well to assemble all ingredients before the start of mixing. Three types of doughs may be prepared: a straight dough, a sponge dough, and a no-time dough.

Straight doughs are most frequently used in food services. Mixing is done by vertical mixer or hand. Dry ingredients are added to liquid and rehydrated yeast. Slow speed and a dough hook are used, and mixing is continued until a firm, solid paste is formed which leaves the sides of the bowl. As mixing continues, lumpiness disappears, and the dough becomes firm as the flour picks up moisture. More mixing causes the dough to relax and become elastic. When taken from the mixer, the dough can be taken in the two hands and stretched out into a sheet that is thin as cellophane. This sheet will show a uniform consistency having no dense areas. A flat hand placed on the dough should leave its impression; when the hand is raised, the points of raised dough will quickly subside. Some properly mixed doughs will show a few bubbles about the size of a silver dollar on the surface in about five minutes, but too many and smaller bubbles indicate an over-mixed dough. Mixing times must be varied to suit the flour strength. Breads made from weak flour should be under-mixed, and slightly less water is usually added to produce firmer dough. A sweet dough should not be developed into as strong a dough as bread or roll doughs. Doughs should come from the mixer from 74° to 84° F.

Sponge dough is usually made by large bake shops in horizontal high-speed mixers. For this, about 60% of the flour and all of the liquid and yeast are mixed together to form a thick batter. Fermentation is from 77° to 80° F. In this process the dough doubles in bulk and becomes wavy or ripply so that at a slight touch it collapses. The dough is then punched, and the remaining flour, all the salt, sugar, shortening, milk solids, and conditioners are added, along with nutrient enrichers. A second fermentation period occurs.

A no-time dough is mixed in the same way as a straight dough. It is used in most operations for dinner rolls. The quantities of conditioner, sugar, and yeast used are raised to maximum levels. The dough should come from the mixer at about 90° F, and fermentation temperature is held at this level. No-time doughs are taken to the bench young, which means that the dough is allowed to rise to about three-fourths of a full rise. There will be noticeable firmness when the hand is pressed into it. Proofing should be less for these doughs than for regular ones. The dough is usually used for the production of rolls when time is short, but it may be avoided by using retarded doughs or by freezing doughs after make-up. Product quality of no-time dough items is not as high as that of the others.

Fermentation

Leavening results when yeast, a plant, multiplies during fermentation. In multiplying, yeast converts glucose to carbon dioxide, water, and alcohol. Diastase, an enzyme, converts starch to maltose, and other enzymes change this to glucose. If the diastatic action is too strong, the dough may become slack and sticky. Millers usually control the amount of diastase that remains in finished flour. Also, finely milled flours speed fermentation by making starch more readily available for diastatic action. Diastase malt or special sirups may be added to assure good diastatic action and food for the yeast. The enzyme, invertase, is carried in the yeast plant so it can change sucrose to glucose and fructose. Protease enzymes are active in fermentation; excessive action by them may be harmful to strong gluten formation. Fresh milk used for bread may be scalded to destroy these enzymes. Usually dry milks used in bread making are treated by heat to reduce the quantity of protease enzymes found in them. Protease activity is reduced in aged flours and when

FIG. 11-7 In making a straight dough, the flour, dry milk, salt and sugar are added to the liquid shown in Fig. 11-6C. Next, add shortening if it is a solid, but if the shortening is a liquid, add it to the liquid ingredients *before* the dry ingredients.

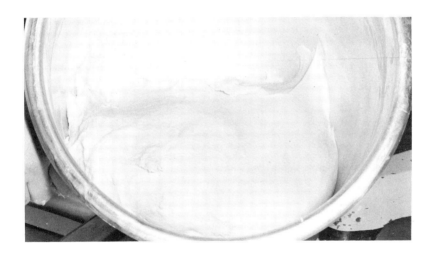

FIG. 11-8 A straight dough at the end of mixing.

conditioners are used. Some proteolytic action is beneficial because it tenderizes gluten.

During fermentation the dough ripens; the gluten completely hydrates and becomes pliable, elastic, and less tenacious. The dough becomes soft, smooth, and almost silky. Extended or too rapid fermentation or too high

(a)   (b)

FIG. 11-9   Sweet doughs are richer than dinner roll or bread doughs. (a) Eggs, best at room temperatures, and (b) sugar are added to the liquid just before the other dry ingredients, as shown here. In addition, more shortening is usually added.

a fermentation temperature may develop excessive acidity and a sour dough. Proper timing and temperature are required, and fermentation rooms are provided if the quantity of yeast products made is high. A humidity of 75% is desirable. If the humidity is not correct, the dough should be covered or brushed on top with oil or shortening to prevent the formation of a crust. Fermentation times vary. Fermentation is indicated when the dough doubles in volume or when the fingers, inserted about three inches into the dough, have little resistance and the dough recedes or puckers away from the fingers.

Doughs made from flours lacking good gluten, such as, graham or rye flour, no-time doughs, and doughs which require considerable handling after fermentation, may be taken to the bench young.

Punch

Punching a dough is not knocking or pushing it down, but folding the dough over from the sides into the middle until most of the gas is expelled. The dough is then turned upside down in the fermentation container. Good punching remixes ingredients so the yeast obtains new food; the gluten is also relaxed. If a bucky, weak, or pastry flour is used, the punch may be omitted and the dough brought directly to the bench to rest. Some straight doughs are fermented a second time after punching. Sponge doughs are punched, given a second mixing, and then fermented again. Usually this second fermentation time is on the basis of one minute for every 1

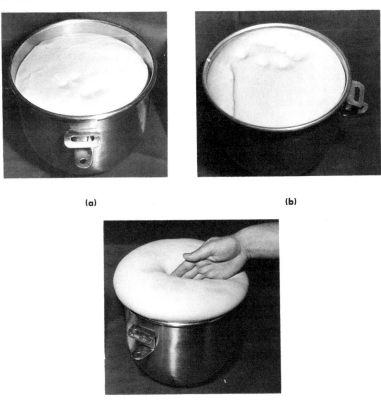

(a)   (b)

(c)

FIG. 11-10 Doughs may be taken to the bench (a) young, (b) moderately young, or (c) fully fermented. Note how in the young doughs there is still resistance to pressure, but in a fully fermented dough there is a collapse of the dough when the hand is inserted.

per cent of the total flour added in this second mixing. Straight doughs are fermented from 1½ to 2½ hours, but sponge doughs are fermented longer. Usually from 70 to 80% of the total fermentation time occurs in the first fermentation of a dough. In bakeshops these ratios are called 70-30 or 80-20 fermentations. There is about a 2% loss in weight in fermenting.

Bench and Rest

When fermentation is complete, the dough is brought to the work bench and given a rest of about 10 to 20 minutes, during which time the dough becomes relaxed and pliable for handling. The rest time for richer doughs may vary from this time.

Make-up

After resting, doughs are ready for make-up. This is a process in which items are shaped for baking. Rolls are divided into proper sizes, rounded or molded, and then panned. Loaf bread is divided, scaled, rounded, given intermediate proof, molded, and panned. For every pound of baked item desired, two extra ounces of dough must be added, for baking loss is around 12%. Allow 1½ dinner rolls per person. Scale dinner rolls at one pound per dozen, and breakfast rolls at two per portion, one ounce each, or two ounces each if only one roll is given per portion.

FIG. 11-11   A punch is not a punch. Rather, the dough is lifted up and turned over. After such a punch, turn the dough completely over, especially in sponge doughs.

Table 11-2

Handling and Flow of Sweet Dough

Mix From Mixer at 74°-84° F

| Normal Fermentation | | | Retarding* | | | |
Sweet Dough	Rolled-in Dough	Danish	Danish	Sweet Dough	Sweet Dough	Rolled-in Dough
Give ¾ to one full rise.	Give ¾ to one full rise.	Let loosen; roll in 2 to 4 oz of butter, margarine, or shortening per pound of dough.	Let loosen; roll in 2 to 4 oz of butter, margarine, or shortening per pound of dough.	Flatten 10 to fit sheet pan; refrigerate.*	Give ¾ normal fermentation.	Give ¾ normal fermentation.
Make-up.	Roll in 2 to 4 oz of butter, margarine, or shortening per pound of dough. Let dough loosen; make up.	Rest 45 minutes; make up.	Make up.	Bring to room temperature.	Make up.	Roll in 2 to 4 oz of butter, margarine, or shortening per pound of dough. Make up.
			Refrigerate.*	Make-up.	Refrigerate.*	Bring to room temperature.
			Bring to room temperature.		Bring to room temperature.	
Proof.				Proof.		
Bake.				Bake.		

*Use retarding method only for richer sweet doughs; refrigerate from 35° to 40° F with relative humidity at 85%; do not retard over 72 hours.

To roll shortening into a dough, roll it out about three-fourths to an inch thick and about three times as long as wide. Margarine, butter, or shortening is then dotted over two-thirds of the surface. The uncovered third is folded over half of the covered part. The remaining covered third is then folded over the top, giving three layers of dough and two layers of

(a)   (b)

(c)   (d)

FIG. 11-12   The making of a sponge dough. The sponge method is oftentimes used when a large quantity of bread is made. (a) Dough coming from the mixer and being dumped into a dough trough. (b) Moving the sponge in a dough trough to the fermentation room. Notice the rough quality of the dough. (c) The temperature and humidity of the fermentation room must be carefully controlled. (d) The sponge after the first fermentation being moved back to the mixer. Note the smoother quality of the dough at this stage. (Courtesy American Baking Institute)

FIG. 11-13 The final steps in making bread are shown. The baker on the near right checks the final fermentation of the dough and feeds it into the divider. The next man checks the dough as it goes through the divider, and the third man in this assembly line places the rounded pieces of dough in an intermediate proofer. (Courtesy Standard Brands, Inc.)

shortening. After a rest, usually under refrigeration, of 35 to 45 minutes for Danish and 10 to 15 minutes for sweet dough, the dough is made up.

Rounding is a process in which a loaf is shaped into a smooth, round ball. For this, the dough should be soft and elastic, as it is worked and gas escapes, it may "squeak like a mouse." The surface should be smooth at the finish, for a rough surface will allow gas to escape in proofing. After rounding, an intermediate proof is given of eight to 12 minutes. This allows the loaf to recover from the effects of make-up. If this rest is not given, the dough is tight and bucky and shapes up poorly in panning. Next, the loaf is molded into desired shape and panned. Adept, rapid motion is desirable in make-up.

Doughs may be retarded or frozen so they can be freshly baked for service. Sugar and yeast are increased slightly in such doughs. The richer doughs lend themselves to this type of handling. They are taken to the bench young, made up, and then retarded or frozen. If desired, the dough may

(a)   (b)

(c)

FIG. 11-14 (a) A baker checks the dough as it leaves the divider and enters into the
rounder. (b) He again checks the product as it comes from the molder and places the
molded loaf in the greased pans. (c) Dough coming automatically from the molder and
being dropped into greased pans. (Courtesy Standard Brands [a] and [b] and American
Baking Institute [c])

(a)

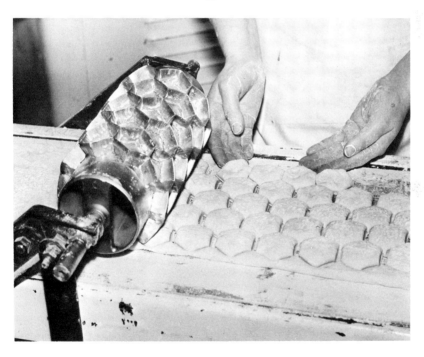

(b)

FIG. 11-15   Here in a large bakeshop an assembly-line production system for producing dinner rolls is shown. (a) The baker shapes the dough just before it goes to make-up. (b) The dough travels along the belt and is cut by the discs shown here. Workers pick up the rolls and place them into pans. The rolls then move to proofing, after which they are baked.

(a)

(b)

(c)

FIG. 11-16 A rolled-in dough is either a dinner roll dough or a sweet dough which has shortening added as shown. (a) The dough is rolled out about three-fourths inch thick. (b) It is next dotted with a plastic shortening shown here; butter, margarine, or a good quality shortening may be used. (c) Fold as shown.

(d)

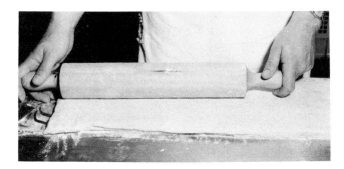

(e)

(f)

FIG. 11-16 (continued)   (d) Divide the dough; allow it to rest, as shown here; and place it under refrigeration from 35 to 45 minutes or 10 to 15 minutes, depending on whether it is Danish or sweet dough.   (e) Roll out to original size as shown, setting the length of the roll parallel to the worker.   (f) Two fingers pressed into the dough indicates that this dough is at its second turn or rolling.

(a)   (b)

(c)   (d)

FIG. 11-17   Making a sweet dough into cinnamon rolls. (a) The dough is rolled into a long rectangular strip which is liberally buttered. It is then spread with cinnamon and sugar (10 sugar to 1 cinnamon). (b) The dough is then rolled lengthwise. (c) Cut and pan on a greased baking sheet as shown. (d) To give variety, cut thicker than cinnamon rolls and crease.

(a)

(b)

(c)

(d)

FIG. 11-18 (a) To make pan rolls, cut dough as shown on the right and roll with both hands. (b) Place a round roll into a muffin pan and divide with a wooden cutter dipped into butter as shown. (c) A quick and easy way to make clover leaf rolls. (d) To make fan tans or butter rolls, roll the dough and then fold, seeing that between folds the dough is liberally spread with butter. Cut and place into pans as shown.

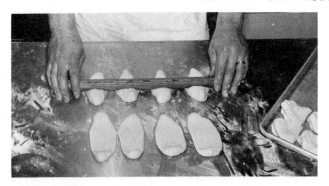

(a)

(b)

(c)

FIG. 11-19   The make-up of (a) Parker House rolls, (b) hamburger buns, and (c) finger or wiener buns is shown.

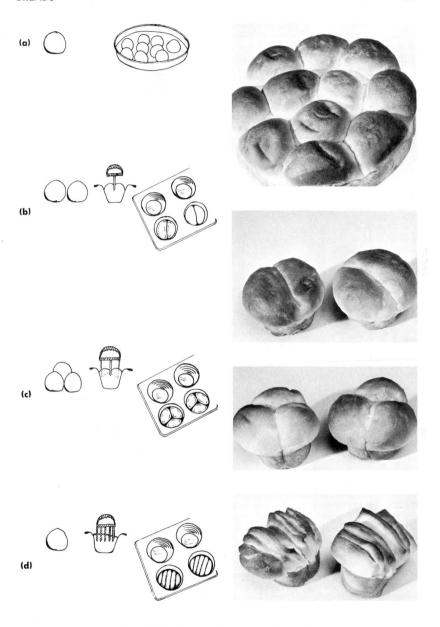

FIG. 11-20 Some techniques used to make
the rolls shown on the right are shown: (a)
pan rolls, (b) twin rolls, (c) cloverleaf rolls,
and (d) fan tans or butter rolls.

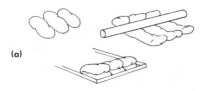

(a)

(b)

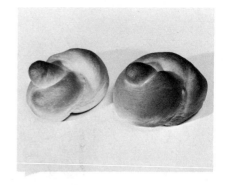

(c)

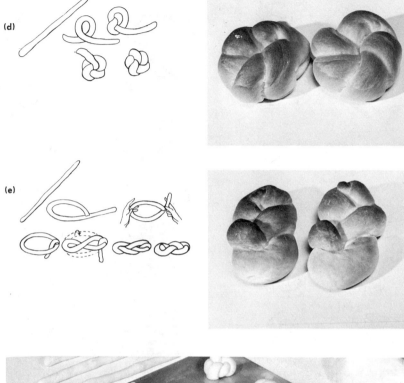

FIG. 11-21 (a) Parker House rolls (b) single knot rolls, (c) double knot roll, (d) kaiser knot roll, and (e) triple or braided rolls are made as shown, (f) Sometimes the single knot and the double knot rolls are called bowknots or rosettes. (Courtesy Wheat Flour Institute)

(a)   (b)

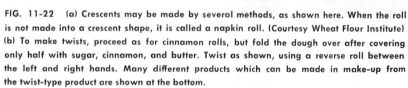

FIG. 11-22   (a) Crescents may be made by several methods, as shown here. When the roll
is not made into a crescent shape, it is called a napkin roll. (Courtesy Wheat Flour Institute)
(b) To make twists, proceed as for cinnamon rolls, but fold the dough over after covering
only half with sugar, cinnamon, and butter. Twist as shown, using a reverse roll between
the left and right hands. Many different products which can be made in make-up from
the twist-type product are shown at the bottom.

FIG. 11-23 Rolls of dough such as those used for cinnamon rolls may be varied in size and made into a wide variety of shapes. By varying filling and cutting, an almost endless variety of products can be offered on any menu.

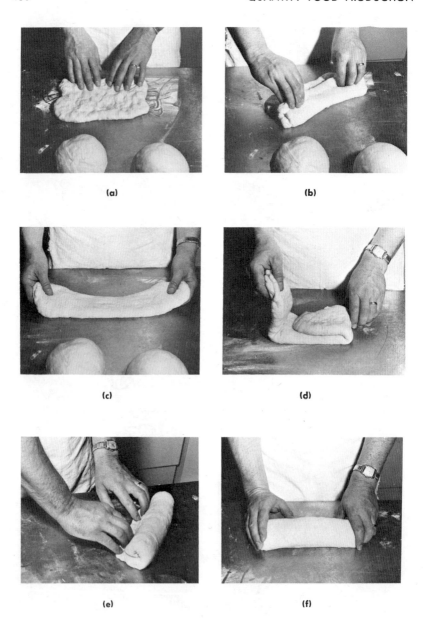

FIG. 11-24   To make a loaf of bread, divide the dough and allow it to rest. (a) Shape the loaf. (b) Fold into a three fold. (c) Stretch into a length double the pan size. (d) Fold again into three. (e) Pat the dough out and fold sealing the edge as shown. (f) The finished loaf should be panned with the seam side down, as shown.

FIG. 11-25   French breads are made from a very lean dough. Here we see a baker making up long loaves for French bread. These are then proofed, placed on a peel, and baked directly on the floors of brick-lined ovens. Steam in baking is used to give a thick, heavy crust.

(a)   (b)

FIG. 11-26   (a) Doughs placed for retarding in a refrigerator. These may be taken later, given a proof, and be ready shortly for baking. (b) Sweet rolls in a freezer. These are removed from the freezer when needed, left at room temperature under original wrap to thaw, then placed into a proofer, and then baked.

be divided into ten-pound pieces, flattened on baking sheets, covered, and retarded or frozen. For retarding, temperatures should be 40° F and relative humidity 85% or more. It is best not to retard doughs longer than 72 hours. Cover to prevent drying out in storage.

Proof

Temperatures should be between 90° to 100° F and relative humidity 80 to 85% in the proof period. The time may vary from 15 to 45 minutes, with 30 to 45 minutes a standard time for loaves. No-time doughs have a shorter proofing period and are usually taken to the oven slightly under-proofed. After proofing, the dough should have about doubled in volume from its make-up size. The outer surface should be smooth and light in appearance. Final conditioning of the dough occurs in proofing, with the gluten becoming quite tender and extended. Firming by baking is now required to preserve structure and shape.

Baking

Baking should proceed immediately after proof. Over-proofing will

FIG. 11-27   Rolls from the proofer, loaded onto a cart and on their way to the ovens.

give an open grain, a gray color to the crumb, and a loss of flavor. Care should be exercised in oven loading, for the dough is now fragile. Heavy loading of an oven may drop baking temperatures too low, and recovery may lag. In such cases, preheat to a slightly higher temperature than desired, add the yeast products, and set the oven temperature at the desired level.

A pound loaf of bread, well proofed, should be baked at 425° F for 15 minutes and then at 375° F for 45 minutes. If slightly under-proofed, bake for an hour at from 375° to 400° F. Larger loaves may require slightly lower temperatures and longer baking. Rolls spaced apart require 15 to 30 minutes at 425° F, but pan rolls and others that touch must be baked nearly as long as loaf breads. Bake rich doughs at slightly lower temperatures than lean doughs.

During the early part of baking, the rise is quite rapid. Not only does the carbon dioxide gas expand, but the enzymatic activity proceeds at a very rapid rate until the temperature of the product reaches 140° F, at which time it is destroyed. This rapid development is known as oven spring. When the starch is completely swelled and the protein coagulated, the

FIG. 11-28 Cool rolls on wire racks. If allowed to cool in the pans in which they baked, they may steam and become soggy.

structure will firm. A shred or break on the side of a loaf occurs because the rise continues after the exterior is set by heat. Small products bake uniformly and do not show this shred. Docking must be used for some products to allow for this final expansion without bursting the product. Color or bloom is now developed on the outside through a caramelizing of sugars and dextrins. Low baking temperatures cause a pale, rubbery crust to form and give poor oven spring and a poor texture. Excessive heat or sugar will cause an over-brown thick crust when done. Steam is used to develop a thick crust on breads. A good bread when done will have a hollow sound when tapped.

Cooling

After baking, loaves, large rolls, and rolls that touch in the pan are dumped from their pans onto cooling racks. This allows steam and alcohol to escape. Drafts or air that is too cool may cause breads to crack. Rolls that are to be served soon after baking while still warm should be completely baked, but rolls that will be cooled and held and then rewarmed in an oven

FIG. 11-29   Sweet rolls shown Figures 11-23 and 11-27 are shown here after baking.

Table 11-3
Trouble-Shooting Bread Failures

Fault	Possible Causes	Possible Remedies
Excessive volume.	Too much yeast.	Reduce yeast to 2 to 3%; check weighing procedures.
	Too little salt.	Maintain from 2 to 2½%; check weighing procedures.
	Excess dough.	Reduce scaling weights.
	Overproofed.	Reduce proofing time; keep between 70-30 or 80-20 fermentation time for sponges.
	Too cool oven.	Increase temperature.
Poor volume.	Weak flour.	Blend strong flour into flour or use a stronger flour; give less mixing, shorter fermentation, and less proofing time.
	Flour too old or too new.	Use aged flour; check age of flour.
	Water too soft or too alkaline.	Use a conditioner; additional salt improves too soft a water.
	Lack of leavening.	Use good yeast and handle it properly; have dough at proper temperature; reduce quantity of salt.
	Undermixing.	Increase mixing times until gluten in dough is properly developed; proper volume of dough to mixer is also a factor to check.
	Overfermented dough.	Reduce fermentation time.
	Overmixing.	Reduce mixing.
	Improper proofing.	Proof between 90° and 100° F and 80 to 85% relative humidity; watch proofing time and maintain proper ratio between fermentation and proofing procedures.
	Too much or too little steam in oven.	Open or close oven dampers; if steam is introduced into oven, establish better controls.
	Too hot oven.	Reduce temperature.
Too dark crust.	Excess sugar or milk.	Reduce; check diastatic action of flour; it may be breaking down too much starch into sugars.
	Overmixing.	Reduce mixing.
	Dough too young.	Increase fermentation and proof periods.
	Too hot oven.	Correct oven temperatures.
	Too long baking.	Reduce baking time.
	Too dry oven.	Close oven damper during part of baking, or use steam.
Too pale or dull color on crust.	Wrong proportion or lack of right ingredients.	Check ratios of sugar, salt, or milk, and diastatic action of flour; increase ingredients to proper ratios; add diastase sirup.
	Soft water.	Increase salt or add conditioner.
	Overfermentation.	Reduce temperature or time of fermentation.
	Excessive dusting flour.	Cover bench only with bare minimum.
	Too high proof temperature.	Reduce temperature.
	Cool oven.	Increase temperature.
	Improper use of steam.	Avoid excessive steam; open dampers to increase oven moisture.
Spotted crust.	Improper mixing.	Follow correct mixing procedures and sequence of adding ingredients.
	Excess dusting flour.	Reduce dusting flour.
	Excess humidity in proofing.	Reduce relative humidity to between 80 and 85%.
	Water in oven or excessive moisture in steam.	Check steam pipes and ovens; open dampers.

Table 11-3
Trouble-Shooting Bread Failures

Fault	Possible Causes	Possible Remedies
Hard crust or blisters.	Lack of sugar or diastatic action.	Increase sugars or check diastatic action of flour; check weighing of ingredients.
	Slack dough.	Reduce liquid; check mixing.
	Improper mixing.	Check mixing procedures and sequence of ingredient addition.
	Old or young dough.	Correct the fermentation time.
	Improper molding or make-up.	Correct procedures.
	Cool oven or too much top heat.	Check damper handling procedures and oven temperatures; check heating elements and heat source to see if functioning properly; check oven circulation.
	Cooling too rapidly.	Cool more slowly; keep out of drafts.
	Too much fat on product.	Reduce brushing of fat after make-up.
Poor shape.	Improper make-up or panning.	Correct procedures.
	Overproofing.	Reduce.
Flat top or sharp corners.	New flour.	Age flour six to eight months under proper conditions.
	Low salt.	Increase; check weighing procedures.
	Slack dough.	Reduce liquid; check mixing.
	Young dough.	Increase fermentation time.
	Excessive humidity in proofing.	Reduce humidity.
Excessive break on side.	Overmixing.	Reduce mixing.
	Improper molding.	Check molding, especially seam folds; place seam folds down on bottom of pan.
	Young dough.	Correct; check proofing time.
	Hot oven.	Reduce temperatures.
Thick crust.	Low shortening, sugar, or milk.	Increase; check scaling procedures.
	Low diastase.	Check diastatic action of flour; add malt sirup or diastase compound.
	Mixing improper.	Correct mixing procedures.
	Improper proofing.	Correct temperature, relative humidity, or time of proofing; check for wet crusts after proofing.
	Old dough.	Correct fermentation and/or proofing time.
	Improper baking.	Correct temperatures and times; reduce steam and check for excessive or insufficient moisture in ovens.
Tough crust.	Old or young dough.	Check fermentation times.
	Improper mixing.	Correct.
	Excess proof or wrong proof conditions.	Correct.
	Oven cold or excess steam.	Correct.
Lack of break or shred.	Excess diastase.	Decrease amount; use non-diastatic malt; check diastatic action of flour.
	Soft water.	Increase salt or use conditioner.
	Slack dough.	Reduce water substantially; check mixing.
	Improper fermentation or proof time.	Correct.
	Too hot or too dry an oven.	Correct temperatures by damper control; introduce steam.

Table 11-3
Trouble-Shooting Bread Failures

Fault	Possible Causes	Possible Remedies
Ragged scaling or shelling on top.	Green or overly old flour.	Use flour properly aged.
	Old or young dough.	Check fermentation or proof times and conditions.
	Stiff dough.	Reduce flour or increase liquid.
	Crusting during proofing.	Increase relative humidity; brush lightly with shortening.
	Excess salt.	Reduce.
	Underproofing.	Increase proofing time.
	Excessive top heat in oven.	Check heat circulation and heat source in oven; check damper control.
	Cold dough.	Add warmer liquid; check mixing, fermentation, and proofing temperatures.
	Excessive dough in pan.	Check scaling.
	Lack of salt or milk.	Check recipe and weighing procedures.
Too close grain.	Low yeast.	Increase; check weighing procedures.
	Underproofing.	Correct.
	Excess dough in pan.	Check scaling procedures.
Too coarse or open grain.	Hard or alkaline water.	Add vinegar or conditioner.
	Old dough.	Excess yeast; reduce fermentation time.
	Slack dough.	Reduce liquid; check mixing times.
	Improper molding.	Correct.
	Overproofing.	Reduce time or check temperatures.
	Improper pan size.	Check.
	Cold oven.	Increase oven temperature.
	Excessive greasing.	Check oiling or greasing of dough.
Gray crumb.	High diastatic action.	Reduce.
	High dough temperature or over fermentation.	Check mixing, fermentation, and proof temperatures and times.
	Cold oven.	Check temperatures and conditions of baking.
	Pans greasy.	Check greasing.
Streaked crumb.	Improper mixing.	Check ingredient sequence of adding in mixing.
	Too slack or stiff dough.	Check liquid or flour quantities; check to see if proper mixing times given.
	Excessive oil or grease, or dusting flour used.	Correct.
	High relative humidity.	Reduce relative humidity in fermentation or proofing.
	Crusting of dough in fermentation.	Increase relative humidity or brush with fat; cover to prevent moisture loss.
Poor texture.	Alkaline or very hard water.	Use conditioner or vinegar.
	Too slack or too stiff dough.	Reduce or increase ingredients to correct ratios; check mixing.
	High sugar or excess yeast.	Check ingredient ratios; check diastase, and decrease or increase as required.
	Lack of shortening.	Increase.
	High dough temperature.	Reduce liquid temperature or temperatures during fermentation or proofing.
	Overfermentation or proofing.	Reduce.

Table 11-3 (Cont.)
Trouble-Shooting Bread Failures

Fault	Possible Causes	Possible Remedies
Poor texture (cont.)	Excessive dusting of flour.	Reduce.
	Low oven temperature.	Increase.
Off- and/or cheesy flavor.	Inferior milk, rancid shortening; paint, gasoline, etc.	Check ingredients used; check flour, other ingredients for off-flavors; check storage areas where ingredients are held; check pans and other equipment for rancidity; check sanitation.
	Improper mixing or method.	Check procedures.
Flat flavor.	Low salt.	Increase salt.

may be slightly underbaked. Brush breads with shortening to prevent crusts from becoming dry in cooling.

Storage

Wrap or place bread in moisture-vapor-proof containers if it is to be stored over eight to 10 hours. Otherwise, store on racks. Breads need protection, and clean, dry containers should be provided even for short storage. Storage near heat should be avoided. Hard, crisp breads should be used as soon as possible, and they should be baked daily. Place these in open boxes or in paper bags.

The staling of bread is a deterioration characterized by a loss of aroma, increase in firmness and crumbliness, and development of a harsh crumb texture. Breads may be held for extended periods if frozen in moisture-vapor-proof wraps. The best quality results when freezing is at –10 to –20° F, with linear air speed at 500 feet per minute. Storage should be at 0° F or lower. To use, unwrap and thaw at 115° F, preferably, or at room temperature. Frozen rolls may be heated uncovered in a 375 to 400° F oven for 5 to 10 minutes and served immediately. Freezing will not restore the freshness of stale or partially stale bread. Breads stale more rapidly under refrigeration than they do at room temperature. French toast, toast, or grilled sandwiches may be made from slightly stale bread without noticeable loss of quality. Overly stale bread can be used for dressings or crumbs.

QUICK BREADS

Quick breads belong to the family of batters and doughs. Baking powder or soda are usually used for leavening, but steam, air, yeast, or baking ammonia may also be used.

Many batters and doughs are closely related, but slight variation in the

Table 11-4

Approximate Ingredient Percentages in Quick Breads
(Based on flour at 100%)

Ingredient	Biscuits %	Muffins %	Cornbread %	Griddle-cakes %	Waffles %	Popovers %	Eclair Paste %
Flour, bread	0 to 50						
Flour pastry	50 to 100	100*	100**	100	100*	100	100
Sugar	0 to 2	10 to 65	5 to 25	2 to 10	15 to 30		
Shortening	20 to 30	20 to 40	6 to 20	5 to 15	50 to 40		100
Eggs	0 to 10	20 to 25	20 to 25	15 to 35	20 to 65	100	175
Liquid	60 to 70***	70 to 80	80 to 90	125 to 200	130 to 180	200	200
Milk, dry. non-fat	7	8	8	10 to 15	10 to 15	20	
Baking powder, double acting	6	6	8½	6 to 10	6 to 8		
Salt	1 to 2	1 to 2	1 to 2	1 to 2	1 to 2	1 to 2	1 to 2

* For greater tenderness, cake flour may be used.

** About 50% of the flour is cornmeal.

***For shortcakes reduce liquid to 50 to 60% and increase sugar to 15 to 20%.

quantity of ingredients or techniques used in mixing, panning, and baking will result in products that differ much more than one would expect. Table 11-4 indicates how the most commonly used batters or doughs vary in ingredient proportions.

FIG. 11-30 Service of quick breads such as shown here wins enthusiastic approval of patrons. (Courtesy General Foods, Inc.)

Mixes are on the market which need only liquid and perhaps egg added to produce high quality products. These save labor and require less skill. Many, with slight variations, are capable of producing a wide variety of items. They have good tolerance in handling and lend themselves well to quantity production. Mixes may be held in storage up to six months.

Standards

Standards for quick breads vary. A high quality muffin is large for its weight. The crust should be crisp, shiny, pebbly and golden brown; a smooth crust of low color may indicate toughness. The top should be well rounded and free from knobs. The interior crumb should be moist, light, and tender with no tunneling. The color of the crust may vary, but plain muffins should have a creamy-white color with an even grain. The flavor should be delicate, not bready or too sweet. Loaf breads, quick coffee cakes,

(a)

(b)

(c)

(d)

(e)

FIG. 11-31 (a) An example of a good loaf of quick bread. (Courtesy Processed Apples Institute). (b) Tender, flavorful scones, biscuits, and square biscuits indicate a high standard. (Courtesy Wheat Flour Institute) (c) High quality in these popovers is indicated by their appearance. (Courtesy Wheat Flour Institute). (d) This muffin sells with its appearance. (Courtesy Processed Apples Institute) (e) The crumb on this cornbread indicates its excellence. (Courtesy General Foods, Inc.)

and many other variety breads are made from batters very similar to those used for muffins, and the standard of the product may be much the same except for shape.

A high quality biscuit should be well shaped and regular, with straight, even sides and a level top. It should have good volume. The crust should be tender but not crumbly, and should have a smooth, golden-brown color. The inside texture should be fine, even-grained, and fluffy, with a creamy-white color free from yellow or brown spots. The biscuit should break with little resistance, and the moist, soft crumb should pull away in thin flakes or layers. Dropped biscuits will vary somewhat from this standard and will be shorter, less perfect in shape, and have qualities of crust similar to those of a muffin.

A popover or eclair paste product should have a rough, irregular top with a delicate tan color. It should be large for its weight with good height. Popovers may be popped over on their sides at the top. They will not have as deep or as even a color as an eclair paste product. The interior of each should be hollow, and the bottom should be even, with no holes. The bottom should possess a good shine. The crust should be crisp, brittle, and tender. The interior should be slightly moist but not pasty, damp, or excessively dry. The hole in the interior should be large. Low volume may indicate improper baking, too much moisture, or failure to mix properly. Too dark a color may indicate too high a baking temperature or too long baking.

A good pancake, also called a griddlecake or hotcake, should have a clear, even, brown color and a good round shape. It should not be pitted on top or bottom. The texture may be moist, slightly heavy, and thin; it is this texture which sometimes gives the cake the name of "flannel." Others may be less moist, firmer, drier, light, porous, open, and about one-fourth of an inch thick. All should be well cooked inside and tender. They should be hot, and the outsides should be firmer and slightly crisp. Flavor should be pleasant and only slightly bready.

Waffles should be a light, even, brown color with distinct grid markings. The shape should be even without ragged edges. Crispness may vary according to the basic recipe and baking time. The interior should be open, with a cream-colored crumb. Tenderness should be evident in both the crumb and the crust. The flavor should be slightly sweet, nutty, and pleasant.

Muffins

The batter for muffins is thick and usually quite lean. This gives a good chance for gluten development in the mixing and handling of the batter. Over development gives a tough muffin. Increasing the richness of the batter or using a weaker flour, such as cake flour, makes it possible to increase mixing. Mixing at about 60° F also retards gluten development. The best mixing technique is to sift the dry ingredients well and repeat, sifting the second time into the mixer. A thoroughly blended mixture of egg, liquid shortening, and liquid is then dumped into the center of the dry mix and the mixer paddle allowed to mix about 15 to 20 seconds at low speed. At this point the flour will have just disappeared and the batter should be rough and lumpy, break-

FIG. 11-32 The basic ingredients for a muffin batter are shown here. Similar to muffins are loaf breads, waffles, hot cakes, and many other products.

ing easily when dropped from a spoon. Some operations mix only the dry mixture and then, as required during service, mix a part of the dry mix with some liquid. It is then baked. Portioning may be done with a No. 16 scoop or by hand dipping and squeezing portions into pans. In portioning, the batter should be taken from the inside of the mixture out, to prevent stirring and thereby toughening the muffins. Gingerbread, cornbread, and other batters may be so thin that they may be poured. If the batter is too deep in the muffin pans or if the muffins are baked at too high a temperature, tunneling may be encouraged. Muffin pans should be conditioned and only lightly greased. Muffins high in sugar or fruit may require slight dusting of flour in addition to greasing to prevent sticking. A batter or dough given little mixing, as is the case with muffins, should be made with fine, not coarse, sugars, so the sugar will dissolve quickly during mixing. Pans should not be washed after use but be cleaned thoroughly with a clean, soft, absorbent cloth. Pan and bake muffins immediately after mixing; otherwise some quality is lost. After baking, dump the muffins from the pans or set them on their sides in the muffin cups so steam may escape, thus avoiding a soggy or over-moist product.

FIG. 11-33   A muffin batter should appear rough and pebbly after a minimum of mixing. In removing muffin batter, start at the outside edge and work out, thus reducing the tendency to toughen the batter by working it.

(a)   (b)

FIG. 11-34   (a) The muffin on the left has been properly mixed, while the one on the right shows peaking and a smooth, evenly colored crust that indicates overmixing. (b) The insides of these two muffins are shown. Note the tunneling in the overmixed muffin.

Mixing procedures may vary. The solid shortening may be cut into the dry ingredients, as for biscuits. The liquid and eggs are then added. The shortening may also be creamed with the sugar, then the eggs and the liquid and flour added at one time, and this mixture blended only until well mixed. If these two variations in mixing are used, more shortening will be required than for the first-mentioned mixing procedure. Some operations develop good basic muffin recipes and use variations of these to make many different kinds of muffins.

If muffins are heavy, the causes may be overmixing or mixing too slowly, too much flour or liquid, insufficient leavening, or too low an oven temperature. Heavy crusts may be caused by over-greased pans or by baking too long or in too hot an oven.

Normally about six to seven pounds of flour or 14 to 16 pounds of batter will give 100 portions averaging about 1½ muffins per portion. About 2½ ounces (a three-inch square one-inch thick) of coffee cake, Sally Lunn, or cornbread makes a portion, and an 18 x 26 inch pan is usually cut 5 by 10 or 6 by 8. A loaf from a 5½ x 10½ x 3 inch bread pan will cut

FIG. 11-35 A Dutch apple cake made from a basic muffin mix. (Courtesy Processed Apples Institute)

into about 25 ⅜ inch slices (two slices per portion) ; about eight pounds of flour or 20 pounds of batter will be required for 100 portions of a hot bread mixture.

Baking Powder Biscuits

The shortening for baking powder biscuits is lightly cut into the sifted flour, baking powder, and salt at low mixer speed until it appears as coarse as cornmeal; too much mixing at this point gives a fine bready texture,

FIG. 11-36   The basic ingredients for a baking powder biscuit mixture.

while too little will give a coarse texture. The liquid is added and the paddle used to blend it in a low speed until a soft dough is formed. Overmixing or overkneading will toughen biscuits. The dough is then taken to a lightly floured bench and the dough kneaded and folded over lightly; use the finger tips to lift it up and then press it down with the heel of the hand. Deft touch and light pressure are required. During this kneading the dough is turned after each kneading, and about 20 turns are given, requiring about 30 seconds of kneading. At the end of kneading, the dough should be soft

(a)

(b)

(c)

(d)

FIG. 11-37 (a) Mix the dry ingredients for baking powder biscuits with the fat until it has the appearance of course cornmeal. After the liquid is mixed in, the mixture should appear rough as shown. (b) Knead on a floured surface, using the palms of the hands to develop gluten as shown. (c) Make into rounds brushed with butter, as shown on the right, or cut with a well buttered baker's cutter into squares, and save time and labor, besides avoiding rerolling the dough, which gives a poorer quality biscuit. (d) The making of scones is shown here. This dough has been patted out onto a sheet; the shapes have been cut, a sharp cut made into the center of the scone with a well buttered baker's cutter, and the scones well buttered before baking.

and springy but not sticky. If the dough is not kneaded, a shorter, crisper, lower-volume biscuit is obtained. Using slightly more shortening and cutting it in the size of a small pea, coupled with good kneading, gives a good flaky biscuit. A dropped biscuit is not kneaded, and the dough is slightly moister than for regular biscuits. The ratio of shortening is slightly less, too. Dropped biscuits are not rolled out but dropped, and the resultant product will have less volume, a rougher appearance after baking, a crisper crust, and a tenderer crumb than a regular biscuit. Flakiness may be achieved by making a dough as slack or slightly more slack than the dropped biscuit and then adding the remaining flour during kneading.

For regular biscuits the kneaded dough is rolled out until about a half-inch thick. The thickness of the dough should be half the final height desired. Cutting should be even and straight down; a twisting cut may give

FIG. 11-38 Dropped biscuits are made slightly more slack than regular biscuits and are not kneaded after mixing. These show the pebbly surface and shape typical of these biscuits.

poor shape. The dough should be even and uniform to give even biscuit size and baking. Many operations cut biscuits from the rolled dough in squares or triangles with a cutter or knife so that all the dough is used in one cutting. Additional reworking of cutting scraps may give tough, compact biscuits. Setting biscuits apart on the greased baking sheet gives a more highly colored, crisper outer surface, especially if the cut biscuit is washed with or dipped into melted butter, margarine, or shortening. The tops may be washed with a milk, evaporated milk, or egg wash before baking to increase color. Shortcakes are rich biscuit doughs containing extra sugar. Dumplings are variations of biscuit dough.

Scones are made from rich biscuit dough containing egg. The dough may also contain raisins, nuts, currants, and other ingredients. Knead and roll as for biscuits, then pat out to cover a baking sheet. Cut next into rectangular shapes about one inch wide by two inches long. This cutting should be done with a scraper dipped into margarine or shortening to permit easy separation after baking. Often the scones are cut on the kneading board and placed on pans without touching. Scones are usually brushed with beaten egg wash before baking. It is also usual to cut deeply into the center of each with a cutter dipped into margarine or butter so that a break appears after baking.

A beaten biscuit is a Southern quick bread, which is not a typical baking powder biscuit since no leavening is used. The biscuit is mixed into a soft dough and then pounded with a stick for a long time. During this pounding, it is folded and refolded to tenderize it and to blend air into it. The flour usually contains phosphates.

The cause of a poor quality biscuit may be:

Defect	From
Heavy or compact crumb.	Overmixed or overkneaded dough.
	Insufficient baking powder or shortening.
	Too much liquid or flour.
	Oven not hot enough.
Pale crust.	Oven not hot enough.
	Baked in too deep a pan.
	Too much flour used.
Poor volume.	Oven not hot enough.
	Insufficient baking powder.
Light but not flaky.	Shortening too finely cut into flour.
	Insufficient kneading.
Poor shape.	Too slack dough.
	Uneven rolling.
	Careless cutting or placing in the pan.

Griddlecakes and Waffles

The batter for griddlecakes is thin enough to pour. Waffles will be between griddlecakes and muffins in batter density. Overmixing or over-manipulation may cause development of the gluten and toughening. As in muffins, richness or the use of cake flours permits more mixing. Thin batters may receive more mixing than thicker batters because the liquid disperses the gluten so it cannot form a cohesive structure. Blending well-sifted dry in-gredients into the liquids is the usual mixing technique. Occasionally beaten egg whites are carefully folded into the batter at the end of mixing. This gives a lighter product, and less baking powder may be required when this is done. Swedish or French pancakes may contain no leavening agents. They are usually thin batters high in egg content, and the resultant product is thin and slightly less tender than the flannel cake. (See Fried Desserts pp. 596 ff.) About two ounces of batter is placed on the griddle for a small, and four ounces for a large, cake. For 100 portions of two large cakes, 17 pounds of flour or 50 pounds of batter (6 gallons) will be required.

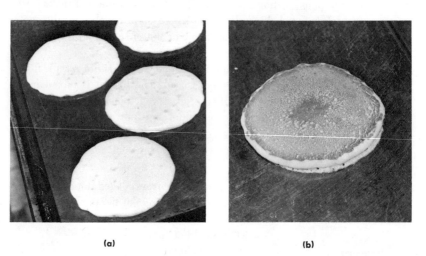

(a)   (b)

FIG. 11-39   (a) These griddlecakes are ready to turn. Note the bubbles on the top and the puffy quality of the batter. (b) The griddlecake turned.

Griddlecakes are baked on lightly greased griddles. If the ratio of the weight of fat to liquid in a hot cake or waffle batter is 1:4, the griddle or waffle grid need not be greased again during baking. The temperature of the griddle should be 350° to 375° F. As the heat strikes the batter on the griddle, volume increases and bubbles rise to the top. When the edge shows a slight drying, the cake should be deftly turned, and baking should be com-

FIG. 11-40 This waffle baker has been filled too full. It will overflow when the lid is lowered.

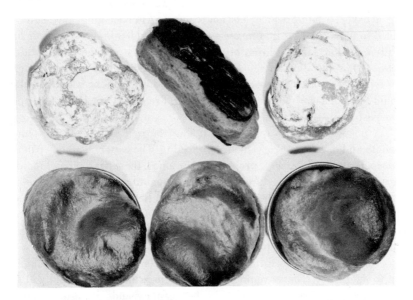

FIG. 11-41 Three popovers are at the bottom; above, a chocolate eclair is shown between two cream puffs. These three products are closely related in that steam is their leavening agent.

pleted on this turn. Additional turning lowers quality. The cake will rise slightly in the center after the turn, and when this recedes and the top becomes even, the cake is done. Heat on the griddle should be uniform. If it is too low, the color and texture of the hot cake will be poor; if it is too hot, the color will be too dark, or the cake will be undercooked and raw in the center. A pitted top side after baking indicates too high a heat or too long a time lapse before turning.

Waffles should be baked in a well conditioned waffle baker. The batter should be placed in the center to about one to 1½ inches from the edge, for baking will spread it out to the edge. About four ounces of batter will be required for one portion, 30 pounds per 100 waffles. Waffle batters usually contain more sugar, fat, and eggs than griddlecake batters, and some may be so rich they are called cake waffles. The crispness of the waffle depends upon the richness of the batter. Increasing the baking time will also give a crisper waffle.

Eclair or Choux Pastes and Popovers

An eclair or choux paste is made by cooking flour, shortening, and water into a smooth paste. An insufficient amount of water or overcooking may cause a broken emulsion. An excess of water will give too soft a paste and a baked product which has low volume. After cooking, the batter is cooled to about 150° F in a mixer and eggs are added in about four or five additions. After each addition of eggs, the batter is mixed well. A critical factor is this blending of the eggs after each addition so that at the end of mixing, a smooth, velvety, shiny paste is obtained. Thickness of the batter should be such as to retain shape in panning. Frequently the batter is shaped from pastry tubes.

A popover batter is quite thin. It must be well beaten to give gluten strength and develop a firm structure in baking. The batter should be panned in deep, heavy muffin tins. If properly conditioned, these pans will not require greasing. Heavy iron pans are desirable for quantity production. These are usually preheated before the batter is poured in. Batter should reach the half-full level, and baking in a hot oven should be immediate after panning. A failure to achieve volume may be caused by improper mixing, insufficient eggs, excess liquid, or too low heat.

The structure formed in the popover or eclair paste product is important to its quality. The leavening agent is steam, which forms rapidly at the base of the batter early in baking. As the steam expands, it pushes much of the paste upward, developing a large hole inside. Once expansion is obtained, baking must proceed so the structure will be made sufficiently firm to support the expansion after the steam condenses. To do this, the baking

FIG. 11-42   The basic ingredients for popovers: milk, flour, eggs, and salt.

FIG. 11-43   The basic ingredients for an eclair or cream puff batter: flour, butter or shortening, eggs, water, and salt.

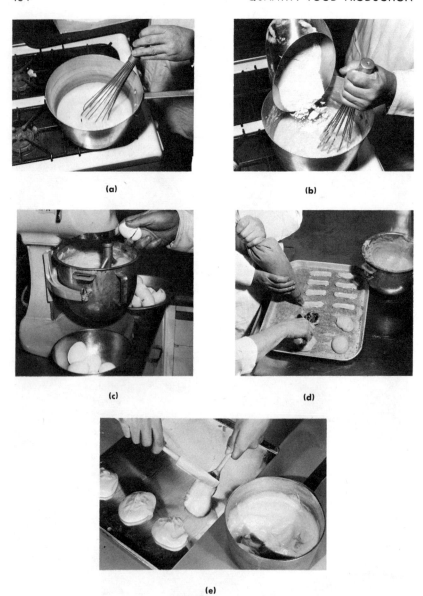

FIG. 11-44 The basic techniques for making an eclair or cream puff batter. (a) Melt the butter in the water over heat. (b) Add the flour, stirring well when adding. The mixture will form a thick, cooked paste. (c) Remove from the stove, cool slightly, and then place in a mixer. Add eggs one at a time, mixing thoroughly after adding each egg. (d) (e) Place on greased baking sheets as shown for cream puffs or eclairs.

temperature is 450° F for 15 minutes, during which time the rapid expansion occurs and the product browns slightly. Then the temperature is dropped to 375° F and baking continues for 30 to 40 minutes. During this last period, the structural walls should be dried out. Browning is not always an indication of doneness. A rapid cold shock upon oven removal will collapse these products. To avert this, they are frequently pulled to the front of the oven and allowed to stand a few moments with the doors open so that heat is reduced gradually. About five minutes before the end of baking, the items may be lightly pricked at the top to allow steam to escape. Cream puffs, eclairs, French crullers (see doughnuts), and other choux pastes are made from eclair pastes. Yorkshire puddings are popover batters.

Some recipes for eclair products may call for baking ammonia, ¼% (to 100% flour). This is used to give rapid and greater expansion, and eggs may be reduced slightly. The ammonia quickly escapes as a gas through the thin walls. Ammonia is not used for popover batters since these are

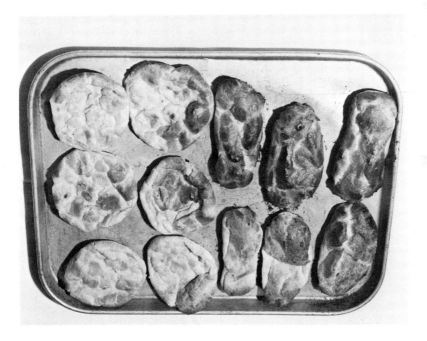

FIG. 11-45   The baking of popovers and eclair (choux) paste products is a critical factor in quality. These products have been baked at too high a heat and taken from the oven too soon. Because they did not develop sufficiently strong walls, they collapsed when cool air struck them after they were removed from the oven.

usually served hot, and the ammonia would still be present in them when they are eaten.

Crumpets and English Muffins

Crumpets and English muffins are yeast leavened, and their production will be much the same as for yeast products. The doughs are usually higher in liquid than those used for regular yeast products. Crumpets leavened by baking powder are sometimes made, but these do not have the chewy, moist

FIG. 11-46   The unbaked choux paste batter, the baked cream puff, and the filled cream puff. (Courtesy Wheat Flour Institute)

texture of the yeast-leavened crumpets. After fermentation the crumpet batter is poured into greased rings (2½ to 3 inches in diameter and about ¾ to 1 inch thick) on a hot griddle. They are allowed to cook until bubbles on the top are firm. They are then turned and cooked on the other side like hot cakes. Most of the baking occurs before the turn, and the top side is open, giving the crumpet a honeycomb or web-structured appearance. The texture of a crumpet should be somewhat chewy.

Table 11-5
Scaling Weights and Baking Temperatures and Times for Breads

Product	Pan Size	Units Per Pan	Scaling Weight	Baking Temperature (° F)	Baking Time (min)
			Yeast Breads		
Rolls, small	8 in.*	12	1 to 1⅓ oz	400 to 425	15 to 20
	17 x 25 in.	72 to 100			
Rolls, medium	8 in.*	8 to 12	1½ to 1¾ oz	400 to 425	15 to 20
	17 x 25 in.	60 to 85			
Rolls, large	8 in.*	8	2 to 2⅓ oz	390 to 420	20 to 25
Cinnamon rolls	8 in.*	8 to 12	1 to 2 oz	375 to 385	25
	17 x 25 in.	72 to 100		375	30
Sweet rolls	17 x 25 in.	24	2 oz	380 to 400	25
Tea rings	8 in.*	1	10 to 12 oz each	375	30
	17 x 25 in.	4	with 2 oz filling		
Topped coffee	8 in.*	1	10 to 12 oz each	375	30
cakes	17 x 25 in.	8	with 2 oz topping		
Fancy coffee	8 in.*	1	10 to 12 oz each		
cakes	17 x 25 in.	3 to 5	with 2 oz filling	375	30
Bread, white	1¼ lb	1	26½ oz	400	60
Bread, rye	1 lb	1	18 oz	400	45
			Quick Breads		
Brown, steamed	4 x 9 x 4 in.	1	1½ lb	Steam	60 to 90
Biscuit, 2¼ in.	17 x 25 in.	88	1¼ oz	425	15 to 20
Dumpling	8 in.*	12	1½ oz	Steam	20 to 30
Cornbread	17 x 25 in.	1	6 lb	425	30
Griddle cakes			4 oz	350 to 375	3 to 5
Muffins, plain			1⅓ to 1½ oz	425	15 to 20
Muffins, bran			1½ oz	425	20 to 25
Breads, quick	7½ x 3½ x 2¼ in.	1	18 oz	350	60
Breads, date and nut	7½ x 3½ x 2¼ in.	1	22 oz	350	60
Breads, quick	4 x 9 x 4	1	1¾ lb	350	60 to 75
Cream puffs			1½ oz**	450	15
Eclairs or popovers			2 oz**	15 min and then	
				375	30 to 40

*round or square pan **Fill cream puffs 2½ oz, eclairs 2 oz, using ¾ oz topping for eclairs.

English muffins are rich yeast doughs, made soft to the point of being almost tacky. They are cut on the bench from the dough by a round cutter and are given a heavy proof (about 15 minutes). They are then carefully dropped into greased rings on a griddle and baked. When browned and partially done, they are turned and baked on the other side. The temperature of the griddle should be about 350° F for both crumpets and English muffins.

FIG. 11-47   Crumpets being baked in their metal shells (left) and English muffins being baked (right).

Table 11-6
Yields from 30-lb Lots of Dry Mixes

Mix	Yield	Mix	Yield
Griddlecakes	725 (4 oz each)	Bran muffins	720 (1 oz)
Waffles	300	Corn bread	375 (2 x 3 in)
Biscuits	720 (2 in)	Corn bread	520 (sticks)
Plain muffins	800 (1 oz)	Coffee cake or	40 (8 in layer)
		Gingerbread	300 (2 x 3 in)

12 Cakes, Cookies, and Frostings

Cakes are not only a popular dessert; they are also well suited to quantity food production. Compared with many other desserts, cakes and cookies are low in cost and easy to prepare, and they can be stored for fairly long periods. The range of cakes that can be produced by only slight variations of basic batters makes it possible to offer wide variety on the menu without

FIG. 12-1 Wide variety may be obtained by using different shapes and different types of frostings as well as different cake batters. Here are just a few of the cherry-type cakes produced in the laboratories of Procter and Gamble Company.

(a)

(b)   (c)

FIG. 12-2   The three main groups of cakes: (a) butter, (b) foam, (c) pound. (Courtesy of
(a) General Foods, Inc., (b) and (c) Standard Brands, Inc.)

requiring a wide variety of worker skills or ingredients. Variety is also easily
achieved by using different-shaped pans and different fillings and frostings.
Many years ago maximum skill was required to overcome the limitations of
ingredients in making *gateaux* (cakes) and *tortes*. At that time cakes were
leavened by air captured in egg foam (sponges), by creaming (pound cakes),
or by gas developed by yeast (baba rhums) ; but today—with our chemical
leavening agents, improved shortenings, and high-stability cake flours—pro-

duction has been simplified. The introduction of cake mixes has further simplified cake and cookie making in recent years.

CAKES—THEIR BALANCE AND STANDARDS

Proportion of ingredients and type of leavening are commonly used to classify cakes. On this basis, cakes may be classified as butter, pound, and foam.

FIG. 12-3 Faulty scales or careless scaling frequently is the cause of cake failures. Keep scales and other portioning equipment clean. Heavy beam scales should be used to weigh large quantities, but small accurate beam scales, as shown here, may be used for small quantities.

There are, however, no distinct demarcations among these groups; recipes for one may closely resemble recipes for another. Established ratios of ingredients must exist, however, if a satisfactory cake of any kind is made. The balance of ingredients is important in itself, but recipe balance may sometimes need to be varied because of the quality and kind of ingredients, the bakeshop and ingredient temperatures; the mixing method; the speed, efficiency, and capacity of mixing equipment; the oven; and the baking conditions. Once a recipe is balanced to an operation, it should not be changed, nor should the conditions affecting its balance be changed.

Butter Cakes

Butter cakes are perhaps the most widely produced of all cakes. The word "butter" may sometimes be a misnomer, because hydrogenated shortenings are now commonly used. Some bakers claim that butter makes a better-flavored cake and still use it. Others use hydrogenated shortening and add butter coloring and flavoring to achieve closely parallel flavors. Butter

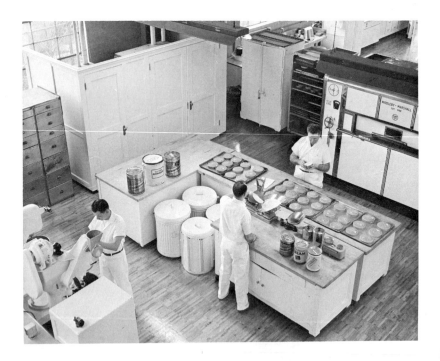

FIG. 12-4 Constant checking for quality must occur if high standards are to be maintained. Here bakers in the Standard Brands laboratories check performance of baking powders in cake making.

Table 12-1

Variations Possible from Three Basic Cake Batters

Cake	Icing	Filling	Basic Batters		
			White	Gold	Chocolate
Almond Fudge	Almond Toffee	Almond Toffee			*
Almond Gold	Almond Toffee	Almond Toffee		*	
Banana	Banana	Banana	*	*	
Bittersweet Fudge	Bittersweet	Marshmallow		*	**
Butterscotch Walnut	Butterscotch Fondant and Walnuts	Butterscotch	*	*	*
Carmel Fudge	Caramel Fudge	Caramel Fudge	*	*	*
Cherry	Cherry Cream	Cherry Cream	*	*	*
Chocolate	Chocolate Fudge	Fudge	*	*	**
Chocolate Chip	Vanilla Fondant and Chocolate Shavings	Vanilla Fondant	*	*	*
Double Dip Caramel	Caramel Fudge and Marshmallow	Butterscotch	*	*	*
Double Dip Chocolate	Chocolate Fondant and Marshmallow	Marshmallow	*	*	*
Double Fudge	Chocolate Fudge	Fudge			
Frosty Silver	Coconut Cream	Coconut Cream	*	*	
Golden Gate	Orange Cream	Orange	*		*
Lady Baltimore	Marshmallow or Nut and Fruit	Fruit and Nut Cream			
Lemonade	Lemon Fondant	Lemon Fondant	*	*	*
Malted Milk	Chocolate Malted Milk	Chocolate Malted Milk	*	*	*
Maple Cream and Nut	Maple Fondant, Walnuts	Maple Cream or Nut Cream	*	*	**
Maple Nut	Maple	Nut Cream	*	*	**
Marshmallow Macaroon	Marshmallow topped with Macaroon Coconut	Chocolate Cream or Marshmallow	*		
Marshmallow Pecan	Marshmallow topped with Pecans	Marshmallow	*	*	*
Orange Coconut	Orange Fondant topped with Orange Coconut	Orange	*	*	
Pineapple Sundae	Pineapple Fondant	Pineapple Fondant	*	*	*
Spumoni	Chocolate Fudge with Chopped Cherries	Fruit Cream	*	*	
Strawberry Sundae	Strawberry Fondant	Strawberry Cream	*	*	

(Adapted from Procter & Gamble materials)

cake ingredients are shortening, sugar, eggs, flour, salt, baking powder, liquid, and flavoring.

A butter cake recipe is considered in balance if:

1. The weight of the sugar exceeds the weight of the flour.
2. The weight of shortening does not exceed the weight of the eggs.
3. The weight of liquids (milk and eggs)[1] is about 1½ times the weight of the sugar.

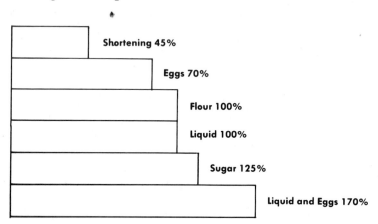

FIG. 12-5   A graph indicating how the ingredients for a typical butter cake might be balanced.

Before the development of high-ratio shortenings and high-stability cake flour, sugar could not exceed flour in butter cakes, but now it may go as high as 150%. Higher ratios of shortening and sugar to flour are found in chocolate cakes, the starch in the cocoa or chocolate evidently allowing the higher ratios. More sugar can be added to butter cakes made by the blending method than to cakes made by other methods of mixing. (For a definition of mixing methods, see page 472 ff.)

It is a common rule in cake balancing that as liquid is increased, eggs and shortening are reduced. (It may be enlightening to a student to follow this change through a true pound cake, to a butter cake, and then to a lean muffin cake formula.) The quantity of liquid in a butter cake is governed more by the quantity of sugar than by the flour. In addition, the quantity and type of shortening and the richness and sweetness desired will control

[1]Whole eggs, whites, and yolks are respectively around 65%, 75%, and 50% moisture; if yolks are used in the place of whole eggs, the liquid is increased proportionately, and if whites are used in the place of whole eggs, the liquid is decreased proportionately.

FIG. 12-6 Typical quality of four different butter cakes: cake mix (lower right), liquid shortening-blended method of mixing (lower left), typical blended method (upper right), and conventionally mixed cake (upper left).

the sugar and liquid balance. If a sirup is used instead of sugar, the liquid in the sirup makes it necessary to reduce other liquids.

The standard for a butter cake varies according to the richness and method of mixing. A good butter cake should be even on all sides, perfectly shaped, and slightly rounded on the top; the rounding will be less on large sheet cakes. The crust should be shiny, golden, tender, thin, daintily crisp and smooth, and not blistered. It may possess a slightly puffy quality. The cut surface should show a fine, even grain that is soft, light, tender, and velvety to the touch. This surface should show no dullness, cloudiness, or streaks. The crumb should be moist and tender. The color varies with the type of cake. The color of chocolate cakes will vary according to batter reactions; an alkaline batter will have a rich, reddish brown, which should not be excessively dark; one not alkaline will have a rich chocolate color, if all other factors exist to make an optimum cake. Butter cakes should have a mild, sweet, rich, delicate, and appealing flavor. Chocolate cakes should have a similar flavor modified by the rich, smooth flavor of chocolate with no trace of bitterness or soapiness from excess alkalinity.

Pound Cakes

A true pound cake has equal weights of sugar, shortening, eggs, and flour as ingredients. No leavening agent is needed, for the leavening comes from air incorporated in creaming and from steam in baking. Salt and flavoring are also ingredients. Pound cake batters are used for fruit cakes, nut cakes, steam puddings, and other products. Products made from pound cake batters keep well. Many pound cake recipes may be modified in ingredient proportions toward a butter cake. When this is done, to maintain balance, shortening and eggs are decreased while sugar is increased; liquid besides eggs is added, and baking powder is then required for leavening.

A pound cake should have an even shape, a slightly rounded top, and a thin, soft, delicately browned crust with the top split slightly in the middle. The crumb should be smooth and rich with no trace of oiliness. The texture should be firm, with fine, compact cells. The flavor should be sweet, delicately rich, and substantial.

Foam Cakes[2]

Typical foam cakes are angel food, sponge, and chiffon. All depend upon air incorporated by egg foam for a major portion of their leavening. Some chiffon and sponge cakes may have baking powder added to assist in leavening. In chiffon cakes, oil is an ingredient. A sponge cake may have shortening added, but an angel food cake will not. Liquid is frequently added to a sponge

[2]See the discussion on egg foams in Chapter 7.

or chiffon cake batter. The light, delicate quality of foam batters requires that high quality cake flour and eggs and fine-grained sugar be used. Foam cakes are usually not prepared in more than 100 portions per batch because their delicate structure may be destroyed by heavy batter weight.

An angel food cake is considered in balance if:
1. The weight of the sugar equals the weight of the egg whites.
2. The weight of the flour is a half to a third the weight of the sugar or egg whites.

Recipes may have variations within these rules; for instance, a successful cake results from 13 ounces of flour (100%), 32 ounces of egg whites (245%), and 26 ounces (200%) of sugar.

Rules for balancing a sponge cake recipe are:
1. The weight of the sugar equals or slightly exceeds the weight of the eggs.
2. The combined weight of liquid and eggs is $1\frac{1}{4}$ times that of the sugar.
3. The weight of the whole eggs or the sugar exceeds that of the flour.
4. The weight of the whole eggs and flour exceeds the combined weight of the sugar and liquid.

A chiffon cake recipe is considered in balance if:
1. The weight of sugar is $1\frac{1}{3}$ to $1\frac{1}{2}$ that of the flour.
2. The weight of yolks is half that of whites.
3. The weight of the oil is half that of the flour.
4. The weight of the liquid is three-fourths that of the flour.
5. The combined weight of the liquid and eggs is about equal to that of the sugar and flour.

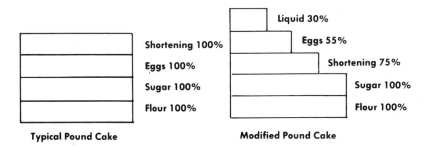

Typical Pound Cake

Shortening 100%
Eggs 100%
Sugar 100%
Flour 100%

Modified Pound Cake

Liquid 30%
Eggs 55%
Shortening 75%
Sugar 100%
Flour 100%

FIG. 12-7 The balances for a typical pound cake and a modified pound cake are shown here. Leavening may be an added ingredient in the modified cake. Note that as the pound cake is modified, its balance tends more and more toward that of the balanced butter cake.

(a)

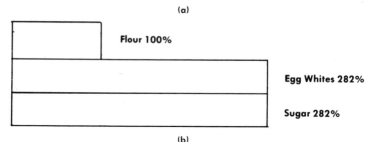

(b)

FIG. 12-8 Ingredients (a) and balance chart (b) for angel food cake. Cream of tartar, unlabeled, is in the paper dish in front.

(It would be well if students and workers would check some recipes for balance and see how, while the rules are broad, most recipes for successful cakes fall within these rules.)

The grain of a good angel food cake should be even, fine, light, feathery, and moist. It is a more delicate and tender cake than a sponge or chiffon. The crumb should not be hard, brittle, or excessively moist, and the color should be clear and white. Cell walls should reflect a delicate sheen. The sides should be even and the top slightly rounded. A delicately browned crust which is not moist or sticky is desired. The cake should stand high for its weight.

The texture of a good sponge or chiffon cake should be delicate, springy, and light. The crumb should be moist and soft and have a delicate flavor. Grain should be even; not coarse, excessively feathery, or moist. The cells should be fine with a soft sheen. Thin cell walls indicate lightness and delicacy. The shape should be high and even; the crust should be lightly browned. Crumb color should be a light lemon-gold in a sponge and slightly lighter in a chiffon, unless other ingredients modify color.

Altitude Adjustment

Even though a cake recipe is in balance at sea level, it may not be at a higher elevation, and the higher elevation will require that the proportion of ingredients be varied. Less change is required in conventionally mixed butter cakes than in those made by the blending method. Altitude adjustment varies for different types of cakes. A rich butter cake or one high in moisture, such as an applesauce cake, require different leavening adjustments from a common butter cake. At 3000 feet, angel cakes need sugar reduced 10 to 12% and cream of tartar increased 20%, while sponge cakes at this elevation require double quantities of cream of tartar, and at 7000 feet a 10 to 12% reduction in sugar. Sponge cakes at 3000 feet will have lemon juice omitted and cream of tartar substituted. For sponge cakes, eggs may be beaten slightly less over 3000 feet. Flour and eggs may have to be increased in butter and pound cakes above 1000 feet to give them a firmer structure. Above 5000

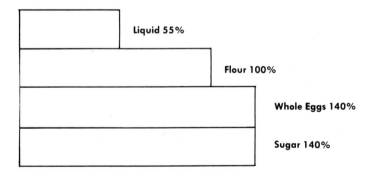

FIG. 12-9 The rules for balancing a sponge cake: Rule 1 — the weight of the sugar is equal to or slightly exceeds the weight of the eggs. Rule 2 — the combined weight of liquid and eggs is 1 ¼ times that of the sugar. Rule 3 — the weight of the whole eggs or the sugar exceeds that of the flour. Rule 4 — the weight of the whole eggs and flour exceeds the combined weight of the sugar and liquids. This chart shows all four rules combined.

feet, shortening in these may need reduction to lessen its tenderizing effect. Since these cakes stick easily at higher elevations, grease pans more heavily. Many bakers increase oven temperatures 25° F above 4500 feet while maintaining the same baking time. Oven dampers may be closed to reduce drying out during at least part of the baking time.

(a)

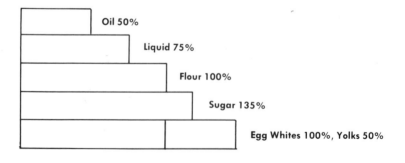

(b)

FIG. 12-10 Ingredients (a) and balance chart (b) for a chiffon cake. Cream of tartar, at the left front, again is unlabeled.

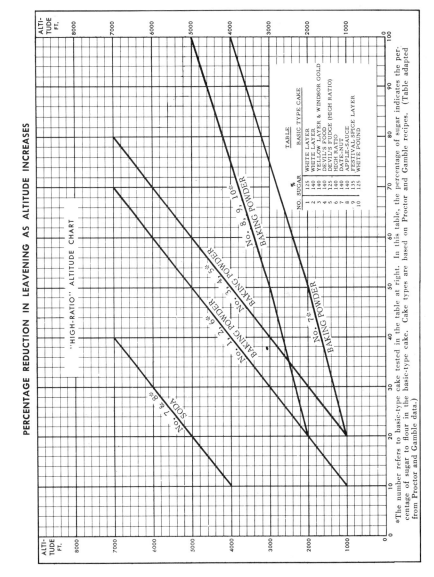

FIG. 12-11

Table 12-2

Approximate Butter Cake Recipe Changes As Elevation Changes

Altitude	Reduction %	Increase %		Altitude	Reduction %	Increase %	
	Baking Powder	Sugar	Moisture		Baking Powder	Sugar	Moisture
1500	5	0	0	6500	43.3	10.5	.056
2000	10	2	.01	7000	46.4	11.5	.06
2500	14.4	3	.015	7500	49	12.4	.067
3000	19.8	4	.02	8000	52.7	13.3	.072
3500	22.8	4.9	.025	8500	54.1	14.6	.077
4000	26.8	5.9	.03	9000	56.5	16	.083
4500	30.4	6.8	.035	9500	58.7	16.8	.088
5000	34	7.8	.04	10000	60.8	17.7	.093
5500	37.2	8.7	.045				
6000	40.5	9.6	.05				

Adapted from General Mills, Inc. materials

CAKE PRODUCTION

Highest quality ingredients, exact measurement, and efficient equipment
are essential if good cakes are to be produced. Recipes should be tested and
balanced to suit conditions in the operation. Layouts should be planned so
that work flows smoothly and efficiently from scaling to mixing, to panning,
to baking, to cooling, and to make-up. Use labor efficiently. Insufficient or
poor pans, mixers, scaling, or holding space may increase labor costs. Establish procedures that save labor but maintain quality. Produce cakes in quantity, and introduce variations to a portion of them. It takes as much time
to scale and mix a small batch as it does a large one.

Efficient equipment must be used. Shortening must be well emulsified
and completely spread throughout a batter. The cake batter should be just
above the mixing paddle when mixing is complete to achieve this result, and
bowl adapters should be used to suit batch volume. Fluctuating heat, poor
temperature control, excessive vibration, warped or sagging shelves, and
uneven baking decks produce poor cakes. Reel ovens should be equipped with
stabilized shelves. Severe vibration makes cakes separate in the center and
have poor volume and crumb. Uneven heat causes cakes to shrink and pull
away from the sides of the pan; it also causes the volume to be low, the
crusts to be dark and thick, and the cakes to have tunnels and high peaks.

Mixing

Butter Cakes

There are two commonly used methods of mixing butter cakes, the
conventional, or creaming, method and the blending method. Two lesser
used methods are the conventional-sponge and the muffin methods.

At one time only the conventional method of mixing was used, but
now the most common method of mixing is the blending method. The con-

ventional sponge and muffin methods are infrequently used. A dump method, in which all ingredients are added at once, as with a new type of blended shortening, promises to revolutionize cake-making procedures. Today the quality of the blended cake is considered best, conventionally mixed cakes next, and the other methods mentioned in this text following in quality.

CONVENTIONAL MIXING

In conventional or creaming mixing, the shortening and sugar are creamed first and then the eggs. Photomicrographs of the various stages of creaming (see student's observations in Figure 12-12) show that the fat is adsorbed on the sugar crystal surface. Air bubbles spread evenly throughout the batter. After eggs are added, moisture from them begins to dissolve the sugar; the eggs also assist in emulsifying the fats. With more cream-

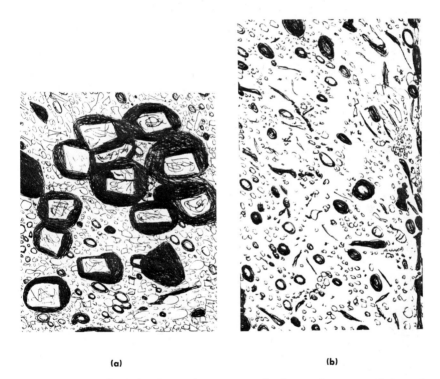

(a)   (b)

FIG. 12-12 A student's drawings and comments on the change of sugar crystal size and fat adsorption in samples which he watched under a microscope as he made a conventional cake. (a) "The sugar crystals looked square and large pools of fat surrounded them. Dark areas represent fat." (b) "After the eggs were added and the mixture beaten for some time, the sugar and fat were more evenly dispersed. The fat globules were now smaller in size."

ing, air cells progressively become finer and more plentiful. Variation in the quantity and size of the air bubbles and their spacing directly affects the final crumb velvetiness.

A vertical mixing machine with paddle is used for creaming. The speed of mixing is low or medium, and the shortening is creamed to a waxy stage; sugar is added, and creaming continues until a light color and a fluffy texture have been obtained. Maximum air incorporation should be achieved. During this and subsequent mixing, scrape down frequently, moving the ingredients from the bottom and sides into mixer action. (Mixing times do not include

FIG. 12-13 Well creamed shortening, sugar, and eggs just before addition of dry ingredients and milk in making a conventional cake.

scraping down.) Add eggs in three equal parts, creaming well at medium speed after each addition. The mixture at the end of creaming should appear smooth and fluffy; the graininess from sugar should have disappeared. (If all the sugar, shortening, and eggs are added at one time and the mixture creamed at medium speed, time and labor will be reduced; but many bakers feel that the cake quality is not as good as when the method described above is used.)

After creaming, one-fourth of the sifted dry ingredients are added, then one-third of the liquid. This blending of dry and liquid ingredients is continued until the batter is complete. Usually there are four additions of dry ingredients and three of liquid. During this blending, use a mixer with paddle at low speed. The resulting batter is thick and smooth and must be spread in panning. Give several sharp raps to the pans after filling to free air bubbles caught in the batter. Overmixing after the addition of flour may give excessive gluten development and leavening loss, resulting in a heavy, compact cake with tunneling. Undermixing gives a coarse, poor crumb.

FIG. 12-14 A conventional cake batter is so thick that it will not spread in the pans by itself but must be spread with a spatula.

In some conventional mixing, only yolks are added during creaming. Whites are beaten separately to a soft, glossy peak (stage three) or are made into a soft meringue with part of the sugar. This is dumped into the middle of the batter just before panning, and the whites are carefully folded in. Use a whip, spoon, or hand to fold, with a down-and-under motion. Machine-blending, using care, may be done at low speed until all egg foam is incorporated. Underblending will give flecks of egg which rise to the surface and give an uneven, blistered crust. Overbeating results in a loss of volume. If egg whites are added this way, less baking powder will be required.

The correct temperature for ingredients in mixing is 75° to 80° F. Shortening should be conditioned at least 24 hours in advance of use. Use a waxy, workable shortening to incorporate air and to give spread and a desirable shortness. Hard or excessively soft fats cream poorly. Temperature of the shortening may be somewhat adjusted to give desired consistency. Emulsifiers in shortenings assist in giving improved creaming action.

Curdling may occur when eggs are added, especially if they are cold. Fine curds may be precursors of a fine cake texture, but most bakers prefer no curdling. Warm eggs and/or the addition of a bit of the dry ingredients during the latter stages of creaming reduces the tendency of the mixture to curdle. Dry eggs, if not added with the sifted ingredients, may be mixed with a part of the liquid needed to refresh them and the remaining liquid added later. This will reduce curdling. Chocolate should be added during creaming, and cocoa should be sifted in with the flour.

MIXING BY BLENDING

The blending method mixes the flour and fat together with a mixer paddle three to five minutes. This coats the flour with particles of shortening, promoting tenderness. Batters made by the blending method also have high tolerance to over- or undermixing. The resultant cakes also have a more even grain and a finer texture than those achieved by other mixing methods.

For best results use an emulsified shortening and a cake flour of high stability. The temperature of ingredients for mixing should be around 75° F, but good tolerance is found from 60° to 80° F. The time and speed of mixing given in the recipe should be followed. Undermixed cakes have a coarse grain and lack tenderness. Overmixed cakes are toughened and have a compact grain.

Frequent scraping down is necessary in using the blending method. If chocolate is used, add it in melted form after the flour and shortening have been partially blended. Sugar, salt, baking powder, and dry milk solids sifted together are next added with a third to one-fourth of the liquid. Cocoa, spices, and other dry ingredients may be sifted in at this time. The addition of liquid in two stages gives a smooth batter without lumps. Mixing continues from three to five minutes. Last, eggs, remaining liquid, and flavoring are added. Mixing continues again for another three to five minutes. The resultant batter will be thin and will pour easily from the bowl. Batter thinness is no indication of poor quality or low cake volume.

One of the most common variations in the blending method is to sift flour, salt, dry milk solids, and sugar into the mixing bowl and add the shortening. Mix at medium or slow speed for two minutes, adding half to two-thirds the liquid early in the mixing. Scrape down frequently. Next, eggs, the remaining milk, and the leavening agent are added and mixing

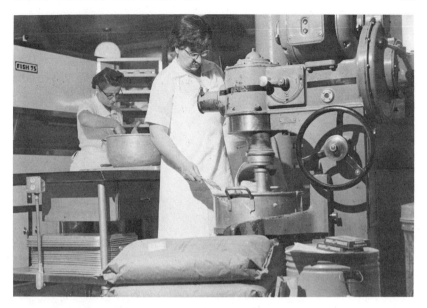

FIG. 12-15 Movement of supplies to the bakeshop, as well as the use of cake mixes, saves time and steps.

continued two minutes. Some bakers vary times to three minutes for the first mixing and only one for the second, claiming that a better cake is thus obtained.

Another variation of the blending method is the dump method. Flour, leavening agent, milk solids, salt, and sugar are sifted together into the mixer. Shortening, eggs, and half the liquid are added. Mixing is done at low or medium speed for one minute. Add the remaining liquid and mix two minutes. Quality is lower with this variation, but with a new liquid shortening appearing on the market, excellent cakes can be made by this method. Scores of cakes made with liquid shortening have been rated higher than paired samples of regular blended cakes. (See Figs. 12-6 and 12-16.)

Muffin Mixing

The muffin method is sometimes used for non-rich cakes. Cakes made by this method should be served soon, for they stale quickly. This method mixes eggs, liquid, and melted shortening (or oil) together. The mixture

FIG. 12-16 One of the latest variations in the blended method, which produces exception-ally high quality cakes, is the use of liquid shortening. Here we see the liquid shortening dumped into a bowl; the blended sugar and dry milk are in the center, and the blended cake flour, salt, and baking powder and the liquid and eggs are on the right. The flour mix-ture and shortening are mixed together first; then the sugar mixture and part of the liquid are added, and last the remaining liquid.

is then poured over the sifted dry ingredients and all are mixed. Quality is lower than that achieved by the two above-mentioned mixing methods.

CONVENTIONAL-SPONGE MIXING

When overly plastic, soft shortening must be used or when shop tem-peratures are high, the conventional-sponge method can be used to give good cakes. The method resembles conventional mixing, but half the sugar is withheld in creaming and no eggs are added. Instead, the dry sifted ingredi-ents are blended into the creamed mixture, followed by liquids and then the dry ingredients until all are blended. Warm eggs with the remaining sugar are beaten into a fluffy sponge and this is carefully folded into the batter.

Cakes of acceptable quality can also be made when soft shortening must be used. First, dissolve the sugar into half to two-thirds of the liquid.

FIG. 12-17 In making a blended cake, the shortening is placed on top of the flour, salt, and leavening, and the mixture is mixed at slow speed three to five minutes until it appears as shown at upper right. One-third of the liquid and the dry milk blended with the sugar are added, and the mixture is again mixed for three to five minutes, after which the eggs and remaining liquid are added. The resulting batter pours easily.

Then the soft shortening and sifted flour, leavening agent, and salt are added. Mixing is approximately three to four minutes at medium or slow speed. Eggs, flavoring, and the remaining liquid are added, and the mixture is beaten one minute at medium speed.

MIXES

Most mixes contain all ingredients required except water, but a few may require eggs. Cakes made from mixes may stale quickly, but increased shortening ratios have improved quality of some on the market. Dry cake mixes should not be stored more than six months, especially if storage temperatures are high. Cost studies show that the cost of cakes made from "scratch" is no less than for those made from mixes, and quality differences between the two are non-significant. Skill, labor time, standardization, and improved management control are other factors favoring use of the mix.

Dry mixes may be prepared. This is done by first blending the flour, shortening, dry emulsifier, and sugar together. The quantity of emulsifier is usually 3/4 to 1% of the total weight of the mix, or 3 to 6% of the shorten-

FIG. 12-18 Two shapes frequently seen in pound cakes. Note the fine, tight grain typical of this type of cake.

ing. If emulsified shortening is used, the quantity of emulsifier used is less. Monoglycerides, diglycerides, or polyoxethylenes, or their derivatives, are usually used for emulsifiers. After the first mixture has been blended, nonfat dry milk solids, salt, sodium acid pyrophosphate baking powder, and dried eggs are added. Cocoa may be added for chocolate cakes.

This dry mixture may be stored and used as desired. The required quantity is scaled, and this, with approximately two-thirds of the required water, is blended at low speed for about one minute. The batter is scraped down and the mixture is mixed four minutes at medium speed. The remaining water is added, and mixing proceeds for one minute at low speed, with scraping down during and at the end of this period. The mixture is then mixed four minutes at medium speed.

Pound Cakes

The best temperature for creaming ingredients for pound cakes is 75° F. After the shortening and sugar are creamed thoroughly, the eggs are added, and creaming is continued until the mixture is light and fluffy. Some flour may be added late in the creaming to prevent curdling. After creaming, flour is blended in. Bread flour up to half of the total flour is frequently used to give strength to the structure. Bakers select flours with good absorptive powers. A strong structure is desirable for fruit cakes, since the batter must support the heavy weight of fruit, which may be one to 1½ times the weight of the batter. A variation in making pound cakes may be used by beating warmed eggs to a sponge with the sugar. The flour is folded in first and the melted shortening next. The quality of this cake is usually not as high as with the creaming method. If only egg whites are used, giving a higher liquid content, 3% baking powder to flour is used. Fine or berry sugar should be used for pound cakes, since coarser sugars dissolve slowly and may detract from cake quality. If a pound cake has a high sugar and liquid ratio, increased volume is obtained, but the grain is more open, and the top crust will tend to break away from the cake more easily.

Foam Cakes[3]

ANGEL FOOD CAKES

The salt and cream of tartar used in angel cake make the egg whites more extensible. The cake is also whiter because the acid reaction of the cream of tartar whitens the flour flavones. Cream of tartar is not a leavener. Egg whites should be beaten with salt and cream of tartar at a temperature of from 110° to 125° F until they reach a soft peak. These peaks should

[3]See Chapter 7 on egg foams. The exact point at which an egg foam is stiff enough to hold the other ingredients and yet is soft enough to allow them to blend in easily is a critical factor in the making of foam cakes. Knowing this point is a matter of experience and judgment.

bend over slightly at the top (stage two, upper level) in egg foams. Over- or underbeating gives a cake of poor quality and low volume. One-third to half of the sugar is folded into the egg whites. The finer the sugar, the finer the cake grain; some recipes call for part powdered and part granulated sugar for this reason. Some chefs roll their sugar with a rolling pin to give it the

(a)

(b)

FIG. 12-19 The making of an angel food cake. (a) Warm egg whites, salt, and cream of tartar are beaten to the upper second foam stage. The sugar is added and is just blended in until the mixture appears as shown in (b). (c) The remaining sugar, blended thoroughly with the sifted flour, is then carefully folded in by hand. Note the spread of the fingers to encourage more rapid incorporation of the flour-sugar mixture.

(c)

desired fineness. Flour sifted thoroughly with the remaining sugar is then carefully folded in until it *just disappears*. The manipulation of the batter in this blending is critical; too much mixing will result in a poor cake. Sifting the flour with a part of the sugar makes the flour easier to incorporate. Blending of whites and flour may be done by machine at slow speed, but most bakers prefer to fold in with a wire whip, a spoon, or the hand.

SPONGE CAKES

Warm whole eggs or yolks are beaten to a stable foam for sponge cakes. Acid ingredients such as cream of tartar, lemon juice, or lemon crystals and salt are added. If the sugar is added to warm eggs during beating, stable foam is formed more rapidly. If desirable, the mixture may be beaten over 150° F water. Egg temperature should be 120° to 125° F, and the sugar may be slightly warm to achieve this temperature. Normally, beating is at high speed for about 10 to 15 minutes, or until the eggs are a thick, lemon-colored foam. Underbeating will cause a tough streak on the bottom of the cake and give a cake of low volume with a heavy, compact grain. If egg yolks replace whole eggs, liquid such as hot water, milk, or lemon juice is added to give sufficient moisture. After beating, the sifted flour is folded in carefully. Machine-folding may occur at slow speed. If baking powder or other dry ingredients are used, they are sifted in with the flour. Sponges may also be made by beating yolks separated from the whites. Half of the sugar is used in the beating. Liquid is added and the flour folded in. The egg whites, cream of tartar, and salt are made into a soft meringue with the remaining sugar, and this is folded into the batter. Overmixing at this point gives a cake with a dry, heavy, close grain which has a tough, rubbery texture. Undermixing gives a coarse texture and uneven grain.

Delicate sponges may have hot milk and/or butter added after the sifted dry ingredients are folded in. The milk is at around 140° F and the butter is melted. Final batter temperature should be around 110° F. Some recipes call for the addition of hot milk alternately with the flour, but this

FIG. 12-20   Hot milk and melted butter are being carefully folded into this sponge batter with a wire whip.

technique requires considerable skill. If the butter solidifies in a butter sponge, the cake will collapse in the oven. Fat breaks down egg foam, and the sponge may lose quality if the melted butter is not blended in skillfully. Hand-mixing is preferred for this process. In place of warm milk or butter, hot water may be added to give a moist, soft, velvety sponge. This is usually blended into the beaten eggs just before the sifted dry ingredients are folded in.

CHIFFON CAKES

The most recent addition to foam cakes is the chiffon cake. It resembles a sponge cake but has a more compact texture and a heavier crumb. Oil is added as a shortening. Chiffon cakes also contain a leavening agent and liquid other than eggs. Mixing procedures for the chiffon cakes are similar to those used for sponge cakes.

Panning

The quality of the cake may be influenced by its panning. To allow for proper expansion, fill pans with butter or pound cake batter to half or two-thirds full. Overfilled pans spill in baking, and the cakes lose quality and may fall. Cake pans with sloping sides result in less volume than when straight-sided pans are used. Do not grease foam cake pans. Foam cakes need to attach themselves to sides to climb up in baking, and greasing lessens this support. Greased sides also reduce butter and pound cake volume. A mixture for greasing may be made, using seven pounds of shortening, one pound of margarine, one pint of salad oil, and four pounds of flour. A bit of butter flavoring and salt may be added. Butter is said to improve cake flavor when used as a greasing medium. Paper liners are desirable for lining bottoms of pans. Remove these when the cake is cooled. Special silicon products may be brushed onto pans to make greasing unnecessary. To prevent crusts on the bottom from becoming dry, use wet paper liners; this may be especially desirable for jelly roll sponges. Cupcakes and muffins may be baked in paper cups. Moist products, such as applesauce cupcakes, may be removed easily from these, but drier products may be removed with difficulty. Overgreasing is indicated by overbrowning and a turning-in of the rims at the edge of the cake.

Black pans give more volume and bake more rapidly because they absorb more heat. If japaned metal pans are new, wipe them clean, place them in a 400° F oven, and allow them to remain until they are tinged with a bluish-black color. Then grease them lightly with oil or a plastic fat and return to the oven to set for three to four minutes. Allow them to cool and wipe them clean. Aluminum pans need not be treated in this manner.

Handle bakery pans with care. Do not bang them around, drop them,

FIG. 12-21   Pound and angel cakes may be scaled as shown above. Professional bakers
are able to scoop and dump rapidly using this hand method. Note how on the balance one
empty pan is set to tare the other and the pound weight is added to assure the addition of
the proper amount of batter. Thin batters may be poured into containers by weight. After
weighing once, the container can be filled without weighing, making repeat filling easier and
quicker to do.

or handle them so they lose shape. Avoid heat warping. Use cake pans only
for cake production. Do not use glass. Glass is fragile, and it is difficult
to brown cakes on the bottoms in glass pans.

Thick cakes may overbake on the outside before the inside is done.
Protect thick cakes on the sides and bottoms from outside heat with half-
inch wooden liners covered with one-fourth-inch asbestos mats. Baking
temperatures for thick cakes are lower than for thinner ones. Ovens having
well controlled heat may eliminate the need for protective mats.

Observe panning weights. Machines that deposit proper weights are used
in large bakeshops. For butter cake batters, use 0.2 ounces per square inch
of pan. The area of a round pan will be approximately 75% that of a
square cake pan having a side equal to the diameter.[4] Pan layer cakes
with greater surface areas are thicker than those with smaller surface areas.

[4]Thus an eight-inch-square pan will take (8X8X0.2) 12¾ ounces of batter, and an
eight-inch-diameter round pan (8X8.75X0.2) 9½ ounces of batter, and an 18 by 26
inch baking sheet (18X26X0.2) 94 ounces (about 6 pounds) of batter.

Foam cake pans should be well filled with batter to build a structure in baking.

Baking

The baking of a cake is critical to its quality. A cake enters the oven as a viscous, aerated, semi-fluid batter and comes out a solid, tender product. Batter movement occurs in baking; the warm portion rises while the cold batter sinks. Slip contributed by shortening and/or liquid is required to allow this movement. During such action, sugars dissolve completely and shortening melts. Leavening makes the cake rise. Firming of the structure results when the starch gelatinizes and the proteins coagulate. The result is a baked cake.

A cake goes through four stages in baking. The first is a rapid rise as leavening develops. The batter is quite fluid. In the second stage, rising

(a)   (b)

(c)   (d)

FIG. 12-22   Stages in the baking of a cake. (a) First stage: the batter is quite fluid and a rapid rise has occurred. (b) Second stage: the rising continues, bubbles rise to the top, and a slight surface tan appears. (c) Third stage: rise is complete and the structure begins to set. (d) Fourth stage: baking is complete, color is deep, and the cake now leaves the sides of the pan. There is a distinct aroma of baked cake.

Table 12-3
Production Scaling Weights, Baking Temperatures, and Times for Cakes

Type Cake	Scaling Weight	Baking Temperature (°F)	Time (min)
Layer			
Butter or Pound (1½ to 2 in. deep)			
6 in.*	6 to 8 oz	375	18
7 in.*	9 to 11 oz	375	20
8 in.*	12 to 14 oz	375	25
10 in.*	20 oz	360	35
12 in.*	1½ to 2 lb	360	
14 in.*	2¼ to 3 lb	360	
Foam cakes			
6 in.*	4 to 5 oz	375	20
8 in.*	9 to 10 oz	375	
10 in.*	16 to 18 oz	360	
12 in.*	1½ to 1¾ lb	360	
Loaf			
Pound, 3¼ x 3½ x 8 in.	1 lb	355	50
Pound, 3¼ x 6 x 11 in.	3 lb	325	100
Fruit, 3¼ x 3½ x 8 in.	1½ lb	315	90
Angel, 3¼ x 3½ x 8 in.	7 to 10 oz	365	
Angel, tube, small	8 to 10 oz		
Angel, tube, 10 in.	1½ to 2 lb	360	50
Sheet			
Butter, 1 x 18 x 26 in.	6 to 7 lb	360	35
Butter, 3 x 18 x 26 in.	8 to 10 lb	350	
Sponge, 1 x 18 x 26 in.	3 lb	360	25
Miscellaneous			
Ring, 6½ in.*	10 to 14 oz	375	
Oval loaf, 6¾ in.	8 oz	375	
Cupcakes, butter, per doz	14 to 16 oz	385	
Cupcakes, foam, per doz	7 to 8 oz	375	
Mary Ann Shells, butter, per doz	1⅛ to 2¼ lb	385	

*diameter

Note: Weights, times, and temperatures are average only; adjust for each cake. Butter cakes made by the blended method may be baked at slightly higher temperatures than those for conventionally made cakes; temperatures given here are for blended type.

continues, the center rising higher than the sides; bubbles rise to the top and a slight surface tan appears; some firmness of batter is evident on the sides. In the third stage, the rise is complete; the structure sets; top browning increases and spreads over the surface; a slight aroma of baked cake is evident. In the fourth stage, browning is complete; the structure sets, and a full-baked aroma indicates that the cake is done. The cake may separate slightly from the pan, and the cake is firm to the touch, springing back and leaving no imprint. (Some very rich butter cakes and foam cakes may lack this spring.) If a toothpick or wire tester is inserted, it should come out clean, indicating doneness.

Temperature is a critical factor in baking. Improved ovens and ingredients have made it possible to increase baking temperatures for cakes. Those mixed by the blending method are usually baked at higher temperatures than those mixed by the conventional method. Small cakes will be baked at higher temperatures than large ones, and thin cakes at higher temperatures than thick ones. Too high a temperature retards flavor and volume; crusts become dark, and the tops of the cakes may split because inside areas are still

FIG. 12-23 Oven temperatures that were just right, too low, and too high caused these effects on identical cake batter.

FIG. 12-24 A cooling rack for cakes and other bakery items. Note that foam cakes are cooled inverted.

rising when the outer area is set in baking. Overbaking of a chocolate or cocoa cake impairs flavor.

The texture of cake is improved if they are set into preheated ovens. In loading the oven, allow room for good heat circulation between cakes. Do not place them against the oven sides where uneven heat occurs. Even heat distribution is essential, and flash heat should be avoided. Pans that touch in the oven reduce batter movement and proper cake development. Ovens should be level. Thermostats on ovens should control temperatures within 10° F of that desired. The heat should come mostly from the bottom and circulate around the cake, but this may vary, as for jelly rolls, where more top heat should be given to keep the bottom soft for rolling.

If the oven temperature is too hot, the outside of the cake will be baked before the interior is baked, and the cake may be tough and too compact. The cake may be humped and show tunneling. Too cool an oven will give a crust that forms too late. This allows cell walls to be overexpanded, and the cake will be flat, with a pale, sticky crust and a coarse, uneven grain. If a cake is underbaked or baked too slowly, the structure may not set sufficiently and the cake may collapse when removed from the oven. A foam cake baked in too hot an oven will become firm before complete expansion has occurred, and the cake will be heavy, with tough texture, poor cell structure, low volume, and a hard crust. If the oven is too cool, the air cells will be overexpanded, giving a coarse-grained cake and a sticky-pale crust. Fruit cakes and other heavy cakes may be steamed instead of baked.

Cooling

Cakes should be cooled, after being removed from the oven, for 15 minutes or longer, depending on their size and shape. Then they should be freed from pan edges and dumped onto racks. They may be turned right side up by reversing on another rack, if desired. Removing them from pans while still warm dissipates bottom moisture and avoids a soggy crumb. Handle gently, however. Cool sponge cakes for jelly rolls to about 110° F. Then roll in slightly moistened cloths and allow to cool in this shape. Unroll, spread with jelly, and then reroll without the cloth; rolling may also be done as shown in Figure 12-25.

Cooling a cake too quickly causes shrinkage. Some thin cakes are allowed to cool in their pans, and while some moisture develops on the bottom, this is not sufficient to give a soggy cake. Butter cakes usually leave the pan easily upon being inverted and loosen around the sides, especially if one side is allowed to come free. Overcooling before removal may cause a cake to stick to the pan, making removal difficult. Allow loaf or pound

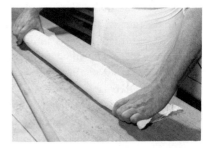

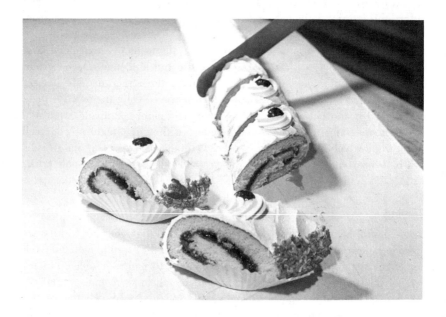

FIG. 12-25 Roll a warm cake into a cloth and let stand securely wrapped until set. Then unroll and fill.

cakes to cool about 30 minutes, and then invert after freeing the edges. Large bride or pound cakes should be removed from frames but not cut when warm. Foam cakes should be inverted upon removal from the oven. Rest these on supports so no pressure is on the cake. Remove the cakes while slightly warm but cool enough to give firmness to the structure. Do not handle while warm. To remove a foam cake, loosen it from the sides and tube with a spatula or knife. Tilt and draw out gently.

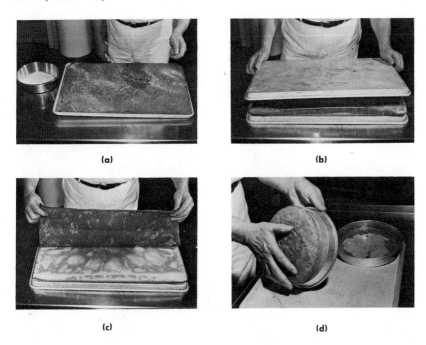

(a) (b)

(c) (d)

FIG. 12-26. (a) To remove a sheet cake from the pan, first sprinkle the top lightly with granulated sugar. (b) Set an empty pan of the same-size bottom down on top of the cake. Invert and remove the top sheet pan. (c) Loosen the paper carefully on the far side of the worker and lift up. (d) Layer cakes can be dumped onto the hand and set onto a pan as shown.

Table 12-4
Butter Cake Production Scaling Weights by Variety

Size Cake	Variety Cake			
	Yellow	Chocolate	White	Wedding
4 in. layer	4 oz	4 oz	4 oz	7¼ oz
6 in. layer	7¼ oz	8 oz	8 oz	12 oz
7 in. layer	10 oz	12 oz	12 oz	1 lb
8 in. layer	13 oz	1 lb	1 lb	1 lb 4 oz
9 in. layer	1 lb 1 oz	1 lb 4 oz	1 lb 4 oz	1 lb 8 oz*
10 in. layer	1 lb 8 oz	1 lb 12 oz	1 lb 12 oz	2 lb*
12 in. layer	2 lb 8 oz	2 lb 12 oz	2 lb 12 oz	3 lb*
14 in. layer	3 lb 8 oz	3 lb 12 oz	3 lb 12 oz	4 lb*
16 in. layer	4 lb 12 oz	5 lb	5 lb	5 lb*
18 x 26 in. sheet	7 lb 8 oz	8 lb 8 oz	9 lb	

*Increase approximately 25% for square cakes; scale an 18-inch-square wedding cake 8 lb.

Note: Adjust all scaling weights to suit *your* batter weights; these are only guides.

FIG. 12-27 Crumbs can be removed from cakes by rolling off the crusts and brushing as shown. This is oftentimes desirable before a cake is frosted.

Storage

Cakes should be stored in a clean, cool place where they will not dry out. At times mold may be a problem. In warm, humid climates, place cakes under refrigeration; staling is more rapid under refrigeration, but this can not be avoided. Many cakes show mold where the cut surface was contaminated by the handler's fingers. By freezing cakes in moisture-vapor-proof wraps, quality may be retained for a long period of time.

Make-up

The make-up of the cake is important to its quality. Appearance and flavor will be significantly affected by the make-up treatment. Many cakes are frosted and filled. Shaping may occur before these treatments are given. Fillings are frequently related to the cornstarch-thickened puddings explained in the chapter on desserts. Jams, jellies, and other sweet products may also be used as fillings.

To prepare good frostings, it is necessary to understand some of the principles and techniques required for the preparation of good sugar mixtures. Sugar cookery takes a great deal of knowledge and skill. The cook or baker who works with sugar must have a complete understanding of the reactions involved and the techniques required to produce a satisfactory item.

SUGAR COOKERY

Starch, dextrin, and sugar belong to the same family, the carbohydrates. Sugar may be complex or simple. Enzymes or acid may break starch down to dextrins, thence to complex sugars, and then to simple sugars, as shown in Figure 12-29. In food preparation we deal with three complex sugars: sucrose, maltose, and lactose; and three simple sugars: fructose, glucose, and galactose. Sucrose is made from cane or beets and is the sugar most commonly used in cooking. Granulated sugar and powdered sugar are almost pure sucrose. Molasses and brown sugar contain large quantities of sucrose, but because they also contain acid, minerals, and other sugars, they react much differently in food preparation from our regular granulated sugars. Maltose is obtained from sprouted barley and is an excellent food for yeast. Malt sugars are also used to flavor foods. Lactose, the third of the complex

FIG. 12-28   A few of the varieties of sugar that may be used in quantity food production.

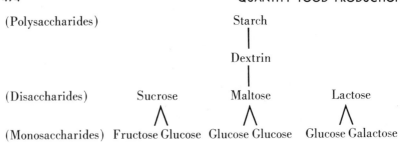

(Polysaccharides)   Starch
                                              |
                                           Dextrin
                                              |
(Disaccharides)   Sucrose   Maltose   Lactose
                          ∧   ∧   ∧
(Monosaccharides) Fructose Glucose Glucose Glucose   Glucose Galactose

FIG. 12-29 A simplified version of the relationships of carbohydrates used in cooking.

sugars, comes from milk; yeast cannot grow in lactose. Its low solubility also causes problems in using it in food preparation.

Glucose (dextrose), fructose (levulose), and galactose are simple sugars found in many plants. Sucrose can be changed into equal parts of fructose and glucose. Maltose breaks down into glucose, and lactose into glucose and galactose.

The changing of sucrose into fructose and glucose is called inversion. The term *inversion* arose because the investigator who named these sugars

FIG. 12-30 The chocolate on the left was filled with a fondant center containing an enzyme which inverted the sugars, turning them into a sirup. The chocolate on the right was filled at the same time with a fondant center having no enzyme added. Note that it remained firm.

found that glucose turns or inverts light to the right, while fructose turns light to the left in a polariscope. He called glucose the right-turning sugar, or dextrose, and fructose he called the left-turning sugar, or levulose. These terms are frequently encountered for these sugars in chemical literature.

The change of starch to complex sugars and complex sugars to simple sugars may be desirable or undesirable in quantity food preparation. A desirable reaction might be one in which the enzymes diastase and maltase turn starch to maltose and maltose to glucose. Another occurs when an acid is used to change cornstarch to corn sirup. Another occurs when the enzyme invertase is added to fondant, changing the sucrose to a sirup in cherry-filled chocolates. The change of sucrose to fructose and glucose retards the crystallization of other sugars in candies, frostings, and other sugar mixtures. If five pounds of sugar, ½ cup or two ounces of cream of tartar, and one quart of water are cooked to 240° F, about 40% of the sucrose is inverted, and the solution will not crystallize. This may be a desirable or undesirable reaction in food preparation. If the strength of the acid or the amount of cream of tartar is reduced so 16 to 23% of the sucrose is inverted, a soft, plastic, moldable crystalline mass results. A 7 to 12% invert sugar content to a fondant gives a firm mixture. Using five pounds of sugar with a half cup of lemon juice or one-fourth ounce of cream of tartar and cooking to 280° F gives about a 15 to 18% inversion. This amount of inversion is suitable in general for fondants. The acid in some items, such as molasses, brown sugar, and lemon juice, may cause undesirable changes in products. Their acid reacting with a starch thickener may turn it into a sirup. This may cause puddings or pie fillings to thin, as is seen sometimes in butterscotch pudding and lemon pie filling. Some sugar-coated fruits become moist and sticky when the acid of the fruit changes the sugar coating to invert sugars.

The amount of inversion that will occur depends upon:

1. The amount of acid in the solution.
2. The strength of the acid.
3. The time of cooking.
4. The temperature to which the solution is cooked.

More and stronger acid must be used if time or temperature are reduced. Many pastry chefs control the time the acid is in contact with the sugar by adding it at the time the sirup comes to a boil. This procedure is better than adding acid at the start. The boiling time from 216° F to doneness is very standard. Some chefs may add a fairly large quantity of cream of tartar after the mixture is cooled and begins to form crystals in mixing. Small quantities of acid may be added to crystallized mixtures to keep them soft and moist in storage. If this acid is in excess, harmful results may occur. Egg whites, fats, gelatin, glycerine, and other substances are also used to retard crystallization. Acids need not be used to obtain invert sugars; they may be obtained directly by adding corn sirup or other mixtures containing invert sugars. One-half to three-fourths of a pound of corn sirup with five pounds of sugar gives about a 15 to 18% inverted sugar to a sirup at the end of cooking; one pound of corn sirup to five pounds of sugar gives about a 20% invert sugar content.

FIG. 12-31   The effect of a strong alkali on a glucose solution.

Soda and other weak alkalis decompose sugars. Sucrose is more resistant to alkalis than maltose, lactose, glucose, or fructose. Breakdown may be indicated by the development of a deep cream or a light yellow color for most sugars, but glucose has a typical dirty gray reaction to alkaline waters. Cooking a sugar solution for a long time in an alkaline solution produces a caramelization and an off-flavor. Adding a bit of acid, such as cream of tartar, will change the alkalinity of most water to acid and prevent this undesirable breakdown from alkaline action.

The sweetest to least sweet sugars are fructose, sucrose, glucose, maltose, and lactose; this order is the same as that of their solubility. The sweetness of a half-fructose and half-glucose solution is slightly under that of a sucrose solution. Acids in a sirup such as molasses, honey, or sorghum lessen the taste of sweetness in the sirup.

Figure 12-32 indicates the solubility of some sugars. Lactose crystallizes easily; the graininess sometimes found in evaporated milk is evidence of this. Mixing dry milk a day ahead of use will permit lactose to go into solution and give a more stable, flavorful product. Glucose crystallizes easily, jams, jellies, and honey that are crystallized are examples of this reaction.

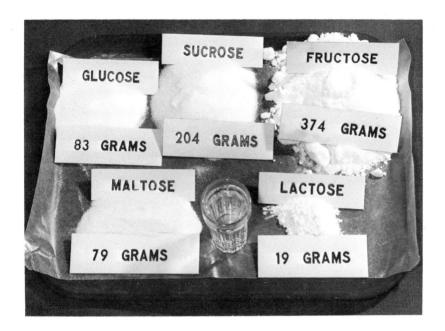

FIG. 12-32 The relative solubility of the sugars used in food preparation. The amounts of the various sugars shown here are soluble at room temperature in the 100 cubic centimeters of water shown here.

The uncrystallized portion of crystallized honey is fructose, which crystallizes with difficulty. Solubility is therefore in this order: fructose, sucrose, glucose, maltose, and lactose.

Warm water dissolves more sugar than cold water. Water dissolves more sucrose if acid, invert sugar, or salt is added. At 195° F water dissolves twice as much sucrose as at room temperature. While fine sugar goes into solution more rapidly, no more will eventually dissolve than of coarse sugar.

A solution holding as much sugar as it should at a given temperature is called saturated. A solution holding more sugar than it should at a given temperature is called supersaturated, and any disturbance of a supersaturated solution will cause it to crystallize. A simple sirup made in excess of two pounds of sugar to one pound of water may crystallize soon after making because, as seen in Figure 12-32, sucrose's solubility is about two of sugar to one of water. Moisture is lost in boiling. A two-to-one sugar-water solution concentrates as it boils. Such a mixture boiled to 240° F and then cooled to 104° F becomes a highly supersaturated solution. Crystallization is quicker in a warm than a cold supersaturated solution; the crystals are also fewer in number and larger. While a solution cooled to 104° F has slower crystallization, a smoother mass is obtained because the crystals are finer and greater in number.

As the quantity of sugar in a solution increases, the boiling point increases. A 10% sucrose solution boils at 213° F, a 50% solution at 216° F, and an 80% solution at 234° F. When no more moisture can be lost, sugars carmelized from heat. Granulated sugar melts at from 320°F to 356°F and begins to burn at 410° F.

Figure 12-33 indicates how the boiling points of sugar solutions drop as the altitude is increased.[5] This is approximately a 1° F drop for every increase of 500 feet. A correction should be applied in sugar cookery above 1000 feet.

When relative humidity is above 50%, it is desirable to cook sirups 1° F higher for every 25% or partial 25% increase in relative humidity over 50%. It is common to see sugar solutions in kitchens cooked two degrees higher in summer than in winter because the humidity in summer is much higher than in winter. A slight excess in humidity may be overcome by extra mixing after crystallization starts. All temperatures in this text are for sea level and a relative humidity below 50%.

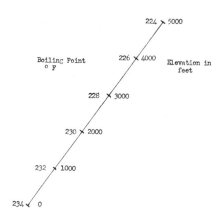

FIG. 12-33 Elevation affects the boiling point of sugar solutions. If a sugar solution boils at 234° F at sea level (4 sugar to 1 water solution), then at the various levels shown on the right, the solution will boil at the temperature indicated at the left.

[5]Denver, Albuquerque, and many other mountain cities in this country are at or above 5000 feet above sea level.

Some sugars are hydroscopic; that is, they draw moisture. Honey, molasses, maltose, brown sugar, and some others draw moisture into foods, making them moist. These sweeteners are used for soft cookies, but not for crisp cookies. Pulled sugar work or hard candies may draw moisture to them on humid days, and for that reason they should be stored in airtight containers. Some storage areas have substances placed in them to attract excess moisture away from pulled sugar goods. When these drying compounds become moist, they can usually be regenerated by heating them in an oven. If a hydroscopic sugar is used in a cooked sugar solution, it may have to be cooked to a slightly higher temperature to correct for the moisture this sugar may attract into the product.

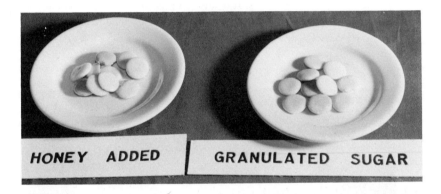

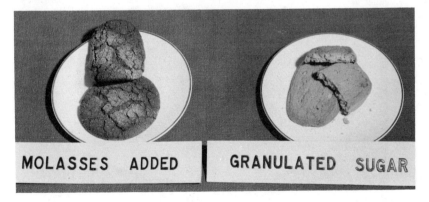

FIG. 12-34 Honey and molasses are hydroscopic sugars. When a formula was varied only by the addition of honey, the mints containing honey became moist and broke down. Similarly, the cookies made with molasses bend easily, while the cookies made only with granulated sugar remain quite crisp and break when bent.

The viscosity or thickness of a sirup will increase as its temperature drops. Some products, such as caramels, peanut brittle, and cooked frostings, may be liquid at higher temperatures and plastic or hard and brittle at lower temperatures. Cold fondants may need warming to work well, but heating above 100° F causes them to become dull and grainy. Caramels and taffy should be warmed slightly before cutting, and sugar work is done before a batch warmer so the sugar mixture remains workable. Moisture, invert sugars, butter, and other ingredients may increase creaminess and plasticity. If the quantity of butter or fat is above 7% that of the sugar, for every 3% increase over this 7%, the final cooking temperature is raised $\frac{1}{2}$° F to counteract the extra softness caused by the fat. Glycerine will also increase plasticity; if it is used, about $\frac{1}{2}$% of glycerine to sugar is considered desirable to give the required softness. It is added to the sirup mixture during boiling. Starch or dextrins cause crystalline mixtures to become firmer. The firmness

FIG. 12-35   The viscosity or thickness of sugar solutions changes with the temperature. The melted caramel mixture on the right is the same as that in the firm caramels on the left. The temperature difference of the two has made the change.

contributed by the starch in cocoa or chocolate should be considered. Some bakers lower final cooking temperatures $\frac{1}{2}°$ F for every 3% that cocoa or chocolate is over 10% of the sugar in a recipe; for instance, if $6\frac{1}{2}$ ounces of cocoa are used to 40 ounces ($2\frac{1}{2}$ pounds) of sugar, the temperature would be dropped $1°$ F, for the excess of cocoa over 10% of sugar is about 6% ($2\frac{1}{2}$ ounces).

The creaminess of a crystalline sugar mass is affected by the size of the sugar crystals and their quantity. Tiny crystals are desired in fondants, fudges, and other creamy crystalline products. Sometimes large, coarse, grainy crystals are desired for coating purposes. Amorphous mixtures, that is, mixtures without definite crystalline form, may be desirable for caramels, nougats, taffy, brittles, and so forth.

Stirring a supersaturated solution encourages crystal development. Smaller crystals, and more of them, will be formed if a solution is cool and if stirring is continuous and vigorous. Kneading a stiff mixture encourages small crystal development. If few crystals are formed, the crystals tend to be large. The size of the first crystal formed in a mass will influence the size of all the remaining crystals. Because of this, fine fondant from a previous batch may be added just before crystallization. This seeds the mixture, promoting the formation of crystals of a similar size. To prevent seeding from coarse sugar, the sides of pans are moistened during cooking so the undissolved crystals clinging to the sides are washed down and dissolved. This prevents them from seeding the mixture later. Pans may also be covered for a short time to dissolve these crystals. Seeding may also occur from dust or other air particles. For this reason, supersaturated solutions are usually covered after they are cooked. Crystals may grow in size in storage. Butter, acid, or other ingredients are added to discourage this growth. Many fondant mixtures are poured from cooking pans onto a cold, flat, smooth surface, such as a greased marble slab, a baking sheet, a stainless steel table, or a platter. The pan is not scraped but all the sirup possible is allowed to drip out. Scraping or disturbing at this point will cause large crystals to form and these can seed the remaining mixture. If the surface on which the sirup is poured is not smooth, the rough spots may encourage large crystalline growth while the mass is hot. If agitation of the hot supersaturated solution occurs, even the movement of a thermometer in the mass, large crystals may develop.

When a liquid changes to a solid, heat is released. This giving off of heat is called an exothermic action. When a sirup crystallizes, the exothermic heat causes the mixture to thin slightly; a loss of sheen is also noticeable. Many use these factors as signals to begin spreading, dropping, or performing other required manipulations before the mixture becomes too firm to handle.

Doneness may be indicated in a number of ways, but unless the worker

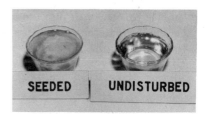

(a)   (b)

FIG. 12-36 The stirring (a), seeding (b), or disturbing (c) of a supersaturated sugar solution when warm causes rapid crystallization. Note how in each case the sample that was untouched remained in an uncrystallized form.

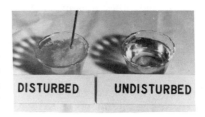

(c)

is experienced, the most satisfactory way is by temperature. A Brix or Baume scale reading may be used to indicate density or doneness of sirups. A Brix of 14° to 16° is a light sirup, 16° to 19° medium, 19° to 21° heavy, and over 21° extra heavy. Some objective tests in judging doneness are:

Water test: Drop sirup into 50° F water; firmness indicates doneness; time in the water is a factor of firmness obtained.

Finger test: Dip the finger into cold water, then quickly into hot sirup; the doneness is indicated by the thread or ball formed.

Spin test: Judge doneness by the length of the thread formed or the manner in which the sirup flows from a spoon or through a perforated ladle.

Bite test: Place a bit of sirup into the mouth. The bite or crack of the sirup will indicate doneness; a sirup that breaks between the teeth without adhering to them is at the crack stage, about 410° F.

Appearance test: Color and appearance are good indicators; the size, type, and viscosity of the bubbles formed in cooking caramels, fudge, penuche, fondant, and other mixtures may be used to tell doneness; when a sirup begins to turn slightly brown, it is at the caramel stage; because thermometers are difficult to use in the burning sugar, sight is a more reliable method to use in indicating doneness of sugars cooked above the caramel stage.

Sound test: When a sirup cracks loudly twice as it is dropped into cold water, the moderately hard crack stage of 310° to 315° F has been reached. When a sugar thread cracks very hard three times as it is wrapped around the finger, the temperature is between 316° F and 320° F. Sugar may discolor slightly at this higher temperature.

It is emphasized again that thermometers are the only reliable guide for non-experts to use, and even experts use them.

Table 12-5

Production Data for Use in Sugar Cookery

Temperature °F of Sirup	Physical Characteristic at this Temperature	Cooking Term Used to Indicate This Doneness	Use of the Product
215 to 217 (30° Baume)	Faint thread forms between thumb and finger when they are separated.	Small thread (lisse or petite fillet)	Light sirups (1 sugar to 3 water).
217 to 220 (31° Baume)	Longer thread formed between thumb and finger when they are separated.	Large thread (grande lisse)	Heavy sirup (1 sugar to 1 water).
221 to 222 (32° Baume)	Thread breaks between thumb and finger.	Little pearl (petit perle)	Extra heavy sirups; can crystalize (2 sugar to 1 water).
222 to 223 (33° Baume)	Holds as thread from thumb to finger.	Large pearl (grande perle)	Working almond paste, flowing fondants.
223 to 225	Strong thread from thumb to finger.	Thread	Large crystals for crystallizing fruits.
230 to 232	Use spin test; dip perforated ladle into hot sirup; tap lightly on side of container; blow through holes and make bubbles fly out.	The blow (au souffle or glue)	Soft, pliable fondant mass; used to glaze fruits and nuts; dip singly and dry; adding a bit of lemon juice retards sugaring.
236 to 239	Soft ball in 50° F water; in finger test, small ball can be rolled between fingers.	Small ball (petit boule)	Fondant for flowing icing on petit fours; thin fudge or penuche.
239 to 243	Medium ball in 50° F water; in finger test ball has more firmness than soft ball above.	Medium ball	Firm fondant for dipping bon bons, fruits, and mints; knead when too firm to stir.
245 to 252	Firm ball in 50° F water; in finger test ball is firm.	Large or firm ball (grande boule)	Soft caramels at lower temperatures; higher temperatures for taffies.
250 to 258	Quite firm ball but still pliable in 50° F water.		Frostings at lower temperatures; divinity sirup, etc. at higher.
258 to 266	Hard ball in 50° F water; in finger test sirup detaches as hard material when finger is placed into cold water.	Small crack (petit casse)	Fondants where fruit juice is added last and temperature brought down to 242° F; nougats, hard taffies, popcorn ball mixtures.
270 to 290	Sirup spins thread; thread snaps between the teeth above 285° F.	Crack (casse)	Butterscotch and hard candies; taffies.
290 to 295	Cracks between teeth; crack is quite sharp.	Hard crack, lower range	Hard nougats, ribbon, English and rock candy.
295 to 310	Very sharp crack between the teeth.	Hard crack, middle range	Coating fruit and nuts; some sugar work.
310 to 316	Very brittle and hard between the teeth.	Hard crack, upper range	Pulled sugar work.
316 to 318	Hard to bite; may shatter.	Hard crack, top range	Flowers in pulled sugar work.
318 to 320	Hard to bite; may shatter.	Hard crack, upper limit	Baskets and woven items in sugar work.
338	Light caramelization noticed.	Caramel sugar	Caramel flavored sugar.
400	Almost black.	Burned sugar	Coloring material.

FIG. 12-37   Barley sugar (left) cooked to approximately 310° F, caramel sugar (center) cooked to approximately 340° F, and burned sugar (right) cooked to approximately 400° F.

Frostings and Icings

Many different types of icings are used on cakes to improve their appearance and flavor. Sometimes frostings are classified as foam or creamed types, such as butter cream, boiled, and meringue; as flat types, such as glazes, fondants, fudge, and plain water, or as combinations of these. But methods of preparation may be a more meaningful classification for the student. For this reason, frostings are discussed under the following subheadings: fondant, or fudge, type; powdered sugar icings, which include butter creams and flat icings; boiled or cooked icings, which include marshmallow and meringue; and royal or decorator's icing. Besides flavor and appearance, icings add richness and prevent moisture loss from cakes. Not all types of cakes require frosting; some foam cakes may be served plain or merely filled, but most other cakes require some type of frosting or sauce.

Use high quality ingredients. Colors and flavorings should be moderate for the most part. Excess coloring or flavoring may detract from, rather than add to, quality. Fillings and frostings should be liberally spread on cakes, but too much will give an oversweetened, overmoist product. The filling and frosting should complement the cake. Warm temperatures or high humidity may make it necessary to emphasize the use of fondant or fudge-type frostings, which are more durable than some others under such conditions. Another problem frequently encountered in the handling of frostings is that they sometimes become quite sticky and handle with difficulty. Stabilizers purchased from a bakery supply house will assist in solving this

FIG. 12-38 Care in frosting cakes pays off in added appearance. (Courtesy Standard Brands)

problem, but agar agar, gelatin, gums, or cereals such as wheat or cornstarch or tapioca flour may be used. It is best to thin frostings with simple or corn sirup rather than with water, for water may curdle or separate some frostings.

Frostings are products high in sugar which may crystallize out. The preparation and use of cooked frostings frequently deals with the problem of retarding or controlling this crystallization.

Fluffy frostings are spread on cakes more thickly than heavier frostings; use about $1\frac{1}{4}$ cups (10 ounces) of filling and $1\frac{1}{2}$ to $1\frac{3}{4}$ cups of fluffy icing for a two-tier eight-inch layer cake, and two to three pints of filling and $1\frac{1}{4}$ to $2\frac{1}{2}$ quarts ($1\frac{1}{2}$ to 3 pounds) of fluffy icing for a single 18 by 26 inch sheet. One dozen cupcakes will require $6\frac{3}{4}$ ounces of butter cream frosting, but if topped with coconut or nuts, reduce to four ounces and use $2\frac{1}{2}$ ounces of coconut or nuts. To coat the sides of eight-, nine- and ten-inch layer cakes allow, respectively, $1\frac{1}{2}$, $1\frac{3}{4}$, and $2\frac{1}{8}$ ounces of coating materials such as chopped nuts and coconut.

(a)

(b)

FIG. 12-39   (a) The three most commonly used frostings for cakes are shown here. Fondant appears on the far left, butter cream frosting on the far right, and a boiled marshmallow frosting in the foreground. (b) Decorator's icing made firm with starch may be used for making many shapes. The castle shown in the background is made of sugar cubes with decorator's icing forming the "cement". A container of decorator's icing, before cornstarch is added to make it firm, is shown on the right.

Fondants

Fondant is a water-sugar mixture usually cooked to 240° F, cooled to 104° F, and mixed until tiny crystals form. Cream of tartar or corn sirup is used to give invert sugars. **Plain fondant is a simple, creamy, white,** smooth crystalline mass. It is best to purchase this already made if use in the operation is high. Fudge icings are rich, cooked fondant containing chocolate or cocoa, cream, butter, and other ingredients. Fudge may be a general term also applied to non-chocolate items such as penuche, maple, and other creamy cooked fondant mixtures. Fondant can be used to make a butter cream icing, but powdered sugar is more satisfactory for this. If fondant is used, eggs should not be added to the butter cream. To thin fondants, use simple sirup; do not heat them above 100° F.

Powdered Sugar Icings

Butter cream icing is a rich, smooth icing, mellow in flavor. Confectioners sugar (size 6X to give good smoothness), butter or margarine or shortening, eggs, flavoring, and other ingredients are used to make it. Eggs, usually egg whites, give lightness and fluffiness. A high degree of creaming also gives lightness and fluffiness. The ratio of fat to sugar is usually one to two, and the ratio of eggs to sugar is usually one to ten by weight. Many variations can be obtained from a basic butter cream. A French butter cream icing can be made by folding in carefully one-fourth pound of softened butter or margarine into two quarts of boiled or marshmallow icing. The icing should be at room temperature. Do not stir or beat, for the soft butter will destroy the foam unless care is taken. Simple or flat icings made from powdered sugar are oftentimes called plain water icings. They are mixtures of water or liquid milk of some type, flavoring, and confectioners sugar mixed to a smooth, thick paste. They are warmed to 100° F to coat Danish pastry and sweet breakfast rolls; they can also be used as a plain fondant for pouring over cakes and coating them as one might do with a plain fondant icing. They usually do not contain fat.

Boiled or Cooked Icing

Boiled icings are made by boiling sugar, water, and glucose or cream of tartar to a temperature of 240° to 250° F. This is poured over egg whites which have been beaten to a soft but firm peak, the upper level of stage two foam. As the hot sirup is added, beating is vigorous. The beating is continued until a crystalline mass forms or the icing is almost stiff enough to spread. Stiffness will depend upon the quantity of egg whites to sirup, the temperature to which the sirup is cooked, and the temperature of the frosting. A marshmallow icing is a boiled icing to which confectioners sugar and

Table 12-6
Variations Obtained from Plain Butter Cream Icing

Variation	To 10 lb Plain Butter Cream Icing Add:	Variation	To 10 lb Plain Butter Cream Icing Add:
Nut	Chopped Nuts, 1 lb	Coconut	Macaroon Coconut Bits, 1 lb
Raisin	Ground Raisins, 1 lb	Fondant	Plain Fondant, 5 lb
Cherry	Candied Cherries. 1 lb	Chocolate (Cocoa)	Cocoa, 10 oz, and Water, 5 oz
Candied Fruit	Candied Fruit, 1 lb	Peppermint Candy	Peppermint Candy Bits, 8 oz
Jam or Marmalade	Jam or Marmalade, 1 lb	Lady Baltimore	Chopped Candied Cherries, Nuts,
Almond*	Almond Paste, 1 lb and		and Raisins, mixed, 1 lb
	Almond Flavoring	Fresh Fruit	Chopped Drained Fresh Fruit, 4 oz

*Thin the almond paste first with a bit of egg white so it goes into the butter cream without lumping.

(a)

(b)

FIG. 12-40 A glaze made from waxy maize starch into a thin paste is shown in (a), and the sheen it gives to products is shown in (b).

gelatin have been added to give stiffness. Commercial meringue preparations are available for making various types of boiled icings.

A glaze is a boiled icing made into a heavy sirup. It usually contains a small quantity of gelatin but no eggs. The glaze may be brushed onto items, or objects may be dipped into it. Glazes may be used to give shine to products; they may be made from fruits, such as apricot pulp, or from a waxy maize-type starch.

Royal or Decorator's Icing

A stiff icing is frequently used for ornamental work. This is frequently made from egg whites, confectioners sugar, flavoring, and cream of tartar

FIG. 12-41   Cakes decorated with fondant icing and decorator's icing.

or lemon juice. Meringue powder with a bit of water may be used instead of egg whites. Uncooked cornstarch is added if extra stiffness is required. It is an excellent icing to use for decorating when other icings may run or weep. Very stiff icing of this kind may be rolled out thin on wax paper and from this a design cut which may be colored or decorated. This same icing in more plastic form may be worked from a pastry tube onto wax paper. After drying, the decorations are then placed onto the cake. The icing may also be used directly on cakes. The unused portion should be kept covered with a damp cloth, for it dries rapidly. To store, cover tightly in an airtight container and place in a refrigerator. After storage, if too stiff, thin with some simple sirup or a bit of egg white. A lighter icing may be made by adding one tablespoon of water to the pound of confectioners sugar and beating the icing more. Decorate with this icing directly onto cakes, for the

air beaten into the mass by this process will make the icing fragile, and
after drying, items will crumble in handling.

Icing Procedures

Cakes should cool before they are iced. Crusts may be removed before icing.
If a damp cloth is placed over the cake, the crust rolls away more easily.
Trim away ragged edges. Frequently shaping is required. Edges on cakes
so shaped should be sharp. Do not attempt to make too intricate a design;
broad outlines make cakes more easily handled and minimize breaking. Use
subsequent decoration to sharpen outlines. Brush away all crumbs from the
cake before icing it.

Before using an icing, be sure it is of the proper consistency for spreading, not so thin as to be runny or so thick as to pull away and break the
cake. Select icings for stability (lack of "bleeding or breakdown"), absence
of stickiness, and a clear, glossy color. If icings become stiff, warm or add
a bit of simple sirup. Use paste colors if these can be obtained; liquid
colors may, however, be used. Any coloring matter should be first blended
with a small quantity of the icing. Color deeply; after the color is worked
well into this smaller mass, use it to shade into the larger batch to give the
desired shade. A good color sense is required, as well as some knowledge of

(a)   (b)

FIG. 12-42   (a) To ice a layer cake with a heavy frosting, such as butter cream, frost the
sides first, then the top, and finish by holding the spatula perpendicular as shown here to
give a smooth edge. (b) When thin frostings are used, pour the frosting over the top and
then work the frosting down to cover the sides completely. Note the use of the decorator's
wheel in these two pictures.

(a)

(b)

(c)

(d)

(e)

(f)

FIG. 12-43 Simple designs can be made as shown in illustrations (a) through (e). (f) The design shown here is obtained by heavily dusting powdered sugar over the cake top covered by a grid and then removing the grid, leaving the design. (Courtesy Standard Brands)

how to obtain various colors. For instance, blue and yellow make green, yellow and red make orange, and red and blue make violet. By shading violet with blue, purple is obtained, but if violet is shaded with red, a red violet results. A red or yellow-orange results when red or yellow, respectively, is blended with orange; and a yellow or blue-green results when green is shaded respectively by yellow or blue. The amateur is known by his excess of color as well as by his excess of flavor. Moderation is the sign of a craftsman.

To ice a layer cake, invert the first layer top down on a turntable or decorator's wheel. If a difference exists in layer thickness, place the thickest layer on the bottom. If a wheel is not available, invert on wax paper. Spread fillings evenly over the first layer; this will be the bottom turned up. Place the second layer on top of this, with the top up. If the icing is thin, deposit a liberal supply in the center of the top and work with a spatula to the sides. Guide the icing down the sides, frosting down with the spatula.[6] If a thicker frosting is used, such as boiled, marshmallow, or butter cream, start to frost on the sides, spreading with a spatula from the bottom toward the top, turning the cake as the side is frosted. Hold the spatula in a nearly vertical position to make a smooth side. When the sides are covered, spread the top with a liberal portion of frosting, using a motion which pushes it toward the edges. Make a smooth surface by dipping the spatula first into water and then smoothing out, or leave the surface irregular. An iced cake should give a feeling of height with the sides even and the top straight. The icing should be liberally piled on the top, and there should not be any "tight, peeled" appearance about it. Allow all iced cakes to dry thoroughly before decorating.

To ice small cakes, free them from crumbs after cutting into proper shapes. Place on a wire grill or rack over a sheet pan, allowing space so the icing will run down the sides of each cake. Pour a thin fondant or water icing over the tops, directing the icing so that it flows down the sides and coats them. Remove the rack, and with a spatula pick up the surplus icing for reuse. Continue with each rack until all cakes are coated. It is sometimes necessary to repeat to get a sufficiently thick coating on the cakes.

Decorating

A pastry bag made of canvas, rubber, or plastic can be used for decorating, but most professional workers prefer to make their own cones from parchment paper. They are simply made, are easily disposed of, and as many can be made for icings as the number of colors required. If parchment paper is not available, use heavy wax paper or brown wrapping paper, but the latter absorbs moisture and soon breaks, while the former is somewhat fragile.

[6]For very thin icings, such as fondant, place the cake on an open rack and frost (as shown in Fig. 12-44 for small cakes) by pouring frosting over it to coat it.

(a)

(b)

FIG. 12-44 (a) To frost small cakes, such as petit fours, cut into the desired shapes and then cover completely with fondant frosting as shown. (b) The finished product.

Table 12-7
Quantities of Frosting to Use Per Cake

Cake Size	Type Frosting	Filling Weight	To Frost Sides and Tops
4 in. layer*	Butter cream		2 oz
6 in. layer	Butter cream		5 oz
7 in. layer	Butter cream	3 oz	6½ to 8 oz
8 in. layer	Butter cream	4 oz	8 to 8½ oz
9 in. layer	Butter cream		11½ oz
10 in. layer	Butter cream		1 lb
12 in. layer	Butter cream		1 lb 7 oz
14 in. layer	Butter cream		2 lb
16 in. layer	Butter cream		2 lb 9 oz
18 by 26 in. sheet	Butter cream		3 to 4 lb (top only)
Cupcakes, per doz	Butter cream		5 oz (tops only)
7 in. layer	Boiled type	2 oz	4 oz
8 in. layer	Boiled type	2¼ oz	5 oz
7 in. layer	Fudge or fondant	3½ oz	9 oz
8 in. layer	Fudge or fondant	4½ oz	10 oz

*All layer cakes are two layer.

FIG. 12-45   Some shapes that may be used for small cakes. (Courtesy Institutions Magazine)

If only writing is to be done, the tip of the cone should not be cut and no metal tip need be inserted; the paper tip should be made the correct size for this. Fill the bag or cone to about half or three-fourths full. In filling, see that the icing is deposited down to the tip away from the top sides, and be sure no air is captured in the icing. Any captured air may ruin a complete decorating job by coming out with a burst during the work. See that the icing is of the correct consistency for the work to be done. For writing, the icing should flow or string out. If too thick, it will break as the tip is moved over the surface. A medium consistency is required for border work. The icing should be stiff enough if used for flowers, leaves, or other objects so petals or other items will stand up. After filling the cone or bag, fold over

Table 12-8
Cutting Sheet Cakes into Fancy Shapes

Shape	Fancy Shape Size (in.)	Make Equal Markings on Sheet Cake Width (18 in.)	Length (26 in.)	Number Pieces per 18 by 26 in. Sheet
Rectangle	1¼ x 2¼	14	10 or 11	140 to 154
Triangle	2⅛ x 2⅛ (each square cut in half diagonally)	8	12	176
Square	1½ x 1½	12	16	192
Diamond	1⅓ to 1½ x 3½	12	7	139 plus 38 triangles
		(See diagram below for markings)		

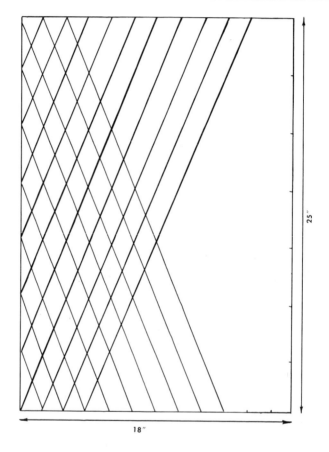

18″

25″

To cut a sheet cake into small diamonds, trim the cake. Mark the width into 12 equal divisions (1⅓ to 1½ inches each). Mark the length into seven equal divisions (3½ inches each). Lay a yardstick or measure diagonally across and mark the cake as indicated here. Cut. Yield: 139 diamonds and 38 triangular pieces.

FIG. 12-46   How to Cut Layer Cakes

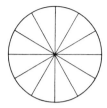

8″ — 2 layer cake
Yield: 12 servings

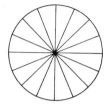

9″ — 2 layer cake
Yield: 16 servings

10″ — 2 layer cake
Yield: 20 servings

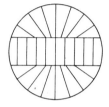

11″ — 2 layer cake
Yield: 26 servings

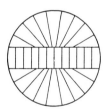

12″ — 2 layer cake
Yield: 30 servings

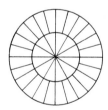

12″ — 2 layer cake
Yield: 36 servings

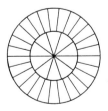

13″ — 2 layer cake
Yield: 36 servings

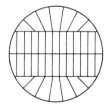

14″ — 2 layer cake
Yield: 40 servings

(Courtesy American Baking Institute)

FIG. 12-47   How to Cut Loaf Cakes

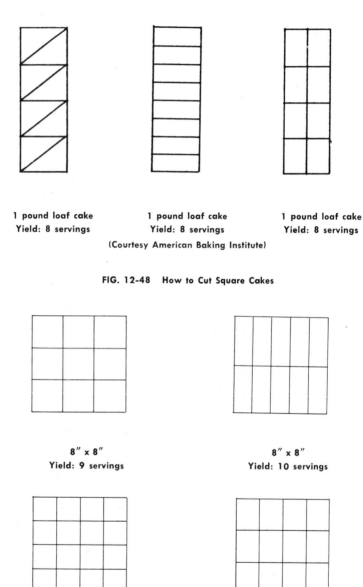

1 pound loaf cake   1 pound loaf cake   1 pound loaf cake
Yield: 8 servings   Yield: 8 servings   Yield: 8 servings

(Courtesy American Baking Institute)

FIG. 12-48   How to Cut Square Cakes

8″ x 8″   8″ x 8″
Yield: 9 servings   Yield: 10 servings

9″ x 9″   9″ x 9″
Yield: 16 servings   Yield: 12 servings

(Courtesy American Baking Institute)

FIG. 12-49   How to Cut Sheet Cakes

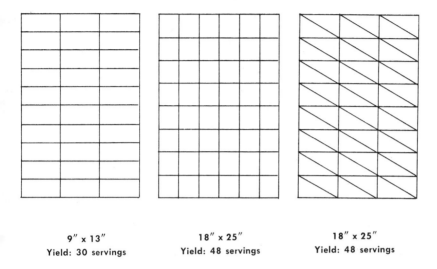

9" x 13"	18" x 25"	18" x 25"
Yield: 30 servings	Yield: 48 servings	Yield: 48 servings

the top, making a double turn to prevent the icing from coming out the top when pressure is applied in decorating.

Many types of metal tips are used to make different designs, but about ten will perform most of the decorating tasks required in an ordinary establishment. Use the right tip for the job.

Apply correct pressure. Holding the bag at the correct angle is also a necessary requisite for making good decorations. A right-handed decorator will apply all the pressure with the right hand; the left is only used to guide or support the cone or to hold items while the right hand directs the tip and applies pressure. Icing coming from the top indicates left-hand pressure. Use an even pressure applied through the fingers and thumb for fine work, or use the four fingers and the palm for more gross work. Relaxing the pressure while moving the tip will cause a break in the icing flow. Exerting heavier pressure will cause a blob of icing to suddenly come from the tip. Hold the cone straight up (vertical) for making drop flowers or other similar items. A 45° angle is required for writing, borders, leaves, flowers, stems, or other objects deposited on top of the cake. If flowers, borders, or other items are to be placed on the sides, hold the bag or cone at a right angle to the side. To set in place preformed and dried decorations, such as those that might be made from royal or decorator's icing, place a small quantity of icing from the tip at the spot where the decoration is to be attached and immediately place the decoration on the spot.

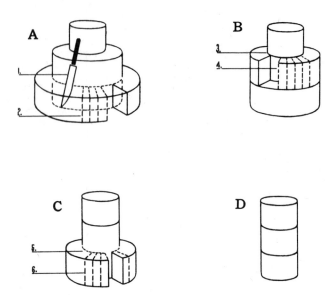

FIG. 12-50 How to cut tier cakes. Proceed as in diagram A, cutting around center of cake, as shown in step 1; then follow steps 2, 3, 4, 5, and 6 in that order. The remaining tiers, shown in D, may be cut into pieces of the desired size. (Courtesy American Baking Institute)

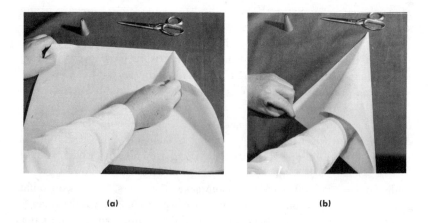

(a)   (b)

FIG. 12-51 (a) To make a paper cone, cut as shown and grasp with the two hands, beginning the roll with the right hand. (b) Finish the cone as shown, keeping the right hand inside to control the shape.

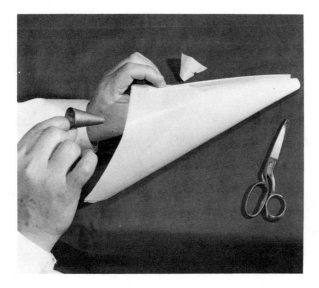

(c)

(d)   (e)

Fig. 12-51 (continued) (c) Cut about a half inch from the cone tip, and insert the metal decorating tip as shown. (d) Fill with frosting, dropping it down into the cone tip. Some bakers make the cone with a triangular piece of paper as shown in the background. (e) Fold the cone with a double fold.

(a)

(b)

FIG. 12-52   (a) Hold the cone at a 45° angle to decorate a cake top. When a large quantity of frosting is required, use the top hand, exerting pressure with the full hand. The bottom hand only guides. (b) When decorating the side of the object, hold cone tip at right angles to the decorated object. When light pressure is required, force the frosting from the tip with light pressure from the right hand (top hand) finger tips as shown.

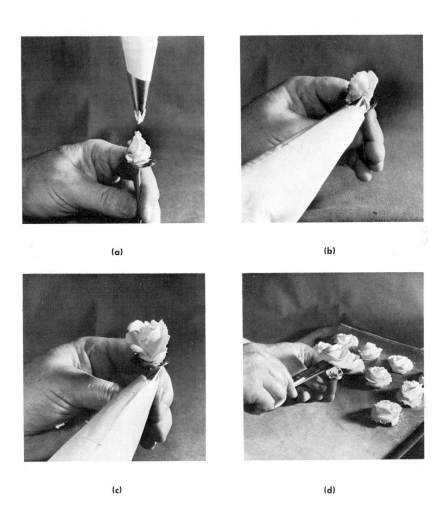

(a)

(b)

(c)

(d)

FIG. 12-53   To make a rose: (a) Using a star tube, set a rosette on top of the decorator's nail. (b) Now, with a petal tip, make petals around the rosette, continuing as shown in (c). (d) Remove the rose with scissors, as shown, and place on wax paper to dry and firm up. Then place into position on the cake.

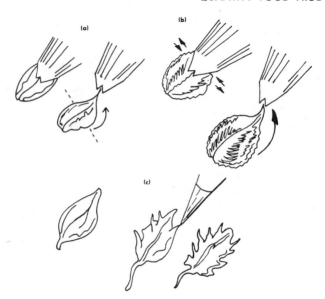

FIG. 12-54   To make leaves, use a leaf tube. Force out a liberal supply of frosting and, at approximately the center of the leaf, release pressure and lift up to form leaf tip as shown in (a). To obtain a jagged edge on the leaf, follow the same procedure but move the tip rapidly back and forth while the other motions are being made as indicated in (b). Or make leaves as indicated in (a) and then with a fine tip, using the same color, add points to the leaves as shown in (c).

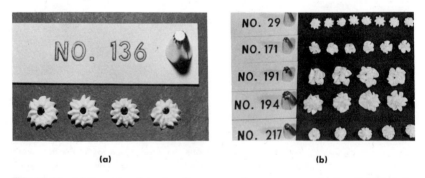

(a)   (b)

FIG. 12-55   (a) To make plain drop flowers, use the proper type of tube. Hold the tube perpendicular above the object to be decorated, or over wax paper where the flowers are to dry, and force out the frosting. The flowers shown here may be filled with items, or another color may be added for the center. (b) Drop flowers can be made with the various tubes shown. The same technique is used as described in (a) except that the tube is twisted to the right as the flower is dropped. Release of the pressure and a quick lift up breaks the frosting and forms the tip.

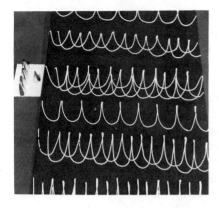

(c)   (d)

(e)

Fig. 12-55 (continued) (c) Some simple string designs. For this type of work the frosting must be slightly thinner than that used for flowers or decorating objects. (d) Many different types of borders can be made with only one tube. The scallop border shown in the first and fourth borders from the top are made by forcing out a fair amount of frosting, then lifting up, and then suddenly releasing pressure as the tip is lowered. A bit of practice is all that is required to make these five borders. (e) Combined string and scallop border designs. As experience is gained, more and more complex designs may be attempted.

COOKIES

Ingredients in cookie recipes are much the same as those used for cakes, and some cookies may be made from batters that are nothing but cake batters. Most cookies, however, are made from doughs which have a higher fat and lower sugar and liquid content. The techniques of mixing are very much the same as cakes for different types of cookies. Sugar, ice box, and other similar types of cookies are made by the conventional or creaming method. Foam-type cookies are made by beating eggs to a foam and carefully folding in other ingredients. Crisp cookies result, with high ratios of fat and sugar and low amounts of liquid, while soft cookies are obtained when the shortening or liquid is high, or when hydroscopic sugars are used to draw moisture into the product. Chewy cookies are usually high in sugar and liquid but low in fat. Eggs give a chewy quality. The degree of baking affects crispness, soft cookies usually being baked a shorter time than crisp cookies. Thickness and size are also factors affecting crispness and softness. Many cookies are tight-grained, but some may be as open-grained as cakes. Baking soda or ammonia is used to give spread. Ammonia is preferred in the amount of $\frac{1}{4}$ to $\frac{1}{2}\%$ of the flour because it leaves little aftertaste. Cookies high in sugar will spread more than those made from a leaner dough, and the coarser the sugar, the more spread the cookie will have in baking. Powdered sugar reduces spread. Large bakeshops usually deposit cookies onto pans by machine, using ammonia to give spread. If a recipe not adapted to machine deposit is used, reduce the leavening agent by half, and replace it with baking ammonia as follows for machine depositing:

> If the recipe calls for baking powder, omit half and replace 40% of this half with baking ammonia. If the recipe calls for soda, omit half and replace 80% of this half with baking ammonia.

Guides such as this are only approximate, however, and other adjustments may have to be made. In using baking ammonia, see that the product in which it is used is thin, not thick, and is not a moist product. The flavor of ammonia may be evident in thick, heavy products.

Cookie Production

A sugar or ice box cookie is usually in balance if the flour is 100%, shortening 100%, sugar 50%, and eggs 10%. In some respects, cookies of this type are a rich pie pastry, high in sugar. Most cookies of this type are made by the conventional method, but a one-stage or dump method may be used in which all ingredients are mixed at one time at slow speed for one or two minutes. The best temperature of ingredients is 70° F. Basic doughs of sugar or ice box cookies may be made into many variations.

Some cookies are made by techniques and ingredients somewhat similar to those used to make foam cakes. Because of the delicacy of the batter, only small batches are usually made. Meringue cookies are made from a hard meringue mixture; the student should consult the discussions of meringues in the chapter on desserts and of egg foam in the chapter on dairy cookery. Kisses, meringue bars, and macaroons are made from egg whites beaten to a second stage foam. Underbeating will give a weak foam and a tough, gummy cookie. Overbeating extends air cells so the product collapses in baking. Kisses require less sugar than hard meringues, and thus are an in-between product between soft and hard meringues. Flour and other ingredients are folded in carefully in the same manner as they are incorporated in the making of foam cakes. Baking temperatures are usually 325° to 350° F. Adding some glucose or invert sugar gives a chewy quality. If glucose, invert sugar, or glycerine is added in the mixing, the tendency of sugar to crystallize is reduced. Weeping of cookies made of egg foam can be reduced by sifting, at the end of beating the egg foam, one-half ounce of cornstarch per pound of egg whites and incorporating. Foam cookies may be glazed while hot with a sirup-gelatin glaze, sometimes called a gelatin shine. Some foam cookies are nothing but slight, if any, modifications of foam cakes. Lady fingers, for instance, are sponge cake batters. Other foam cake batters may be used to make foam-type cookies with slight modifications. In quantity preparation, macaroons are made from a base of almond paste, sugar, flour, and unbeaten egg whites. Mixing of these ingredients is at 85° F.

Panning

Chill stiff cookie doughs before they are cut. Doughs store well for several days if they are well wrapped, and they freeze well in vapor-moisture-proof wraps for holding a longer time.

The time and labor involved makes it almost prohibitive to roll cookie doughs and cut cookies from them. In addition, the extra handling toughens the cookie. If rolling and cutting *must* be done, use a canvas cloth for an underliner. Roll about 1/8 inch thick. Cut the dough as economically as possible so little dough will be left to rework into another rolling.

Semi-soft batters are used for drop cookies. About one to 1½ ounces are dropped for this type of cookie; ice cream scoops, size 30 and 20 respectively, will give these quantities. Scooping and depositing may be by spoon or pastry bag. To deposit by hand, scoop a handful of the batter, using the side of the hand as a scoop, and then with a squeezing motion place the correct quantity on the baking sheet. Macaroons, kisses, and meringues may be deposited in this manner. Deposit semi-soft batters approximately two inches apart.

After depositing non-meringue type macaroons, allow to stand eight to twelve hours before baking. Holland or split macaroons are placed under refrigeration overnight, and in the morning are cut through the center with a sharp knife. After baking, a split appears in the center. Kisses, meringues,

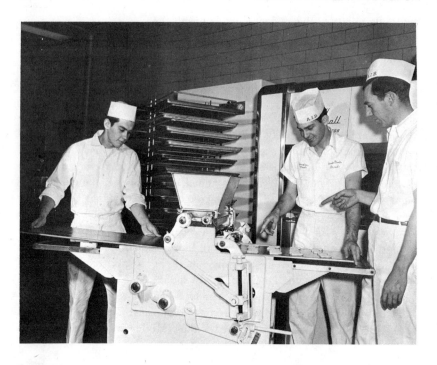

FIG. 12-56   Machine-dropping cookies onto baking sheets at the American Baking Institute.

and paste macaroons may be placed on greased paper, silicon-coated baking sheets, greased and flour-dusted pans, or thin sheets of rice paper. Using a wet spatula or pancake turner, remove while still warm, or hold the baking sheets a moment over heat to loosen. Rice paper can be broken away and left on the bottom, for it is edible. Lady fingers may be deposited by making small fingers of sponge cake batter with a pastry tube about three inches long and a half inch wide. Allow at least one inch between cookies of this type. Many foam-type or semi-soft batters may be machine-deposited. Batters or doughs with nuts or chopped fruits, however, sometimes do not deposit well by machine.

Some semi-soft or soft batters, such as nut squares and brownies may be spread evenly onto baking sheets about a half inch thick. After baking, while still warm, they are cut into the desired shapes. If the cookies are frosted, cutting may have to be done when they are cold.

Quite stiff doughs are made up into rolls to make ice box cookies. For large cookies, scale off three pounds and make into two-inch-diameter rolls. These are wrapped in wax paper or plastic and then refrigerated or partially frozen. Each roll of this size will make approximately 50 cookies. Small rolls—about 1½ pounds each, made into rolls ¾ to one inch in diameter—produce tea-type cookies. A sharp knife or a kitchen slicing machine may be used to cut the cookies about ⅛ inch thick. Space in pans about one inch apart. If the dough contains ammonia for spread, slice thicker and space on pans a greater distance apart.

Some stiff doughs are made into long rolls about one to 1½ inches in diameter, and then pieces about one ounce each are cut, using a pastry blade or sharp knife. Place on well greased pans about two inches apart. These are then flattened into thin discs on the pan. Items such as peanut butter cookies can be flattened with a fork, or a small can may be placed in a moistened cloth, the cloth-covered end dipped into granulated sugar, and this end used to press pieces of dough out into flattened discs. The cloth is dipped again into granulated sugar and another cookie is flattened. Fruit bars, hermits, and other similar cookies are made into 1¾ pound rolls. These are flattened to about three- or four-inch strips on well greased baking sheets. About four flattened rolls can be placed on an 18 by 26 inch baking sheet. Each strip is glazed with a wash before baking. After baking, each strip is cut into 1¾-inch-wide bars, obtaining about 12 to 13 bars per strip.

Use level, clean baking sheets. Some need not be greased; others may need liberal greasing and dusting with flour. Have pans cool before cookies are placed on them. Liberal greasing encourages spread. If dusting flour is used, spread is reduced. If pans are too lightly greased, cookies high in egg or sugar will be difficult to remove and may color too heavily at the edges. Many cookies are glazed either before or after baking.

Some cookies spread but little; others may double in diameter. A small cookie is about the size of a 50¢ piece after baking, and a medium cookie is about the size of a silver dollar. Large cookies may be three inches in diameter. Bar or fruit cookies are usually scaled ¾ to one ounce each, and sugar cookies half an ounce or less. Many recipes call for yields of 32 to 34 cookies to the pound of dough or mix. A dozen 3½-inch-diameter sugar cookies will weigh between 11 and 12 ounces before baking and about 10 ounces after. Small cookies may be scaled three or four to the ounce. Scale meringue or other foam-type cookies one-half to two-thirds ounce each, or six to 10 ounces per dozen.

Baking

Normally, cookies are baked at higher temperatures than cakes. Watch carefully, for a slight overbaking will overcolor the cookies and ruin their flavor. Chocolate cookies burn easily. When cookies are done, they are of the proper color and spring back slightly to the touch. Too low an oven temperature will give a light-grained cookie with poor color. If the oven temperature is

Table 12-9

Scaling Weights and Baking Temperatures and Times for Cookies

Product	Pan Size	Units Per Pan	Scaling Weight	Baking Temperature (°F)	Baking Time (min)
Brownies	17 x 25 in.	100	7½ to 8 lb	350 to 360	20 to 45
Butter, tea			⅓ to ½ oz	375	8 to 10
Drop, medium			¾ oz*	350 to 400	8 to 15
Ice box, medium			1 oz	375	8 to 10
Rolled, small			½ oz	375	7 to 10
Rolled, large			1½ oz	375	9 to 12

*Use No. 40 scoop.

too high, the cookies will lack spread and will be overly dark. Closing the damper to the oven in the early stages of baking holds some steam inside, which assists in giving spread. Crisp cookies may be soft while they are still warm but will crisp on cooling. After baking, protect cookies from drafts and too rapid cooling. Many cookies should be removed from the pans while they are still warm.

Storing

Most cookie batters or doughs freeze well, except foam types. Stiff doughs should be thawed under refrigeration, but softer mixes may be thawed at room temperature. Baked cookies should not be packed while warm. Cool and then pack. They may be placed into airtight containers or held in drawers for demand. If the package is removed from the freezer and opened, the cookies will thaw in about 15 to 20 minutes. Sometimes a moist product, such as a cut apple, is stored with soft cookies to keep them moist. Do not attempt to pack soft cookies. Foam-type cookies dry out easily. Make these in batches that will be used quickly. Store in airtight containers.

13 Pies[1]

Pies and pie-like products may be costly from the standpoint of labor requirements, but no one can deny their popularity on a menu. If the types of pies are wisely selected, if a convenient layout is set up for the work, and

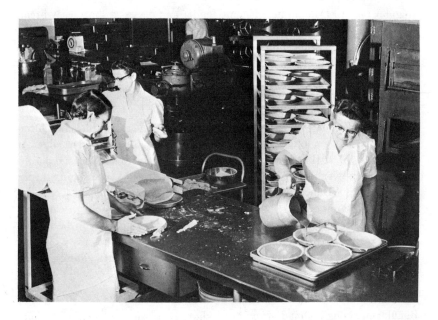

FIG. 13-1 With assembly-line methods, these three workers rolled the crust and filled 160 pumpkin pies in 171 worker minutes, in contrast to 471 worker minutes when the three workers worked separately on the same job.

[1] The National Restaurant Association's *Technical Bulletin — Pies* is an excellent treatise on the making of pies. This dessert, according to the bulletin, makes up 27 to 35% of all desserts served in quantity food services.

if good production techniques are used, the cost of pies and pastries can be reduced. To achieve satisfactory costs, one must establish production standards. In one operation, an experienced baker hand-rolled 200 pie dough pieces in an hour. Where a large number of pies are to be produced, assembly-line production methods give increased worker efficiency. Three workers, working with pre-cut dough discs and a pumpkin filling already prepared and using a mechanical pie-rolling machine, produced 160 pumpkin pies ready for baking in 171 worker minutes. (See Fig. 13-1).

Pies may be single or double crust. These may be filled with fruit, cream filling, egg custard, gelatin, or other sweetened and thickened mixtures. Ice cream, mousse, or other frozen desserts may be placed into baked pie shells and served as pies. There are many pastries closely related to pies, such as tarts and dumplings. Besides variation in filling or shape, variety is obtained from the use of different crusts, such as puff paste, graham cracker, dark chocolate wafer, and meringue.

STANDARD

Regular pie crust should be crisp and tender and possess a short, easy break. It may be flaky, semi-flaky, or mealy, depending upon the type of crust. The surface color should be golden or cream, darkening to a golden brown at the edge. The appearance should be rough and blistery on the surface rather than smooth, but this roughness will vary with the flakiness of the crust. The crust should cut easily but not crumble. Oiliness may be tested by rubbing the crust between the fingers.

The filling may vary in consistency and type. A starch-thickened filling will be delicate, smooth, and soft, sagging only slightly at the cut edge. An egg custard filling should have a sharp edge, be firm with no flow, and possess a good sheen over the cut surface. A fruit filling should ooze slightly at the edge. The appearance should be rough and blistery on the surface, rather bottom crust but not over the plate. Each piece of fruit should be clear and distinct. The color should be clear and bright. Fillings should be neither gummy or pasty. Flavor should be moderately sweet and possess a pleasing characteristic flavor for the product. The flavor of custard fillings should be sweet and mellow, not eggy.

DOUGH INGREDIENTS

Regular pie dough is made from flour, shortening, salt, and water. The flour and liquid form a paste. The shortening serves as a lubricant separating the gluten strands of the flour so that a tender product results. Salt is added for flavor, usually dissolved in the water. Since salt strengthens gluten in the flour, however, an excess should be avoided. Milk powder or liquid milk may sometimes be used to improve color and flavor, but the crust will then be

(a)

(b)

FIG. 13-2   (a) The All-American pie. Note the soft, lush filling of apples delicately seasoned
with cinnamon candies. The blistered and delicately colored crust also indicates goodness.
(b) A single crust pie is also highly popular. Note the gentle sag in the filling indicating
tenderness; yet the filling is sufficiently firm to hold its shape. Pies such as these can bring
much customer satisfaction to an operation. (Courtesy Procter & Gamble)

less crisp. If dry milk is used, it is usually added with the flour. To improve color and flavor, glucose or corn sirup in the ratio of 2% of the flour is added with the water. Some specialty pie or tart doughs are almost as rich as cookie doughs. These may have eggs as an ingredient. Eggs improve color but raise cost and reduce crispness, and more fat must be used to give correct shortness. Baking powder does not improve crust quality, but vinegar or

FIG. 13-3   (a) This slice of apple pie with its traditional piece of cheddar cheese shows a good standard. The crust is tender, yet sufficiently firm to hold its shape. Just a bit of the filling oozes out onto the plate. (Courtesy Armour & Co.) (b) Both pies shown here have good-appearing crusts, but the one on the right has a filling that is too soft, which detracts greatly from the appearance of the product.

cream of tartar may be used to reduce water hardness, increase gluten tenderness, and make the dough whiter.

The percentages of ingredients in a regular pie dough are:

Flour, pastry	100%
Shortening	50 to 75%
Salt	2 to 3%
Water	25 to 30%

Pastry flour is most frequently used for pie dough. It contains about 10% gluten, which gives sufficient strength to give a good pliable dough that holds up well in rolling but not enough strength to give toughness unless the dough is handled improperly. When puff paste or extremely flaky doughs are made, bread flour is used. Bread flour gives a dough that will spread out into thin sheets of paste between layers of shortening. Steam formed in baking between these sheets lifts them up, developing flakiness.

Tenderness is an important factor for quality, and the amount of shortening used is an important factor in achieving tenderness. The amount of mixing given the dough and the method of blending the shortening into the flour are other key factors. A flour possessing a small amount of gluten or a weak gluten will require less shortening and can take more mixing than a stronger flour. To give sufficient tenderness, a strong bread flour may require a ratio of shortening by weight as high as 80 to 100% that of the flour. Hard wheat flour will mix less easily into the shortening. Bread flour gives a dough a chewy quality which may be desirable.

If soy flour is added to a pie dough, a shorter and mealier crust results. Soy flour gives a creamy color to the crust and reduces flakiness. Specialty-type crusts may have ground pecans, almonds, filberts, or other products re-

FIG. 13-4   Basic ingredients for a pie crust.

placing up to 25% of the flour; such replacement favors shortness and the development of a mealy crust because of the lower gluten content of the dough.

For proper crust tenderness, a shortening with good tenderizing power is required. It should be sufficiently plastic to work well within a range of 50° to 80° F. The shortening power of the fat and its plasticity are factors governing the quantity that must be used. Highly unsaturated or emulsified shortenings will not develop flaky doughs because of their tendency to blend easily into the flour. Lard is a good shortening for pie crust, for it gives good tenderness and flavor and has the correct plasticity. Butter or margarines are sometimes used for flavor, but the amount to flour must be 65 to 100% to give sufficient shortness unless the curd and moisture are first removed by kneading and washing. Edible oils can be used, but the dough may be sticky and oily and hard to handle. Oils permeate the flour to such an extent that it is difficult to make flaky crusts with them. Hot-water pie crusts may be made using oil or shortening. The proportion of fat or oil in a hot-water pie crust is the same as that in a regular pie crust.

Only that quantity of water required to give a soft, pliable dough should be used. Besides making the dough workable, water furnishes steam inside the dough layers, causing the crust to flake. If the crust is too dry, an insufficient quantity of steam develops, and the crust is less flaky. Avoid a sticky dough, for it is difficult to roll and handle. Excess water also encourages toughness, possibly by allowing more complete hydration of the gluten. As the quantity of shortening in a dough increases, moisture is also increased.

PRODUCTION

Precise scaling, good ingredients, and skillful techniques are required to produce good pies. A horizontal cylinder, slow-speed mixer may be used to make large quantities of pie dough, but most operations will use the vertical type, operating it at low speed. Many use a pie crust blade for cutting the shortening into the flour and a flat paddle to blend the water into this mixture; others use only the flat paddle for both operations. Some bakers prefer to mix small quantities of dough by hand because they can work the shortening into the flour better and feel the dough development more surely. Good rollers, pastry boards or canvas tops, cutters, and other equipment are essential. Mechanical rollers reduce time and labor. A cool dough rolls and handles better than a warm one.

Mixing

The short and flaky qualities of a pie crust depend not only upon the type of ingredients and their quantity and quality, but also on the method of mixing. If the shortening is blended into the flour well, a mealy crust results. If a limited amount of mixing occurs, so the fat is in large pieces and not well blended into the flour, the pie crust is apt to be flaky. The flakiness of a flaky crust, puff pastes, and strudels results from rolling and rerolling sheets of dough and shortening so that many finely separated layers of each are made.

The amount and vigor of mixing is critical to pie crust quality, especially after water is added. The gluten then has moisture for development. Excess speed or time of mixing favors gluten development. Warmth also favors this; hence, doughs should be kept cold. The best temperature for mixing most shortenings into the flour is 60° F. At this temperature the shortening blends well into the flour but still retains sufficient firmness to give particles for developing flakiness. The friction of mixing and the absorption of shortening by the flour develop heat. Water at around 40° F or colder should be used. If the fat is too cold, the crust will be toughened; if too soft, it is difficult to make a flaky dough. Excess development of gluten gives a dough which shrinks badly in baking. Resting the dough after mixing for about 15 minutes decreases shrink, allowing the gluten to completely hydrate. This makes the dough easier to roll. Some bakers state that ripening the dough for 12 to 24 hours improves quality; others say it makes little difference.

Add all the water, with the salt dissolved into it, at one time, spreading it well over the blended shortening and flour. Mix at low speed only until the water is blended. The dough should *just* leave the sides of the bowl. (In hand-mixing, the water may be sprinkled over the shortening and flour mixture.) Normally, on an upright mixer, blending of the flour and shortening takes from 15 to 90 seconds at slow speed, the time depending upon the size of the shortening particles desired. About 40 seconds at slow speed are sufficient for mixing after the water is added.

A very short and tender crust, commonly called a mealy crust, may be

FIG. 13-5   From left to right, a flaky, a semi-flaky, and a mealy pie crust.

made by blending the shortening into the flour until the mixture looks like coarse cornmeal, or half the shortening may be blended well into the flour and the remainder then added and mixed until the shortening is no longer sticky. A ratio of 50 to 60% shortening to flour is used. A mealy crust will be short and quite tender, and will soak less than flaky types. It bakes with low shrinkage and colors well. It is used for the undercrusts of double pies and for custard pies and others where soaking may be a problem.

A batter method may be used to make a mealy crust. For this, 80% of the flour is mixed with all of the shortening until the mixture looks like

FIG. 13-6   Mealy pie crusts made with 60% shortening to flour. From left to right, crust made by blending shortening and flour well together; crust made by blending half the shortening into the flour and mixing the remainder until the shortening is no longer sticky; crust made by the batter method; and crust made by the creaming method. Very little difference appears among the three.

cornmeal. All of the liquid and the rest of the flour are then mixed together to make a slurry. This is added to the other mixture. Then the two are blended only until the first mixture is moistened. Overmixing after the moisture is added will produce a tough crust with high shrinkage.

A creaming method is also used to make a mealy crust. About 50% of the flour is mixed with all of the shortening until a smooth paste is formed. The remaining flour is added and mixed until the mass is crumbly in texture. Salt and sugar, the latter an optional ingredient, are dissolved into the water and added to the flour and shortening mixture. The mass is mixed only until the dough leaves the sides of the bowl. This method is simple and gives good results for the inexperienced worker.

To make a semi-flaky crust, a ratio of from 60 to 75% shortening to flour is required. Good plasticity of the shortening is required so the particles will flatten out well between sheets of the dough paste. The shortening is cut into the flour until it is large pea size. Another method is to blend from one-third to one-half of the shortening well into the flour; the remaining shortening is added and blended until it is about the size of hazelnuts. Semi-flaky dough has good tenderness and crispness, and is considered best suited for all purposes. It colors well in baking.

A flaky crust can be made by cutting the shortening into the flour the size of small walnuts. The shortening should possess good plasticity so it will spread and layer well. From 75 to 100% shortening to flour is required. A flaky crust is best made by a folding and rolling method which, while it may develop gluten, gives maximum sheeting of the shortening and the dough. To do this, mix water into the flour-shortening mixture until it *just* blends. Then roll the dough into a one-inch-thick rectangle twice as long as it is wide. Brush away excess flour. Fold the right and left outside fourths into the middle. Then fold at the middle to obtain four folds. Chill for 25 to 30 minutes. Roll the rectangle out again to its original size and repeat the folding. This will give 16 layers or sheets of paste and shortening on a four-fold dough. The dough may now be used, or allowed to rest under refrigeration again, and then rolled in the same manner and folded. The dough now has 64 layers. Too much layering will make the sheets of paste and shortening too thin, causing them to break, and flakiness will be lost. Excess rolling and handling will toughen the dough and cause high shrinkage in baking.

A highly successful flaky crust will resemble puff paste in texture and to some extent in appearance. It makes excellent baked single crust shells, but absorbs moisture readily after fillings are added. Fillings should be added to this crust just before service. It is good for top crusts of fruit pies and for tarts or tartlets, small pastry shells, tops for deep-dish pies, meat or poultry pies, and so forth. It is seldom used for bottom crusts of double crust or custard pies because of its tendency to soak. The trimmings of semi-flaky and flaky doughs may be rerolled with mealy dough for bottom crusts of double crust pies.

Some operations use a hot-water pie crust. The formula is similar to that for regular pie crust. Ratios to flour by weight are salt 2 to 3%, shortening 50 to 65%, and water 30%. The water is brought to a boil and added to the shortening in the mixer. This is then beaten until it is smooth and fluffy. The salt and flour are next added, and the mixture is mixed only until it is smooth and the wet spots have disappeared.

Pie doughs may be stored about a week under refrigeration after make-up. Some bakers shape about six pounds of regular pie dough into three-inch-diameter cylinders from 15 to 18 inches long. These are placed in moisture-vapor-proof wraps or under slightly moistened cloths. The cylinders are chilled and then cut with a dough cutter into round pieces about an inch thick. These discs then may be rolled into pieces for pies. Pie dough mix may be left dry and kept stored for use as required, but storage should not be over 10 days.

A graham cracker crust is sometimes used for pies, small tart shells, and other products. A formula of 100% graham cracker crumbs, 30% sugar, and 55% butter or margarine gives a good crust. Cinnamon, almond flour, powdered sugar, and other ingredients may be added. Gingersnaps, vanilla wafers, chocolate wafers, and other dried crumbs may also be used in place of graham cracker crumbs. About two ounces of the mixture is used for a nine-inch pan, and the crumbs are spread evenly and packed firmly on the sides and bottom. Another pan is firmly pressed onto the crumbs. The crusts are baked 10 minutes in a 350° F oven or left in a refrigerator overnight. Some of the crumb mixture may be saved for sprinkling over meringues or whipped cream toppings.

(a)

(b)

(c)

(d)

FIG. 13-7   Technique for making puff paste. (a) The dough paste is rolled out about three times as long as wide and about a half inch thick. It is then covered with about a half-inch-thick layer of puff paste shortening over two-thirds of the surface. (b) The uncovered third is then folded over. (c) The folding is completed to make three folds. The dough is then allowed to rest in a refrigerator for about 20 to 25 minutes. It is then rolled out again into its original shape, but the width of the first turn is now rolled into the length of this second turn. (d) Here we see the worker making a four-fold dough. After four to six rollings or turns, the dough is ready to use; rests of 20 to 25 minutes in the refrigerator occur between turns. (Courtesy Swift & Company)

The products made from puff paste are attractive because of their puffy, light quality. In a Continental kitchen, puff paste is called pâte feuilletée, feuilletée meaning "many leaves." At one time puff paste could only be made by the accomplished pastry chef, but with special shortenings and an understanding of the principles and techniques required, almost anyone can make an acceptable product. Shortenings for puff pastes must be highly plastic. There are special puff paste margarines on the market. If either butter or regular margarine is used, wash it thoroughly in cold water to remove moisture and curd. Then knead until highly plastic. Frozen puff paste may also be purchased in some areas ready for shaping and baking.

Puff pastes are made of bread flour. In ratio to flour, use 100% shortening, 1% salt, and 35 to 50% water. Modern recipes call for eggs in the proportion to flour of 3 to 12% and cream of tartar 0.75%. The cream of tartar is sifted in with the flour. It contributes to a tenderization of the gluten and gives a whiter dough. The eggs contribute color, strength, and nutritional value to the paste. The flour, salt, and water are mixed until the mass is smooth, soft, and pliable. Sufficient strength of gluten is required so the dough will form a tenuous sheet or layer over and under the layer of shortening. Do not develop until stringy or ropy, however. Water and flour may be mixed together at 60° F for approximately two minutes, using a pie blade and slow speed. Some pastry chefs add 15 to 20% of the shortening in this mixing. After mixing, the paste is allowed to rest for approximately 10 to 15 minutes. Then it is rolled into a half-inch-thick rectangle twice as long as it is wide. Excess flour should always be brushed off in the rolling procedures. The shortening is next spotted evenly over two-thirds of the rectangle, leaving about a half-inch margin at the edges. The unspotted third is then folded over one-half of the spotted portion. Then the remaining one-third of spotted dough is folded over this folded portion, giving a three-fold dough. A four-fold dough is sometimes made; this is a process in which the dough is marked into fourths and covered with shortening on the two inside fourths, and each outside fourth is folded in over this. After being brushed free of flour, one of the tops of the fourths is dotted with shortening and another fold made. After either a three- or four-fold, the dough is allowed to rest for 20 to 25 minutes under refrigeration. It is then taken to the bench and the dough is given a half turn, so the former length becomes the width in the rolling out and folding that occurs.

After resting, the dough is again rolled into a rectangle of the same dimensions as the original rectangle. Smooth, even rolling is necessary to distribute evenly the paste and shortening. The paste and shortening should be of the same consistency to give even working of the dough and prevent rupture of paste walls because of slippage of the shortening. The dough

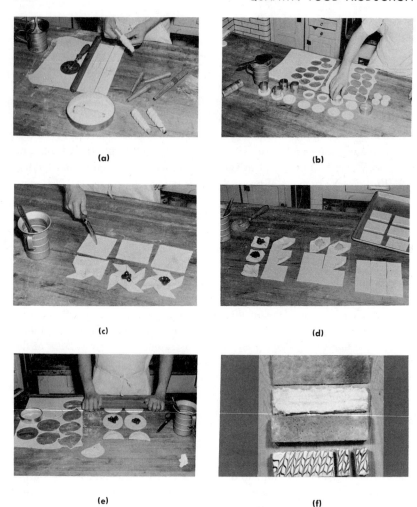

(a)   (b)

(c)   (d)

(e)   (f)

FIG. 13-8   Some techniques for making items from puff paste. (a) Cream horns are made from strips of dough ⅛ inch thick, 1¼ inches wide, and about 15 inches long. Roll the completed horn in sugar and bake after a 30 minute rest. (b) Cut rounds with a plain cutter from dough 1/16 inch thick. Cut ⅜-inch-thick dough with the same cutter, and cut out the centers with a smaller cutter. Wash first rounds with a bit of water around the edges with the pastry brush and place the rings upside down on top of the discs. (c) Cut ⅛-inch-thick dough about 5 by 5 inches square and wash with water. Using a pastry wheel or scraper, cut into center as shown, leaving about one inch in the center uncut. Press every other corner into the center and fill with washed or glazed fruit. (d) and (e) Variations in shapes are shown. (f) Napoleons are made from strips of baked puff paste spread with a filling and topped as shown. (Courtesy Swift & Company)

is not spotted again with shortening, but another three- or four-fold dough is prepared, and a 20 to 25 minute rest under refrigeration is given. Care in folding is required so that in subsequent rolling and folding the desired sheeting of the paste over and under the layers of shortening occurs. As folding and rolling occur, thinner and thinner and more and more layers of paste and shortening are made. Each time a turn is given and the dough rolled, the dough is given a half turn; that is, it is turned at right angles from its former position so the length is parallel to the worker, and with each turn

(a)

(b)   (c)

FIG. 13-9   Making tartlets. (a) Puff paste or special tart shell dough is rolled out, cut into rounds, and placed into tartlet molds. Beans are placed in paper cups, which are placed in the tarts. Peas, rice, or rock salt may be used instead of beans. (b) On the upper top, the tartlet dough, shell, and rock salt used are shown. In the second row, the tartlet shell, thin round of cake, cream filling, and placement of the cake filling are shown. In the next row, fruits are placed in position, and in the bottom row the tart is shown glazed. (c) A franchipan batter is placed into a well greased tartlet shell and baked as shown on the row at the top. The second row shows shaping and the third the filling of the item. The bottom row shows the finished product. (Courtesy Culinary Institute)

the folds crisscross at right angles to each other. Pastry chefs indicate the number of turns a dough has received by showing a finger indentation in the dough, one indentation meaning one turn, two meaning two, and so forth. The maximum number of turns with three folds is six, and with four folds, four. (See Fig. 11-16, which shows this same technique being used on bread dough.) Excessive folding and rolling toughens the dough, giving too thin a paste sheet to give good flaking. Puff paste trimmings are usually gathered together, made into a dough, rolled out, given a three fold, and used again, but the quality of this reworked dough is usually lower than that of the original dough.

Puff paste can also be made by using hard wheat flour 100%, puff paste shortening 100%, water 35%, salt 1%, and cream of tartar 0.75%. About three-fourths of the shortening is mixed thoroughly into 25 to 30% of the flour, and this mixture is given a 20 minute rest in a refrigerator. The remainder of the flour, and all the water, salt, and cream of tartar are mixed into a heavy dough, and this is allowed to rest 30 minutes under refrigeration. Instead of paste on the outside and shortening on the inside, the procedure is reversed and the paste mixture spread over two-thirds of the

FIG. 13-10 A tray of finished puff pastries and tartlets ready for service. (Courtesy Institutions Magazine)

rectangle of the shortening and flour mixture. Folding then occurs as described above.

Rolling and Make-up

Regular crusts are usually rolled about ⅛ inch thick, although some crusts may be somewhat thicker. Bottom pieces should be cut around six ounces and tops five ounces for nine-inch pies. Crust thickness will govern the amount. Experienced bakers may require less since they will have little or no waste in rolling. For machine-rolling, pieces for top and bottom are eight ounces.

To hand-roll dough, use a pin or roller approximately 1½ inches in diameter and 18 inches long, slightly tapered at either end. Have a smooth surface or board with only a little dusting flour on it. If canvas is used, less

(a)   (b)

FIG. 13-11   Stretching a pie dough will cause shrinkage in baking. Two identical pie dough discs are shown; the one on the left was stretched in cutting; the other was not stretched, and the shape remained close to that of the original cut. (b) Single crust shells are best baked double-panned. Note how the shape is best in the double-panned shell shown in the upper left. Docking is next best, as indicated in the upper right, while baking without double-panning or docking results in a non-usable crust.

dusting flour is required. Keep the rolling pin and the top of the dough lightly dusted with flour. Dough can be toughened by the addition of too much flour during rolling. Quick, deft strokes starting from the center that roll the dough into a nearly perfect circle will give a crust which will have low waste and shrinkage. Roll, do not force the dough out. In the early rolling, the dough is rolled into an oval shape; it is then turned and the circle made. The dough should be lifted and turned as frequently as necessary. When this is done, a check is made to see that dusting flour remains underneath the dough. Dough should be cold but not overly stiff for rolling. When the crust is in the desired shape, it is folded once in the center and placed into a pan

FIG. 13-12   Roll with deft, light strokes, working the dough
out to all sides so that a good round about ⅛ inch thick
is obtained.

without stretching. It is then unfolded easily and shaped to the pan. Some
bakers fold the dough over the rolling pin, lift to the pan, and unfold into the
pan with the pin. Docking, a process that makes holes in the crust, is required
for single crust pie shells so they do not blister in baking. If single crust
pie shells are baked between pie pans, docking is not necessary. Some bakers
like to invert pie pans and bake docked shells on the outside of the pan.
This reduces the tendency of the dough to shrink and fall into the pan.

In making double crust pies, time is saved if the excess from the bottom
and top crusts is removed at the same time. Excess dough should be removed
by a quick, deft turning motion between the two hands. The finished edging
of single or double crust pies may be made attractive by pinching the dough
lightly with the thumb and index finger slightly open and pressing in with
the index finger of the other hand. The use of a pie crimper, roller-docker,
pastry cutter, bench brush, and scraper facilitates handling of the dough.
The bottom and top crusts of double crust pies should be carefully sealed
around the edges to lessen the possibility of boil-out in the oven. Moistening
the edge of the bottom crust before adding the top assists in giving a tight
seal. Washing of the top with milk, cream, evaporated milk, eggs and milk,
butter or margarine may be done to give extra color to the crusts. The type
of wash will govern the finished appearance of the crust. Usually, well made
crusts need no wash. Butter and margarine are best for homemade-type

washes and finishes. If a hole is made in the center of the crust and temperature is controlled, boil-out of the filling is usually not a problem.

Pie dough may be used for many other items besides pie. Small pies,
tarts, tartlets, turnovers, dumplings, and others items are made from it. To
hold dough in place, beans or rice may fill shells lined with dough. When
this is done, docking is omitted. Afterward, the rice or beans are stored in
jars and reused for the same purpose whenever required. Baked pastry
dumplings or turnovers may be filled with meat, fruit, or other items. For
these, the dough is usually rolled to a $\frac{1}{8}$ inch thickness, a No. 12 scoop of
filling is added in the center, and the product is folded over. A No. 10 can
makes a good-size cutter for a semi-circular product. If the item is to be
deep-fried, a special type of dough is required (see fried desserts in Chapter
14). If special tartlet tins are not available, muffin pans may be used to make
individual shells. For this, rounds of dough are cut the proper size to fit over
the outside, and the pieces are docked and baked over these. Frequently
a rich pastry dough resembling a cookie dough is used for tartlets. Pastry
rings or tin hoops may be placed on greased baking sheets and lined with
dough for larger tarts. These are pinched to give a border at the edge. They
are then docked and baked. Small tartlet shells may be purchased already
baked.

FIG. 13-13 Trim excess dough by rotating and cutting with
the palms of the hands at the same time.

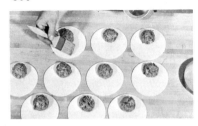

(a)   (b)

FIG. 13-14   (a) Filling fruit turnovers and brushing tops with water to give a good seal.
(b) Sealing in the edge previous to baking. Note that the tops have been pierced so steam
may escape. (Courtesy Procter & Gamble)

Baking

Single crusts are usually baked at from 425° to 450° F in about 15 minutes,
and double crust pies at 425° to 450° F for 10 minutes. Then the temperature is dropped to 350° or 375° F. From 45 minutes to one hour is
required to bake a double crust fruit pie. Many bakers prefer a straight
baking temperature of 350° to 375° F for double crust pies. Brushing lower
crusts with flour or egg is not as effective in avoiding soaking as proper
baking temperatures. If a pie is cooked at too low a temperature, the crust
will be toughened. Overbrowning will result if the heat is too high, and the
filling of double crust pies may not cook properly. The time required to
bake a double crust pie is lessened if the filling is hot when the pie is placed
into the oven for baking.

FIG. 13-15   From left to right: too low a baking temperature, just right, and too high a
baking temperature.

PIE FILLINGS

A pie filling should be made with the same care as the crust, for the filling
gives identity to a pie. A wide variety of fillings are used for single crust
pies. These may be blanc manges, cream puddings, bavarians, layers of
cream pudding over which thickened layers of fruit filling are poured, gelatin chiffons, frozen fillings, and others. Toppings may be meringues, whipped
cream, toasted coconut, crumbs, or nuts. Unbaked single crusts may also be
filled with custards, chiffons, soufflés, or other uncooked fillings and baked.
Double crust pies usually have fruit fillings. Lattice tops are sometimes used
for these instead of solid crusts. A streussel-like topping may also be baked
on top instead of a top crust. This crust may be called "French" or "Dutch."

About 1½ pints to one quart, or 1¼ pounds to two pounds, of filling
will be required for a nine-inch pie. When pies are topped with a meringue or
whipped cream, the smaller quantity is used. Many fillings for single crust
pies are similar to desserts, and the methods for preparing these fillings and
soft meringues will be found in the next chapter (on desserts). Fruit fillings
for double crust pies and custard fillings, however, need explanation here.

Fruit Fillings

The type of fruit, the proper thickening agent, the proportion of thickening
agent, and the methods of preparation are four factors affecting pie filling
quality. Low quality fruits should be avoided. The fruit may be broken,

FIG. 13-16 Testing the doneness of a pumpkin custard pie. (Courtesy Armour & Co.)

for appearance is not as critical as when fruit is served alone, but it should have some form. Fresh fruit should be kept under refrigeration. Before use it should be picked over, moldy or over-ripe fruit discarded, and the good fruit then washed and drained. Sugar, thickeners, and other ingredients may be added and the fruit allowed to stand for an hour or so. Open canned fruits just before use; long standing will cause a loss in quality. Frozen fruits may be partially defrosted and placed in a steam-jacketed kettle, a small quantity additional sweetening and be thickened. Cold or hot setting starches may be used and the fruit carefully blended into the thickened juice after it is poured over the fruit. Allow to stand for two hours. Frozen fruits may also be partially defrosted, placed into a steam-jacketed kettle, a small quantity of water added, and the temperature brought quickly to 185° to 190° F, at which time it is thickened. Carry-over pie fillings should not be held for long periods. If it is necessary to store fillings, temperatures should be between 50° and 52° F for best quality retention. Many bakers add freshly made filling to stored products and use immediately to obtain a fresh-tasting product.

Extending a filling by adding excessive quantities of water and then thickening with starch so a sufficiently heavy pie filling is obtained is not recommended. The quantity of water required will be governed by the type of fruit, and it is difficult to establish exact ratios, but in final form ratios of fruit to liquid of 2:1 or 3:1 are common.

Cornstarch and flour are commonly used as thickeners. Fruit pie fillings are best thickened with a waxy maize starch because of its clarity and brilliance. The thickened filling will be soft and have the same consistency when hot as when cold. It has good tolerance in use and gives a more standard thickened product than other types of thickeners. The following are average quantities of thickeners used per gallon of liquid for fruit fillings:

Waxy maize starch	10	to 10½	oz	(8% solution)
Cornstarch	13	to 15½	oz	(10 to 12% solution)
Flour	20½	to 30	oz	(16 to 20% solution)

Some bakers add gums such as carboxy-methyl-cellulose (CMC), gum trag-acanth, locust bean gum, and low-methyoxyl pectin to thicken and provide high clarity and brilliance to the fruit and juice.

Usually the thickener is mixed with the sugar and blended into the hot liquid. The thickener can also be blended with some of the liquid and added as a slurry. Cooking should continue until thickening is complete, which for cornstarch occurs at 203° F and for waxy maize starch at 195° F. Rapid cooking and cooling is desirable to prevent the breakdown of the thickener by the fruit acid. To make a lemon cream pie filling, blend the cornstarch, sugar, and salt together. Pour this into the water with good agi-

FIG. 13-17   The relative quantities of waxy maize starch (left), cornstarch (center), and flour (right) required to give equal thickness to a pie filling and the resultant products. Note the softness of the waxy maize and the sheer firm qualities of the cornstarch compared with the flour. Clarity is also a variable.

FIG. 13-18   Waxy maize starch is not suitable for cream pie fillings. Note how the cream filling made from waxy maize starch on the left flows and is overly soft compared with the sheerer, yet softer qualities given the filling on the right by cornstarch.

tation while the water is boiling. The grated lemon rind can be placed directly in the water before this. When thickening is complete, take a small quantity of the hot mixture and stir into lighty beaten (stage one) egg yolks. Blend this yolk mixture with good agitation into the thickened mixture.[2] Cooking is continued for three to five minutes while the mixture is stirred. Temperature should reach 195° F. The lemon juice and butter are then added after the mixture is removed from the heat. Cooling should be rapid.

In thickened fruit fillings, if the quantity of sugar used is high, some may be withheld and added after thickening. This will prevent excess sugar from retarding gelatinization of the starch. If one pound of starch is heated with seven pounds of sugar in 1¼ gallons of water, swelling or gelatinization of the starch may be prevented, and a dull, thin, watery, unflavorful filling will result. If the same starch is mixed with only three to four pounds of sugar, good thickening will occur, and the remaining sugar can be added later.

Cold-setting starches are becoming popular for thickening fruit pies. The drained liquid is thickened with this and then poured over the drained fruit, and this mixture is allowed to stand two hours. The fruit pies are then filled, covered with top crust, and baked. Good quality is obtained and

FIG. 13-19   Waxy maize starch can be frozen without a breakdown of the custard formed, but many other starches cannot. On the left a meat pie filling that was made from waxy maize starch and frozen six months, and a control sample thickened with flour.

much labor is saved. A hot-setting starch or flour may be added to a fruit filling; this mixture is put into a double crust and the pie baked, the filling thickening as the pie bakes. This is not considered the best procedure, however. Tapioca is used in this manner or is used to thicken fillings before they are added to the pie.

[2]This procedure is described for blanc manges in the chapter on desserts that follows.

Custard Fillings

Custard pies are usually made with 2½ pounds of whole egg to one gallon of milk or liquid. If yolks are used, the proportion of eggs may be reduced. A finer custard also results when yolks only are used. A higher proportion of eggs than that used for a dessert custard is desirable to give a firmer custard and keep the crust drier. Techniques for mixing and baking are much the same as for dessert custards (discussed in the next chapter). Chiffon pies have baked fillings much like dessert soufflés, but some chiffon pies are made of egg whites incorporated into starch-thickened or gelatin-thickened mixtures. These are not baked but are poured into baked pie shells and allowed to set.

Gelatin desserts are used to make chiffon pie fillings. These are actually snows or sponges, bavarians or whips. Gelatin desserts may also be combined

FIG. 13-20 Set up marking and control procedures for portion control so that all portions are alike.

with fruits and used as pie fillings. A parfait pie filling is a gelatin dessert mixture into which soft ice cream and fresh or frozen drained fruits have been folded just before the gelatin sets.

MAKE-UP AND SERVICE

In many food services, single crust cream pies are not filled until just before use. This avoids crust soaking. The filling is cold and at such consistency that it can be spread in the pie and yet hold its shape when cut. Meringues or other toppings are added shortly before service. Use pie markers to indicate cuts on a pie. Many fruit pies are improved if they are slightly warm at service.

14   Desserts

A dessert is a food, usually sweet, that completes a meal. This definition would include cakes, cookies, and pastries, but, for the purpose of this chapter, desserts are defined as other sweet foods, such as puddings, frozen or gelatin products, and even plain fruit eaten in hand at the end of a meal.

A dessert should blend with and complement the meal it ends. Factors needing consideration in its selection are flavor, richness, color, variety, texture, form, appearance, and quantity. The dessert should suit the occasion. If a light meal is served, a heavy dessert, such as a steamed pudding and hard sauce, is in order. At a bridge luncheon, a meringue filled with a delicate custard and topped with crushed ripe berries might be served. A stuffed baked apple might be served after a pork roast dinner. Just as certain foods are selected to begin a meal by sharpening the appetite, desserts should be selected to give final satiety and satisfaction—to "top off" the meal.

Desserts provide an opportunity for decoration and color, but these should not take the place of goodness. Succulent, flavorful, delicate desserts, properly selected and prepared, and merchandised in a unique manner, can do much to improve the standards of food served in any operation.

STANDARDS

The standard for a good dessert varies according to its type. In general, desserts should not be cloyingly sweet or bitingly tart. Good form and attractive shape are essential. The texture should be crisp or soft, depending upon the type; soft for some puddings, crisp for meringues, and in between for frozen desserts. Pasty texture, insipid, untrue, or overabundant flavor, or excessive color is not the mark of a good dessert. Hot desserts should be served hot, and desserts that need chilling should be cold upon service.

FIG. 14-1 High quality is indicated in this French apple dessert, worthy of the standard of almost any food service operation. (Courtesy Processed Apples Institute)

FRUITS

One of the simplest and finest desserts that can be served is fruit. Fresh fruit served as a dessert should be tart yet sweet and full of flavor. Use fresh fruit to bring color and flavor into a meal. Serve fresh fruit cold.

Berries in season may be served plain, dipped in powdered sugar, or with cream and sugar. At times, slightly sweetened crushed fruit may be served over custard, pudding, or biscuit. Clean fresh berries by washing them, about one to two quarts at a time, either by running cold water over them or by placing them into a colander and dipping them into cold water. Sort and examine. Fresh berries should be served chilled. About three ounces or a half cup is sufficient for a portion.

Fresh fruit, such as apples, apricots, bananas, cherries, oranges, melons, pears, peaches, and pineapple, may be served whole, halved, or in pieces. Many are served plain, but some may be served with cream and sugar. Grapefruit and oranges may be cut into halves, any seeds removed, and the sections loosened with a sharp knife. They are usually served in the half-section. They may also be thinly sliced after peeling, and grapefruit is an excellent dessert when lightly broiled; the addition of a bit of *creme de menthe* or grenadine after broiling adds interest and flavor. Oranges and grapefruit peel best when dropped into very hot water for three to five minutes. The white part of the peel should be completely removed, since it is apt to be bitter.

Many fruits, such as peaches, apricots, and bananas, may darken when cut or peeled. If these are dipped into a solution containing a small quantity of ascorbic acid, lemon juice, pineapple juice, or commercial anti-oxidant, discoloration may be retarded. Salt water is not as effective. Sugar added to some fruits prevents discoloration. Using stainless steel, glass, or silver knives avoids discoloration from iron salts.

Frozen raspberries, strawberries, blueberries, pineapple, peaches, and apricots are used for desserts or for dessert preparation. If a few crystals of ice remain, acceptability is increased. About three to four ounces (half cup) makes a portion. The fruit is usually purchased sweetened with sugar in the

(a)   (b)

(c)   (d)

FIG. 14-2   Fruit is an excellent dessert. (a) A fruit salad used as a dessert. (b) Fruit desserts: left, the traditional cheese, wafers, and fresh fruit; right, a small plate of assorted fruit; center bottom, a fresh fruit cup; center top, pears cooked with candied ginger. (c) Fresh fruit combines well with pastry. (Courtesy Procter & Gamble) (d) Nothing is better than a baked Roman Beauty apple.

ratio of 4:1 (berries to sugar). Frozen sweetened berries in five-pound cartons at 0° F, when removed to room temperature, take two to three hours to thaw sufficiently, and four to five hours if removed to refrigerated space.

Cooked fruits are also served. Such sauces may be purchased canned in various weights of sirup. If prepared from fresh fruit, retention of color, shape, and flavor must be considered in cooking. Rapid boiling breaks up fruit. Sugar strengthens the cellular structure of fruit. If fruits are dropped

Fig. 14-3   At the top of this illustration are shown five apple slices cooked gently in heavy sirup, while at the bottom are shown five slices from the same apple after being boiled in water.

into hot sirup and cooked gently with the cover on, the fruit will not break up as much as it will when cooked uncovered in water at a rapid boil. Fruits with some cellular strength, such as pears and apples, are easily baked in light sirup. Delicate fruits may be covered and baked at low temperatures to retain shape. Browning may be done quickly under a broiler after baking is completed. At times it is desirable to have a fruit which is soft and broken up, such as applesauce. Fruits cooked in light or medium sirup are called stewed fruits or fruit sauces. If cooked in a heavy sirup, they are called compotes. Whole fruits cooked in heavier than 23.9° Brix sirup are also called preserves.

Table 14-1
Densities of Sirups for Cooking Fruit

| Type of Sirup | To Make One Gallon of Sirup | | | | Brix Reading |
| | Sugar | | Water | | |
	(pounds)	(quarts)	(pounds)	(quarts)	(degrees)
Light	3	1¾	7½	3¾	11 to 13.9
Medium	4 to 5	2½ to 2¾	7 to 7¼	3½	14 to 19.9
Heavy	7 to 8	4 to 4½	6½ to 7	3	20 to 23.9

For quantity production, approximately 15 pounds EP of fruit cooked in about 1½ gallons of light or medium sirup will give 100 half-cup portions. Four No. 10 cans of fruit will usually serve 100, but the count of fruit per can is oftentimes a controlling factor.

Dried fruits may be stewed and served as a dessert. The pulp may also be prepared for dessert preparation. Many dried fruits can be prepared by being washed in cold water, drained, and then just covered with boiling water; after 24 hours of soaking, the fruit will be plump and tender and may be served without cooking. However, dried fruits, after soaking, are most often simmered until tender. Rapid cooking from the dry state will give a tough fruit lacking plumpness. Ten pounds of dried apricots or figs and 12 pounds of peaches, pears, or prunes will give approximately 100 half-cup portions. Some helpful conversions to calculate yields are: one pound dried prunes yields 10 ounces (2 c) pitted prunes; 1½ pounds (4 c) cooked prunes yields one pound (3 c) pitted prunes; and 1¼ pounds pitted prunes equals one quart.

Low-moisture fruits contain about 5% or less moisture. They take little storage space, give good quality products, are low in cost, and do not

Table 14-2
Low-Moisture Fruit Equivalents

| | Equivalent Per Pound of Low-Moisture Fruit | | | |
	Fresh AP	Canned Regular Pack No. 10 Can	Canned Solid Pack No. 10 Can	Evaporated or Dried
Apple nuggets (sauce)	10 lb	3	1¼	3 lb
Apple nuggets (sauce)	10 lb	3		3 lb
Apple pie slices	10 lb	3	1¼	
Apricot slices			1	3 lb
Peach slices			1	2½ lb
Pitted prunes				2½ lb

require refrigerated storage to prevent insect infestation in warm, humid climates. They are usually soaked and then cooked slowly. They may also be started in cold water, brought slowly to a simmer, and cooked until plump and tender. Sugar may be added at the start or after cooking, depending upon the fruit and the firmness desired. The yield of one pound of low-moisture prunes will be about $2\frac{1}{4}$ pounds, giving about 12 medium-size portions.

FRUIT DESSERTS

Fruit may be a predominating ingredient in many desserts. For the most part, these fruits are puddings.

Crisps and Bettys

Crisps are made by topping fruits with a mixture of flour, sugar, and fat. This is baked in an oven, resulting in a crisp top with soft fruit underneath. Oatmeal rather than flour may be used. Brown bettys are made by spreading layers of bread or cake crumbs between layers of fruit, butter, and sugar; the mixture is then baked. The interior and bottom are a soft mixture of fruit and crumbs, while the top is crisp. Crisps and bettys are best served warm with a light sweet-tart fruit sauce, whipped cream, or hard sauce. Carry-over fruits or small quantities of odds and ends of fruit may be utilized in these preparations.

(a)

(b)

FIG. 14-4 (a) A blended mixture of flour, shortening, and brown sugar is being spread over seasoned peach slices to make a peach crisp. (b) The making of an apple betty is shown, alternate layers of apples, crumbs, and sugar being spread in the pan and drizzled with butter. (c) Fruit and bread cubes are used to make a bread pudding. (Courtesy American Baking Institute)

(c)

Biscuit Fruit Desserts

Shortcakes are a popular biscuit-type fruit dessert. The dough is slightly richer and sweeter than for a baking powder biscuit but is otherwise made the same way. Two layers of dough, about a half-inch thick, are rolled out. The lower layer is buttered and the top layer is placed over it. Sometimes

(a)   (b)

FIG. 14-5   (a) A peach shortcake makes a substantial dessert with which to top off a meal. (b) Strawberries being placed into small sponge cakes for a strawberry shortcake. (Courtesy General Foods, Inc.)

the top may be sprinkled with sugar. It may be docked and baked in a sheet. For serving, cut into portion sizes, split the layers apart, and cover the center and top with crushed fruit. Top with whipped cream or serve with plain cream. Biscuits may be cut from the dough and split later as the portion is prepared for service. It is usually desirable to serve shortcakes slightly warm. Keep the fruit chilled, however.

Cobblers are baked in an oven with biscuit toppings set over sweetened fruit. They are usually served hot. Some cobblers are made with a pie crust topping. A Dutch cake is biscuit dough over which fruit, such as peach or apple slices, is heavily dotted. Sugar, spices, and melted butter or margarine may be sprinkled over the top, and the product is baked. This is usually served hot with a warm, sweet-tart sauce over it.

Fruit rolls are made by placing fruit in biscuit dough and rolling as for a cinnamon roll. About inch-thick slices are cut from this and baked on a greased pan. A roly-poly is a fruit roll baked without slicing. Slices are cut after baking. Fruit dumplings are made by rolling a rich biscuit dough about one-fourth-inch thick. The center is filled with fruit, and the edges of the dough are folded over to make a tight seal. These are placed into pans, cov-

FIG. 14-6   A variation for a cobbler. (Courtesy Processed Apples Institute)

FIG. 14-7   A cherry cobbler with a pie crust topping instead of biscuit.

ered to about a half of the dumpling with a fruit sauce, or slightly sweetened water, or water alone, and then baked or steamed. After baking, a thickened sauce surrounds the dumpling and is spooned over it when it is served. A greater quantity and a thinner sauce is obtained when the dumplings are steamed; the sauce may then require some thickening. Many like to brown dumplings under a broiler to improve their appearance. Some dumplings may be deep-fried. Fruits rolls, roly-polies, dumplings, and other fruit-biscuit desserts are usually served slightly warm with a fruit sauce, hard sauce, brandy sauce, or foamy sauce.

PUDDINGS

Wide variety is possible in puddings. Most puddings are easily made in quantity, low in cost, and require small labor expenditures. For this reason some institutions serve puddings too frequently and cause them to lose appeal.

FIG. 14-8   The making of a fruit roll. It will be sliced and baked and then topped with a hot fruit sauce at service. When the roll is not cut but baked whole, it is called a roly-poly.

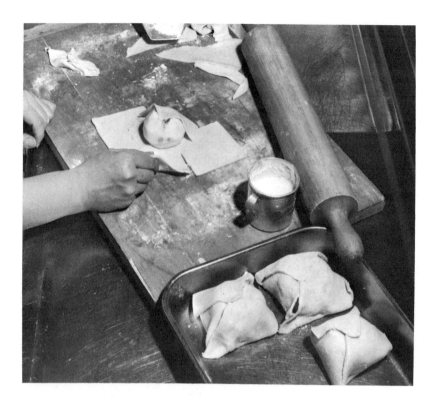

FIG. 14-9   The making of apple dumplings.

There are many desserts which are made like cakes but are served as puddings. A date pudding is a dessert of this type. Shortening, sugar, and eggs are usually creamed, and the sifted flour and other dry ingredients are added alternately with the liquid. Floured fruit and nuts are blended in last. Such desserts usually contain high ratios of fruit. They may be served hot or cold.

Boiled or Steamed Puddings

Zest and lightness are qualities lost if steamed or boiled puddings are served cold. They are usually made with suet as the shortening. Bread crumbs, strong flour, and eggs act as binders for heavy ratios of fruits and nuts. Only a small quantity of moisture is added if the fruit used is moist. The leavening agent is usually soda, which gives a porous texture and darkens the fruits, nuts, molasses, and many other ingredients if they are in the batter.

Steamed puddings are heavier in texture than baked ones. The grain is apt to be tight and waxy, but it should not be pasty. The ratio of batter to fruit and nuts may vary from one to one to 2½ to one. Many steam pudding batters approximate pound cakes in the proportions of flour, shortening, and sugar used. Lighter puddings may be made which resemble rich muffin batters. These are apt to be open-grained and more delicate in texture.

Containers in which puddings are cooked may be large or individual. Grease, flour, and fill only two-thirds full to allow for expansion in cooking. Covers should be provided or the tops covered with foil. The containers may be steamed for about 2½ to three hours, baked in a 330° F oven in pans of shallow water while covered with damp cloths, or placed into pots of boiling water and cooked on top of the range. To boil a pudding in a bag, take a strong muslin cloth and dip into cold water; wring out dry. Turn it inside out and dip into flour. Turn the floured side in and drop in the batter. Tie loosely, allowing for expansion in cooking, and lower into water that is just boiling. The bag may be also suspended in a bath of steam. When

(a)

(b)

(c)

FIG. 14-10   (a) There are many varieties of steamed puddings, but variation may also be obtained by steaming in different containers as shown here. (b) To steam, place pudding batter in well greased and floured containers, cover, and place in a steam chest, or (c) to use the traditional method, place in a bag and steam or boil in a covered container.

cooked, remove, dip into cold water, and free the cloth; let the pudding cool under cover or in water so that it does not form a tough skin. Usually, in quantity preparations, steaming is done in pans or containers. In these, the pudding may be stored for short periods and then reheated. If desired, puddings may be allowed to cool to a point at which they may be handled. Then they may be removed, wrapped in foil, and refrigerated. These puddings may be reheated in their foil wraps in steam or in a 325° F oven for about 45 minutes, or they may be reheated after being replaced in their original containers. Very sharp or serrated knives should be used for cutting. Individual puddings may be reheated in roll or bun warmers. The sauce should be hot unless it is hard sauce. Select a sauce that complements the pudding in flavor and color. Vanilla, lemon, orange, rum, foamy, and other types of hot sauces are used.

FIG. 14-11 Two ways of mixing ingredients for a starch-thickened pudding. Dry starch, cocoa, and sugar may be blended together as shown on the lower left, or the dry starch and cocoa may be blended with a bit of the milk (upper center). The former is blended into the hot milk slowly with good agitation, while the latter is blended into a hot milk and sugar mixture. Salt may be added at any time, but vanilla and butter are usually added after the pudding has been removed from the heat.

Starch-Thickened Puddings

Blanc manges and cream puddings form the base for many desserts. Blanc mange is another name for cornstarch pudding made from hot milk, sugar, vanilla, and a bit of salt, with cornstarch, arrowroot, or some other starch used as a thickener. The proportion of cornstarch may vary from six to 12

FIG. 14-12 A cream pudding is a cornstarch pudding (blanc mange) that has eggs added to it. To blend in the eggs, mix them well, add a bit of the hot pudding mixture, and stir to blend in the eggs thoroughly; then, as shown here, with good stirring, blend this egg mixture into the hot pudding mixture.

ounces per gallon of liquid, depending upon the consistency desired. If the pudding is served molded, use 12 ounces of thickening. If eggs are used for part of the thickening, the product is not a blanc mange but a cream pudding, the quantity of starch thickening being reduced because of the eggs. A chiffon or light, fluffy texture may be given to a cream pudding by adding only the yolks for thickening, beating the whites into a meringue with part of the sugar, and then folding them in while the mixture is hot. The hotter the mixture when poured over the meringue, the firmer will be the pudding.

The procedure for making a blanc mange or cream pudding is to heat the milk, reserving a small quantity of cold milk to blend with the sugar and cornstarch or the cornstarch alone, then blending this mix into the hot milk. Add a bit of the hot milk mixture to the cold milk and cornstarch mixture and blend well. Add this with good agitation to the hot milk mixture. An alternate method is to mix the sugar and cornstarch well together, blending the mixture with rapid stirring into the hot milk. Cook for about 10 minutes or until the temperature is well above 200° F. If eggs are added, beat slightly and blend some of the starch-thickened mixture into them. Return this mixture with good agitation to the hot mass until well blended. Cooking to 195° F is recommended to complete thickening of the eggs. When either a blanc mange or cream pudding contains a large quantity of sugar, withhold a part until the starch and eggs are cooked. Then add it. This will prevent the sugar from interfering with the thickening of the starch and eggs.

Tapioca puddings are made by adding tapioca to sweetened milk or fruit juices and cooking until the mixture is thickened. Either pearl or granular tapioca, the latter the quick-cooking type, is used. Pearl tapioca requires soaking before cooking; the granular does not. A less ropy product results when granular tapioca is used. Overmixing causes ropiness and lowers quality. A tapioca cream contains eggs. The egg yolks are cooked with the

Table 14-3
Quantity of Starch and Eggs Required to Thicken One Gallon of Pudding

Type of Starch Thickener	Amount of Thickener*	Whole Eggs
Cornstarch	4 to 5 oz (1c)	1½ lb (1½ pt or 16 eggs)
Flour	8 oz (1 pt)	1½ lb (1½ pt or 16 eggs)
Rice, uncooked	9 to 14 oz (1 to 1½ pt)	
Rice, cooked	1 to 1½ gallon	
Tapioca, granular	6 to 9 oz (1½ to 2 c)	1½ lb (1½ pt or 16 eggs)
Tapicoa, pearl	12 oz (3 c)	1½ lb (1½ pt or 16 eggs)
Cake or bread crumbs	1 to 2 lb (1 to 2 qt)**	
Cornmeal, farina, or other	1 lb (1 qt)	

*Increase thickener if eggs are omitted.
**Quantity will depend upon moistness of crumbs.

tapioca and hot milk and part of the sugar. Flavoring is added, and this very hot, thickened mixture (above 180° F) is poured over a meringue made of the sugar and beaten egg whites. The mixture is carefully folded, giving a light, fluffy texture. Sage, farina, and cornmeal are also used to make starch-thickened puddings. Indian pudding is a pudding thickened with corn-meal. Molasses and raisins are also ingredients. Serve about a half cup of pudding per portion; about 3¼ gallons will be required for 100 portions.

FIG. 14-13 A tapioca cream pudding is being prepared here. The hot tapioca mixture is being folded into an egg white meringue. The hotter the pudding mixture when it is stirred into the meringue, the stiffer will be the final pudding.

Egg-Thickened Puddings

Custards

A baked custard is made with 1½ to two pounds of whole eggs to a gallon of liquid. If egg yolks are used, the quantity required may be slightly less. Poor quality eggs make a weak custard. Proper baking temperature is between 325° and 340° F. If the temperature is too low, a weak custard is obtained; if it is too high, the custard has a watery, open texture instead of a firm, smooth, solid clabber. This watery, open condition is called syneresis.

The cut surface of a custard should be even and sharp, possessing a soft sheen tinted a slight creamy tan. The top should be delicately browned. Cereals such as bread, rice, or cake crumbs make it possible to reduce the quantity of eggs two ounces for every eight ounces of cereal used. Some

FIG. 14-14   One of the ways to test for doneness in a custard pudding is to insert a knife. If it comes out clean, the custard is done.

recipes may call for a small quantity of flour or other thickening agent in addition to eggs. Custards should be baked in pans of water or ovens so that direct heat will not come in contact with the custard and cause syneresis. Custards cook after they come from the oven; for this reason, they are usually removed before they are completely cooked. The time of removal must be judged carefully. A custard is cooked when the tip of a small, pointed knife comes out clean. An experienced baker can tell the doneness of a custard by moving the pan in the oven and noting the firmness. If desired, custards may be steamed rather than baked, but if steamed they should be covered to keep steam condensation out.

In making a custard, have the milk hot; the final temperature of the mixture going into the oven should be 140° F. Add flavoring, sugar, and eggs, and blend well. Pour into pans or molds. To stop a custard from cooking after removal from the oven, set in a well aerated place or in a pan of cold water.

Stirred or soft custards are similar to baked custards in quantity of ingredients used, but they are stirred instead of baked. Upon cooling they have the consistency of thin to medium white sauce. Syneresis is a problem in their cooking, and constant stirring is required to prevent curdling. Coagulation is an endothermic action, and 185° F is used as a guide to indicate when coagulation begins. As soon as the thermometer rises above 185° F, coagulation is apt to be complete. Disappearance of foam is also an indication of doneness. Soft custards can be made in one- to two-gallon batches in a steam-jacketed kettle or over hot water, but good stirring is necessary. If hand-stirred, quantities up to two or three quarts can be made. Again, preheating the milk so the mixture with the eggs and sugar is at 140° F makes a firmer and more satisfactory custard.

Soft custards are excellent poured over fruit or slices of plain cake. Floating island is a soft custard which is poured over soft meringue, or soft meringues are placed on top of the custard.

Baked Soufflés

Soufflés are desserts thickened with eggs; frequently a starch thickener is used, too. They are delicate desserts, and the most satisfactory product results when they are prepared to order. A typical soufflé may be made by beating the yolks separately with sugar, blending in flavoring ingredients, and then folding in stiffly beaten egg whites. They are made in a manner similar to that discussed for foamy omelets under egg cookery. The product is then baked in a slow or moderate oven. Service must be immediate, since they may collapse. If other types of thickening besides eggs are used, the product will be less fragile.

FIG. 14-15   A fruit soufflé. (Courtesy Poultry and Egg National Board)

Meringues

A meringue is a complex emulsion of air cells dispersed in a heavy sugar sirup. Egg whites are the stabilizer for the emulsion. Hard meringues are often used as a base for desserts, while soft meringues are used largely for toppings for pies, puddings, and other products.

Hard meringues may have moisture added to the egg whites in a ratio of about one ounce of water per pound of egg whites. This helps to bring the sugar into solution. A quarter ounce of cream of tartar to each pound of egg whites is used to give tenderness to the meringue and assist the egg whites in beating up to a stable foam, but if one ounce of vinegar or lemon juice is added per pound of whites, moisture and cream of tartar are omitted. From 1¾ to 2½ pounds of sugar are used to each pound of whites. Bake for 1½ hours at 275° F or for 50 minutes at 325° F. They should be dried out, rather than baked, but not so dry that they shatter easily in serving. Heavy ovens may be preheated to 325° F, the heat turned off, and the meringues placed into the oven and left overnight. Baking may be on ungreased brown paper or on non-resinous wooden boards, one inch or more thick. Per pound of egg whites used for soft meringues, use half a pound to a pound of sugar, and three-quarters of a teaspoon of cream of tartar. The ratio of sugar to egg whites may go as high as 3 to 2, giving a more tender and flavorful meringue with a high degree of sweetness. Bake soft meringues five minutes at 475° F, six minutes at 425° F, or 12 to 18 minutes at 350° F, the last time and temperature being recommended for quantity work. The length of cooking will also depend upon the depth of the meringue. At times, soft meringues may be browned with a torch or a red-hot, flat, iron instrument and served at once, but this does not destroy Salmonella bacteria, if present.

FIG. 14-16 The ingredients and the making of a soft meringue for topping pies.

In making a soft meringue for pies:

(a) Prepare just before use.

(b) Put meringue on warm (122° F) or hot (158° F) filling, never on a cold filling.

(c) Bake at a low temperature for a relatively long time, rather than at a high temperature for a short time.

(d) If frozen egg whites are used, thaw not above 45° F to avoid food poisoning from *Salmonella* in such eggs.

In making meringues, have the whites at 110° F for whipping. Extra-fine sugar should be used to give rapid solution and prevent graininess. The greater the quantity of sugar, the more stable and finer the grain of the meringue. Make a good foam, third stage, adding salt and acid (cream of tartar, or lemon juice, or vinegar) at the start of beating. Then add the sugar in small additions, beating in well to blend and dissolve. Failure to have the eggs at a sufficiently stiff stage will cause a thin meringue, lacking volume, which may weep and have slippage. Care should be taken not to overbeat

(a)   (b)

(c)

FIG. 14-17 (a) The ingredients for making a hard meringue: egg whites, sugar, cream of tartar, and salt. (b) Placing the meringues on a baking sheet previous to baking. (c) Upper right shows a soft meringue on a lemon pie. The individual heart-shaped hard meringue (upper left) will be filled with strawberries and topped with whipped cream for a Valentine's Day dessert, while the large meringue pie shell, partially shown, will be filled with pistachio ice cream, topped with shaved bitter chocolate, and served.

the eggs before adding the sugar, for this, too, will cause a meringue failure. Meringues, especially soft ones, develop a condition called leakage. This is moisture separating as tiny droplets or gathering under the meringue. Leakage may result from excess moisture, improper beating, or placing the unbaked meringue on too cold a filling before baking. Meringues for cream pies contain a substantial amount of sugar, and this high sugar content may encourage weeping. During baking, the egg white is partially coagulated; this reduces its stabilizing effect on the sugar sirup. To prevent moisture loss, stabilizers such as locust bean gum, gum arabic, gum tragacanth, powdered carageenin gum, or agar agar are used. The two latter stabilizers should be put into solution in a small quantity of boiling water before being added. Some formulas call for cornstarch or tapioca flour in the amount of a half ounce to every pound of whites. This is usually dusted over the meringue and incorporated during the last stage of beating. Prepared stabilizers for meringues may be obtained from bakery supply houses. To prevent slippage on a cream pie topped with a meringue, attach the meringue well to the edge of the crust. Scale meringue shells at $1\frac{1}{4}$ ounce each, or about 15 to 18 ounces per dozen. Scale on a nine-inch pie five to six ounces of meringue for a liberal topping.

Besides soft meringues, two other meringues may be used for topping desserts or pies. One is Italian meringue, which is a boiled frosting having a ratio of sugar to egg whites of 1:1, with the sugar cooked in half its weight in water until it reaches 244° F; then it is beaten into a stage three foam (lower limits) of the egg whites. The other is Swiss meringue, which has the same sugar ratio as common meringues; the mixture is beaten over boiling water and finished in a mixer with a whip at medium or high speed until the meringue is quite stiff, rather than having 110° F egg whites beaten at room temperature, as is done with the soft meringue. A meringue made for use as a frosting, the seven-minute frosting, may also be used as a topping much as a meringue is used.

Dried egg whites or meringue powders may be used for meringues with satisfactory results. Underbeating or overbeating is less a factor with these products than with regular egg whites. Normally, one quart of lukewarm water and one pound of sugar are used to six ounces of meringue powder.

JUNKET DESSERTS

The use of rennet for desserts is declining, but some may still desire it as a dessert for special diets or, for specific reasons, as a menu item. Rennet is an enzyme that sets the curd of milk into a custard or a clabber. If unpasteurized milk and sugar as a solution are warmed to 98° F and flavoring added, junket will set this mixture into a flavorful, delicate dessert.

About four tablets dissolved in a bit of lukewarm water will be sufficient to set a gallon of milk. Manufacturer's directions should be followed. The mixture, after addition of the dissolved junket, is stirred only to mix it into the milk, and the entire mixture is then poured into cups, glasses, or molds and kept at a lukewarm temperature until it sets, after which it is chilled. Jarring or stirring will break the curd. Portions are a half to three-fourths of a cup. Simple variation of junkets is possible by using almond, orange, caramel, cinnamon, grated chocolate, macaroon, or cake crumbs. Color may be used to give additional variation.

GELATIN DESSERTS[1]

Gelatin desserts are easily made and have low labor and material costs per portion. Presentation and merchandising are required, however, to maximize these favorable factors. Fortunately, they are adaptable for utilizing carry-over fruits, foods, or fruit juices. They store well and are not highly perishable under proper storage. It is possible to make a wide variety of these desserts.

FIG. 14-18 A plain gelatin mixture may be used for the preparation of many salads. (Courtesy General Foods)

[1]See the chapter on salads for more information on the preparation of gelatins.

(a)　(b)

(c)

FIG. 14-19 (a) To chill a hot gelatin dessert mixture quickly, add chipped ice to equal the total liquid required. (b) Gelatin dessert cubes. (c) Riced gelatin may be served many ways. (Courtesy General Foods Corporation)

Color, form, and shape may be varied considerably. Ricing, cubing or whipping are possible. Gelatin mixtures poured over cake cubes or crumbs make attractive desserts. Have the gelatin mixture at the sirupy stage ready to set, to prevent soaking of the cubes or crumbs. The proportions for a gelatin dessert mixture should be 1½ pounds of gelatin dessert powder per gallon of liquid. If gelatin only is used, three ounces per gallon of liquid is used as the base; sugar, flavoring, and color must be added.

Whipped egg whites, whipped cream, blanc manges, cream puddings, or melted ice creams may be blended with gelatin desserts or gelatin to

(a)   (b)

(c)

FIG. 14-20   (a) To whip a gelatin dessert, have the gelatin mixture about this thick, and (b) place in a mixer bowl in chipped ice, and beat at high speed. (c) Many types of service are possible. Here a whipped raspberry gelatin dessert is served with frozen raspberries. (Courtesy General Foods Corporation)

make different types of desserts. Pineapple snow or sponge can be made, using lemon- or lime-flavored dessert gelatin, with water and pineapple juice as the liquid. This is chilled until sirupy and whipped until double in bulk. Shredded pineapple and whipped egg whites may be blended into a whipped gelatin dessert and the mixture allowed to set. Apple sponges or snows, apricot or prune sponges, and so forth, are variations of this dessert.

When whipped cream is folded into a sweetened gelatin mixture, the result is called a bavarian. The finest bavarians contain milk instead of water as the liquid base. Cooked rice or such items as cake crumbs, ground nuts, and fruits may be added. Bavarian-type desserts can be made by blending blanc manges or cream puddings with gelatin mixtures. Stiffly beaten egg whites, or whipped cream, or a soft ice cream, may be blended into the mixture just before it sets. Some Bavarian mixtures may be whipped to a foam previous to the addition of other ingredients.

A Spanish cream is made by making a thin, stirred custard and adding flavored gelatin in sufficient quantity to make the product set. When it is still sirupy, whipped cream is folded in and the product allowed to set. Stiffly beaten egg whites may be substituted for whipped cream. There are many variations.

FROZEN DESSERTS

Among the most popular dessert items on any menu are frozen desserts. They are low in cost compared with many other desserts, and if purchased

(a) (b)

FIG. 14-21 (a) Beaten dry milk and gelatin being folded into a chocolate cream pudding mixture to make a low-calorie bavarian cream. (b) An orange marmalade bavarian made from a General Foods recipe.

prepared, they are low in labor cost. Variety may be endless, so they can be offered frequently on a menu.

Types

Ice cream is a frozen mixture of cream and milk, sugar, flavoring and stabilizers. The milk fat content may vary from 8 to 22%. Eggs may be an added ingredient, as well as fresh fruits, nuts, or fruit juices. Nuts and fruits are usually added just before the product is frozen completely. Other ingredients are usually added with the basic mix. Stabilizers form a gel structure which holds moisture in the frozen crystals, preventing spread and retarding crystalline growth. Gelatin or vegetable gums are the most commonly used stabilizers, but eggs or cooked starch may also act in this

(a)   (b)

FIG. 14-22   Ice cream may be merchandised in many ways. (a) Vanilla ice cream placed into individual pie shells and topped with shaved chocolate. (Courtesy Armour & Co.) (b) Rolling lemon sherbet balls into shredded coconut and serving over frozen strawberries. (Courtesy General Foods, Inc.)

manner. Purchased mixes usually contain stabilizers. Eggs will give increased volume and overrun to frozen desserts. Extra-dry milk solids improve texture and acceptability. A sherbet is a frozen mixture of milk, sugar, fruits and/or fruit juices, and a stabilizer. An ice is a frozen mixture similar to a sherbet except that no milk is used. Egg whites are usually added to an ice to give volume and act as a stabilizer. Ice cream, sherbets, and ices are mixtures frozen with air incorporated by mechanical mixing in freezing. Desserts such as mousse, parfait, frozen pudding, and whole, sliced, or crushed canned fruits packed in heavy sirup are not whipped during freezing; they are whipped either before or not at all. Slushes or granites are only partially mixed during freezing. All mixes should be pasteurized.

Quality Factors

Texture

The texture developed during freezing is important to the quality of
the frozen dessert, and this is dependent upon crystal size, overrun, ingredients, and storage.

It is a phenomenon of gas to give off heat when compressed and to take
up heat when it expands. Compression may change the gas to a liquid, and
when this liquid vaporizes, heat is required. Gases such as ammonia, sulfur
dioxide, and freon are easily compressed into a liquid by mechanical com-
pressors. This liquid is then allowed to expand in coils located in a cooling or
freezing unit. This expansion requires heat, which is taken from the item to
be frozen. Ice cream freezing units are operated on this principle. Coils
around the freezing chamber allow liquids to expand into a gas, and the heat
absorbed comes from the mixture to be frozen.

Crystal Size

The larger the crystals in a frozen mass, the coarser the texture. Rapid
freezing produces small crystals and a smooth texture. Good agitation encourages small crystal formation. Ingredients such as milk solids, gelatinized
starch, stabilizers, and egg solids give smoother frozen mixtures. Frappes,
slushes, and some other frozen mixtures require coarse crystals, and techniques used in freezing are directed to this end.

Overrun

Air incorporation will affect flavor and smoothness of texture. The
smoothness obtained by creating a foam is similar to that obtained in whipping cream or eggs. The openness of texture and volume given by overrun
aids in achieving palatability. When liquids freeze, they swell; and this
increase, plus that gained when a foam is made, may give an increase in bulk
double that of the original liquid. This increase in bulk is called swell, or
overrun. A doubling in volume from overrun is said to be 100% overrun.
Ice cream should have from 80 to 100% overrun. An ice which contains no
milk but some egg whites to encourage foam will have an overrun of 20
to 25%. Sherbets will increase 30 to 50%, but the best quality results from
overrun at the lower levels. If overrun is excessive, the dessert is frothy and
foamy and lacks quality. A failure to obtain sufficient overrun gives a
product lacking fullness of flavor. It is compact, pasty, and heavy.

Ingredients

The quality of frozen desserts is affected by the ingredients. Milk fat
tends to make these desserts hard, and fillers such as non-fat milk solids and
eggs are used to counteract it. Excess milk fat may cause graininess when

FIG. 14-23 Overrun is a term used to indicate the amount of air beaten into a frozen dessert. Maximum overrun that should be permitted for ice cream is 100%. In other words, the gallon and a half of ice cream mix shown here may be permitted to whip in freezing so it fills the three-gallon container shown on the right. Best quality results in ice creams when overrun is from 80 to 100%.

(a)

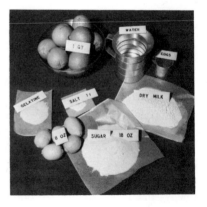

(b)

FIG. 14-24 The ingredients for one gallon of finished ice cream. These ingredients make a rich ice cream frequently called French ice cream because it contains eggs. Ground vanilla may be used in place of the liquid vanilla for this ice cream. (b) The ingredients used to make one gallon of orange sherbet. A small amount of coloring, not shown, may be added.

rapid agitation churns the fat into small butter globules. This may be partially overcome by homogenizing the mix. Operations making their own mixes should have homogenizers as well as freezers and hardening cabinets. Fruits and nuts may affect texture. Canned milk, if used, may give a graininess caused by lactose crystallization. Smoother desserts are obtained if mixes containing dry milk are refrigerated 24 hours before using.

Storage

If the storage temperature is high, crystalline growth will be encouraged. Storage should be at 0° F or below, and for dishing it should be at 8° to

FIG. 14-25 Have ice cream at about 8° to 12° F for best results in dishing. (The angle used for taking the picture distorts the reading, which showed 8° F.)

12° F. At dishing, if the product is too hard or too soft, the texture is poor. Fluctuating temperatures speed crystalline growth, while stabilizers retard it. Frozen desserts easily absorb flavors from other foods.

Freezing Mechanics

Freezing units vary, but basically all must freeze and whip. Small freezers will reach freezing temperature of 28° F or below in about 10 to 15 minutes. Temperatures below 24° F may harden the mixture too quickly and also overburden the motor. After five to eight minutes of freezing, batch consistency should be checked; if the mix is ribbony and appears dry and dull, and if the proper amount of overrun has been secured, freezing is completed.

If the mass is overfrozen at this point, overrun is poor. Just before withdrawal, flavoring ingredients are added. Prechilled cups or cans should be used as the mixture is forced out of the freezer at low speed. Move the frozen product rapidly into hardening cabinets. The faster the hardening, the better the quality of the dessert. It is usually desirable to have more than one person working when individual portions are drawn off so that movement to the hardening cabinet proceeds rapidly. Follow manufacturer's directions for equipment use, and post these where workers will see them.

Overloading the machine or freezing mixes too hard causes excessive wear and strain on equipment. Some freezing units are operated on the same compressor as the hardening cabinet; this complicates operation, since the compressor must be operated at higher speeds when the freezer unit is operated.

Extreme care must be taken to see that the freezing area, storage spaces, and freezing and storage equipment are clean and sanitary. Special solutions for sterilization are available; if they are not used, it is necessary to boil or steam-clean all equipment after thorough washing. It may be desirable to give the freezer a preliminary rinse before dismantling for cleaning. After washing and reassembling, the sterilizing solution should be added to about half the freezer capacity and the machine run for approximately one minute. The solution is drawn off, but the equipment is not rinsed. Leave the machine open for free air circulation. Before the freezer is operated again, it is rinsed, sterilized, and then rinsed again. All the auxiliary equipment and cans should be thoroughly rinsed, washed, rinsed, dried, and then sterilized.

Frozen desserts are usually purchased ready for service. Only when the quantity made is quite large does it pay to make one's own. Many operations that make their own frozen desserts purchase the mixes already prepared. If a mix is prepared from basic ingredients, be sure that the quality is high and the proportions correct. Blend well, for poor blending will make a poor product. If butter or other fats are used instead of cream with non-fat dry milk solids, homogenization must occur. Mixes for ice cream are usually 10% milk fat or higher, but mixes used for milk shakes and malts may be lower than this. In addition, a good ice cream mix will contain between 9 and $12\frac{1}{2}$% milk solids, 14% sugar, and $\frac{1}{2}$% stabilizer. Some mixes may go as high as 22% milk fat and 18% sugar. Corn sirup may replace about 30% of the total sugar. Use only quality flavorings. Gelatin or other approved products must be used for stabilizers or emulsifiers at $\frac{1}{2}$%.

Quality

Judge the quality of frozen desserts on the basis of flavor. This should be pleasant and true, with proper acidity and sweetness. Texture, smoothness, and feel in the mouth are called *body*. Fineness of grain, creaminess, and firmness are desirable. Too frothy or open a product is inferior. Defective texture may be described as fluffy, weak, crumbly, watery, icy, soggy, or gummy. Appearance should be bright and smooth, and products with little or no milk solids should possess good brilliance.

(a)

(b)

FIG. 14-26 (a) The proper type and size of scoop will be required to obtain best results in the service and merchandising of frozen desserts. (Courtesy Ice Cream Merchandising Institute) (b) The size of the scoop indicates the number of scoops obtained per quart. Shown here from left to right are: No. 40, No. 30, No. 24, No. 20, No. 16, No. 12, and No. 10. Normally, about half as many scoops are obtained per quart of frozen dessert as indicated on the scoop because of packing and scooping.

Service[2]

If frozen desserts are purchased, avoid excess stocks; obtain them in 2½, 3, or 5 gallon containers. Rotate stocks as quickly as possible. Vanilla, strawberry, and chocolate ice cream are usually stocked as standard items, and sherbets and ice creams of different flavors are stocked with these for variety. Orange and pineapple sherbets are usually standard items. If frozen desserts are purchased, establish good specifications which will guarantee quality. Place orders so that frozen desserts may be conditioned at 8° to 12° F in the dishing cabinets at least 24 hours before use.

It is easy to destroy quality by improper service. Scooping incorrectly or having the dessert at the wrong temperature will pack and destroy texture. Normal shrinkage in scooping should be from 40 to 45%. Normally, five gallons of ice cream will give 100 No. 10 scoops or 130 No. 12 scoops. To estimate dipping efficiency, weigh five or six portions on a scale, and from this calculate the average weight of each portion; then divide this into the net weight of the full container. For instance, if five dips weigh one pound, or an average of 3.1 ounces each, and a five-gallon container weighs 22 pounds six ounces, or 358 ounces, the yield will be approximately 116 dips. Usually 62, 51, 42, 35, 26, and 20 dips are obtained per gallon of dessert respectively from No. 30, 24, 20, 16, 12, and 10 scoops. Many fountain operators recommend the following for portions:

Fountain Item	Size Scoop	Number of Scoops Per Portion
Banana Split	No. 30	3
Bowl of Ice Cream	No. 30	4
Parfait	No. 30	3
Ice Cream Soda, Malt, or Milk Shake	No. 24	2
Pie, Cake, or Pudding a la Mode	No. 20	1
Sundae	No. 20	2
Table d'hote, Plain	No. 16	1
Sundae, Meal Portion	No. 12	1
A la Carte Portion	No. 10	1

Scoops should be clean and smooth, possessing a good sharp edge without nicks; they should be dipped into clear water before scooping. If the scoop is cold, the dessert will stick and pack. The procedure for scooping correctly is illustrated in Figure 14-28. Have the dessert at the right temperature; if it is too hard or soft, packing will occur. Portioning and cupping frozen desserts as they are withdrawn from the freezer and then hardening them saves packing loss. Freezing into bricks and slicing also reduces scooping loss.

[2]Food services will get much helpful information for serving ice cream from the Ice Cream Merchandising Institute, Barr Building, Washington, D. C.

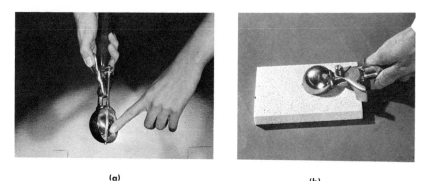

(a)   (b)

FIG. 14-27   (a) Use a good sharp-edged scoop. See that it is in good working order. (b)
To scoop, dip into cool water, drain the scoop for a moment on a pad, and then use.

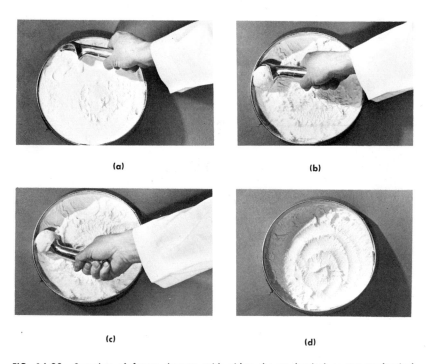

(a)   (b)

(c)   (d)

FIG. 14-28   Scooping of frozen desserts with either the mechanical or non-mechanical
scoop is much the same. Shown here is the use of the non-mechanical scoop. (a) Insert
the scoop about a half-inch deep into the frozen dessert, starting at the outer edge or
where the last scoop left off. (b) Draw lightly and evenly across the surface, rolling the
dessert into a ball. (c) When the scoop is filled, turn up with a twist of the wrist, breaking
off the ice cream. (d) Keep the surface smooth, working evenly across the top as shown here.

(a)   (b)

(c)   (d)

FIG. 14-29 Standardize your ice cream service. Here are some of the commonly accepted standards recommended by the Ice Cream Merchandising Institute: (a) Different styles of sundaes may be made. Two of the most popular are the (b), (c), (d), and (e) tulip, made with two No. 24 scoops in a tall tulip-style glass, and the double sundae, made with two No. 24 scoops side by side in the flat double or duplex sundae dish. (f) For a parfait, use three No. 30 scoops of ice cream alternated with layers of fruit or sirup in a tall, slender

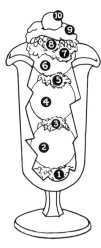

① 1 SODA SPOON SYRUP
   OR CRUSHED FRUIT

② 1 #30 DIPPER
   ICE CREAM

③ 1 SODA SPOON SYRUP
   OR CRUSHED FRUIT

④ 1 #30 DIPPER
   ICE CREAM

⑤ 1 SODA SPOON SYRUP
   OR CRUSHED FRUIT

⑥ 1 #30 DIPPER
   ICE CREAM

⑦ ½ SODA SPOON SYRUP
   OR CRUSHED FRUIT

⑧ 1 SODA SPOON OF NUTS
   OR NUTS IN SYRUP

⑨ WHIPPED CREAM

⑩ CHERRY

(e)   (f)

banana splits

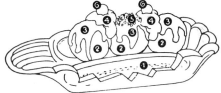

① MEDIUM RIPE BANANA   ④ WHIPPED CREAM

② 3 #24 DIPPERS ICE CREAM   ⑤ GROUND NUTS
   ASSORTED FLAVORS

③ ½ OZ EACH OF 3 TOPPINGS   ⑥ CHERRY OR GARNISH

(g)   (h)

parfait glass. Marbelizing is accomplished by running a spoon handle down the side of
the glass. A different fruit or ice cream may be used for each layer. (g) and (h) For a
banana split, select a medium-size, ripe banana, and split it in half lengthwise with
the peel on. Place the halfs flatside down on each side of the dish as shown. Remove the
peel. Place a No. 24 dipper each of vanilla, chocolate, and strawberry ice cream on
top of the banana. Top with a half ounce of chocolate sirup over the chocolate, a half

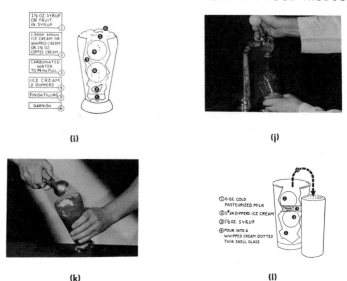

(i)   (j)

(k)   (l)

ounce of pineapple sundae mix over the vanilla, and a half ounce of strawberry sauce over the strawberry. Garnish with whipped cream, nuts, and a cherry. (i), (j), (k) The making of a soda is shown here. Note how the fine stream of soda water is directed to the side of the glass just above the contents until the glass is three-fourths full. Then add a No. 24 scoop of ice cream, as shown, and finish by filling the glass with a coarse stream, directing the stream slowly from side to side of the glass. Avoid slopping over of the foam. (l) The consistency of the milk shake or malt will be governed by the proportion of ice cream to milk, the temperature of the ingredients, and the mixing time. The mixing whips in air, but overmixing breaks down the foam. Proper temperature for ingredients should be ice cream 10° F, milk 32° F, and sirup and mixing cup cool. If the milk is at this temperature, the increase in volume will be 90 % ; if at room temperature, volume increase will be only 20 %. Mix only until thoroughly blended. (m) To make an ade or freeze, use fresh lemon, orange, or lime juice, or other flavors combined with fresh lemon juice. Citric acid may be required to give desired tartness. About two ounces or more of fresh juice, depending upon the type, about 1 1/2 ounces of simple sirup, and two to four soda spoons of extra-fine or bar sugar are stirred into a glass. Add about three ounces of cracked ice or several ice cubes and stir again. Fill the glass with plain or carbonated water and blend. A float can be made by adding one No. 16 scoop of sherbet or ice. A fruit ade made with carbonated water may be called a rickey. To make a freeze, use about 1 1/2 ounces of fruit juice made sufficiently tart with lemon or lime juice or citric acid, two No. 24 scoops of fruit sherbet, and five ounces of carbonated water. Mix in a mixer about one minute. Pour the mixture over a scoop of cracked ice in a glass, fill to the top with a fine stream of carbonated water, and top with fresh fruit or a cherry. A freeze float can be made using another scoop of the same or different ice or sherbet. (n) To make a frappe, place 1 1/2 ounces of milk, three No. 24 scoops of ice cream, and one ounce of crushed fruit or sirup into a shaker, and whip on the malt machine about one minute. The product is served in a glass topped with whipped cream, a dash of nutmeg, and a cherry. Sometimes a coarsely frozen mixture similar to this is called a slush or a granite.

freezes and floats

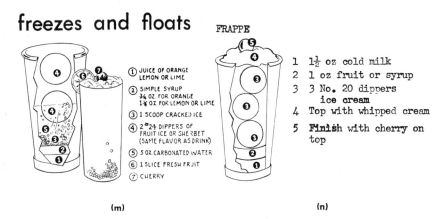

FRAPPE

① JUICE OF ORANGE
  LEMON OR LIME

② SIMPLE SYRUP
  ¾ OZ. FOR ORANGE
  1¼ OZ FOR LEMON OR LIME

③ 1 SCOOP CRACKED ICE

④ 2 #24 DIPPERS OF
  FRUIT ICE OR SHERBET
  (SAME FLAVOR AS DRINK)

⑤ 5 OZ CARBONATED WATER

⑥ 1 SLICE FRESH FRUIT

⑦ CHERRY

1   1½ oz cold milk
2   1 oz fruit or syrup
3   3 No. 20 dippers
    ice cream
4   Top with whipped cream
5   Finish with cherry on
    top

(m)   (n)

FIG. 14-30   To make a gallon of simple sirup, use six to seven pounds of granulated sugar, one gallon of boiling water, and one-fourth cup of lemon juice or one tablespoon of cream of tartar. Blend and stir.

Frozen desserts may be served in a number of ways. Meringue shells filled with vanilla ice cream may be covered with fruit and topped with whipped cream. A baked Alaska, made by placing a No. 24 scoop of ice cream on a two-inch square of sponge cake, surrounded with soft meringue and baked until the meringue is delicately browned, will have high appeal. Frozen log rolls, cupcakes, and eclairs filled with frozen desserts, bombes, coupes, and other desserts all bring interesting variety to a menu without high cost. Combining flavors of ice cream, sherbets, and ice; adding interesting accompaniments; and using different and unusual toppings, such as toasted coconut and grated bitter chocolate on vanilla ice cream—all give menu interest. *A la modes*, frozen desserts of varied shapes and colors, and combinations of frozen desserts with other foods assist in increasing sales. Standard methods of preparing some of the most common fountain items are shown in the illustrations.

FRIED DESSERTS[3]

Fritters

While not a common item on a menu, fritters can be a popular dessert item, giving good variety. Fritters are usually deep-fried, but occasionally they may be pan-fried in a liberal quantity of fat. Many are simply fruit dipped into a batter and then fried. Others may be batter mixtures containing

FIG. 14-31   Two types of fritters. The apple fritters on the left have been batter-dipped and fried. The ones on the right are banana fritters made by mixing diced bananas into a fairly stiff fritter batter and frying.

[3]See also deep-fat frying in the chapter on meat cookery.

leavening agents into which fruits are mixed; the batter is scooped out with a No. 30 scoop and deep-fried. There are many variations.

(a)   (b)

FIG. 14-32   (a) Rolled crêpes or French pancakes. These are filled with strawberry preserves; powdered sugar is dusted over them. (b) Crêpes suzette should be filled with an orange butter cream filling, folded in this manner, and then flamed with rum or brandy or a mixture of liqueurs.

(a)   (b)

FIG. 14-33   (a) To make fried pies, use a dough about midway in richness between a baking powder biscuit and pie dough. Fill as shown. (b) Fry as shown, placing a screen or another basket lightly over the pies so they will be submerged in the frying fat. (Courtesy Procter & Gamble)

Pancakes or Crêpes

Thin batters that resemble plain omelet mixtures slightly thickened with flour are used instead of regular pancake batter to make dessert pancakes or crêpes. No leavening agent is used. The cakes are thin; small ones will be from two to three, measuring four to five inches in diameter, in a portion. Large cakes may also be made, filled with a sweet filling, rolled, dusted with powdered sugar, and served on a platter, at one per portion. The small pancakes are either rolled or folded in four, the latter folding being typical of *Crêpes suzette*. Many different types of filling may be used.

To make, pour the batter into a hot pan in which butter has been brought to a delicate brown stage. Only the minimum quantity of batter to cover the pan bottom should be used. The pan should then be quickly tilted around so the batter flows to the edges, covering the entire surface with a thin coating. Cooking should be fairly rapid. When the bottom is nicely browned, the pancake should be turned and browned on the other side. Since this second side will never brown as well, it should be the interior of the pancake at service. Pancakes may be made ahead of service and rewarmed. They may also be frozen, thawed, and rewarmed. When warm, the pancake is placed on a clean surface and filled. Butter cream fillings, hot applesauce, *bar-le-duc* jelly, red currant jelly, marmalades, and other sweet items are popular. Serve very warm. Pancakes are usually sprinkled with powdered sugar by sifting powdered sugar through a sifter. Some may be scored with a hot poker, as are omelets. Others may be served with a hot sweet sauce over them. Many are flamed with brandy or rum. A small quantity of granulated sugar over the top of the pancakes aids in drawing the liquor up for burning. The liquor burns better if it is slightly warmed, and should be 100 proof or better.

Doughnuts

There are several kinds of doughnuts: cake, yeast, and French. The first is made from a lean cake or rich muffin dough, the second from a sweet yeast dough, and the French from a rich eclair paste (choux paste). All are deep-fat fried. In some areas, twisted cake doughnuts are called crullers, but the term is usually reserved to describe the French doughnut. Cake doughnuts may be made into balls, fingers, and other shapes. Frequently, yeast doughnut dough is also made into bismarcks, longjohns, and other-shaped deep-fried products. Quality will depend upon recipe balance, ingredients, techniques of mixing and handling of the dough, frying, and subsequent handling after frying.

Normally, a doughnut recipe is considered in balance if it is within the following ratios:

Ingredient	Type Doughnut		
	Cake	Yeast	French (cruller)
Flour, bread*		65 to 100%	50 to 100%
Flour, pastry or cake*	100%	35 to 0%	0 to 50%
Sugar	10 to 50%	8 to 20%	
Eggs, whole	5 to 25%	3 to 15%	125 to 155%
Liquid (water)	50 to 60%	50 to 70%	155%
Shortening	2 to 8%	8 to 20%	30 to 65%
Baking powder, double-acting	2 to 4%		
Salt	½ to 1%	½ to 2%	1 to 2%
Mace, nutmeg, or other spice	¼ to ½%	¼ to ½%	
Vanilla, lemon, or other flavoring	¼ to ½%		
Milk, non-fat dry	5 to 11%	5 to 7%	0 to 3½%
Egg yolks	0 to 16%	2 to 8%	
Yeast		2 to 6%	
Baking ammonia**			0 to ¼%**

*Pastry flour may be used in place of blends of bread and cake flour; overly tender cake doughnuts would result from 100% cake flour unless a quite lean dough is used.
**Best to omit baking ammonia since this breaks down the frying fat.

FIG. 14-34   A variety of cake and yeast doughnuts.

Variation in any of the major ingredients will make it necessary to adjust the others to obtain a desirable product. The qualities desired in a doughnut may be varied oftentimes by the type or quantity of ingredients used. If mixes are used, storage should only be up to three months.

FLOUR

The flour used for cake doughnuts is usually pastry, but where large quantities are made, special soft wheat flours less finely ground than ordinary flour and coming from the middle streams will be used. The coarse texture and lower gluten content of such flours gives a tenderer doughnut. About 5% corn or potato flour may be added to increase tenderness. A flour mixture containing 9 to 10% gluten is usually desirable for cake doughnuts. If a rich dough is made of 50% bread flour, with cake or pastry flour making up the remainder, the cake doughnut will be satisfactory. Lean doughs in which too much gluten development occurs will give a tough, poorly colored doughnut with a large hole. It will have a rough, uneven surface and a poor break; the shape that a doughnut takes in frying is called a "break," a good break being a good circle with a small hole and symmetrical development. The flour used for yeast or cruller doughnuts must be adjusted to dough richness. Because of the structural strength desired in both, some bread flour is always used.

For cake doughnuts, mixing time and dough temperature must be adjusted to the strength of the flour and to dough richness. Strong flours should be mixed a minimum time. If the dough is from 50° to 60° F, or if the flour is weak or the dough is rich, more mixing can occur. If a machine mixer is used, usually mixing from a half to one minute at low speed gives an undermixed cake doughnut, from two to three minutes a good product, and from five to six minutes an overmixed doughnut. Overmixing gives excessive gluten development and a tough product. Sufficient mixing must occur to give a good break and structural strength. Undermixing may give poor color and break, a rough surface, and high grease absorption. When cake doughnuts are cut, mixing must be less to allow for the handling of the dough in rolling out and cutting.

LIQUID

Water is the liquid used in most recipes, and non-fat dry milk solids are added if milk is required. If a dough is too slack, the texture and grain will be poor, and excessive fat absorption and a poor break will occur. If the dough is too stiff, improper break, poor expansion, and a rough, broken surface with deep cracks will result. The liquid is used to control dough temperatures according to the following formula:

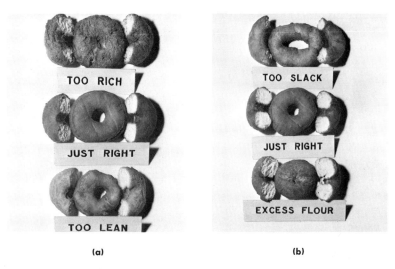

TOO RICH

JUST RIGHT

TOO LEAN

(a)

TOO SLACK

JUST RIGHT

EXCESS FLOUR

(b)

FIG. 14-35 (a) The results of making a cake doughnut too rich, too lean, and just right with sugar and shortening. (b) The results of making a cake doughnut too moist, too stiff, and just right.

$$\frac{(\text{Desired } °F \text{ of dough} \times \text{Final dough wt [lb]}) - (\text{Dry mix } °F \times \text{Its wt [lb]})}{\text{Weight of water (lb)}}$$

equals required water temperature. For example, if a dough is desired at 60° F and five pounds of water are used to ten pounds of dry mix which is at 70° F, the calculation will be: $\dfrac{(60° \text{ F} \times 15) - (70° \text{ F} \times 10)}{5}$ equals 40° F.

The color, keeping qualities, and flavor of cake doughnuts are improved if dry milk solids are added up to 10% of the flour. If more is used, the color may be too dark and the texture tough and soggy. Some French doughnut recipes call for milk to improve color, flavor, and texture.

OTHER INGREDIENTS

Use fine sugar for cake doughnuts so it will go rapidly into solution and reduce mixing. Coarse sugar is apt to give a porous grain, increase grease absorption, and give a poor crust. An excess of sugar in a dough weakens it and gives a coarse, open grain. From 2 to 8% sugar should be used for cake doughnuts made of cake flour, but if pastry flour is used, from 2 to 5½% has been found to be most desirable. An excess of shortening weakens the dough and gives a coarse, open grain and a rough surface. Cracks develop in frying, which invite additional fat absorption. If sugar and shortening are creamed, only sugar twice the weight of the shortening should be added in this process, the remainder being added with the eggs.

Spices and flavorings are added during creaming.

Dried or frozen eggs make good doughnuts. Dry eggs should be added with the dry ingredients, and additional liquid required to give the equivalent of fresh eggs should be added with the liquids used in the recipe. High quality eggs make the best doughnuts. An excess of eggs will give too compact a grain. Eggs are desirable to give structural strength and reduce fat absorption. Egg yolks produce a short doughnut and, if used in excess, will produce the same result as too much shortening. Improved cake doughnuts have been found to result when a mixture of half yolks and half whole eggs is used. If cake or pastry flour is used, more eggs should be added to give a stronger structure. When extra eggs are added, reduce the liquid by 50% of the volume of the eggs. If soft shortening is used, the eggs and sugar may be beaten to a smooth foam and then blended with the soft shortening, a technique quite similar to that explained under cake production when soft fat must be used.

An excess of leavening will give poor grain and texture, an excessively cracked surface, and high fat absorption. An insufficient amount of leavening will give poor expansion and a tight grain. The rate of release of leavening

FIG. 14-36 (a) Using excess baking powder, cutting poorly to give rough edges, and frying in too cold a fat are mistakes which affect doughnut quality.

gas is important in securing a good break. If baking ammonia is used in a French doughnut, the quantity of eggs is reduced slightly, but many bakers avoid ammonia because it breaks down the frying fat.

Mixing

Hand-cutting of cake doughnuts is used when production is occasional and the quantity prepared is small. When the doughnuts are hand-cut,

FIG. 14-37   The results of undermixing, overmixing, and the correct amount of mixing.

the dough must be stiffer than when they are dropped mechanically. To stiffen or soften a dough for machine production, reduce or increase sugar and moisture, either separately or combined. Scale cake doughnuts at one ounce each.

Yeast doughnuts are made in a manner similar to that described for sweet yeast doughs, but the dough should be slightly slack. A 4% yeast to 100% flour will receive its first punch in $1\frac{1}{4}$ to $1\frac{1}{2}$ hours and go to the bench 15 to 20 minutes later. Six pounds of flour will make 13 pounds of dough, yielding about 10 dozen doughnuts. Yeast doughnuts should be given maximum proof before frying. Handle carefully when adding to fat. Machine- or hand-cutting may be used. Scale at $1\frac{1}{2}$ ounce each and proof 10 to 20 minutes before frying. Holes may be made as shown below.

French doughnuts are made in the same manner as described for eclair (choux) paste under quick breads. The batter, preferably warm, is put into a large pastry bag fitted with a large star tube; and about two-inch-diameter circles, slightly under one ounce each, are made, either on greased, heavy brown paper or on a light metal plate. The paper or plate is then care-

FIG. 14-38   A hole can be made in a yeast-raised doughnut by pressing through the center carefully, as shown, just as the doughnut is dropped into the frying fat.

(a)   (b)

FIG. 14-39 To make French doughnuts, make a choux (eclair) type of paste and place on greased paper as shown. Instead of paper, metal plates may be used, sized to fit the fryer. The paper or metal plate is lowered into the fat, and when the doughnuts begin to swell, they free themselves and rise to the top. At this time the paper or metal plate may be removed and the doughnuts fried as shown in (b).

fully slipped into the hot fat, and when the doughnuts free themselves, the paper or plate is removed. The doughnut must be crisped thoroughly before it is removed from the fat, and usually four turns are required to cook it properly. If it is removed from the fat before it is completely cooked, it will collapse for the same reason a cream puff, eclair, or popover collapses if it is not completely cooked before removal from the oven. The serrated edges left by the star tube should appear on the tops of the crullers. French doughnuts may be machine-shaped, if quantities produced are large.

Frying

Cake doughnuts should be fried 1½ to two minutes at 385° to 395° F; 390° F is generally considered best. Yeast doughnuts should be fried two to 2¼ minutes at 360° to 365° F, and French doughnuts two to 2¼ minutes at 365° F. Temperatures must be adjusted so the doughnut is completely cooked when the desired color is obtained. Excessive heat will give a dark doughnut with a raw interior, a tight, compact grain, and low volume. The surface appearance will also be poor. Too low a temperature will give excessive expansion with a poor color, break, and texture and a high fat absorption.

Hand-cut doughnuts should be slid into the fat. If a mechanical dropper is used, it should not be more than two inches above the fat. The surface should not be crowded, and the quantity fried should allow for expansion and turning.

Normal fat absorption will be around three ounces per dozen. Four

FAT ABSORPTION IN RELATION TO FRYING TEMPERATURE AND DOUGH RICHNESS

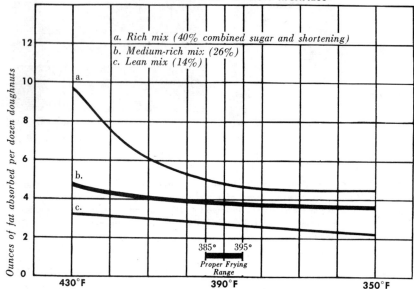

Frying Temperature

FIG. 14-40 Fat from 385° to 395° F fries the doughnut rapidly and seals the surface. This reduces fat absorption. Lower temperatures do not seal the surface as rapidly, and thus the doughnut absorbs more fat. Above 395° F absorption is less, but the danger of scorching or of breaking down the fat is greatly increased.

ounces or more is considered excessive. If too much fat is absorbed quality is lost and cost increased. Desirable absorption is three ounces per dozen. Factors which might increase fat absorption are undermixed dough, an overly rich or too cold dough, excessive leavening, poor shape, rough surfaces which increase the surface area exposed, and poor quality or handling of the fat. Increasing flour may decrease absorption, but increasing eggs or liquids in some doughs may retard it. Proper selection of the frying fat is important, not only for quality but also for long frying life.

When hand-frying, turn doughnuts as soon as they come to the top of the fat. Some operators use a screen to hold the doughnuts beneath the fat, thus doing away with turning. Automatic fryers drop the doughnut, turn it, and remove it from the fat. Many machines automatically keep the frying fat at desired levels.

Finishing

Doughnuts may be dipped into various coating materials. Cool to 80° F before coating in granulated sugar, crumbs, chocolate, powdered sugar, chopped nuts, or other coatings. If they are dipped while warm, escaping

FIG. 14-41   Choux (eclair) paste can be given many shapes to give many types of desserts. In the upper row, shapes are shown to make the body, head, and neck of a swan. A basket handle may be made to use for a basket. Eclairs and cream puffs are also shown.

moisture will soak the coating. If the doughnuts are greasy, the coating may also appear soaked. Good coatings may also be destroyed by improper storage. Powdered sugar coatings may be stabilized somewhat if from 5 to 10% starch or non-fat dry milk is added. A fondant or plain powdered sugar icing will soak less if some fat, 10 to 15% of the total icing weight, is creamed into the icing. A glaze consisting of 40% water, 10% glucose or 5% invert sugar, 1/10% cream of tartar or 3% glycerine brought to a boil, with 100% 4 to 6X sugar and 1% gelatin stirred in after removal from the fire, will be satisfactory for the dipping of cake or yeast doughnuts. The glaze should be at around 110° F when the hot doughnuts are dipped. They are then placed on a wire screen over a pan, and the excess glaze drips off. Doughnuts may be iced and decorated with various products. Yeast doughnuts are best dipped into fine granulated sugar or sugar and cinnamon, or glazed. Yeast doughnuts, and especially longjohns and bismarcks, may be filled with jellies or jams, custards, marshmallows, or butter creams and occasionally with whipped cream or fresh fruit fillings. Consistency of fillings is important; if too soft, they will soak, and if too firm, they will not work well in filling, giving a pasty texture to the doughnut. Most doughnuts are filled with a cream puff filler or similar machine. Occasionally French doughnuts are filled, but most often they are merely dusted with powdered sugar, or a plain fondant or a butter cream icing may be brushed over them.

Bibliography

General

Bryan, Mary de Garmo, *The School Cafeteria*, Appleton-Century-Crofts, New York, 1938.

Dunning, Frances, *Standards for Cafeteria Service*, Burgess Publishing Co., Minneapolis, 1949.

Fitch, Natalie K., and Francis, Charlotte A., *Foods and Principles of Cookery*, Prentice-Hall, Inc., New York, 1948.

Halliday, Evelyn G., and Noble, Isabel T., *Food Chemistry and Cookery*, University of Chicago Press, Chicago, 1943.

Harris, Florence LaGanne, and Henderson, Ruth Adele, *Foods, Their Nutritive, Economic and Social Values*, D. C. Heath and Co., Boston, 1954.

Huges, Osee, *Introductory Foods*, 3rd ed., The Macmillan Company, New York, 1955.

Justin, Margaret M.; Rust, Lucile Osborn; and Vail, Gladys E., *Foods*, 4th ed., Houghton Mifflin Co., Boston, 1956.

Lowe, Belle, *Experimental Cookery*, 7th ed., John Wiley & Sons, Inc., New York, 1955.

Macleod, Annie L., and Mason, Edith H., *Chemistry in Cookery*, 2nd ed., McGraw-Hill Book Co., Inc., New York, 1937.

Stanley, Louise, and Cline, Jessie, *Foods, Their Selection and Preparation*, Ginn and Co., Boston, 1950.

Sweetman, Marion D., *Food Selection and Preparation*, 3rd ed., John Wiley & Sons, Inc., New York, 1943.

U. S. Department of Health, Education, and Welfare, *Quantity Food Preparation, a Curriculum Guide*, Circular No. 526, Washington, 1958.

U. S. Navy, *Applied Cookery*, Navsanda Publication 277, Washington, November 1955.

Ward, Artemas, *Encyclopedia of Food*, Peter Smith Press, New York, 1941.

Welch, John M., *Instructor's Guide*, Extension Service, University of Missouri, Columbia, 1963.

West, Bessie Brooks, and Wood, Levelle, *Food Service in Institutions*, 3rd ed., John Wiley & Sons, Inc., New York, 1955.

Williams, Matthieu, *Chemistry of Cooking*, Appleton & Co., New York, 1906.

Planning

Aldrich, Pearl J., "Tailor-made Recipes for Modern Service," *Journal of American Dietetic Association* 31, No. 9, September 1955, pp. 898-900.

American Home Economics Association, *Handbook of Food Preparation*, revised ed., Washington, 1959.

Callahan, James, and Aldrich, Paul J., "New Methods of Calculating Yield Recipes," *Journal of American Dietetic Association* 35, No. 11, November 1953, p. 1089-93.

Callahan, James, "Recipe Expansion Made Easy," *Institutions* 46, No. 2, February 1960, pp. 116-18.

Cranmore, Mary K., "How to Set Up a Master Recipe File," *Food Service* 22, No. 10, October 1960, pp. 37-41, 76-79.

Department of Food Economics and Nutrition, School of Home Economics, Kansas State College, *Practical Cookery*, 21st edition, Wiley & Sons, Inc., New York, 1947.

Easton, Alice, *More Meat for your Money*, Dahl Publishing Co., Stamford, Conn., 1946.

Easton, Alice, *Recipes and Menus for Restaurant Profits*, Dahl Publishing Co., Stamford, Conn., 1941.

Ericson, Myrtle H., "Recipe Standardization," *Cornell University Hotel and Restaurant Quarterly* 1, No. 1, May 1960, pp. 55-59.

Farmer, Fannie M., *Boston Cooking School Cook Book*, Little Brown & Co., Boston, 1946.

Fowler, Sina Faye; West, Bessie Brooks; and Grace Shugart, *Foods for Fifty*, 4th ed., John Wiley & Sons, Inc., New York, 1961.

Gray, Madeline, and Vass, De Lo Padua, *How to Cook for Profit*, Greenberg, New York, 1947.

Hart, Constance C., *Recipes at Moderate Cost for School, Institution and Commercial Food Service*, 2nd ed., Appleton-Century-Crofts, New York, 1942.

Janssen, Pearl Z., "Recipe Construction," *Journal of American Dietetic Association* 29, No. 2, February 1953, pp. 125-30.

Janssen, Pearl Z., "Up-to-date Recipes," *Journal of American Dietetic Association* 34, No. 2, February 1958, pp. 133-37.

Kinder, Faye, *Meal Management*, The Macmillan Co., New York, 1956.

King, Florence B., and Kirkpatrick, Mary E., *Manual for Food Preparation Study*, John Wiley & Sons, Inc., New York, 1941.

Kraft Foods Co., *Tested Quantity Recipes*, Chicago, n.d.

Libby, McNeill, and Libby, *A Quantity Recipe Book*, Chicago, n. d.

MacFarlane, Alberta M., "Standardized Recipe System Works," *Institutions* 44, No. 1, January 1959, pp. 13-20.

McLean, Beth, *Meal Planning and Table Service*, Charles A. Bennet Co., Inc., Peoria, Ill., 1949.

National Canners Association, Home Economics Division, *Canned Foods Recipes*, Washington, 1946.

Richards, Lenore, and Treat, Nola, *Quantity Cookery*, Little, Brown & Co., Boston, 1939.

Simpson, Jean T., and Taylor, Demetria M., *The Frozen Food Cook Book*, Simon and Schuster, New York, 1948.

Smith, Evelyn A., *Handbook on Quantity Food Management*, Burgess Publishing Co., Minneapolis, 1955.

Smith, Frances Lowe, and Stoddard, Florence B., *Recipes and Menus for Fifty*, M. Barrows & Co., Inc., New York, 1948.

Sullivan, Lenore, *Quantity Recipe File*, Iowa State Press, Ames, Iowa, n.d.

Sutherland, Elizabeth, and Nelson, Mabel P., *Food Preparation*, 5th ed., Wm. C. Brown Co., Dubuque, Iowa, 1958.

Terrell, Margaret E., *Large Quantity Recipes*, J. B. Lippincott, Philadelphia, 1951.

U. S. Department of Agriculture, *Planning Food for Institutions*, Agr. Handbook No. 16, Washington, 1951.

U. S. Department of Agriculture, *Food Yields*, Agr. Handbook No. 102, Washington, 1956.

U. S. Department of Commerce, *Establishing and Operating a Restaurant*, Washington, 1957.

U. S. Navy, *Navy Recipe Service*, Washington, 1962.

Voegele, Marguerite C., and Woolley, Grace C., *Menu Dictionary*, Ahrens Publishing Co., Inc., New York, 1961.

Welch, John M., "Analyze Your Food Cost," Circular 723, Agr. Extension Station, University of Missouri, Columbia, Mo., 1960.

Welch, John M., "Standardizing Recipes," Paper No. 2362, Agr. Extension Station, University of Missouri, Columbia, Mo., 1961.

Wenzel, George L., *Wenzel's Menu Maker*, Austin, Texas, pub. by the author, 1948.

Work Methods

Alford, L. P., *Principles of Industrial Management*, The Ronald Press Company, New York, 1940.

Barnes, Ralph M., *Motion and Time Study*, John Wiley & Sons, Inc., New York, 1958.

Kotschevar, Lendal H., "Cut Costs with Better Work Methods, Part I," *Drive-in Management*, Duluth, Minn., January 1963, pp. 38-40.

Kotschevar, Lendal H., "Cut Costs with Better Work Methods, Part II," *Drive-in Management*, Duluth, Minn., February 1963, pp. 40-43.

Kotschevar, Lendal H., "Cut Costs with Better Work Methods, Part III," *Drive-in Management*, Duluth, Minn., March 1963, pp. 38-41.

Kotschevar, Lendal H., "Standards for Labor Control," *Drive-in Management*, Duluth, Minn., August 1963, pp. 28-29, 50.

Kotschevar, Lendal H., *Work Simplification*, 2nd ed., *Institutions Magazine*, Chicago, 1962.

Kotschevar, Lendal H., and Terrell, Margaret E., *Food Service Planning*, John Wiley & Sons, Inc., New York, 1961.

Niebel, B. W., *Motion and Time Study*, Richard D. Irwin, Homewood, Illinois, 1955.

Schell, Erwin Haskell, *Production Line Technique*, McGraw-Hill Book Company, New York, 1944.

Sanitation

Adams, H. S., *Milk and Food Sanitation Practice*, The Commonwealth Fund, New York, 1947.

Bryan, Arthur H., and Bryan, Charles G., *Principles and Practices of Bacteriology*, College Outline Series, Barnes and Noble, New York, 1955.

Dack, Gail Monroe, *Food Poisoning*, 3rd ed., Chicago University Press, Chicago, 1959.

Robinson, Arthur C., *Food and Beverage Service Workers Manual*, Washington State Department of Health, Division of Public Health Engineering, Olympia, Washington, 1955.

Yaffee, Charles D.; Byers, Sohrman H.; and Hosey, Andrew D. (technical editors), *Encyclopedia of Instrumentation for Industrial Hygiene*, University of Michigan Institute of Industrial Health, Ann Arbor, 1956.

Salads, Sandwiches, Appetizers

American Baking Institute, Consumer Service Department, *Modern Sandwich Methods*, Chicago, 1952.

American Baking Institute, Consumer Service Department, *Turn to Sandwiches*, Chicago, 1957.

DeGouy, Louis P., *Sandwich Manual for Professionals*, Dahl Publishing Co., Stamford, Conn., 1939.

Duffy, Patrick G., *The Standard Bartender's Guide*, Revised, Permabooks, New York, 1962.

Elliott, Janet, "A Sandwich Symposium," reprint from *Vend Magazine*, Chicago, 1962.

Fruit Dispatch Co., Home Economics Department, *Banana Salad Bazaar*, New York, 1941.

General Foods, Inc., *Album of Jellied Salads and Aspics*, White Plains, New York, 1955.

Good Housekeeping's Sandwich Manual, Hearst Corporation, New York, 1961.

Knox Gelatine Company, *Knox Gelatin Book*, Johnstown, New York, 1958.

National Restaurant Association, *NRA News*, Vol. 1, No. 5, June 1958.

National Restaurant Association, *Sandwich Maker's Album*, Chicago, 1956.

National Restaurant Association, *Sandwich Meals Are Profitable*, Technical Bulletin 122, Chicago, 1956.

National Restaurant Association, "Sandwich Time," *NRA Ad Builder*, Chicago, 1957.

Pierre, J. Berard, *Pierre's 60 Profitable Sandwiches*, No. 14, Dahl Publishing Co., Stamford, Conn., n. d.

Shircliffe, Arnold, *The Edgewater Beach Hotel Salad Book*, Hotel Monthly Press, Evanston, Ill., 1930.

Sunkist Growers, Inc., *Fresh Citrus Quantity Handbook*, Los Angeles, 1959.

Swift & Company, *Helpful Hints on Salad Dressing Preparation*, Chicago, January 1955.

U. S. Department of Health, Education, and Welfare, Food and Drug Administration, *Dressings for Foods*, Washington, June 1957.

Stocks, Sauces, Soups, and Gravies

Breithaupt, Hermann A., *Commercial Cooking for Prospective Hotel and Restaurant Workers*, TCH Pub. 3-936, File No. 3008, Chadsey High School, Trade Division, Board of Education, City of Detroit, 1959.

Breland, John H., *Chef's Guide to Quantity Cookery*, Harper and Bros., New York, 1947.

Culinary Institute of America, Inc., *Professional Quantity Cooking*, Dahl Publishing Co., Stamford, Conn., 1958.

Culinary Institute of America, Inc., *Professional Quantity Cooking, Basic Courses, Method and Formulas*, Dahl Publishing Co., Stamford, Conn., 1957.

Culinary Institute of America, Inc., *The Professional Chef*, revised ed., Institutions, Chicago, 1963.

Diat, Louis, *Cooking a la Ritz*, J. B. Lippincott Co., Philadelphia, 1941.

Escoffier, A., *The Escoffier Cook Book*, Crown Publishers, New York, 1959.

Fellows, Charles, *A Selection of Dishes and Chef's Reminder*, The Hotel Monthly Press, John Willy, Inc., Evanston, Ill., 1944.

Fellows, Charles, *The Culinary Handbook*, The Hotel Monthly Press, John Willy, Inc., Evanston, Ill., n. d.

Fougner, G. Selmer, *Gourmet Dinners*, M. Barrows and Co., Inc., New York, 1941.

Gancel, J., *Culinary Encyclopedia of Modern Cooking*. 7th ed., Van Rees Press, New York, 1920.

Given, Meta, *Modern Encyclopedia of Cooking*, J. G. Ferguson and Associates, Chicago, 1954.

Hirtzler, Victor, *Hotel St. Francis Cook Book*, The Hotel Monthly Press, John Willy, Inc., Evanston, Ill., n. d.

Ranhofer, Charles, *Epicurean*, The Hotel Monthly Press, John Willy, Inc., Evanston, Ill., 1920.

Shircliffe, Arnold, *Principles of Cooking*, Naval Air Technical Training Center, NTSCH (Cooks and Bakers), 1942. (Out of print.)

Beverages

Campbell, C. L.; Dawes, R. K.; Deolalkar, S.; and Merritt, M. C., *Effects of Certain Chemicals in Water On the Flavor of Brewed Coffee*, The Coffee Brewing Institute, Inc., Publication No. 38, New York, March 1958.

Clements, Robert L., and Deatherage, F. F., *Chemical Study of Coffee Flavor*, The Coffee Brewing Institute, Inc., Publication No. 26, New York, October 1957.

Gardner, D. G., *Water Composition and Coffee Brewing*, The Coffee Brewing Institute, Inc., Publication No. 31, New York, March 1958.

Lentner, C., and Deatherage, F.F., *Organic Acids in Coffee in Relation to The Degree of Roasting*, The Coffee Brewing Institute, Inc., Publication No. 45, New York, 1958.

Little, Angela C.; Chichester, C. O.; and Mackinney, G., *On The Color of Coffee, II*, The Coffee Brewing Institute, Inc., Publication No. 37, New York, November 1958.

Little, Angela C.; Chichester, C. O.; and Mackinney, G., *On the Color of Coffee, III, Effect of Roasting Conditions on Flavor Development for a Given Color. Role of Initial Moisture Level on Roasting Characteristics of Green Coffee Beans*, The Coffee Brewing Institute, Inc., Publication No. 48, New York, May 1959.

Lockhart, Ernest E., *Characteristics of Coffee Relation to Beverage Quality*, The Coffee Brewing Institute, Inc., Publication No. 40, New York, May 1959.

Lockhart, Ernest E. *Chemistry of Coffee*, The Coffee Brewing Institute, Inc., Publication No. 25, New York, September 1957.

Lockhart, Ernest E., *Coffee Grinds, II, Classification and Analysis*, The Coffee Brewing Institute, Inc., Publication No. 39, New York, 1959.

Lockhart, Ernest E., *Coffee Solubles and Beverage Acceptance*, The Coffee Brewing Institute, Inc., Publication No. 27, New York, November 1957.

Lockhart, Ernest E., *Storage Properties of Vacuum Packed Coffee*, The Coffee Brewing Institute, Inc., Publication No. 30, New York, February 1958.

Lockhart, Ernest E., *The Coffee Hydrometer*, The Coffee Brewing Institute, Inc., Publication No. 43, New York, February 1958.

Lockhart, Ernest E., *The Strength of Coffee*, The Coffee Brewing Institute. Inc., Publication No. 44, New York, October 1959.

Lockhart, Ernest E.; Tucker, C. L.; and Merritt, M. C., *Water Impurities and Brewed Coffee Flavor*, The Coffee Brewing Institute, Inc., Publication No. 6, New York, February 1956.

Merritt, M. C., and Proctor, Bernard E., *Effect of Temperature During The Roasting Cycle On Selected Components of Different Types of Whole Bean Coffee*, The Coffee Brewing Institute, Inc., Publication No. 46, New York, November 1958.

Merritt, M. C., and Proctor, Bernard E., *Extraction Rates For Selected Components in Coffee Brew*, The Coffee Brewing Institute, Inc., Publication No. 47, New York, November 1958.

Niven, W. W., Jr., and Shaw, B. C., *Critical Conditions for Quantity Coffee Brewing*, The Coffee Brewing Institute, Inc., Publication No. 19, New York, April 1957.

Nejelski & Company, Inc., *Survey of Beverage Coffee*, The Coffee Brewing Institute, Inc., Publication No. 5, New York, January 1956.

Ruffley, J., *About Good Coffee*, Research Department Bulletin, No. 21, National Restaurant Association, Chicago, Ill., 1958.

Rhoades, John W., *Coffee Aroma Analysis By Gas Chromatography*, The Coffee Brewing Institute, Inc., Publication No. 34, New York, July 1958.

Segall, Stanley, and Proctor, Bernard E., *The Influence of High Temperature Holding Upon the Components of Coffee Brew*, The Coffee Brewing Institute, Inc., Publication No. 41, New York, January 1960.

Segall, Stanley, and Proctor, Bernard E., *The Influence of High Temperature Holding Upon the Components of Coffee Brew, II, Volatile Reducing Substances*, The Coffee Brewing Institute, Inc., Publication No. 42, New York, August 1959.

Dairy and Eggs

Aldrich, Pearl J., and Miller, Grace A., *A New Milky Way for Your Own Favorite Quantity Recipes*, Circular Bulletin 225, Agr. Experimental Station, Michigan State University, East Lansing, April 1958.

Aldrich, Pearl J., and Miller, Grace A., *Whole and Nonfat Dry Milk in Quantity Food Preparation*, Circular Bulletin 223, Agr. Experimental Station, Michigan State University, October 1956.

American Dry Milk Institute, *Quantity Recipes*, Bulletin 503, Chicago, 1947.

Domestic Engineering, *Poultry and Egg Specialties*, Institutions Magazine, Chicago, 1957.

"Faster Eggs," *Fast Foods Magazine*, January 1961, pp. 64-66.

National Dairy Council, *Newer Knowledge of Cheese*, revised ed., Chicago, 1954.

National Dairy Council, *Newer Knowledge of Milk*, revised, Chicago, 1954.

Poultry and Egg National Board, *Eggs*, Chicago, n. d.

Poultry and Egg National Board, *Ways with Eggs*, Chicago, n. d.

U. S. Department of Agriculture, Human Nutrition Research Branch, *Cooking with Dried Egg*, Bulletin No. 50, Washington, 1956.

U. S. Department of Agriculture, Human Nutrition Research Branch, *Milk and Its Products, Facts for Consumer Education*, Washington, May 1954.

Vegetables

Cruess, W. V., and MacKinney, G., *The Dehydration of Vegetables*, Bulletin 680, Agr. Experimental Station, University of California, Berkeley, 1943.

Frozen Food Distributors Association of California, Inc., *A Short Course in Frozen Food Cookery*, San Francisco, 1949.

MacFarlane, Alberta M., *Cooking the Modern Way*, Groen Mfg. Co., Chicago, 1953.

MacFarlane, Alberta M., *Cooking with Steam*, Market Forge Co., Cleveland, Ohio, 1946.

MacFarlane, Alberta M., *Economical Gourmet Entrees*, Durum Wheat Institute, Chicago, 1958.

National Restaurant Association, *White Potatoes*, Technical Bulletin No. 101, Chicago, 1953.

Olsen, Grace E., "Fresh versus Pre-processed Vegetables," *Journal American Dietetic Association* 30, No. 8, August 1954, pp. 762-68.

U. S. Army, *Cooking Dehydrated Foods, TM* 10-406, Washington, 1943.

U. S. Department of Agriculture, Human Nutrition Research Division, *Green Vegetables for Good Eating*, Bulletin 41, Washington, October 1954.

U. S. Department of Agriculture, Human Nutrition Research Division, *Potatoes in Popular Ways*, Bulletin 55, Washington, 1957.

U. S. Department of Agriculture, Economic Research Division, *Use of Frozen Foods by Restaurants*, Marketing Research Report No. 144, AMS, Washington, 1956.

Meats, Fish, and Poultry

American Lamb Council, *Outdoor Barbecuing*, AIC Bulletin No. 8, Denver, Colo., 1960.

Holland, Madeline, *Fact Sheet on Frozen Meat*, American Meat Institute, Chicago, 1956.

National Livestock and Meat Board, *Cooking Meat in Quantity*, 2nd ed., Chicago, n. d.

National Livestock and Meat Board, *Meat Manual*, 4th ed., Chicago, 1950.

National Livestock and Meat Board, *Ten Lessons on Meat*, 7th ed., revised, Chicago, n. d.

National Restaurant Association, *Fish*, Special Bulletin No. 111, Chicago, 1953.

National Restaurant Association, *Turkey*, Research Bulletin, Chicago, n. d.

National Turkey Federation, *Turkey Handbook*, Mount Morris, Ill., n. d.

Patrick, George, "The Fabulous Fry Kettle," *Food Service Magazine*, No. 10, October 1957, pp. 30-34.

Poultry and Egg National Board, *Golden Treasury of Turkey Cookery*, Chicago, 1953.

Proctor & Gamble Research Kitchens, Cincinnati, Ohio:

    The Art of Preparing French Fried Potatoes, 1950.

    The Chicken Book, 1957.

    Deep Frying Pointers, 1958.

    Turnovers and Dumplings, 1952.

    Proper Frying, n. d.

"Profits from Turkey," *Restaurant Management*, October 1959, pp. 38-42, 68-71.

Ruffley, J. J., "How to Use Deep Fat Frying Effectively," *National Restaurant News*, August 1957, pp. 10-13.

Staggs, Reba, *Meat Cookery the Modern Way*, talk before Electrical Women's Round Table, Inc., January 25, 1950, New York City, published by National Livestock and Meat Board, Chicago.

U. S. Department of Interior, Washington 25:

    Burtis, Jean, and Kerr, Rose G., *How to Cook Crabs*, Bulletin No. 10, 1956.

    Burtis, Jean, and Kerr, Rose G., *How to Cook Shrimp*, Bulletin No. 7, 1958.

    Kerr, Rose G., *Fish Cookery for 100*, No. 1, 1957.

    Kerr, Rose G., *Basic Fish Cookery*, No. 2, 1957.

    Kerr, Rose G., and Burtis, Jean, *How to Cook Oysters*, No. 3, 1957.

    Osterhaug, Kathryn L., and Kerr, Rose G., *How to Cook Salmon*, No. 4, 1958.

    Osterhaug, Kathryn L., and Kerr, Rose G., *How to Cook Clams*, No. 8, 1958.

    Osterhaug, Kathryn L., and Kerr, Rose G., *How to Cook Halibut*, No. 9, 1957.

Bakery Ingredients

Bialey, L. H., *Development and Use of Baking Powder and Chemicals*, U. S. Department of Agriculture, Circular No. 138, Washington, May 1940.

General Foods Corporation, *Baking Powder in Action*, White Plains, New York, 1934.

(See also general references in bibliography.)

Breads

American Institute of Baking, *Freezing of Danish Pastry*, No. 100, Chicago, 1961.

Procter and Gamble Bakery Service, *Make-up Ideas for Sweet Doughs*, Cincinnati, Ohio, 1952.

Richards, Paul, *Breads, Rolls and Sweet Doughs*, Baker's Helper Press, Chicago, 1946.

Snyder, Clara Bebhard, *ABC, A Primer of Bread Baking*, Wheat Flour Institute, Chicago, 1952.

Wilfahrt, Julius E., *Treatise on Baking*, Standard Brands, Inc., New York, 1950. (Out of print.)

U. S. Department of Agriculture, *Bread*, AIB, No. 142, Washington, November 1955.

U. S. Department of the Army, *Bread Baking*, TM 10-410, Washington, 1956.

Pies, Cakes, and Desserts

Amendola, Joseph, *The Baker's Manual*, 2nd ed., revised, Ohrens Publishing Co., New York, 1960.

American Dry Milk Institute, *Cakes*, Bulletin No. 102, Chicago, 1953.

Bisno, Lou, "Pie Production," *Baker's Digest*, April 1962, pp. 81-89.

Briant, Alice M., *et al.*, "Variations in Quality of Cream Pies," *Journal of the American Dietetic Association*, No. 7, July 1954, pp. 678-81.

California Prune Advisory Board, *Full O'Prunes*, Flanley and Woodward, Inc., New York, 1958.

Corn Products Sales, Co., *Snow Flake Milo Starch for Pie Fillings*, New York, 1957.

De Gouy, Louis P., *Soda Fountain and Luncheonette Drinks and Recipes*, Dahl Publishing Co., Stamford, Conn., 1940.

Ice Cream Merchandising Institute, Inc., *Ice Cream Profit Maker*, Nos. 1, 2, 3, and 4, Washington, 1956.

Fisher, Harry S., "Starch Helps Flavor," *Baker's Review*, August 1958.

Ford, Thomas W., "New Starch for Fruit Pies," *Baker's Weekly*, 1957.

Fruit Dispatch Company, *Banana Recipes for Large Service*, New York, 1941.

Fruit Dispatch Company, *Bakery Formulas Using Fresh Ripe Bananas*, New York, 1941.

General Electric, *Ice Cream Recipes for the U. S. Navy*, Bloomfield, N. J., 1944.

General Mills, *Quality Cakes and Icings*, revised ed., Minneapolis, Minn., 1959.

"Great Dessert Dilemma," *Drive-In Restaurant*, September 1961, pp. 7-9.

Handy, Etta H., *Ice Cream for Small Plants*, Hotel Monthly Press, John Willy Co., Evanston, Ill., 1937.

Henderich, George W., *Let's Sell Ice Cream*, Ice Cream Merchandising Institute, Inc., Washington, 1952.

Kite, Frances E., *et al.*, "Thick-boiling Starches," *Baker's Digest*, August 1957.

Meister, John E., *Vest Pocket Pastry Book*, Hotel Monthly Press, Evanston, Ill., n. d.

Meloripe Fruit Company, *Bananas and How to Serve Them*, Boston, 1941.

National Restaurant Association, *Pies*, Technical Bulletin No. 121, Chicago, 1953.

National Starch Products, *Clearjel—a Fruit Pie Stabilizer*, New York, n.d.

Otterbacher, T. J., and Kite, Frances E., "The Milo Starches," *Baker's Digest*, October 1958, pp. 19-24.

Processed Apples Institute, Flanley and Woodward, Inc., New York:
Happy Apple Recipes, 1957.
New Quantity Recipes, 1959.

Taste-tempting Recipes, January 1961.

Procter and Gamble Research Department, Cincinnati, Ohio:
   Dollars from Doughnuts, 1950.
   High Ratio Cakes, 1956.
   The Evolution of a Cake Formula and Formula Balance, 1942.
   Pie Formulas, 1940.
   Quality Pies, 1940.

Prouty, W. W., "Quality Evaluation of Baked Products, Pastry and Cake," *Baker's Digest.* April 1962, pp. 71-77.

Richards, Paul, *Pastry for the Restaurant,* Hotel Monthly Press, Evanston, Ill., n. d.

"The Great Dessert Dilemma," *Drive-In Restaurant,* September 1961, pp 7-9.

Tricks of the Trade. Lyons Magnus, Inc., San Francisco, n.d.

Wilfahrt, Julius E., *Treatise on Cake Making,* Standard Brands, Inc., New York, 1950. (Out of print.)

Wilton, McKinley, and Wilton, Norman, *Cake Decorating,* 1st ed., Wilton Enterprises, Inc., Chicago, 1960.

Wilton, McKinley, and Wilton, Norman, *Modern Cake Decorating,* 2nd ed., Wilton Enterprises, Inc., Chicago, 1954.

Glossary of Terms
Used in
Cooking and Food Service

Glossary[1]

A la, a le, (au, aux)	*To the, with, at* or *in;* in the mode of style; *a la Colbert,* with Colbert sauce; *au jus,* with natural juice; *a la moutarde,* in mustard.
Abaisse	Thin bottom or under crust.
Abalone	Tenderized, thin muscle of a large sea snail; the portion looks much like a veal cutlet in shape and is like a scallop in texture, flavor, and color.
Abatis	Giblets; *abatis,* heads, liver, kidneys, giblets, and so forth.
Absinthe	A liqueur having a licorice-like flavor.
Acids	Acidulated liquids used in cooking, such as plain or seasoned vinegar, lemon juice, tomato juice, and other tart liquids.
Agar Agar	Seaweed product with gelatinous properties used to make permanent emulsions.
Aide	Kitchen or dining room helper.
Aiguilettes	Small strips of cooked meat; stuffed puff pastes served as hors d'oeuvres.
Ail	Garlic; *aillade* or *aioli,* mayonnaise garlic sauce that may also contain mustard.
A la king	With cream or bechamel sauce containing mushrooms, green peppers, and pimientos.
A la mode	In the usual fashion; *boeuf a la mode,* braised larded beef; *cake or pie a la mode,* topped with ice cream.
Alimentary Pastes	Macaroni products, rice, and so forth.
Allemande	Velouté sauce thickened with egg yolks, *a l'allemande,* German style.
Almond	*Amande* (Fr.); *a l'amande,* slivered almonds sautéed lightly in butter and served over fish; *amandine,* served with almonds.
Almond Paste	Ground almonds, sugar, and egg whites; also called marzipan.
Ambrosia	A mixture of fruit and coconut used as a dessert; *ambrasin* (Fr).
Amontillado	A semi-dry sherry.

[1]Diacritical markings to indicate pronounciation in many foreign words are omitted in this text. The author has taken the viewpoint that these words are now so commonly used in the food service field that in a text of this type such markings are not necessary. Many of these words may now be considered to be Anglicized. For instance, there is no longer a need to write *purée* when we no longer write *fricassee* with the accent. To avoid mispronunciation, the author has at times used the markings. This should be taken, not as a lack of consistency, but as a necessary guide to those not acquainted with such terms.

Anchovy	A small salted fish used for appetizers and seasoning; *anchois* (Fr).
Andalouse	Spanish style; mayonnaise mixed with heavy red tomato puree and perhaps chopped peppers and pimentos; not to be confused with our Spanish sauce made of whole tomatoes, onion, peppers, and garlic, which is more heavily seasoned.
Angel Food	A white cake leavened with egg whites.
Angels on Horseback	Oysters broiled with strips of bacon around them and served on toast.
Anisette	A cordial heavily flavored with anise seed, giving it a licorice flavor.
Annatto	A yellow food coloring frequently used to color cheese and butter.
Antipasto	Italian hors d'oeuvres, relishes, and other foods used as a first course or as snacks.
Arroz con Pollo	A Spanish dish of chicken and rice; the sauce usually has tomatoes in it.
Artichoke	*Artichaut* (Fr); bud of a plant belonging to the thistle family and usually called Globe or French artichoke in contrast to the Jerusalem or Girasole artichoke, which is a tuber resembling a potato.
Aspic	Gelatin-set mixture; may be clear or seasoned with meat stock, spices, tomato puree, or other foods; may be used as a glaze or as a body in which to set other foods.
Attereaux	Skewers; to alternate pieces of food on a skewer and then bake or broil or cook.
Au Beurre	Cooked in butter.
Au Bleu	Live fish stunned with a sharp blow on the head, cleaned quickly, and plunged into a boiling, acidulated liquid or court bouillon; the flesh turns slightly blue.
Au Four	Baked in an oven; *petit fours,* small cakes; *paté de petit four.* pastry of the little oven; *four* is French for oven.
Au Gras	See *gras (au).*
Au Gratin	Escalloped and covered with cheese; food covered with a sauce (usually cream or bechamel), sprinkled with crumbs and cheese, and baked; cheese may be omitted.
Au Lait	With milk.
Au Jus	With natural gravy.
Au Maigre	With no meat; a Lenten dish.
Au Naturel	According to nature; cooked simply, or uncooked.
Baba	A light yeast raised cake or rich sweetened bread; usually served soaked with rum and called baba rum (see *brioche*).
Bagels	Crisp hard rolls in the shape of a ring, frequently served with lox (salmon) during Jewish holidays.
Bagration	Fish-base soup, made from a thin velouté, cooked macaroni, sole, fish quenelles, crayfish, and so forth; the macaroni and velouté base are the characteristic features.
Bain-Marie	A hot-water bath for holding foods for service; a double boiler in which foods are cooked.
Bake	To cook by dry heat; now usually done in an oven, but occasionally in ashes, under coals, or on heated stones or metals; when

	applied to meats it is called roasting.
Baked Alaska	Ice cream on cake covered with meringue and baked in a quick oven.
Banbury	A small tart filled with spiced citrus peels and raisins; also a small round English cheese.
Bannock	Scotch cake made usually of oatmeal or ground barley.
Barbecue	To roast slowly on a gridiron or spit, or over coals, or on hot stones in a covered pit or trench; while cooking, the food is usually basted with a highly seasoned sauce, or it may be cooked in the sauce, which is made of tomato catsup or puree, chili sauce, mustard, vinegar, spices, chopped vegetables, and perhaps some sweetening.
Barde	Bacon or salt pork slices used to cover poultry or fish in roasting.
Bar-le-Duc	A preserve of white currants, but also may be red currant jelly, gooseberry, strawberry, or other fruit preserve; seeds should be removed.
Baron	Double sirloin of beef; saddle and leg of lamb or mutton.
Barquettes	Small pastry shells for filling for hors d'oeuvres or desserts.
Baste	To moisten food while cooking for added flavor or to prevent drying out; the liquid is usually melted fat, meat drippings, stock, water, water and fat, or a sauce.
Batter-dip	To dip into a batter consisting of egg, milk, flour, salt, leavening, and perhaps sugar; used for deep-frying.
Bavarian	A fruit gelatin mixture into which whipped cream has been folded before setting; called also bavarian cream; Fr. *bavarois*.
Bearnaise	Hollandaise sauce seasoned with tarragon; *a la bearnaise*, Swiss style; means from Berne, Switzerland.
Beat	To mix vigorously to incorporate air.
Beaten Biscuit	A Southern unleavened bread made light by pounding and folding; phosphates have usually been added to the flour.
Bechamel	One of the basic sauces; made of chicken or veal stock, thickened with *roux*, and finished with rich milk or cream.
Beef Steak Pie	A meat pie, two-thirds beef and one-third kidneys, with vegetables in a gravy; baked with a biscuit crust.
Beignets	Fritters.
Bel Paese	A soft, rich Italian cheese.
Benedictine	Orange-flavored liqueur originated by Benedictine monks.
Bercy	A sauce of white wine or lemon juice, onions, meat marrow, demiglaze, and melted butter; a fish sauce.
Beurre	See *butter*.
Bifsteck	A steak cut from the butt or large end of the beef tenderloin, weighing about 5 to 6 ounces.
Bigarrade	Brown sauce seasoned with orange peel and juice; may be slightly sweet and used with roast duck; the sour and bitter Seville orange is best to use, if available.
Bill of Fare	The menu.
Biscuit	A small roll, either yeast or quick bread; a rusk, toast, and so forth; in French *biscotte* usually means a rusk.
Bisque	A thick cream soup made of shellfish; also indicates a frozen dessert, ice cream with finely chopped nuts added.

Blanc	White; white sauce.
Blanch	To precook or cook in boiling water or steam (1) to inactivate enzymes and shrink food for canning, freezing, or drying (vegetables are blanched in boiling water or steam, fruits in boiling fruit juice, sirup, water, or steam); or (2) to aid in removal of skins from nuts and fruits; many items after blanching are then dipped into cold water.
Blanc Mange	Cold pudding made of cornstarch, milk, sugar, and flavoring; usually molded.
Blanquette	Stew or ragoût in white cream or velouté sauce; the meat is white, such as veal or chicken breast; a light fricassee.
Blend	To mix thoroughly two or more ingredients; a creaming paddle, wire whip, or pastry cutter may be used on a mechanical mixer; see *beat*, *cut*, *knead*, and *mix*.
Blue Points	Small oysters, usually from Chesapeake Bay.
Boil	To cook in water or a liquid largely water at a boiling temperature (212° F at sea level).
Boitelle, a la	Cooked with mushrooms.
Bombe	Molded dessert of two or more ice creams; may also be called *bombe glacé.*
Bon Bons	Candies or sweets.
Bonne Femme	Term used for soups, stews, and so forth; simple home-style.
Bordelaise	Brown sauce seasoned with red wine, garlic, shallots, and diced or sliced poached marrow; onions are reduced in white wine and added to a velouté sauce and finished with butter, after which tarragon is added for a white *bordelaise* or a *bonnefoy sauce.*
Border	(Fr) *bordure (en)*; to surround with a border, such as a planked item circled with duchess potatoes.
Borscht	Russian or Polish soup containing beets and cabbage and garnished with sour cream.
Boston Cream Pie	Two layers of cake filled between with cream pudding custard sauce and topped with powdered sugar or whipped cream.
Bouchee	Small cake or small patty shell or choux paste with cream filling; literally, "mouthful"; may also be small hors d'oeuvre made from puff paste.
Boucher	Butcher.
Bouillabaisse	Thick fish soup or stew; served in large soup plates or dishes with toast; may be seasoned with saffron, and should contain five or six different fish, among which should be mussels, clams, and lobsters; also called *soupe marseillaise.*
Bouillon	Soup; stock is richer than a broth and usually comes from beef; (Fr) *bouilli*, boiled beef.
Boulanger	Baker.
Boulettes	Forcemeat balls.
Bouquet Garni	Parsley, bay leaves, thyme, onions, and other herbs finely chopped; usually tied in a small cloth and cooked with the food but removed when proper seasoning is attained; also called *sachet* or *fagot.*

Bourgeois	Natural; plain, family style; *a la bourgeoise*, to serve with vegetables; sometimes confused with *Bourguignonne*.
Bourgignonne	A brown sauce for fish, meat, and eggs, reduced with red wine and small cooked onions, with mussels added; for snails, a basic butter seasoned with chopped thyme, tarragon, garlic, chervil, marjoram, parsley, and lemon juice; cleaned, drained snails are returned to the shells and baked with this sauce.
Braise	To brown meat or vegetables in a small amount of fat, then cook slowly in a covered utensil in small quantity of liquid; the liquid may be juices from meat, water, milk, cream, stock, tomato juice, and so on.
Bread	(1) To coat with bread crumbs alone; (2) to coat with egg or liquid and then crumbs; or (3) to coat with flour, egg, and/or liquid and then crumbs; "to egg" usually means to bread.
Bread Sauce	Milk flavored with onions, bay leaf, and cloves, thickened with fresh white bread crumbs.
Brie	A soft, rich French cheese.
Bretonne	Brown sauce with tomatoes, chopped onions, and garlic; or cold tart sauce with mustard and horseradish slightly sweetened.
Brioche	Baked yeast bread, frequently sweetened and almost rich enough to be called a cake; may be somewhat like sweet dough products.
Brochet	A skewer; *en brochette*, meat and food roasted or broiled on a skewer; *a la broche* is also used.
Broil	To cook by radiant or direct heat.
Brouillé	Scrambled.
Brown Betty	Rich cake or bread crumb pudding, heavy with apples or other fruit.
Brown Bread	Steamed bread served with baked beans; the bread usually is distinguished by the ingredients of white and rye flour, cornmeal, molasses, and raisins.
Brown Sauce	One of the four basic sauces; see *espagnole*.
Brunoise	Vegetables or meat diced in ⅛ inch squares.
Brunswick Stew	Southern dish of chicken or rabbit or ground meat with corn, onions, okra, salt, pork, tomatoes, potatoes, and lima beans; the true stew is made of squirrel meat.
Brush	To clean with a stiff brush; to brush on ingredients such as butter and fondant frosting.
Bubble and Squeak	Corned beef and cabbage.
Buffet	A large table displaying foods that are served from it; see *Russe*.
Burn	To burn sugar on top of food with a hot poker, as for an omelet.
Butter	(Fr) *Beurre*; *au maitre d'hotel*, with soft butter spread over or with butter melted until it froths; *au meuniere*, with browned butter; *au beurre noir*, with black butter; each is butter with a bit of lemon juice, a bit of cayenne, and parsley added. *Beurre fondu*, melted butter; *beurre d'anchois*, softened butter seasoned with anchovy paste. Many basic butters are used as spreads for canapes or in cooking as seasonings.

Café	Coffee; *café noir*, black coffee; *café au lait*, coffee with milk; also used to indicate coffee house or restaurant.
Camembert	A rich, soft, French cheese.
Canapé	A small open-faced sandwich used for an appetizer; may be on a fried or toasted piece of bread or crisp cereal product; the spread is tangy.
Canard	Duck; *canardeau or caneton*, young or female duck, respectively.
Candy	(1) When applied to fruit, fruit peel, or ginger, it means to cook in a heavy sirup until plump and transparent, then drained and dried; can also be called crystallize. (2) When applied to sweet potatoes and carrots, it means to cook in sugar or sirup.
Canneloni	Thin strips of Italian paste stuffed with meat and cooked.
Capers	Small pickled buds used for garnish or seasoning; (Fr) *cappone*.
Capon	Desexed male chicken weighing usually from five to six lbs.
Caramel	Sugar heavily browned; to caramelize is to heat sugar or foods containing sugar until a brown color and a characteristic flavor develops.
Carne	Spanish for with meat; *chili con carne*, beans with meat.
Carré	Back and shoulders; the rack.
Casserole	A hollow mold of rice or potatoes or other products; a dish in which foods are braised or baked; a *cassolette* is an individual casserole.
Caviar	Salted roe of the sturgeon; see *roe*.
Cepe	A wild mushroom.
Cervelat	A smoked bologna sausage.
Chablis	A white, good-bodied wine; sometimes called white Burgundy.
Champignon	Mushroom.
Chantilly	Sweetened and flavored whipped cream.
Chapon	Capon (Fr); a crust of bread boiled or soaked in the soup; a crust of bread rubbed with garlic and placed in a salad for flavoring.
Charlotte Russe	A mold lined with bread, cake, lady fingers, or sponge cake and filled with a bavarian; may also be bread or cake soaked with fruit sauce and served cold with whipped cream.
Chartreuse	A famous liqueur; a dish consisting of only vegetables and no meat, after the custom of the monks who founded this order.
Chasseur	A sauce consisting of equal parts of brown and tomato sauce with chopped onions or shallots, parsley, and a bit of lemon juice; oftentimes, on American menus, called *hunter sauce*.
Chateau, au	Specialty of the house; see *maison*.
Chateaubriand	A steak weighing about 12 oz or more cut from the center of a beef tenderloin; may be cooked variously; also the name given to a cold or hot sauce served with this steak.
Chaud	Hot.
Chaud-froid	Cooked meat prepared for service cold; frequently highly decorated; a sauce used to cover cold decorated meats; called *mayonnaise collée* if from mayonnaise, *chaud-froid brun* if from brown sauce, and *chaud-froid blanc* if from velouté sauce.
Chausson	Fruit jam in a pastry puff; a covered tart.

Chef de Cuisine	Head chef; *chef de nuit*, night chef; *sous chef*, assistant chef.
Chef's Salad	Tossed greens and chopped vegetables garnished with strips of tongue, ham, cheese, or chicken and served with French dressing.
Chemise (en)	Cooked with the skins on (usually potatoes); *chemiser* (Fr), to line or coat a mold.
Chenoise	China cup; a strainer.
Cherries Jubilee	Dark cherries in sirup slightly thickened with starch, covered with kirsch, and ignited, and perhaps served with a garnish of ice cream or whipped cream.
Chevalier	Food dipped in batter, fried, and served with cream sauce.
Chicken Cacciatore	Chicken sautéed in olive oil, then braised with diced onions, green peppers, whole tomatoes, and a bit of consomme and white wine, until tender. Mushrooms may be added.
Chiffonade	Shredded or minced vegetables; shredded or minced onions, beets, parsley, green peppers, and chopped egg in French dressing.
Chili con Carne	Beans with meat.
Chipolata	Brown sauce with onions, mushrooms, little veal sausages, bacon, and carrots, seasoned with madeira or sherry wine; can also be tiny sausages served as hors d'oeuvres.
Chitterling	Fried or pickled sausages made from hog intestines.
Chop	To cut into small pieces with a knife or other sharp tool.
Chop Suey	Chinese mixed vegetables seasoned with meat and soy sauce and served with rice.
Choux	Cabbage.
Choux Paste	An eclair or cream puff batter.
Chowder	A thick soup containing diced potatoes and sautéed onions and bacon or salt pork.
Chow Mein	Chicken or pork Chinese vegetable dish, with fried noodles and soy sauce.
Chutney	A sweet East Indian relish made of mangoes and other ingredients; the usual accompaniment for curry.
Civet	Rabbit stew or ragoût; see *jugged*.
Clairet	Claret wine.
Clam Bake	Roasting ears of corn, lobster, fish and clams, and potatoes, rolled with wet seaweed, then in wet cloths, and baked in a barbecue pit or 350° F oven; typical procedure is to bake on hot stones in a pit dug in the sand.
Cloche	Glass bell used for covering a dish; *sous cloche*, under cover or bell.
Cochon	Pig; *cochon de lait*, suckling pig.
Cockie-leekie or Cocky-leeky	A Scotch soup; chicken broth with celery and leeks; cooked prunes may be served separately, and many recipes call for the stock from a rooster or cock.
Coddled Egg	Boiling water is poured over an egg; as it stands in the water, the egg is allowed to cook to desired firmness; in quantity cookery, placing eggs in cold water, bringing to a boil, and removing from heat to cook until done.

Colbert	Brown sauce seasoned with onions previously reduced in white wine; sauce is finished with maitre d'hotel butter; consommé with spring vegetables and poached egg.
Coleslaw	Shredded cabbage with boiled dressing or mayonnaise; hot slaw served after heating in a hot dressing.
Collops	Cutlets; may also be called *escalopes*.
Compote	Stewed fruit; occasionally poultry stew.
Confit	Preserve or jam; may also be called *confiture*.
Conserve	A preserve; fruit or vegetables in heavy sirup.
Consommé	A strong, clear, clarified soup made of two or three kinds of meat.
Coq-au-vin-rouge	Chicken sautéed in red wine and brown sauce with mushrooms and onions.
Coquille	Shell of shellfish used for *au gratin* fish dishes; coral of lobster.
Corned Beef	Pickled beef.
Côte	Rib, cutlet, or chop; *côtes de boeuf*, ribs of beef.
Cotellette	Cutlet or cutlet-shaped.
Cottage Potatoes	Thinly sliced raw potatoes sautéed in shallow fat.
Cottage Pudding	Warm cake served with hot fruit sauce over it; baked pudding served with a warm dessert sauce.
Coulis	Rich meat juice; frequently jellied strained gravy.
Country Style	Served with salt pork or fat bacon.
Coupe	Cup, goblet, or bowl; diced fruit served in a coupe glass topped with a frozen dessert or whipped cream.
Court Bouillon	Water, vinegar or wine, herbs, and seasonings in which fish is cooked or over which it is steamed; fish bones and trimmings may be used to enrich the stock.
Couvert	Setting; cover; place setting.
Cover Charge	Fixed charge added to a meal or food prices for entertainment.
Cream	To work one or more foods to a soft and creamy mass using a spoon, mixer, or other tool; applied to thorough mixing of fat and sugar to incorporate a large quantity of air, which gives a light, fluffy mixture; on mechanical mixer, creaming paddle is used.
Cream Sauce	A white sauce to which cream or rich milk has been added; a term sometimes incorrectly applied to bechamel sauce.
Crecy	With carrots.
Creme de Menthe	A liqueur flavored with mint; there are white and green varieties.
Creole	Louisiana-type cookery, using green peppers, rice, *filé* seasoning, okra, saffron, and so forth, in dishes.
Crêpe	Pancake; *crêpes suzette,* thin pancakes rolled with orange butter, with cream center, covered with warm brandy or rum, and served flaming; the Russians call crepes *blinis* or *piroshki*, depending upon the type of filling used.
Crevette	Shrimp; *crevette rose*, prawn about 1½ to 2 inches long.
Crimp	To make deep gashes on salmon, cod, haddock, or skate as it leaves the water; soak in cold water for an hour or so, and then boil in salted water, and cook only to doneness.

Crisp	To moisten and refrigerate until crisp; to cook until the outer surface is crisp.
Croissant	Crescent-shaped rolls or croutons; also crescent-shaped confectionery.
Croquette	Chopped meat, cone-shaped, breaded and deep-fried; binder of meat is usually heavy white sauce; sometimes applied to sweet deep-fried pastries.
Croustade	Hollow, fried bread square into which food in a sauce is placed; may also be any starch product shaped to contain other foods.
Croute (en)	Placed under crust.
Crouton	Toasted or fried bread; frequently used as a soup garnish; *croutes* (Fr).
Cuisinier	A cook.
Cuisson	Meats braised or cooked in their own juices.
Cullis	A puree soup made of pulped flesh of game, meat, poultry, or fish.
Cumberland	A sauce made of currant jelly, lemon juice, port wine, lemon and orange rind, mustard, onions, and ginger; may be hot or cold.
Curaçoa	An orange-flavored liqueur.
Curry	East Indian stew containing curry seasoning; frequently-cooked meat added to a bechamel sauce which has been seasoned with curry; served with chopped nuts, shredded coconut, chutney, and other dishes.
Cut	(1) To chop. (2) To incorporate fat into dry ingredients with the least amount of blending; on a mechanical mixer the pastry blender paddle is used.
Dagout	Drippings; see *fond*.
Danish Pastry	Yeast, sweet dough, and shortening rolled out similar to puff paste to give a flaky soft bread; used for breakfast rolls and other rich rolls.
Dariole	A mold lined with thin paste, filled with custard, and topped with whipped cream.
Daube	To braise in wine.
Dauphenoise	Braised dish in sauce topped with buttered crumbs.
Decouper	To cut up.
Degust	To cook; to reduce or get rid of.
Dejeuner	Breakfast; *dejeuner a la fourchette*, luncheon.
Delayer	To soak; see *soak*.
Delicatessen	Place where cold buffet foods are sold.
Dente (al)	Means *to the tooth;* a slight firmness remaining in foods after cooking, as in vegetables or macaroni products, giving some chew.
Denver Sandwich	Filling of chopped cooked ham added to lightly beaten egg; frequently served on toasted bread.

Devil	(Fr) *Diable;* usually tangy sauce with meat-stock base, seasoned with mustard, cayenne, and onions, reduced in white wine; pimientos, green peppers, and other minced items may be added; sometimes a tangy tomato sauce; deviled crab or deviled eggs are tangy preparations.
Devonshire Cream	Cream clotted by scalding it and removing clots as they form on the surface; served chilled.
Dice	To cut into cubes around ½ to ¼ inch in size.
Dinde	Female turkey; *dindon,* male turkey; *dindonneau,* young turkey.
Diplomate	Normandy sauce seasoned with lobster.
Dobos Cake	Thin layers of sponge cake filled with rich chocolate cream.
Dock	To pierce, prick, gash, or cut.
Dolma	Turkish forcemeat; ground meat mixture cooked in cabbage leaves.
Dredge	To coat lightly; see *flour.*
Dresser	To garnish.
Duchesse	Usually applied to mashed potatoes that contain egg yolk; the mixture is frequently used for potato puff; used also as a topping for baked meat pies; can be forced from a pastry tube into forms, piped around planked items, or used otherwise and baked.
Dugléré	With tomatoes.
Du jour	Food ready to be served; *du jour* means "of the day."
Eau	Water.
Eau de Vie	Brandy; literally, "water of life."
Eclair	Finger-like choux pastes filled with cream or pastry cream; frequently chocolate-frosted.
Ecarlate	Any sauce containing red food, such as lobster coral, beets, and red tongue.
Ecrevisse	Crayfish.
Egg	See *bread.*
Emince	Finely minced; mincemeat; sometimes used to indicate thin slices.
Empanades	See *pasty.*
En Bellevue	In aspic; literally, "in good sight."
Enchiladas	Mexican tortillas filled with a chicken, cheese, tomato mixture, grated cheese on top; usually some raw chopped lettuce is added at the last minute.
En Cocotte	In small individual casserole.
En Coquille	In shell.
English Monkey	See *monkey.*
English Muffin	Round yeast bread baked on griddle.
En Papillote	To cook in paper bag.
Entrecote	Literally, "between the ribs"; frequently used to indicate a steak.
Entrée	Main dish.
Entremets	Desserts served either cold *(froid)* or hot *(chaud); entremets de danseur,* desserts served at the end of a course meal; may also be applied to buttered vegetables or large salads.
Epaul de Mouton	Shoulder of mutton.

Epigramme	Small cutlet of tender meat.
Espagnole	Brown sauce; one of the basic sauces made from brown stock and browned roux; a small quantity of tomatoes may be added.
Essence	Rich stock of meat or vegetable flavors; an extract of meat flavors; finely divided or pulped foods used to give predominant flavor to a food; dessert flavorings may also be called this.
Estouffade (Etuver or Etouffer)	Smothered and braised; frequently a term used to indicate chicken cooked in this manner.
Etuvee	Type of stew.
Fagot	Celery, bay leaf, pepper corn, thyme, and garlic wrapped together and used as a *bouquet garni.*
Faisan	Cock pheasant; *faisans,* hen pheasant; *faisandeau,* young pheasant.
Fanchonette	Small pie or tart topped with meringue.
Farce	Forcemeat stuffing; *farci,* stuffed, filled with forcemeat.
Farina	(Fr) *farine;* coarsely ground endosperm of wheat; French are apt to call all finely ground flours *farine.*
Fariner	To dredge with flour; see *flour.*
Fausse Tortue	Mock turtle; usually a soup made of green peas in imitation of real turtle soup; seasoned with sherry or madeira wine; stock is usually rich veal, and diced meat from cooked calves' head may be added.
Fermiere	"Farmer's wife" style; baked in earthen dish with minced green onions, chives, parsley, butter, and a bit of white wine.
Feuilletée (pâte)	Puff paste; means "many leaves;" reworked scraps are called demi-feuillitée.
Filet	Boneless piece of meat, usually the tenderloin; *fillet,* boneless piece of fish.
Financière	"Banker's style"; brown sauce containing diced ham, usually seasoned with mushrooms, truffles, and white or madeira wine.
Fines Herbes	Finely cut green herbs used for seasoning or garnish.
Finnan Haddie	Lightly smoked salted haddock.
Flamande	Velouté sauce seasoned with rich fish stock, mustard, lemon juice, and chopped parsley; carrots, pickles, and grated horseradish may sometimes be added.
Flamed	(Fr) *Flambé;* set afire with brandy, liqueur, or other product, usually served flaming.
Flan	Custard; open tart.
Florentine	With spinach; frequently means an item served over creamed spinach; Florentine soup is cream of spinach soup.
Flour	To coat with flour; to dredge in flour; usually salt, pepper, and other seasonings are added to the flour, and paprika may be added for color.
Foie	Liver; *foie de veau,* calf's liver; *foie gras,* goose liver.
Fold	To combine by using two motions, cutting vertically through the mixture and turning over and over by sliding the implement across the bottom of the mixing bowl with each turn; usually done with a spatula or whip; can be done with care with whip in mixer; with very delicate products, such as a butter sponge, the hands should be used.

Fond   Drippings in a pan; *fond brun*, brown drippings; also a rich
                            stock of meat and vegetables.
Fondue   Melted or blended; a light custard-like entree that resembles a
                            soufflé; hot melted cheese entree; *Swiss fondue*, melted Swiss
                            cheese in white wine seasoned delicately with kirsch and dipped
                            up with French bread; custard of eggs and milk poured over
                            bread and diced meat or fish added, and product baked.
Forcemeat   Pulped meat bound together with soft crumbs and egg yolks and
                            poached in tiny balls or pieces; used as a garnish.
Four   Oven.
Fourré   Coated with sugar, cream, or other preparations.
Franconia   Browned; potatoes browned with the roast.
Frappé   Partly frozen; coarsely frozen.
French Dressing   Oil and vinegar or lemon in the ratio of 2:1; a variety of season-
                            ings may be added to give many variations.
French Ice Cream   Rich ice cream containing eggs; may also be seasoned with
                            ground vanilla bean.
French Onion Soup   A bouillon soup thick with sautéed, thinly sliced onions and
                            served in a *petite marmite* dish, topped with a slice of French
                            bread covered with grated parmesan cheese, the whole dish
                            richly toasted under a broiler before serving.
French Toast   Bread dipped in egg and sautéed.
Friandines   Small patties or croquettes.
Fricandeau   Larded and braised leg of veal; can also be large larded slice
                            from the rump.
Fricassee   To cook by braising; usually applied to fowl, rabbit, or veal;
                            for white fricassee, no browning occurs.
Fricot   Stew or ragoût.
Frit   Fried.
Froid   Cold.
Fromage   Cheese; *fromage glacé*, ice cream molded in shape of cheese.
Fruit   Fruit; *fruit divers*, mixed fruit; *fruit glacé*, candied fruit;
                            fruit secs, dried fruit.
Fry   To cook in fat; (1) cooking in a small amount of fat and also
                            called sautéing or pan-frying; (2) cooking in deep fat, called
                            deep-fat frying.
Fumet   Stock from fish, game, or meats, reduced with wine and slightly
                            more concentrated than an essence; a rich stock over which
                            foods are steamed.

Galantine   Decorated boneless meat, game, or poultry piece; frequently has
                            a crust around meat with decoration in the meat; boned meat or
                            poultry cooked in a casing and served cold.
Garbure   Baked stew or thick soup containing much cabbage and salt
                            pork.
Garde Manger   Cold meat cook.
Garnish   An edible food used to decorate another; (Fr) *Garniture*.
Gateau   Cake; *gateaux assortis*, assorted cakes.
Gaufre   Waffle; a crisp ice cream wafer.

Gelee	Jelly; any type of jel.
Genevoise	Rich fish essence reduced with red wine; sauce contains no meat; Geneva style, not Genoa style.
Genoise	Genoa style; rich in butter and eggs.
Glacé	Iced, frosted, frozen, glassy, glazed, candied, crystallized; some desserts are said to be *glacé* when covered with a thick sauce; a glaze; to coat with a thin sirup cooked to the crack stage, or to cover with a starch- or pectin-thickened gel; in the latter, pies, tarts, and bread may be glazed with apricot or strawberry glaze, a jam or jelly, and so forth; *glacé de viande*, meat glaze; *glacé de boeuf*, beef glaze; *glacé de veau*, veal glaze.
Glacé Royale	An icing; a sauce made of mousseline sauce and mornay sauce or cream sauce blended in equal amounts.
Glaze	A rich stock reduced one-fourth in volume used to heighten flavor in stocks, sauces, or meat dishes; a demi-glaze is rich stock reduced one-half; to coat meat, poultry, or fish with a meat essence containing a high amount of gelatin; to give a glossy, shiny coat; to place vegetables in a mixture of butter or margarine and sugar or sirup and coat with a glaze by sautéing or ovenizing.
Gnocchi	Italian pastry or cracker seasoned with parmesan cheese; Italian dumpling.
Godiveau	Forcemeat made of veal kidney.
Golden Buck	Welsh rarebit over poached egg.
Gorgonzola	Italian cheese resembling Roquefort cheese.
Goulash	Hungarian stew heavily seasoned with paprika.
Gras (au)	*Gras* is French for fat; cooked in fat, or covered with a rich meat gravy.
Gras-double	Tripe.
Gratin (au)	Browned; a food covered with sauce, sprinkled with crumbs and perhaps grated cheese, and browned.
Greek	(Fr) *Grecque;* Greek style; usually seasoned with olive oil and garlic.
Grid	The part of a broiler on which foods are placed for broiling.
Grill	To fry on a griddle; sauté or toast; (Fr) *grille*, broiler; the term is no longer used in indicate broiling.
Grind	To reduce to small particles by cutting, crushing, or grinding.
Grits	Coarsely ground hominy cooked as a porridge and served for breakfast; (Fr) *gruau*, oatmeal, grits, groats, gruel.
Groseille	Gooseberry; *groseille rouge*, red currant; *groseille noire*, black currant.
Gruyere	Cheese resembling Swiss cheese.
Guava	An apple-like fruit that makes a tart, deep pink (almost red) jelly.
Gumbo	Also indicated by the term "okra"; a Creole-type dish; usually contains okra, tomatoes, and rice.
Hachis	Hash; minced meat, sometimes spelled *hachée*.
Haggis	Scotch sausage cooked in sheep's stomach.

Ham	Cured, smoked leg of pork. *Smithfield*, Virginia ham from pigs eating a heavy diet of peanuts; a drier, more heavily cured ham. Westphalia, Prague, Polish, and Bayonne hams are similar to the Smithfield and require slow and extended cooking to tenderize.
Hard Sauce	Creamed butter and powdered sugar, flavored variously; used as a dessert sauce.
Haricot	Kidney or navy bean; stewed meat with turnips; *haricot vert,* green bean; *haricot d'Espagne,* red bean.
Harlequin	See *Neapolitane.*
Hasenpfeffer	Rabbit stew cooked with tart wine; may be finished with sour cream.
Hash Browned Potatoes	Boiled potatoes, sliced, chopped, or diced, and sautéed until they have a crisp outer crust.
Hashed Potatoes in Cream	Boiled, sliced, or diced potatoes in rich bechamel or cream sauce.
Hatelet	Small skewer; silver skewer.
High Tea	A formal tea more elaborate than an ordinary tea.
Hodgepodge (hotchpotch)	A mixture; a stew; *hoche pot* is a mixture of meat and vegetables served with broth in a soup dish.
Hollandaise	Sauce made of egg yolks, butter, lemon juice or vinegar, and seasonings.
Homard	Lobster.
Hors d'oeuvre	Appetizer; side dish after the soup in a very formal meal; means dishes served outside of the ordinary dishes.
Huître	Oyster.
Hungarian Goulash	See *goulash.*
Hush Puppies	Cornmeal paste deep-fried; a Southern dish, and very delicious.
Ice	Sweetened fruit juice and water; frozen.
Imperatrice	Rich supreme sauce; also name of a consommé.
Indian Pudding	A New England dessert of baked cornmeal, milk, brown sugar, eggs, raisins, and flavoring.
Indienne	Generally used to indicate dishes flavored with curry.
Irish Stew	A stew made of lamb or mutton with dumplings.
Italienne	Dishes distinguished by the use of Italian pastes and grated parmesan cheese; may also be used to indicate use of tomato sauce; ground meat sauce with vegetables and oregano used with spaghetti.
Jackson (a la)	A cream of potato soup; vegetables and macaroni may be added.
Jambalaya	Creole rice dish containing tomatoes, onions, saffron and other seasonings, and fish, shellfish, poultry, or meat.
Jambe	Leg; *jambon,* ham.
Jardinière	Mixed garden vegetables with carrots and turnips usually included; usually cut in strips ⅛ inch thick by 1 inch long, or diced.
Jolie Fille	Dishes fair to look upon; usually decorated pieces.
Jugged	Braised, and usually served in a casserole, as in "jugged hare."
Julienne	Vegetables or meats cut into matchlike strips; used for garnishing and seasoning.

Junket	A dessert of sweetened and flavored milk set to a clabber with rennet.
Jus	Juice of fruit, vegetable, or meat; see *au jus*.
Kebabs or Kebobs	Marinated pieces of lamb or mutton cooked on skewers; may also have vegetables or other foods between pieces of meat.
Kiev	Stuffed with seasoned butter.
King	See *a la king*.
Kippered	Lightly salted and smoked fish; *kippers*, smoked herring.
Kirschwasser	Liqueur made from cherries.
Kisses	Meringue-type dessert.
Knead	To work a thick product with a pressing motion by folding and stretching; to knead with a mechanical mixer is to use the dough hook.
Knöpfli	Tiny Swiss dumplings; made much like *spaetzle* except that dough is thicker; *klösse* (Ger).
Kosher	Food handled according to Jewish religious customs.
Kuchen	German cakes, not necessarily sweet; see *lebkuchen* below.
Kummel	Caraway; liqueur seasoned with caraway seed.
Lachs	Smoked salmon; *lox* or *locks*, a Jewish dish of thinly sliced smoked salmon served with bagels.
Lait	Milk.
Langouste	Spiny-back lobsters with no claws; only tails used.
Langues de Chat	Small cakes called "cat's tongues."
Lard	Bacon, salt pork, pig's fat; *to lard* is to pull strips of salt pork, bacon, or fat through meat previous to cooking it; *lardoon*, larding needle; *lardon*, strips of fat used for larding.
Lasagne	Broad, ribbon-like Italian noodle.
Lebkuchen	German cakes which are quite sweet; usually honey is a part of the sweetener used.
Legumes	Group of vegetables composed of beans, peas, and lentils.
Liaison	Thickening agent such as starch, yolk of eggs, and so forth.
Limburger	A soft, strongly flavored German cheese aged similar to the manner in which camembert is aged.
Limpa	A Swedish bread.
Locks	See *lachs*.
Loin	Area from last rib to rump, except on pork, which is from shoulder blade tip to rump; *longe* (Fr); *longe de porc*, loin of pork; *shortloin*, area from last rib to edge of hip bone.
London	*London mixed grille* is an English (double or two sides of loin) chop with kidney, bacon, small sausage, and mushrooms; a London broil is tender flank steak cooked rare and sliced thin.
Lox	See *lachs*.
Lucullus	Rich brown sauce garnished with truffles, cocks' combs, quenelles, foie-gras, chicken kidneys, and mushrooms; seasoned with sherry; applied to costly dishes.
Lyonnaise	Heavily seasoned with onions and perhaps some parsley.

Macaroon	Small cake or cookie made of beaten egg whites and sugar and almond paste or fine coconut.
Macedoine	Mixture of vegetables, either raw or cooked, for salad or vegetable; can also refer to a mixed fruit sauce or mixture of fruit.
Madeira	A wine much like sherry; brown sauce reduced with madeira wine; some make a madeira sauce with half brown sauce and half tomato sauce, and season with madeira wine or sherry; *Madere* (Fr).
Maggi	A flavoring essence, largely monosodium glutamate (MSG), used to add flavor to stocks, sauces, and gravies.
Maigre (au)	Without meat; food other than meat; used to indicate Lenten dishes.
Mais	Corn; sometimes used to refer to wheat or other cereals.
Maison (a la)	Specialty of the house.
Maitre d'Hotel	Person in charge of dining room; head waiter; see *butter*.
Manhattan	A cocktail made from bourbon whiskey and sweet (French) vermouth.
Marasquin	A liqueur made of maraschino cherries.
Marengo	Chicken fried in oil and braised in white wine and mushrooms; garlic and tomatoes are frequently added.
Marinade (also Marinate)	To soak in oil and vinegar or wine to give added flavor in the case of meats, also to tenderize; sometimes the marinade may be a pickling or brine solution.
Marmite	Small soup dish in shape of pot (see *petite marmite*); *grande marmite*, soup in which large pieces of meat cooked in the soup are sliced and served with the soup.
Marseillaise	Chopped onions, fine herbs, garlic fried in oil, reduced in red wine and chopped anchovies added to tomato sauce; *soupe a la Marseillaise* is a bouillabaise.
Martini	A cocktail made of gin and dry (Italian) vermouth.
Maryland	Meat or poultry dredged with flour, egg, and crumbs and fried; served with cream gravy and corn fritter.
Marzipan	Almond, egg white, and sugar paste confections in shape and color of fruit or vegetables; see *almond paste*.
Mask	To cover completely; usually applied to a cover of mayonnaise or other thick sauce, but may refer to a cover with forcemeat or jelly.
Matelote	Sailor fashion; onions and mushrooms sautéed, then reduced in red wine, with rich essence of fish added, and brown sauce; a dish of different sorts of fish (eel, carp, perch, and so forth) braised with vegetables and red or white wine.
Matignon	Minced raw or cooked mashed vegetables used for seasoning foods.
Mayonnaise	Oil, eggs, and vinegar or lemon juice in emulsified form for use as a salad dressing or preparation of other sauces; *mayonnaise collee* (see *chaud-froide*).
Meat Loaf	Ground meat with diced or minced vegetables shaped into loaf form and baked; loaf may be made of ground beef, ground veal, ground ham, or mixed ground meats or fish mixtures.

Meat Pie	Diced meat with vegetables in gravy, usually cooked under a biscuit or pastry crust; see also *pasty, pirog, piroshki, ruff, shortcake, tourtiere, turnover.*
Medaillon	A cake shaped like a large medal; beef tenderloin tips or small pieces of *foie gras* or other items.
Melba	Usually a dessert consisting of a half peach on ice cream, covered with Melba sauce (pureed raspberries or strawberries seasoned with Curaçao).
Mêlé	Mixed.
Melt	To liquefy.
Mere Poularde	A flat, unfolded plain or French omelet.
Meringue	Egg whites beaten stiff with sugar, used to top pies or desserts; adding more sugar makes a stiff meringue used as a base for many desserts.
Meuniere	Dredged with flour and sautéed in butter; see *butter.*
Mexican	Usually a dish containing *frijole* beans, onions, tomatoes, hot chili peppers, mild peppers, and kernel corn.
Mignon	A delicate morsel; *filet mignon*, the butt of the tenderloin cut as a steak and frequently wrapped in bacon; the French use the small end of the tenderloin for the *filet mignon.*
Milanaise	A dish with tomato sauce combined with *allemande* or *bechamel* sauce with some Italian pastes; some add parmesan cheese.
Mince	*Emince* (Fr); to cut or chop into small pieces.
Minestrone	Thick Italian vegetable soup distinguished by a leafy vegetable, red kidney beans, and an Italian paste among other products; usually served with parmesan cheese; there are at least four distinct types of minestrone soup originating in various districts of Italy.
Mint	*Menthe* (Fr); *crème de menthe*, a mint-flavored after-dinner liqueur; *menthe poivree*, peppermint; a mint sauce may be served hot or cold and is made of mint, vinegar, water, and sugar combined with the drippings of meat (usually lamb or mutton); some chefs add a bit of orange marmalade.
Minute Steak	Steak (usually sirloin) ½ inch thick cooked only a short time.
Mirabeau	A velouté sauce from rich chicken stock with crushed garlic added; may also be applied to an egg, steak, or garnish varying considerably in ingredients used.
Mirepoix	Diced vegetables used for imparting flavor to dishes.
Miroton	Cold meats warmed up.
Mix	To combine ingredients so as to blend them together.
Mixed Grill	A Frenched chop, kidney, bacon, sausage, broiled or grilled tomato, and mushroom.
Mock Turtle Soup	See *fausse tortue.*
Mold	To obtain a desired form by placing in a mold or device (see *shape*).
Monkey	Very similar to rarebit (rabbit), except thickening agent will be soft bread crumbs soaked in milk, instead of flour or other starch thickener; normally served over toasted English muffins;

	usually called English monkey; burned sugar dissolved in water to give a brown color to foods.
Montmorency	Dark or pie cherries used in a product; a sweet-sour cherry sauce sometimes served over baked ham.
Mornay	A bechamel, white, or cream sauce seasoned with grated parmesan cheese.
Mousse	A froth or foam; used to describe a delicate, aerated, smooth mixture; a frozen dessert made from a base of whipped cream.
Mousseline	A custard-like forcemeat made of egg whites and cream; a very smooth mixture; *mousseline sauce*, one part whipped cream to two parts mayonnaise or hollandaise sauce; see *glacé royal*.
Mulligatawny	Chicken broth, rice, corn, raw apples, and curry combined to make a soup; vegetables, meats, and chutney may be added.
Muscat	The large muscat raisin; *muscatel*, a sweet (dessert) wine.
Nantaise	Normandy sauce with shrimp, chervil, and tarragon added; also called *Nantira sauce*.
Napoleon	Puff paste pastry consisting of sheets of puff paste filled with custard filling, frosted, and cut into finger shapes.
Natural	*Au naturel* (Fr); in the natural form.
Neapolitane (Napolitaine)	A dish containing spaghetti; a brown sauce containing some currant jelly, diced ham, nutmeg, thyme, and a bit of malaga wine; some chefs add a bit of horseradish; name also indicates two or more layers of ice cream, ice, or sherbet in brick form; also indicates gelatin layers in different colors; *harlequin* is used synonymously; see *panache*.
Neutral Sauces	Sauces that contain no meat stock, such as hollandaise, mayonnaise, and bread sauce.
Newburg (Newberg or Newburgh)	Bechamel or cream sauce flavored with sherry; may be thickened by a liaison of egg yolks.
New England Boiled Dinner	Boiled beef or ham or both with boiled cabbage, carrots, rutabagas, turnips, onions, parsnips, and potatoes.
New Orleans	Same as *Creole*.
Nivernaise	Shredded vegetables in poulette sauce; glazed carrots.
Noisette	Nuts, hazel nuts; the kernel or eye of the main loin muscle *(longissimus dorsi)* or fish fillets; pieces from small end of beef tenderloin (see *tournedos*) about 1½ in. in diameter and usually two or three served as a portion; a *noisette* of lamb may be a piece from the loin; *noisette sauce*, a hollandaise or supreme sauce to which a small amount of hazelnut butter or paste is added just before service and served with salmon, trout, or other boiled fish.
Noix	Nut or walnut; *noix de coco*, coconut; *noix de pistache*, pistachio nut; *noix de veau*, veal cutlet taken from the muscle called the kernel on the leg.
Normandy	Rich fish velouté and cream reduced; a bit of cayenne may be added; for desserts *a la Normandy*, means a delicate, smooth mixture often containing whipped cream.

Nougat	Almond cake; an amorphous confectionery containing chopped or whole almonds.
Nouilles	Noodles or shredded egg paste; see *knöpfli, spaetzels,* and so forth.
O'Brien	Chopped green pepper, onion, and pimiento added; usually applied to cooked potatoes diced and sautéed with these items added.
Oeuf	Egg: *ôeufs brouillés,* scrambled eggs.
Oka	A cheese; see *port salut.*
Onion Soup	See *French onion soup.*
Orly	A dough using beer for a liquid.
Ovenize	To place in an oven to sauté or fry; to oven roast.
Pailles	Straws; *pailles au fromage,* cheese straws; *pailles pommes de terre,* shoestring potatoes.
Pain	Bread.
Pain de Boeuf	Meat loaf.
Panache	Two or more kinds of one item in a dish; panache ice cream may also be called *neapolitan* or *harlequin* ice cream.
Panade	Bread soaked and squeezed dry and used for stuffings, dressings, or forcemeats; *empanades,* a pasty.
Panard	Thick white sauce used as binding for croquettes.
Pan-Broil	To cook on a hot frying pan or grill without added fat or liquid; fat is poured off as it accumulates.
Paner	To cover with bread crumbs; also called at times *panure.*
Pan-Fry	Sauté or cook in small quantity of fat in a sauté pan.
Panier	Basket.
Papillote (en)	In paper; to bake in paper; *cotellette en papillote,* cutlet baked in paper; term is also used to indicate paper frills on chops and other items.
Parboil	To partially cook by boiling.
Pare	To trim or cut off outside covering; see *peel.*
Parfait	Vari-colored foods; a frozen dessert served in a parfait glass with layers of ice cream separated by layers of fruit or sirup and topped with whipped cream; a smooth mousse-like frozen dessert.
Parfumer	To flavor or season.
Parisienne	Paris style; cut into small, round ball shapes; *parisienne potatoes,* small round potato balls, deep-fried.
Parker House Rolls	A rich yeast dinner roll folded in half like a pocket book and baked.
Parmentier	Name of man who introduced potatoes into French cookery; *a la Parmentier,* with potatoes.
Parmesan	A hard Italian cheese, usually grated and used as a seasoning with macaroni products.
Passer	To strain.
Pastrami	A highly spiced corned beef brisket.
Pastry	Made of pie or puff paste dough, such as pies or tarts; *pâtisserie* (Fr).

Pasty	Flaky pie dough filled with diced meat and potatoes in gravy and baked; *empanades* (Fr).
Pâté or Paste	May mean fine paste mixture, a pie, or thick dough; a patty which may be a shell of puff paste, a small, round, flat cake, or a hamburger, potato, or vegetable patty.
Paupiette	Thin slices of meat spread with forcemeat, rolled, dipped in batter, and fried; a *roulade* or *rouleau*.
Paysanne	In peasant style; usually a dish served with shredded or diced cooked vegetables; the name given a fairly thick country type soup; a diced product.
Peel	To remove outside skin or rind by mechanical means or heat; *pelure* (Fr).
Pêle-mêle	Mixed up; tossed.
Pepper Pot	Soup popularized in Philadelphia; salt pork, onions, green peppers, potatoes, and other vegetables diced with sliced julienne tripe in a rich stock, usually beef.
Perigeux	Truffles; served with truffles; Perigord is a district in France known for its fine truffles.
Persillade	With parsley; *persillées,* new potatoes boiled, buttered, and dusted with chopped parsley.
Petit	Small, little, tiny, dainty.
Petit Dejeuner	Breakfast.
Petite Marmite	A vegetable or *pot au feu* soup containing sliced beef or chicken, served in a small individual pot and topped with a cheese-toasted crouton; see *marmite*.
Petit Fours	See *au four*.
Petit Lait	Buttermilk.
Petits Pois	Green peas.
Pfeffernüsse	Hard German cookies that contain a small amount of ground black pepper; literally, pepper nuts.
Philadelphia Ice Cream	Simplest type of ice cream, consisting of thin cream, sugar, and flavoring.
Pièce de Resistance	Main dish, the most important dish.
Pièce Montée	A display piece.
Pilaff	Turkish rice dish; *pilau* (Fr).
Pipe	To place a border around an item; see *border*.
Piquant	*Piquante* (Fr); tangy sauce containing vinegar, white wine, and sautéed onions with chopped capers and fine herbs added; some chefs add brown sauce; served with hot or cold pork, mutton, or fatty meats.
Piqué	Larded with strips of salt pork or bacon.
Pirog	Minced or finely diced meat baked in yeast, pastry, or biscuit dough; *calzoni* (It).
Piroshki	Baked biscuit dough filled with meat, cheese, vegetable, or fish mixture; sometimes means pancakes rolled with a filling of this type.
Pizza	Italian pie with crisp yeast bottom baked with a seasoned tomato mixture, cheese, and other items on top.
Plank	To broil fish or meat on a plank, surrounded with vegetables and a border of duchess potatoes, and serve.

Plat	Plate or platter; *plateau*, tray.
Plombiere	A mixture of candied fruits with ice cream.
Pluck	Lights, heart, liver.
Poach	To simmer in a small quantity of water that barely covers the item; *pôcher* (Fr).
Poëler	To brown in a saucepan in butter and then cover and braise; the cooking is fast and excess moisture is avoided in braising; a process between braising and roasting; sometimes a white mirepoix is called a *poële*.
Pois	Peas.
Poisson	Fish; *poissonier*, fish cook.
Poivrade	A tangy, tart brown sauce used on game meats, especially venison; a part of the marinade in which meat is soaked.
Polenta	Dish made of cornmeal or farina; grated parmesan cheese is usually sprinkled over it.
Pollo	Chicken (It or Sp).
Polonaise	Polish style; velouté sauce made slightly tart with lemon juice and a bit of horseradish; may also mean with beet, horseradish, and cabbage with sour cream.
Pomme	Apple; *pomme de terre*, potato; *pomme d'amour*, tomato.
Pompano	A fine fish caught in Florida or Caribbean waters.
Popover	A bread made of a mixture of flour, milk, and eggs and leavened by steam.
Port (du) Salut	A soft, richly flavored cheese also called *oka* or *trappist* after the Trappist monks, who originated it.
Potage	Soup, usually thick; *potagier*, soup cook.
Potato Chips	Thinly sliced rounds of potato cooked to a crisp stage in deep fat.
Pot-au-feu	Literally, "pot on the fire"; a soup made from rich stock of somewhat nondescript character because the ingredients are waste items obtained in other food production; usually a flavorful vegetable soup; may also refer to a stock pot cooking on a range or in a steam-jacketed kettle.
Poulet	Young fowl; *poularde*, a fat pullet; *poulette sauce*, egg yolks added to supreme sauce for thickening; may contain chopped mushrooms; normally a chicken stock is used for the basic velouté sauce, but some poulette sauces used for fish are made from a fish stock.
Praline	A confection made of brown or maple sugar and pecans; mixed broken pecans caramelized; brown sugar or maple sugar nougat; sometimes refers to burnt almond flavoring.
Prawn	A large shrimp.
Printaniere	Spring vegetables cut in small dice with peas and asparagus; the name of a consommé containing these vegetables.
Profiterolles	Tiny choux (eclair) pastes filled with vegetables, meats, or tangy fillings; sometimes used as a garnish for soup; may also be filled with sweetened mixtures and used as a dessert.
Prosciutto	An Italian ham, usually thinly sliced.
Provençale	Brown sauce heavily diluted with tomato puree and seasoned with garlic; the true sauce is made by cooking tomatoes with

	minced garlic and a few onions, salt and pepper, and a bit of oil and then sieving.
Provolone	A smoked Italian cheese with a rich, mellow flavor.
Puff Paste	Mixture of strong flour and water layered with shortening between folds and rolled out many times until thin sheets of dough and shortening are in thin layers; baked and used as a pie dough.
Pumpernickel	Bread made from whole rye flour.
Puree	Foods rubbed through a sieve; slightly coarser than pulped foods; a soup made from pureed food.
Quadrillé	Checkered by layering.
Quenelles	Oval or other fancy-shaped forcemeats.
Quiche Lorraine	A pie dough overlaid with bacon and Swiss cheese in a custard and baked; nutmeg may be sprinkled on top; used as an hors d'oeuvre.
Rabbit	See *rarebit.*
Ragoût	A stew of meats and vegetables, usually quite thick and savory; a thick concentrate of an item, such as tomato puree, often called tomato ragoût.
Ramekin	Small individual baking dish or pastry shell, or item baked in it; small cheese cake served as an hors d'oeuvre.
Rare	Underdone.
Rarebit	Also called *rabbit* or *Welsh rarebit;* melted cheese dish made with white sauce or stale beer or ale thickened with an egg yolk liaison; seasoned rather heavily; see also *fondue, golden buck, monkey,* and *Yorkshire buck;* when seasoned with anchovy and served with oysters, the dish is called *Capetown Rarebit.*
Rasping	Crumbs; grated cereal particles; *râpé* (Fr).
Ratafia	Name of a liqueur.
Ravigote	Cold sauce, quite tart, with chopped eggs and fine herbs and capers; usually made of oil and vinegar but sometimes with mayonnaise; also may be a tart sauce with fine herbs served hot; means to give appetite or vigor.
Ravioli	Small Italian pastes filled with meat, cheese, or vegetables, served in a rich tomato sauce and sprinkled over with Parmesan cheese.
Réchauffé	Warmed over.
Recherché	The best; the most refined.
Reduce	To evaporate part of a liquid by simmering or boiling. The recipe should state the amount of reduction.
Reforme	Dishes named after the famous Reform Club of London; a poivrade sauce made quite tart with gherkins, capers, cooked white of egg, and tongue, all cut julienne.
Refroisir	To cool or chill.
Regency (Regence)	Allemande sauce with mushrooms and truffles diluted with rich stock from the item it is to accompany.
Reine (Regina)	Chicken soup; creamed, or sweetbreads in patty shell; means also young or fat chicken.

Releves (Removes)	Roasts and boiled meats on the menu; entrees but in larger quantity than just a serving; *relever*, to improve.
Remoulade	Mayonnaise seasoned with mustard, chopped dill pickles, anchovy, capers, and fine herbs, usually highly seasoned with ground pepper; may mean in cookery to reduce to a paste or grind.
Render	To free fat from a connective tissue by means of heat.
Rhin	Rhine; *Rhin du vin*, Rhine wine.
Riblette	Thin slices; a rasher.
Riced	Put through a ricer, as is frequently done with hot boiled potatoes.
Richelieu	Sauce, usually over a tenderloin steak, consisting of brown sauce seasoned with madeira sauce and tomato paste; also a consommé or a garnish.
Ris	Sweetbread; *ris de veau*, veal sweetbreads.
Risotto (Rizotto)	A rice dish.
Rissolé	Browned or seared; with a brown or toasted coat; oven-browned potato.
Roast	To bake; applied to certain foods, such as meats and chestnuts; see *bake*.
Robert	Rich brown sauce with minced onions, mustard, and white wine.
Rockefeller	Creamed spinach and fine herbs; usually spread over raw oysters topped with bread crumbs and Parmesan cheese and baked; worcestershire. tabasco, anchovy paste, and absinthe or anisette may be added to the mixture for seasoning.
Rocks	Semi-hard dropped cookies or cakes containing raisins and nuts.
Roe	Fish eggs; buluga caviar is best quality; pressed sturgeon caviar widely used for spreads, pastes, and so forth; codfish and white-fish roe (both hard and frequently colored gray or black) and herring and salmon (both soft, the latter tinted red) and other roe are used as substitutes for caviar.
Roly-Poly Pudding	Rolled pastry or biscuit dough covered with fruit paste or jam and steamed or baked; served with a hot sauce.
Roquefort	Famous French bleu cheese; *Roquefort dressing*, about 5 oz Roquefort cheese to quart of French dressing; chopped chives may be added.
Rothschild	See *Angels on Horseback*.
Rouennaise	A dish featuring duck; made famous in the city of Rouen, France.
Rôtir	To roast; *rôti or rôt*, a roast; *rosbif*, roast beef; *rôtisseur*, roast cook; *rôtisserie*, equipment for roasting before an open fire, usually on a spit.
Roulade	Roll; rolled meat; term *rouleau* is used synonymously.
Roux	A mixture of equal parts of flour and fat used to thicken sauces and other foods.
Royale	In the royal style; a custard plain or combined with other foods used as a soup garnish.
Ruff	A meat pie or fried meat turnover.
Rusk	A crisp twice-baked bread.
Russe	Russian style; *Russian buffet*, foods on a buffet distinguished by caviar and Russian fish in a large glass or ice bowl on a stand.

Sachet	See *bouquet garni.*
St. Florentin	Deep-fried mashed potato croquettes containing diced ham.
St. Germain	A split pea soup; a dish containing puree of peas.
St. Hubert	Hunter style.
Salamander	A small broiler used for browning dishes in the cook's section.
Salisbury	A steak made of ground beef, milk, bread crumbs, and seasonings.
Sally Lunn	A breakfast coffee cake about the richness of a muffin.
Salmagundi	An old English dish of fresh and salted meats, fish, onions, and various seasonings.
Salmis	Also *salmi;* a stew of roasted game or meat in a rich brown sauce.
Salpiçon	Finely diced or chopped meat and vegetables (sometimes mushrooms and truffles are included) for flavoring sauces and other dishes; a mixture used for croquettes.
Saratoga	Indicates fried potato chips; also a shoulder or neck lamb chop.
Sauce	A concentrated, flavored accompaniment to food, usually liquid; *saucer,* to cover with sauce; *saucier,* sauce cook; *sauciere,* sauce-boat; *sauce vin blanc,* a velouté made of rich fish stock.
Saucisse	Sausage.
Sauerbraten	Pot roast (German) marinated in wine or water, vinegar, and seasonings; *sauer,* sour; *sauerkraut,* soured or pickled cabbage.
Sauté	To fry quickly with just enough fat or butter to prevent sticking; see *fry* and *pan-fry; sautoir,* a frying pan.
Scald	To heat liquid to just below boiling point or to dip an item into very hot or boiling water so that removal of an outer surface is facilitated or for other reasons; see *blanch.*
Scallop	Also *escalope;* to bake food, usually cut in pieces, in a sauce or other liquid; top is usually covered with crumbs; food and sauce may be mixed together or placed in alternate layers; *au gratin* may be used synonymously; to cut food on a bias.
Scallopine	Veal cutlet sautéed; *scallopine Bolognese,* ham and potatoes served with cutlet or minced veal with sauce, seasoned with Parmesan cheese.
Scallops	Meat or muscle of the sea or bay scallop, a shellfish.
Schnitzel	Breaded and sautéed; see *wiener schnitzel.*
Scone	A rich biscuit dough baked usually in triangular form; a Scotch tea cake made from wheat, rye, or barley flour.
Score	To cut lightly across an item; to mark lightly, as scoring an omelet by burning.
Scotch Broth	Soup made from mutton stock containing cooked barley and vegetables; often called Scotch mutton broth.
Scotch Woodcock	Half of hard-cooked or chopped creamed eggs seasoned with anchovy paste.
Scrape	To remove in thin layers with a sharp or blunt instrument.
Scrapple	Diced or ground pork cooked in cornmeal and seasoned.
Scrod	Cod or haddock about 2½ pounds in size.
Sear	To brown the surface by a short application of heavy heat; used to develop flavor and color.
Sec	Dry; *sauté sec,* braise in dry white wine.

Semolina Paste	Macaroni products; semolina is the endosperm of durum wheat, which makes a high quality macaroni product.
Shake	To toss vigorously up and down in a container.
Shape	To form into desired pattern either with hands or with molds.
Shepherd's Pie	A meat pie covered with mashed potatoes and baked.
Sherbet	A frozen dessert consisting of fruit juices, milk, sugar, stabilizer, and coloring; *sorbet* (Fr).
Shir	To bake.
Shore Dinner	Combined sea foods and shellfish served with French fried, shoestring- or baked potatoes and cole slaw.
Shortbread	A rich Scotch cookie.
Shortcake	A rich biscuit dough slightly sweet, split, with fruit in between and on top, and served with whipped cream or plain cream over; shortcake biscuit covered with meat in gravy.
Shred	To tear or cut into small pieces.
Simmer	To cook in a liquid at a temperature around 185° F with bubbles forming slowly and breaking at the surface.
Simple	A menu term meaning coffee or tea or other light food served without another food.
Singe	To remove hair or feathers by fire.
Skewer	A wood or metal pin for securing meat or on which to place meat for roasting or barbecuing; also used as a verb, as to *skewer* a roast; see *attereaux* and *hatelet.*
Slice	To cut with a knife or mechanical slicer into thin pieces in fairly substantial sizes; not cut or chopped; to carve.
Smorgasbord	A buffet of light foods acting as appetizers in which herring, butter, and rye bread are a part.
Smothered	Covered; *calf's liver smothered,* grilled calf's liver covered with fried or sautéed onions.
Soak	To immerse for an extended period of time in a liquid to rehydrate, to prevent from drying out, to keep from tarnishing in the air, or as a preliminary step in cleaning.
Soubis	A sauce made from cooked pureed onions added to a bechamel sauce.
Soufflé	Puffed: a dish made light, usually by folding in beaten egg whites and baking; a puffed-up French fried potato, either Irish or sweet.
Sous chef	Assistant to head chef.
Sous cloche	See *cloche.*
Southern Fried Chicken	Dredged in flour and deep-fried; see *Maryland.*
Spaetzle	Austrian noodle made by running heavy noodle batter through colander into boiling stock; used with braised meats; *spätzle* (Austrian).
Spanish	A tomato sauce with chopped ham or bacon, celery, carrot, and onion sautéed in bacon or ham fat, with added brown or tomato sauce; *Spanish omelet,* filled with tomatoes, peppers, onions, mushrooms, olives, celery, parsley, and spices; *Spanish cream,* a custard mixture firmed with gelatin and with whipped cream usually folded in just before the mixture sets.

Spareribs	Rib sections of pork behind the area from which the bacon is taken; would be the bone section behind the plate and brisket in beef.
Spit	A skewer on which meat is turned before open heat.
Sponge	A cake made light with beaten eggs; a soft bread batter considered the first stage in bread production, with the second addition of flour occurring after fermentation has proceeded to a certain point; a soft, light, aerated mixture.
Spoonbread	A Southern soft bread made of cornmeal paste, eggs, and milk; actually a soufflé.
Springerle	A cookie pressed with a mold before baking.
Spumone	A rich Italian ice cream; sometimes spelled *spomoni*.
Squab	A young pigeon that has not left the nest.
Squid	A seafood related to the octopus; usually deep-fried after batter-dipping for hors d'oeuvres, or cooked with tomato or other sauces.
Steak and Kidney Pie	See *beef steak pie*.
Steam	To cook in steam with or without pressure; the steam may be applied directly to the food, as in a steamer or pressure cooker.
Steep	To allow a substance to stand in liquid below the boiling point for the purpose of extracting flavor, color, or other qualities.
Stew	To simmer or boil in a small bit of liquid; for meat, temperature is around 185° F; a meat and vegetable dish in gravy.
Steward	Person in charge of purchasing and ordering, who may plan menus with chef; is largely responsible for food cost.
Stilton	An English bleu-type cheese with a brown outer crust.
Stir	To mix foods with a circular motion in order to blend or obtain a uniform consistency.
Stock	A liquid seasoned by meat or vegetable essence.
Stollen	A German yeast-leavened cake containing milk, eggs, butter, sugar, fruits, and nuts in addition to basic bread ingredients.
Stroganoff	Sautéed beef in sauce of sour cream, mushrooms, and onions.
Strudel	Viennese dessert consisting of thin sheets of cooked paste, fruits, cheese, honey, and other items.
Succotash	A vegetable mixture of fresh corn and lima beans; tomatoes may sometimes be added.
Suèdoise	Swedish, a whipped cream sauce containing horseradish and applesauce.
Suki Yaki	A Japanese dish of mixed vegetables sautéed in a light oil seasoned with beef or other meat and a bit of sugar.
Supreme	Of finest quality; velouté sauce to which heavy cream is added.
Sweetbreads	Thymus glands of animals.
Sweetdough	A yeast-leavened dough rich with sugar and eggs.
Sweetmeats	Candies.
Swiss Fondue	See *fondue*.
Swiss Steak	A braised steak.

Tamale	Meat in cornmeal roll flavored with chili and baked or boiled in corn husks.
Tartar Sauce	Chopped onions, dill pickles, celery, shallots, chives, and parsley in mayonnaise with capers; most chefs specify *no sweet pickles*.
Tarte	Small pie or pastry-filled item; *tartelette*, small tart.
Tasse	Small cup.
Tea	A beverage; tea served with dessert items such as tarts, cookies, small cakes, sandwiches, or other foods; *high tea*, elaborate service with quite fancy foods; see *simple*; *thé* (Fr).
Terrine	A stew or ragoût; an earthenware pot resembling a casserole.
Thermidor	Cream sauce seasoned with wine and herbs; cream added to *sauce vin blanc*.
Thicken	To add eggs, flour, or other products to foods and cook them until more firm: gelatin, rennet, and other products may be added to foods to thicken when cold.
Thousand Island Dressing	Mayonnaise and chili sauce with chopped eggs, green peppers, chives, and other items.
Timbale	A chopped or pureed meat, vegetable, or other food bound with eggs and baked in a mold or pan; may also be a crust or case in which foods are served.
Toad-in-the-Hole	Sausages or meat baked or fried in batter.
Tomato Sauce	Fine herbs sautéed, usually in salt pork, seasoned with bay leaf, thyme and other seasonings; next cooked with tomato puree or paste and white or brown stock; then thickened with roux. This sauce is considered one of the basic sauces; may contain no meat stock.
Torte	Pie or cake; may be rich, cake-like product.
Tortillas	Mexican flat pancake-type items containing cornmeal, flour, eggs, and seasonings into which seasoned meat or other items are rolled.
Tortoni	A frozen dessert containing tortoni biscuit (ground dried macaroons and chopped blanched almonds); usually a very rich ice cream is the base.
Toss	To mix lightly.
Tournedos	Small steak cut from the narrow part of beef tenderloin about 1½ inch thick. They resemble kernels or noisettes, which are the eye of the meat taken from lamb loins, pork loins, or other animals; weight is about 2½ oz each; cooked much like filets, Chauteaubriands, or other tenderloin steaks.
Tourner	To cut or shape vegetables; an expression used to indicate curdling.
Tourtiere	Canadian meat pie containing salt pork.
Tranche	Slice of meat or bread; *tranche de saumon*, slice of salmon; *trancher*, to slice or carve; see *slice*.
Trifle	Sponge cake soaked in wine and served with sauce or whipped cream.
Tripe	Stomach of cattle.

Truffle	*Truffe* (Fr); fungi grown in France in clusters below ground under oaks; pigs are trained to root them out; they resemble mushrooms, are black in color, and are used for flavor and garnish of meat dishes; see *Perigeux*.
Turbot	A delicately flavored, white-fleshed fish.
Turn	To carve or trim in some manner; a *turned olive* is a pitted olive, and a *turned mushroom* is a mushroom carved or decorated on the top, which also may be called a *mushroom crown*.
Turnover	A baked or fried food encased in pie or puff paste.
Turtle	Reptile used largely to make soup; tenderest parts may be used for steaks.
Tutti-frutti	A mixture of fruits.
Veal Cutlet	Slice of meat from the leg; *veal cutlet Holstein,* breaded cutlet sautéed in butter and served with fried egg, anchovy, and potatoes; see *wiener schnitzel; cotelette du veau* (Fr); *veal birds,* dressing or forcemeat rolled in thin slices of veal cutlet and braised.
Velouté	A basic sauce of white stock thickened with *roux;* means "velvet" or "smooth"; may also be used to indicate a white stock. There is also a fish velouté, which is a white stock or sauce made from lean white fish flesh and bones; the sauce is seasoned with white wine and may be called *sauce vin blanc.*
Venison	Flesh of all antlered members of the deer family: deer, antelope, elk, moose, and so forth.
Verjuice	Juice of unripe fruit; usually tart juice of grapes or apple; *verjus* (Fr).
Vichy	Famous springs in France; vegetables cooked in the water had excellent flavor; now a term used to indicate boiled and buttered vegetables, usually sprinkled with parsley; usually applied to carrots.
Vichysoisse	Hot or cold cream of potato soup; when cold, served with garnish of chopped chives on top.
Villeroi	Allemande sauce seasoned with the article which it accompanies; may be seasoned with mushroom and ham stock or with onions or tomatoes.
Vin	Wine; *vin de Xérès,* sherry or madeira-type wine.
Vinaigrette	Tart sauce; see *ravigote.*
Vin Blanc Sauce	See *velouté.*
Vol-au-vent	Puff paste shells to be filled with sauce mixtures, such as creamed chicken, braised lamb kidneys and mushrooms, and crab Newburg.
Waldorf	Term used to indicate an apple salad containing celery and walnuts with a boiled or mayonnaise dressing.
Welsh Rarebit	See *rarebit.*
Western Sandwich	Chopped ham, green peppers, onions, and beaten egg, fried and served as a sandwich.
White Sauce	Seasoned milk thickened with a starch paste; one of the basic neutral sauces; if cream is added, it is called a cream sauce.

Wiener Schnitzel	Breaded veal cutlet braised until tender and served with slice of lemon and anchovy filet; some bake cutlet in sour cream or tomato sauce.
Woodcock	Small game bird; see *Scotch woodcock*
Yankee Pot Roast	Braised pot roast with vegetables; frequently accompanied by dumplings or corn fritters.
Yorkshire Buck	Welsh rarebit on poached egg on toast; *Yorkshire rabbit,* bacon instead of egg is used.
Yorkshire Pudding	Popover batter poured into roast beef drippings and baked; served with roast beef with some *au jus* spooned over it.
Zeste	The colored part of the peel of citrus fruit.
Zwieback	Hard, crisp bread toasted and then baked again until thoroughly dry; a rusk.

Appendix

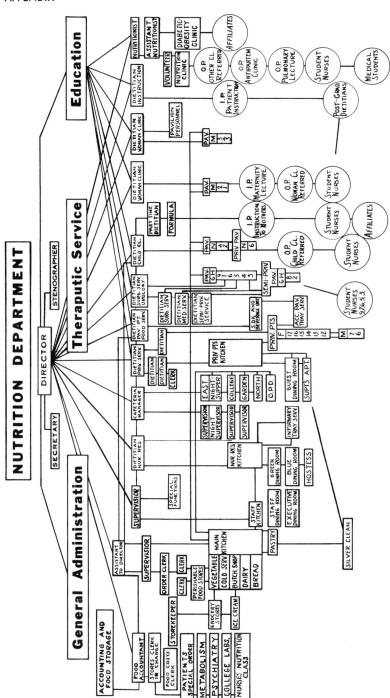

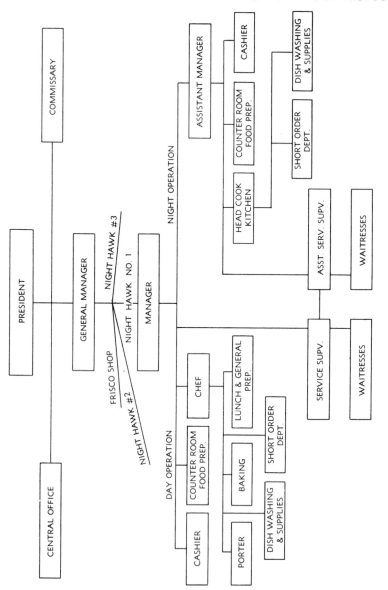

THE NIGHT HAWK

FOOD SERVICE
Staff Organization — 1956 to 1957

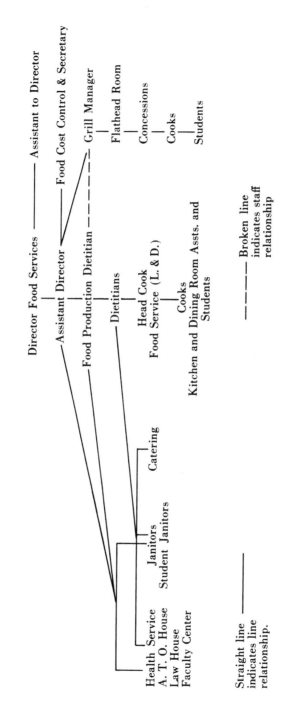

Director Food Services ———————— Assistant to Director

Assistant Director ———— Food Cost Control & Secretary

Food Production Dietitian – – – – Grill Manager

Dietitians ——— Flathead Room

Head Cook ——— Concessions
Food Service (L. & D.)

Cooks ——— Cooks
Kitchen and Dining Room Assts. and
Students ——— Students

Catering

Janitors
Student Janitors

Health Service
A. T. O. House
Law House
Faculty Center

Straight line
indicates line
relationship.

– – – – Broken line
indicates staff
relationship

FOOD AND NUTRITION BOARD, NATIONAL ACADEMY OF SCIENCES—NATIONAL RESEARCH COUNCIL

RECOMMENDED DAILY DIETARY ALLOWANCES[1], REVISED 1963

DESIGNED FOR THE MAINTENANCE OF GOOD NUTRITION OF PRACTICALLY ALL HEALTHY PERSONS IN THE U.S.A.

(Allowances are intended for persons normally active in a temperate climate)

	Age[2] Years from to	Weight kg. (lbs.)	Height cm. (in.)	Calories[3]	Protein gm.	Calcium gm.	Iron mg.	Vitamin A Value I U	Thiamine mg.	Riboflavin mg.	Niacin Equiv.[4] mg.	Ascorbic Acid mg.	Vitamin D I U
Men......	18-35	70 (154)	175 (69)	2,900	70	0.8	10	5,000*	1.2	1.7	19	70	
	35-55	70 (154)	175 (69)	2,600	70	0.8	10	5,000	1.0	1.6	17	70	
	55-75	70 (154)	175 (69)	2,200	70	0.8	10	5,000	0.9	1.3	15	70	
Women.....	18-35	58 (128)	163 (64)	2,100	58	0.8	15	5,000	0.8	1.3	14	70	
	35-55	58 (128)	163 (64)	1,900	58	0.8	15	5,000	0.8	1.2	13	70	
	55-75	58 (128)	163 (64)	1,600	58	0.8	10	5,000	0.8	1.2	13	70	400
Pregnant (2nd and 3rd trimester)				+ 200	+20	+0.5	+5	+1,000	+0.2	+0.3	+3	+30	400
Lactating				+1,000	+40	+0.5	+5	+3,000	+0.4	+0.6	+7	+30	400
Infants[5]......	0- 1	8 (18)		kg.x115 ±15	kg.x2.5 ±0.5	0.7	kg.x1.0	1,500	0.4	0.6	6	30	400
Children...	1- 3	13 (29)	87 (34)	1,300	32	0.8	8	2,000	0.5	0.8	9	40	400
	3- 6	18 (40)	107 (42)	1,600	40	0.8	10	2,500	0.6	1.0	11	50	400
	6- 9	24 (53)	124 (49)	2,100	52	0.8	12	3,500	0.8	1.3	14	60	400
Boys	9-12	33 (72)	140 (55)	2,400	60	1.1	15	4,500	1.0	1.4	16	70	400
	12-15	45 (98)	156 (61)	3,000	75	1.4	15	5,000	1.2	1.8	20	80	400
	15-18	61 (134)	172 (68)	3,400	85	1.4	15	5,000	1.4	2.0	22	80	400
Girls	9-12	33 (72)	140 (55)	2,200	55	1.1	15	4,500	0.9	1.3	15	80	400
	12-15	47 (103)	158 (62)	2,500	-62	1.3	15	5,000	0.9	1.5	17	80	400
	15-18	53 (117)	163 (64)	2,300	58	1.3	15	5,000	0.9	1.3	15	70	400

[1] The allowance levels are intended to cover individual variations among most normal persons as they live in the United States under usual environmental stresses. The recommended allowances can be attained with a variety of common foods, providing other nutrients for which human requirements have been less well defined. See text for more detailed discussion of allowances and of nutrients not tabulated.

[2] Entries on lines for age range 18-35 years represent the 25-year age. All other entries represent allowances for the midpoint of the specified age periods, i.e., line for children 1-3 is for age 2 years (24 months); 3-6 is for age 4½ years (54 months), etc.

[3] Tables 1 and 2 and figures 1 and 2 in text show calorie adjustments for weight and age.

[4] Niacin equivalents include dietary sources of the preformed vitamin and the precursor, tryptophan. 60 mg tryptophan represents 1 mg niacin.

[5] The calorie and protein allowances per kg for infants are considered to decrease progressively from birth. Allowances for calcium, thiamine, riboflavin, and niacin increase proportionately with calories to the maximum values shown.

* 1,000 I U from preformed Vitamin A and 4,000 I.U. from beta-carotene.

Source: National Research Council, Publication 589

Table 15-1

Conversion of Water From Measure to Weight

Cups	Pints	Quarts	Ounces*	Pounds and Ounces*	
½	¼	⅛	4.15	0	4
1	½	¼	8.31	0	8¼
1½	¾	⅜	12.46	0	12½
2	1	½	16.62	1	½
2½	1¼	⅝	20.77	1	4¾
3	1½	¾	24.93	1	9
3½	1¾	⅞	29.08	1	13
4	2	1	33.24	2	1¼
4½	2¼	1⅛	37.39	2	5¼
5	2½	1¼	41.55	2	9½
5½	2¾	1⅜	45.70	2	13¾
6	3	1½	49.86	3	1¾
6½	3¼	1⅝	54.01	3	6
7	3½	1¾	58.17	3	10¼
7½	3¾	1⅞	62.32	3	14¼
8	4	2	66.48	4	2½
8½	4¼	2⅛	70.63	4	6½
9	4½	2¼	74.80	4	10¾
9½	4¾	2⅜	78.94	4	15
10	5	2½	83.10	5	3¼
10½	5¼	2⅝	87.25	5	7¼
11	5½	2¾	91.40	5	11½
11½	5¾	2⅞	95.56	5	15½
12	6	3	99.72	6	3¾
12½	6¼	3⅛	103.87	6	8
13	6½	3¼	108.03	6	12
13½	6¾	3⅜	112.18	7	¼
14	7	3½	116.34	7	4¼
14½	7¼	3⅝	120.49	7	8¼
15	7½	3¾	124.65	7	12½
15½	7¾	3⅞	128.80	8	1
16	8	4	133.00	8	5

*For whole milk equivalents multiply by 1.032, and for light sirups (20° Brix) multiply by 1.373.

Table 15-2

Equivalents of Heat and Energy

1 Btu = 0.2520 Calories

1 Calorie = 3.968 Btu's

1 Btu = 778 foot-pounds (i.e., will raise 1 lb 778 feet against gravity)

1 Hp = 33,000 ft-lb/min (i.e., will raise 33,000 lb 1 ft in 1 min)

1 Hp = 42.42 Btu/min or 2545 Btu/hr

1 Hp = 746 watts

1 Kw = 1.341 Hp

Table 15-3

Dry and Liquid Measure Equivalents

Dry

2 pt	1 qt	1.101 liters
8 qt	1 peck	8.808 liters
4 pecks	1 bu	35.24 liters

Liquid

4 gills	1 pt	473.25 cubic centimeters
2 pt	1 qt	0.9465 liters
4 qt	1 gal	3.786 liters
31½ gal	1 barrel	
2 barrels	1 hogshead	

Table 15-4

Liquid Measure Conversion Table

United States measure	United States measure				Imperial measure (British)				Metric measure		Weight of indicated volume of water	
	Gallon	Quart	Pint	Gill	Gallon	Quart	Pint	Gill	Liter	Cubic centimeter	Pound (avoirdupois)	Kilogram
1 gallon........	1	4	8	32	0.833	3.33	6.66	26.66	3.785	3,785.4	8.33	3.785
1 quart........	.25	1	2	8	.208	.833	1.666	6.67	.946	946.4	2.08	.946
1 pint.........	.125	.5	1	4	.104	.417	.833	3.33	.473	473.2	1.04	.473
1 gill.........	.031	.125	.25	1	.026	.104	.208	.833	.118	118.3	.26	.118
Imperial measure (British)												
1 gallon........	1.2	4.8	9.6	38.4	1	4	8	32	4.543	4,543.5	10	4.543
1 quart........	.3	1.2	2.4	9.6	.25	1	2	8	1.136	1,135.9	2.5	1.136
1 pint.........	.15	.6	1.2	4.8	.125	.5	1	4	.568	567.9	1.25	.568
1 gill.........	.038	.15	.3	1.2	.031	.125	.25	1	.142	142.0	.312	.142
Metric measure												
1 liter........	.264	1.057	2.11	8.45	.220	.880	1.761	7.044	1	1,000	2.20	1.
1 cubic centimeter.	.0003	.001	.002	.008	.0002	.0009	.002	.077	.001	1	.002	.001

See also Table 15-9

Table 15-5

Weights, Measures, and Their Abbreviations

Measure	Abbreviation	Equivalent
Teaspoon	t	3 t or 1 T
Tablespoon	T	16 T or 1 c
Cup	c	2 c or 1 pt
Pint	pt	2 pt or 1 qt
Quart	qt	4 qt or 1 gal
Gram	gm	
Ounce	oz	28.35 gm or 1 oz
Pound	lb	16 oz or 1 lb
Gallon	gal	

Note: 2 T of liquid or solid matter usually equals 1 oz; $5\frac{1}{3}$ T equals $\frac{1}{3}$ c, 4 T equals $\frac{1}{4}$ c, a pinch equals about $\frac{1}{16}$ t and a dash less than $\frac{1}{8}$ t.

Table 15-6

Measures in Ladles, Spoons, and Scoops

(Ladles)

Cup Size	Ounces
$\frac{1}{4}$ c	2 oz
$\frac{1}{2}$ c	4 oz
$\frac{3}{4}$ c	6 oz
1 c	8 oz
1 qt (No. 56 dipper)	32 oz

(Scoops)

Scoop Size*	Level Measure	Ounces
No. 6	$\frac{2}{3}$ c	5
No. 8	$\frac{1}{2}$ c	4
No. 10	$\frac{3}{8}$ c	$3\frac{1}{4}$
No. 12	$\frac{1}{3}$ c	$2\frac{3}{4}$
No. 16	$\frac{1}{4}$ c	2
No. 20	$3\frac{1}{5}$ T	$1\frac{1}{2}$
No. 24	$2\frac{2}{3}$ T	$1\frac{1}{3}$
No. 30	$2\frac{1}{5}$ T	1
No. 40	$1\frac{3}{5}$ T	0.8

*Scoop number refers to number of scoops per quart.

(Spoons)
Ordinary cooking spoon serves approximately 3 oz.

Table 15-7

Conversion Table: Grams, Ounces, Pounds

Grams	Ounces	Pounds	Grams	Ounces	Pounds	Grams	Ounces	Pounds
28.35	1	.06	198.45	7	.44	340.20	12	.75
56.70	2	.13	226.80	8	.50	368.55	13	.81
85.05	3	.19	255.15	9	.56	396.90	14	.88
113.40	4	.25	283.50	10	.63	425.25	15	.94
141.75	5	.31	311.85	11	.69	453.60	16	1.00
170.10	6	.38						

Table 15-8

Volume Conversion Table

Fluid Ounces to Milliliters

Fl. Oz.	Ml.	Fl. Oz.	Ml.
1	29.6	17	502.8
2	59.1	18	532.3
3	88.7	19	561.9
4	118.3	20	591.7
5	147.9	21	621.0
6	177.4	22	650.6
7	207.0	23	680.2
8	236.6	24	709.8
9	266.2	25	739.3
10	295.7	26	768.9
11	325.3	27	798.5
12	354.9	28	828.1
13	384.5	29	857.7
14	414.0	30	887.2
15	443.6	31	916.8
16 (1 pint)	473.2	32 (1 quart)	946.4

Table 15-9

Equivalents of Household Food Measures

Quarts	Pints	Standard Cups	Fluid Ounces	Table-spoonfuls	Tea-spoonfuls	Milli-liters
1.0	2.0	4.0	32.0	64.0	192.0	946.4
0.5	1.0	2.0	16.0	32.0	96.0	473.2
0.25	0.5	1.0	8.0	16.0	48.0	236.6
0.125	0.25	0.5	4.0	8.0	24.0	118.3
....	0.125	0.25	2.0	4.0	12.0	59.2
....	....	1.125	1.0	2.0	6.0	29.6
....	....	....	0.5	1.0	3.0	14.8
....	....	....	......	0.33	1.0	4.9
....	....	....	......	......	0.2	1.0

Table 15-10

Relation of Steam Pressure and Compartment Temperature

Gauge Pressure Lb. per Sq. In.	Temperature °F
0 (14.7 atmospheric pressure)	212.
1	215.2
2	218.3
3	221.3
4	224.2
5	226.9
6	229.5
7	231.9
8	233.3
9	236.6
10	238.8

Table 15-11

Gauge Pressure and Boiling Temperature Relationships at Various Altitudes

The following table shows the extra pressure (gauge pressure) in pounds per sq. in. needed above atmospheric pressure to produce boiling temperatures at various altitudes:

| Temperature | | Sea Level | Elevation — Feet Above Sea Level | | | | | | |
Degrees C.	Degrees F.		500	1000	2000	3000	4000	5000	6000
100.0	212	0.0	0.2	0.5	1.0	1.5	2.0	2.4	2.9
104.4	220	2.5	2.7	3.0	3.4	3.9	4.4	4.9	5.3
110.0	230	6.1	6.3	6.6	7.1	7.6	8.0	8.5	9.0
115.6	240	10.3	10.5	10.8	11.3	11.7	12.2	12.7	13.1
121.1	250	15.1	15.4	15.6	16.1	16.6	17.1	17.5	18.0
126.7	260	20.7	21.0	21.2	21.7	22.2	22.7	23.1	23.6

Table 15-12a
Definitions of Heat

Specific heat	Number of Btu's or Calories required to raise, respectively, 1 lb or 1 Kg of a substance 1° F or 1° C. (The specific heat of water is 1.0 and ice 0.48. Thus, to raise ice at 0° F to 212° F will require 32° [32-0] × 0.48 *plus* 180° [212-32] × 1.0, or 195.36 Btu's.)
Latent heat of fusion	Heat required to change a solid to a liquid. (Ice requires 144 Btu's, and we must add this to the specific heat to calculate the total heat required: 144 + 195.36 = 339.36 Btu's.)
Latent heat of vaporization	Heat required to change a liquid to a vapor; the lower the temperature at which the change occurs, the more heat is required. (To change 1 lb of water at 212° F to steam at the same temperature requires 970 Btu's, but to change water at 60° to vapor at 60° requires 1158 Btu's.)

Table 15-12b

Equivalent Fahrenheit and Centigrade Degrees

Fahrenheit	Centigrade	Fahrenheit	Centigrade	Fahrenheit	Centigrade
0	-17.8	60	15.6	120	48.9
10	-12.2	65	18.3	150	65.6
15	-9.4	70	21.1	200	93.3
20	-6.7	75	23.9	212	100.0
32	0	80	26.7	250	121.1
35	1.7	85	29.4	300	148.9
40	4.4	90	32.2	350	176.7
45	7.2	95	35.0	400	204.4
50	10.0	100	37.8	450	232.2
55	12.8	110	43.3	500	260.0

Rule: Fahrenheit to Centigrade: Subtract 32 from Fahrenheit degrees and multiply the remainder by ⅝; product is centigrade degrees.
Centigrade to Fahrenheit: Multiply centigrade degrees by 9/5 and add 32; product is fahrenheit degrees.

Table 15-13

Equivalents Between Fresh and Frozen Foods

Food Item	Frozen	Fresh	% Waste Eliminated
(Fish and Sea Food)			
Cod and Haddock Fillets	5 lb	15 lb	67
Flounder Fillets	5 lb	20 lb	75
Halibut Fillets and Steaks	5 lb	10 lb	57
Lobster Meat	1 lb	32 lb	62
Mackerel Fillets	5 lb	9 lb	42
Red Perch Fillets	5 lb	25 lb	80
Swordfish Steaks	5 lb	6¼ lb	20
(Vegetables)			
Asparagus	2½ lb	5.4 lb	54
Broccoli	2½ lb	5.5 lb	55
Cauliflower	2½ lb	10.0 lb	75
Brussels Sprouts	2½ lb	7.0 lb	64
Corn, cut	2½ lb	2 doz ears	
Green Beans	2½ lb	4.0 lb	48
Wax Beans	2½ lb	4.0 lb	48
Beans; Limas, Fordhook, or Baby	2½ lb	7½ to 9 lb	63
Peas	2½ lb	7½ to 9 lb	67
Peas and Carrots	2½ lb	6 to 6¾ lb	63
Pumpkin	2½ lb	4.0 lb	48
Spinach	2½ lb	3.9 lb	63
Squash	2½ lb	6.9 lb	37
Succotash	2½ lb	4.0 lb	63
Mixed Vegetables	2½ lb	4.0 lb	63
(Poultry)			
Broilers, 12 to 24 oz	1 lb	1½ lb	33
Fryers, 1½ to 2½ lb	2 lb	3 lb	33
Fowl, 2 to 3½ lb	2½ lb	3¾ lb	33
Ducks, 3½ to 5 lb	4 lb	4¾ lb	30
Turkeys, 9 to 30 lb	22½ lb	30 lb	25
Geese	7 lb	10 lb	30
(Fruits) *			
Apples	30 lb (7:1)	35:4 lb	24
Apricots	30 lb (5:1)	26⅔:5 lb	6
Berries	30 lb (4:1)	25:6 lb	4
Cherries	30 lb (5:1)	27:5 lb	8
Canteloupe	30 lb (7:1)	52:4 lb	50
Peaches	30 lb (4:1)	31½:6 lb	24
Pineapple	30 lb (4:1)	47:6 lb	48
Rhubarb	30 lb (3:1)	25⅔:8 lb	14

*Most frozen fruit is packed in some sugar, and the ratio of fruit to sugar normally packed is shown in parenthesis after the 30 lb container size. In the next column for the fresh product, the quantity of fruit plus the sugar put in with it to equal the 30 lb is given. Waste is the excess over 30 pounds.

Table 15-14
Approximate Substitution Equivalents in Quantity Food Production

Ingredient	Substitute	Measure	Weight
Flour (2 c, 8 oz)	Cornstarch	1 c	13½ oz and 2½ oz cornstarch
Cake flour (1 qt, 1 lb)	Hard or all purpose flour	3¾ c and ¼ c cornstarch	
Sirups, honey, etc. (1 pt, 1 lb 6 oz)	Sugar	2½ c sugar, ½ c water, ⅛ t cream of tartar	1¼ lb sugar, 4 oz water, ⅛ t cream of tartar
Chocolate, bitter (2 c, 1 lb)	Cocoa	3½ c, ¾ c shortening	12½ oz, 3½ oz shortening
Milk, whole (1 qt, 2 lb)	Dry milk, whole*	⅞ c, 3⅞ c water	3¾ oz, 1⅞ lb water
Milk, whole (1 qt, 2 lb)	Dry milk, non-fat*	¾ c, 3½ c water, 2 T shortening	3½ oz, 1¾ lb water, 1 oz shortening
Milk, non-fat (1 qt, 2 lb)	Dry milk, non-fat*	¾ c, 3⅞ c water	3½ oz, 1⅞ lb water
Milk, whole (1 qt, 2 lb)	Evaporated milk	No. 1 tall can plus water to equal qt	14½ oz plus water to equal 1 qt
Eggs, whole (1 pt, 1 lb)	Dried whole eggs	1¼ c, 1¾ c water	5 oz, 12½ oz water
Eggs, whites (1 pt, 1 lb)	Dried whites	1⅛ c, 1¾ c water	3 oz, 14 oz water
Eggs, yolks (1 pt, 1 lb)	Dried yolks	1⅛ c, 1¾ c water	6 oz, 11 oz water
Eggs, whole (1 pt, 1 lb)	Frozen whole	1 pt (10 eggs)	1 lb
Eggs, whites (1 pt, 1 lb)	Frozen whites	1 pt (18 whites)	1 lb
Eggs, yolks (1 pt, 1 lb)	Frozen yolks	1 pt (24 yolks)	1 lb
Butter (1 pt, 1 lb)	Margarine	1 pt	1 lb
Butter or margarine (1 pt, 1 lb)	Fat or oil	1⅞ c plus ½ t salt, 2 T water	14 oz, ½ t salt, 1 oz water
Cream, coffee, 18% (1 qt, 2 lb)	Milk, non-fat and butter	3½ c milk, ¾ c butter	26 oz milk, 6 oz butter
Cream, whipping, 40% (1 qt, 2 lb)	Milk, non-fat and butter	3 c milk, 1⅓ c butter	20 oz milk, 12½ oz butter
Leavening agents			
Tartrate baking powder (¾ c, 4 oz)	SAS/baking powder phosphate	⅜ c	2 oz
Tartrate baking powder (¾ c, 4 oz)	Soda and cream of tartar	3 T and ⅔ c	1 oz and 3 oz
SAS Phosphate baking powder (⅜ c, 2 oz)	Phosphate baking powder	½ c plus 1 T	3 oz
SAS Phosphate baking powder (⅜ c, 2 oz)	Soda plus liquid	3 T plus 1 c sour milk or 1 c buttermilk or 1 c milk, 1 T vinegar or lemon juice or ½ to 1 c molasses	

*Measure equivalent is for regular dry milk; for instant use 1⅓ c for every ¾ of regular.

Table 15-15
Food Equivalents, Weights and Measures

Food	Weight	Approximate Measure
Beverages		
Cocoa	1 lb	4½ c
Coffee, urn grind	1 lb	4½ c
Coffee, instant	1 oz	½ c
Tea	1 lb	1½ qt
Cereals and Cereal Products		
Barley, pearl	1 lb	2½ c
Bran, all-bran	1 lb	2 qt
Bran flakes	1 lb	3 qt
Bread, crumbs, dry	1 lb	1¼ qt
Bread, crumbs, fresh	1 lb	2½ qt
Bread, crumbs, dry sifted	1 lb	1 qt
Bread, soft, broken, ¾ in. cubes	1 lb	2¼ qt (packed 2 qt)
Bread, slices, ⅝ in.	1 lb	16 slices
Cake crumbs, soft	1 lb	1¼ qt
Crackers, crumbled	1 lb	2 to 2½ qt
Crackers, crumbs	1 lb	1¼ qt
Crackers, graham	1 lb	40 crackers
Crackers, small, square saltines	1 lb	108 crackers
Crackers, large, soda	1 lb	56 crackers
Cracked wheat	1 lb	3½ c (5 to 6 c cooked)
Cornflakes	1 lb	1¼ gal
Cornmeal	1 lb	3½ c (3 qt cooked)
Cornstarch, stirred	1 lb	3½ c (1 c = 4¾ oz, 1 oz 3½ T)
Farina	1 lb	2⅔ c
Flour, graham or whole wheat	1 lb	3½ c
Flour, cake, unsifted	1 lb	3¾ c
Flour, cake, sifted	1 lb	1 qt
Flour, rye, straight grade, sifted	1 lb	1¼ qt
Flour, white, bread, sifted	1 lb	1 qt
Flour, white, bread, unsifted	1 lb	3¾ c
Farina	1 lb	2⅔ c
Hominy grits	1 lb	2½ to 3 c (6½ lb or 3¼ qt cooked)

Macaroni, 1 in. pieces	1 lb	3½ to 4 c (3¾ lb or 2½ qt cooked)
Noodles	1 lb	6 to 8½ c (3¾ lb or 2¼ qt cooked)
Oats, rolled	1 lb	4¾ c (2¼ qt cooked)
Rice	1 lb	2⅛ c (2½ lb or 2½ qt cooked)
Spaghetti, 2 in. pieces	1 lb	1¼ qt (4 lb or 2½ qt cooked)
Soya flour	1 lb	1¼ to 1½ qt
Tapioca, quick cooking	1 lb	2⅔ c (7½ c cooked)
Tapioca, pearl	1 lb	2¾ c (soaked and cooked 7½ c)
Wheat cereals	1 lb	2⅞ c (cooked 6 c)
Wheat, shredded	1 lb	20 small biscuits

Dairy Products

Butter or Margarine (see also fats)	1 lb	2 c
Cheese, grated or ground	1 lb	2¼ c light pack, 3¾ c loose pack
Cheese, cubed	1 lb 1 oz	1 qt
Cheese, cottage	1 lb	2¼ c
Cheese, Philadelphia cream	1 lb 9 oz	3 c
Cream, 18%	8¾ oz	1 c
Cream, 30 to 40%, whipping	1 lb	1 pt (doubles volume in whipping)
Milk, condensed, sweetened	11 oz	1 c
Milk, dry, instant	1 lb	5¾ c
Milk, dry, non-fat, regular	1 lb	1 qt
Milk, dry, whole, regular	1 lb	3¾ c
Milk, evaporated	1 lb	1⅞ c
Milk, fresh, liquid	8½ oz	1 c

*Eggs, large**

Eggs in shell	1½ lb	1 doz
Eggs, whole	1 lb	1 pt (9 to 11)
Eggs, whites	1 lb	1 pt (17 to 20)
Eggs, yolks	1 lb	1 pt (19 to 23)
Eggs, hardcooked, chopped	1 lb	2½ c (1 doz = 3½ c)
Eggs, dry, whole, packed	1 oz	¼ c
Eggs, whole dry	1 lb	1¼ qt (1½ c (6oz) and 1⅞ c water= 1 doz eggs)
Eggs, whites, dry	1 lb	2 qt (¾ c (2 doz) and 1½ c water= 1 doz whites)
Eggs, yolks, dry	1 lb	4¼ c (1⅛ c (4 doz) and ⅝ c water= 1 doz yolks)
Meringue	6 oz	1 c

*Eggs lose approximately 11 to 12% weight in shelling. Medium eggs are about 10% less in weight than large.

Table 15-15 — Continued
Food Equivalents, Weights and Measures

Food	Weight	Approximate Measure
Fats and Oils		
Bacon fat	15 oz	1 lb (1 lb = 2⅛ c)
Butter or margarine	14 oz	1 pt
Creamed fat	1 lb	2½ c
Hydrogenated shortening	14½ oz	1 pt
Oil	1 lb	2¼ c
Suet, chopped	1 lb	3¾ c
Fruits		
Apples	1 lb	3 size 113 (3 c pared, diced or sliced)
Apples, sliced	1 lb	4 to 4½ c
Apples, diced half inch	1 lb	1 qt
Applesauce	1 lb	1⅞ c
Apples, canned, solid pack	1 lb	1 pt
Apple nuggets	1 lb	6⅔ c
Apricots, dried	1 lb	3¼ c (1¾ lb or 5 c cooked)
Apricots, canned, heavy pack	1 lb	1 pt
Apricots, canned, halves, no juice	1 lb	1 pt (21 halves)
Apricots, fresh	1 lb	8 medium
Avocados, Calavos, medium size	1 lb	2 to 3
Bananas, AP, medium size	1 lb	3 (peeled 10 oz)
Bananas, peeled	1 lb	2½ c diced, 1 medium banana = 30 ⅛ in. slices or ¾ c or ⅓ to ½ c mashed
Blackberries, fresh	1 lb	1 qt
Blackberries, water pack, drained	1 lb	3 c
Blueberries, fresh	1 lb	3 c
Cantelope	1 lb	1 melon 4 in. in diameter
Cherries, red, heavy pack, drained	1 lb	3 c
Cherries, Royal Anne, drained	1 lb	3 c
Cherries, candied	1 lb	3 c or 120 cherries
Cherries, Maraschino	1 qt	60 to 70 cherries
Citron, chopped	1 lb	2½ c
Cranberries, fresh	1 lb	1 qt (1 lb AP = 3¼ c sauce)
Cranberries, dehydrated	1 lb	8½ c

Cranberries, whole	2½ lb raw	1 qt cooked
Currants	1 lb	3½ c (1 c = 4½ oz)
Dates, pitted	1 lb	2¾ c (1 c = 6 oz, 1 c = 8¼ oz if packed)
Dates		
Dates, unpitted	1 lb	2½ c (1¾ c pitted)
Figs, dry	1 lb	3 c (1 c = 5 oz)
Grapefruit, 32's	1 lb	12 sections, 1¼ c juice
Grapes, whole, stemmed	1 lb	1 qt
Grapes, cut	1 lb	2⅔ c
Oranges, 88's, diced with juice	1 lb	2¼ c (1 orange = ½ c diced or ⅓ c juice)
Oranges, 88's, Florida	1 doz	1 qt juice
Oranges, rind, grated (also lemon)	1⅔ oz	¼ c (1 t = ⅛ oz)
Oranges, rind, grated (also lemon)	6½ oz	1 c
Peaches, canned, sliced with juice	1 lb	⅞ c
Peaches, fresh	1 lb	3 to 5 peaches
Peaches, dry, loose pack	1 lb	1 qt
Pears, canned, drained, diced	1 lb	2½ c
Pineapple, slices	1 lb	8 to 12 slices (2½ c)
Prunes, dried, size 30 to 40, uncooked	1 lb	3 c (2½ lb or 5 to 6 c cooked)
Prunes, cooked, pitted, with juice	1 lb	2¼ c
Pumpkin	1 lb	2½ c
Raspberries	1 lb	3½ c (2¼ c cooked)
Raisins	1 lb	3 c (1 c = 5¼ oz, 1 lb cooked = 1 lb 9½ oz or 1 qt)
Rhubarb, raw, 1 in. pieces	1 lb	1 qt (cooked 1⅜ lb or 2½ c)
Strawberries, fresh	1 lb	3¼ c
Meats		
Bacon, diced, packed	1 lb	2¼ c
Bacon, raw, sliced	1 lb	15 to 25 slices
Bacon, cooked	1 lb	85 to 95 slices
Beef, dried, solid pack	1 lb	1 qt, scant
Beef, ground, raw	1 lb	1 pt
Beef, cooked, diced	1 lb	3 c
Chicken, ready-to-cook	5 lb	5 c cooked, diced meat (40% yield)
Chicken, cooked, cubed	1 lb	2½ c
Crabmeat, flaked	1 lb	3 c
Ham, cooked, diced	1 lb	3¼ c
Ham, cooked, ground, packed	1 lb	1 pt
Ham, raw, AP	1 lb	1 c fine diced cooked

Table 15-15 — Continued
Food Equivalents, Weights and Measures

Food	Weight	Approximate Measure
Meats, chopped, cooked, moist, packed	1 lb	1 pt (loose pack = 1 qt)
Oysters, 1 qt, Eastern	2 lb	40 large, 60 small
Salmon, canned	1 lb	1 pt
Sardines, canned	1 lb	48, 3 in. long
Sausage, link	1 lb	16
Sausage meat	1 lb	1 pt
Shrimp, 2 lb AP	1 lb EP	3¼ c (5 lb in shell = gal)
Tuna Fish	1 lb	1 pt
Turkey, ready-to-cook	30 lb	15 lb clear meat
Weiners	1 lb	10 (frankfurters 6 to 7)
Miscellaneous		
Chocolate, see spices		
Compressed yeast	½ oz	1 cake
Compressed yeast	8½ oz	1 c
Dry active yeast	1 lb	2½ lb compressed
Gelatin, granulated, unflavored	1 lb	3½ c (1 oz = 3½ T)
Gelatin, prepared, flavored	1 lb	2⅓ c (1 oz = ¼ c)
Marshmallows (1¼ in.)	1 lb	80
Nuts		
Almonds, shelled	1 lb	3½ c (¼ lb shelled)
Almonds, blanched	1 lb	3 c
Coconut, shredded	1 lb	4½ c to 7 c depending on type shred and tightness of pack
Coconut, ground or fine shred	2⅜ oz	1 c
Coconut, shredded, medium	1 oz	7 T
Filberts	1 lb	3⅓ c (½ lb shelled)
Peanut butter	1 lb	1⅞ c
Peanuts, chopped	1 lb	1 qt (⅔ lb shelled)
Pecans	1 lb	4¼ c (⅓ lb shelled)
Walnut meats	1 lb	4¾ c (½ lb shelled)
Walnut meats, chopped	1 lb	1 qt
Nut meats, ground	4¼ oz	1 c

Salad Dressings and Condiments

Catsup or Chili Sauce	9 oz	1 c
Cooked Salad Dressing	1 lb	1 pt
French Dressing	1 lb	2⅛ c
Horseradish, ground	1 lb	2¼ c
Mayonnaise	1 lb	2⅛ c
Olives, small	1 lb	3½ c or 135 olives, 1 No. 10 = 4½ lb drained weight or 350 large olives
Pickles, chopped	1 lb	2½ c
Pickles, small	1 gal	80 (about 225 gherkins or 25 large per gal)

Spices, Seasonings, Leavenings

Allspice, ground	1 lb	4½ c (1 oz — 4½ T)
Baking Powder	1 lb	2½ c (1 T = 7/16 oz, 1 oz = 2½ T)
Celery Seed	1 lb	1 qt (1 oz = ¼ c)
Chili or Curry Powder	1 oz	3 T
Chocolate, grated	1 lb	1 qt (1 lb = 16 squares)
Chocolate, grated	1 oz	5 T (1 c = 3¾ oz)
Chocolate, melted	1 lb	1⅞ c (1 oz = 2 T)
Cinnamon, ground	1 lb	1 qt (1 oz = ¼ c)
Cloves, ground	1 lb	3¾ c (1 oz = 3¾ T)
Cloves, whole	1 oz	5 T
Cream of Tartar	1 lb	3 c (1 oz = 3 T)
Flavoring Extracts	⅜ oz	1 T (⅛ oz = 1 t)
Ginger, ground	1 lb	4¾ c (1 oz = 4¾ T)
Mustard, ground	1 lb	5 c (1 oz = 5 T)
Nutmeg, ground	1 lb	3½ c (1 oz = 3½ T)
Paprika	3¼ oz	1 c (1 T = ⅜ doz)
Pepper	1 oz	¼ c
Sage, ground	1 oz	½ c
Salt	1 lb	1⅔ c (1 oz = 1 T, 2 t)
Soda	1 lb	2½ c (1 oz = 2 T, 6½ t = 1 oz)
Vinegar	1 lb	2 c (1 oz = 2 T)
Worcestershire Sauce	9½ oz	1 c

Sugars and Sirups

Corn sirup	11 oz	1 c
Honey	12 oz	1 c
Jam or jelly	1½ lb	1 pt

Table 15-15 — Continued
Food Equivalents, Weights and Measures

Food	Weight	Approximate Measure
Sugar, cocktail cube	1 cublet	½ t (small cube = 1 t, tablet = 1½ t, 96 cubes, medium, per lb)
Sugar, granulated	1 lb	2¼ c (superfine 2 c)
Sugar, confectioners, stirred	1 lb	3½ c
Sugar, confectioners, 4 X, sifted	1 lb	4½ c unsifted 2¾ c)
Sugar, brown	1 lb	3 c (packed 2¼ c)
Molasses	11 oz	1 c
Vegetables		
Asparagus, fresh	1 lb	20 stalks
Asparagus, canned tips, drained	1 lb	19 stalks
Asparagus, canned, cuts, drained	1 lb	2½ c
Beans, baked	1 lb	1⅞ c
Beans, dried, lima, small, AP	1 lb	2⅓ c (2½ lb or 1½ qt cooked)
Beans, lima, fresh, unshelled	1 lb	⅔ c shelled
Beans, lima, fresh, shelled	1 lb	2¼ c
Beans, lima, drained, cooked fresh or canned	1 lb	2⅔ c (1½ lb = 1 qt)
Beans, kidney, dry, AP	1 lb	2⅓ c (2¼ lb or 1½ qt cooked)
Beans, string, cut, uncooked, EP	12 oz	1 qt
Beans, navy, dry, AP	1 lb	2⅓ c (2½ lb or 1¾ c cooked)
Bean Sprouts	1 lb	1 qt
Beets, cooked, diced, drained	1 lb	2¼ c (3 to 4 medium whole)
Beets, cooked, sliced, drained	1½ lb	1 qt (1 lb = 2¾ c)
Brussels Sprouts, AP	1 lb	1 qt
Cabbage, shredded, EP	12 oz	1 qt (1 lb = 5½ c or 1 lb = 7 c loose pack)
Cabbage, AP, shredded, cooked, drained	1 lb	3½ c
Carrots, half inch cube, raw	1 lb	3¼ c
Carrots, diced, cooked, drained	1 lb	2½ to 3 c
Carrots, ground, raw, EP	1 lb	3¼ c
Carrots, AP	1 lb	4 medium, 6 small
Cauliflower, 1 crate	12½ lb, net, EP	10 qt
Cauliflower, head, medium	12 oz	4 to 5 portions
Celery, diced, EP	1¼ lb	1 qt (1 lb = 3¼ c)
Celery, dehydrated	1 lb	9½ c

Item	Amount	Yield
Corn, cream style	1 lb	1⅞ c
Corn, whole kernel, drained	1 lb	2⅓ c
Cucumbers, diced	1 lb	2½ c
Eggplant, diced half inch cubes	1 lb	4½ c
Eggplant, sliced, 4 in. diameter, half inch thick	1 lb	8 slices
Garlic, crushed	1 oz	6 to 9 cloves
Lettuce, average head	1 lb	10 to 12 leaf cups
Lettuce, shredded	1 lb	8 c (packed 5 c)
Lettuce, leaf	1 lb	30 salad garnishes
Onions, AP	1 lb	4 to 5 medium
Onions, chopped	1 lb	2½ to 3 c
Onions, grated or minced	5 oz	1 c
Onions, dehydrated	1 lb	9½ c
Mushrooms, fresh	1 lb AP	1⅓ c cooked
Parsley	1 lb	3 bunches (6 c chopped)
Parsnips, AP	1 lb	3 to 4 medium
Parsnips, diced, raw	1 lb	2½ to 3 c
Parsnips, diced cooked	1 lb	2½ c
Parsnips, mashed	1 lb	1 pt
Peas, fresh, 2½ lb AP	1 lb EP	1 pt scant, 5 portions
Peas, canned, dried	1 lb	2¼ c
Peas, dried, split	1 lb	2⅓ c (2½ lb or 5½ c cooked)
Peppers, green	1 lb	5 to 6 medium
Peppers, green, chopped	1 lb	3½ c
Pimientos, chopped	8 oz	1 c
Potatoes, white, medium, AP	1 lb	3 to 4 (¾ lb pared, 1 pt mashed)
Potatoes, dehydrated cube	1 lb	4¾ c
Potatoes, dehydrated, flake	3½ oz	1 c
Potatoes, granule, dehydrated	7 oz	1 c
Potatoes, cooked, diced half inch cube	1 lb	3 c
Potatoes, sweet	1 lb	3 medium
Potato chips	1 lb	5 qt (20 1 c portions ¾ oz)
Pumpkin, cooked	1 lb	1 pt
Radishes, whole, topped and cleaned	1 lb	1 qt
Rutabagas, cubed, cooked	1 lb	3 c
Rutabagas, raw, cubed, EP	1 lb	3⅓ c
Sauerkraut, uncooked	1 lb	3 c
Spinach, raw	1 lb	5 qt, loose pack

Table 15-15 — Continued
Food Equivalents, Weights and Measures

Food	Weight	Approximate Measure
Spinach, 1 lb raw, AP, cooked	13 oz (EP)	1½ c cooked, 3 portions
Spinach, canned, drained	1 lb	1 pt
Squash, summer, AP	1½ lb	1 3 in. diameter
Squash, Hubbard, cooked, mashed	1 lb	2⅛ c
Tomatoes, canned	1 lb	1 pt
Tomatoes, dried	1 lb	3½ c
Tomatoes, fresh	1 lb	3 to 4 medium
Tomatoes, fresh, diced	1 lb	2¼ to 2¾ c
Turnips, AP	1 lb	4 to 5 medium
Turnips, raw, diced	1 lb	3½ c
Watercress	1 lb	5 bunches

Table 15-16
Standard Portions

Food	Portion and Serving Method
Meats	
American chop suey	4 oz ladle, rounded
with corn soya	2 T, No. 32 scoop
with rice	No. 16 scoop
Baked hash, beef or corned beef	No. 10 scoop or heaped serving spoon, 5 to 6 oz
Beef or other meat and noodles	No. 8 scoop rounded or 6 oz ladle rounded, about 7 oz (¾ c)
Beef patty	No. 8 scoop before cooking, use tongs
Beef or other meat stew	6 oz, (¾ c), ladle
Chili con carne	6 oz ladle rounded to give 8 oz
Corned beef and cabbage	3 or 4 oz sliced beef, tongs; 3 to 4 oz cabbage, spoon
Cold cuts	3 oz, tongs or spatula
Cabbage rolls	2 rolls, 3 oz each (use 2 oz meat filling), use spoon
Creamed meats	½ c, 4 oz ladle; use 8 to 10 lb cooked meat per 100; serve over toast, biscuits or No. 16 scoop rice
Croquettes	No. 10 or 12 scoop for 1; No. 20 scoop for 2; 1½ oz sauce
Frankfurters, 6 to 7 lb	2, tongs
with sauerkraut	1 rounded serving spoon, 3 oz
Fritters	2, tongs; portion with No. 20 scoop; 2 strips bacon
Ham a la king	4 oz ladle rounded
Ham, baked, boned	5 to 6 oz before cooking, tongs
Ham, baked, slices	3 to 4 oz after cooking, tongs
Ham, fried	6 oz before cooking, tongs
Hamburgers	2, portion with No. 20 dipper, tongs
Liver, braised	3 to 4 oz before cooking, 2 strips bacon, tongs
Meat balls and spaghetti	No. 20 scoop, 2 balls, 2 serving spoons spaghetti and sauce
Meat sandwich, hot	2 oz meat, 1 or 2 slices bread, tongs; 2 oz ladle gravy
Meat loaf	4 to 5 oz cooked, slice and use spatula or tongs
Meat pie	2 serving spoons, rounded, 8 oz
with pie crust	Cut 17 x 25 baking pans 5 x 9, 45 portions
with biscuit	2½ in diameter, serve 1 with 6 oz stew
Meat turnover	2 oz meat, No. 16 scoop; serve with 2 oz gravy, ladle
Mock drum sticks	5 oz before cooking, serve 1
New England boiled dinner	6 oz before cooking, 3 to 4 oz after, tongs, 5 oz vegetables and 5 oz potatoes
Pork chop	3 to lb before cooking, serve 1; 6 to lb serve 2
with dressing	2 to 3 oz; use serving spoon or No. 16 scoop
Pork chop with pocket	3 to lb, 1½ oz stuffing; tongs
Roasts, meat or poultry	3 oz cooked, tongs
with dressing	2 to 3 oz meat cooked; 4 oz (½ c), No. 10 scoop rounded of dressing
Sausage, bulk	3 oz before cooking, tongs
Sausages, link, 14 to 16 per lb.	2, tongs
Spareribs	8 to 12 oz before cooking, tongs
Steak, braised, Swiss, etc.	6 to 7 oz raw, 4 to 5 oz cooked, spoon
Steak, dinner, dry heat type	8 oz AP, no bone, tongs; size may vary with institution
Steak, ground	3 to pound, No. 8 scoop rounded; 4 oz cooked, tongs
Steak, stuffed	5 to 6 oz before cooking; 1½ oz dressing, tongs
Stew	No. 8 scoop rounded or 6 oz ladle rounded (¾ c)
Veal birds	5 oz before cooking; 1½ oz dressing; spoon
Veal cutlet	4 oz before breading; 5 oz breaded
Veal chop	5 oz
Weiners, 10 to lb	2, tongs

Table 15-16 — Continued
Standard Portions

Food	Portion and Serving Method
Fish	
Fillet, baked or fried	3 to pound before cooking; 4 oz if breaded
Steak	3 to pound unless wasty in eating, then 6 oz
Creamed fish dishes	4 oz ladle rounded; 1 slice toast, 1 biscuit or No. 16 scoop of rice
Shrimp wiggle	4 oz ladle rounded; slice of toast or biscuit or No. 16 scoop of rice
Shrimp, deep fried, fantail	4 to 5, tongs
Strips, breaded and deep fried	1 oz each, serve three, tongs; about 35% breading
Croquettes	No. 10 scoop for 1; No. 20 scoop for two; 1½ oz sauce
Loaf	4 oz slice; in 17 x 25 pan, cut 5 by 9, in 12 by 20 pan, cut 4 by 6; bake in these 1 in. deep
Scalloped salmon, tuna, etc.	1 4 oz ladle rounded, 5 to 6 oz; if thick, rounded serving spoon
Fish and noodles	Serving spoon rounded, 5 to 6 oz
Tuna fish, potato chip dish	Serving spoon rounded, 5 to 6 oz
Souffle	Cut 17 x 25 pan, 5 by 9, 12 by 20 pan 4 by 6
Poultry	
Chicken fricassee, unboned	12 oz raw meat, spoon
Chicken, creamed	6 oz (¾ c); about 2 oz cooked chicken meat per portion
Chicken, fried	2 pieces or half (12 oz before cooking)
Chicken or turkey, roast	2 to 3 oz with dressing, 4 oz without, 2 oz gravy
Duck or geese	12 oz to 1 lb before cooking
*Luncheon Entrees**	
American noodles	5 oz, serving spoon well rounded
Baked beans	6 oz ladle or two serving spoons or one heaped
Baked lima beans	6 oz, serving spoon heaped
Baked eggs, creole	4 oz ladle, rounded
Beef biscuit roll	1, 4 in. diameter, 2 oz ladle gravy
Buttered apples with sausage	3 apple halves, 2 sausages
Cheeseburgers	1 No. 16 scoop, 2 each, slice cheese ¾ to 1 oz each
Cheese fondue	4 oz, 1 oz sauce; cut 12 by 20 pan 4 by 6, spoon and ladle
Rice and cheese baked	5 oz (⅔ c), well rounded serving spoon
Creole spaghetti	1 serving spoon well rounded (6 oz)
Eggs a la king or creamed eggs	2 halves egg on half slice of toast; 2 oz sauce
Omelet	4 oz, spoon; if cut, use spatula
Goulash	6 oz ladle
Italian delight	4 oz ladle
Italian spaghetti	1 heaped serving spoon spaghetti, 4 oz ladle sauce
Macaroni and cheese	1 heaped serving spoon, 5 to 6 oz
Macaroni hoe	1 heaped serving spoon, 5 to 6 oz
Meat souffle	1 heaped serving spoon, 1½ oz sauce
Pizza Pie	Cut 18 x 20 in baking sheet 4 by 5, use spatula
Scalloped ham and potatoes	1 heaped serving spoon, 5 to 6 oz
Scalloped meat dishes	1 heaped serving spoon, 5 to 6 oz
Scrapple	4 oz, 2 slices
Spanish rice	1 well rounded serving spoon, 5 oz
Stuffed cabbage	1 or two

*A 12 by 20 in. baking pan 4 in. deep with food (16 to 18 lb of food) may be cut 5 by 8 to give 40 6 to 7 oz portions. (Use 6 in. deep pan)

Table 15-16 — Continued
Standard Portions

Food	Portion and Serving Method
Swedish meat balls	2 2 oz each after cooking; portion with rounded No. 20 scoop
Tamale pie	1 heaped serving spoon, 5 to 6 oz
Welsh Rarebit	½ c, 4 oz ladle, on toast, biscuit or No. 16 scoop rice

Vegetables

Most canned vegetables	3 oz (½ c), 1 rounded serving spoon
Apples, buttered	½ c, 3 to 4 pieces, serving spoon
Asparagus tips	3 to 5 canned, 4 to 6 fresh
Beans, navy, lima or other	4 to 5 oz, serving spoon
Beets, Harvard	½ c, serving spoon rounded
Beet greens, other greens	3 oz (½ c), tongs or serving spoon
Broccoli, buttered	2 to 3 pieces, 3 to 4 oz, tongs
Cabbage, steamed, fried, etc.	3 oz (½ c), serving spoon
Onions, creamed	2 to 3 small onions, serving spoon
Potato puff	5 oz, ⅔ c, spoon
Potato, browned, steamed, etc.	5 oz, serving spoon
Potato, au gratin, creamed, etc.	4 to 5 oz, serving spoon
Potato, baked	5 to 6 oz, tongs
Potato, hash brown, etc.	4 to 5 oz, serving spoon
Potato, mashed	1 No. 10 scoop or serving spoon, 4 oz
Potato, French fried	4 oz, 8 to 10 pieces, tongs or spoon
Potato cakes	4 oz, serving spoon
Rice, steamed	No. 10 scoop rounded (⅔ c)
Squash, acorn, baked or steamed	⅓ or ½ squash
Squash, hubbard	6 to 7 oz piece before baking
Squash, mashed	4 oz, rounded serving spoon
Sweet potatoes, baked	5 to 6 oz, tongs
Sweet potatoes, candied or glazed	2 slices, 4 oz
Scalloped sweet potatoes and apples	4 oz, serving spoon
Tomatoes, escalloped or stewed	4 oz ladle
Vegetable pie	5 oz, well rounded serving spoon
Vegetables, creamed	3 to 4 oz

Salads

Cole slaw	3 oz, serving spoon
Cottage cheese	No. 20 scoop
Deviled egg	2 halves
Gelatin	12 by 20 pan, 1 in. deep, cut 5 by 10, 50 portions
Mixed fruit	1 rounded serving spoon, No. 12 scoop
Mixed vegetable	1 rounded serving spoon
Sliced tomato	2 large or 3 medium slices
Head lettuce, 1 lb average	⅛ head, 2 oz serving
Potato, cold or hot	1 No. 10 or No. 12 scoop (4 to 5 oz)
Waldorf	1 rounded serving spoon, 3 oz
Fish or meat salad. entree type	5 to 6 oz, 1 c
Brown bean	4 to 5 oz

Table 15-16 — Continued
Standard Portions

Food	Portion and Serving Method
Dressings and Sauces	
Mayonnaise, boiled, etc.	1 to 2 T; portion depends upon salad size
French or other liquid	1 to 2 T; portion depends upon salad size
Cranberry sauce, applesauce, etc.	2 to 2½ oz, scant serving spoon or No. 16 scoop
	1 to 2 T
Soup	
Cup	6 oz, ¾ c
Bowl	8 oz, 1 c
Tureen	10 to 12 oz, 1¼ to 1½ c
Breads	
Biscuits	2 to 3 1 oz each**
Bran rolls	2 1 oz each
Cinnamon rolls	2 1½ oz each
Cornbread, coffee cake, etc.	1 piece 2 oz, cut 18 x 26 in. baking sheet 6 by 8
Muffins	2 2½ oz each
Griddle cakes	3 3 to 4 oz each
Potato doughnuts	2 2 oz each
Hot rolls	2 1 oz each
Sweet dough items, breakfast	1 3 oz each
White or other bread, sliced	1 to 2 slices, 1 oz each

Desserts	Pan Size	Portion
Cakes, butter		
Sheet, 1 layer	18 x 26 in.	Cut 6 by 8, 48 portions
	13½ x 22⅞ in.	Cut 5 by 9 or 6 by 8, 45 or 48 portions
	12¾ x 23 in.	Cut 5 by 9 or 6 by 8, 45 or 48 portions
Sheet, 2 layer	18 x 26 in.	Cut 12 by 5, 60 portions
	13½ x 22⅞ in.	Cut 3 by 20, 60 portions
	12¾ x 23 in.	Cut 3 by 20, 60 portions
Square, 1 layer	9½ x 9½ in.	Cut 3 by 4, 12 portions
Square, 2 layer	9½ x 9½ in.	Cut 3 by 7, 21 portions
Round, 2 layer	8 in. diameter	Cut 12

Eight 8 in. round layer cakes will serve 96
Six 9 x 13 in. sheets will serve 96
One 9 x 13 in. sheet, two layer, will serve 30
Four 12 in. round layer cakes will serve 120
Three 14 in. layer cakes (round) will serve 120

(See also portioning information in chapter on cakes and cookies)

Angel food	16 oz	Cut 16
Chocolate roll, jelly, ect	18 x 26 in. rolled	34 to 36 portions
Cup cakes	1 No. 16 scoop	1 each
Doughnuts, cake	1 oz	2
Cookies		
Brownies, date bars, etc	18 x 26 in.	Cut 54, serve one
	13½ x 22⅞ in.	Cut 5 by 9, 45 portions

**weight is calculated from raw weight before baking

Table 15-16 — Concluded
Standard Portions

Desserts	Pan Size	Portion
Pies		
One or two crust	10 in.	Cut 8
(use marker)	9 in.	Cut 7
	8 in.	Cut 6
Crust, double	9 in.	12 oz
Crust, single	9 in.	6½ oz
Filling, cream	9 in.	1½ to 2 pt (1½ to 2 lb)
Filling, custard type	9 in.	1½ pt (1½ lb)
Filling, fruit	9 in.	1½ pt (1½ lb)
Puddings		
Apple crisp, brown		4 oz
betty, etc		
Apricot whip		¾ c
Bread Pudding	13½ x 22⅞ in.	½ c, cut 5 x 9
Cobblers, etc	13½ x 22⅞ in.	½ c, cut 5 x 9
	12 x 20 in.	½ c, cut 6 x 8
Cream, rice, tapioca, etc		½ c, No. 10 scoop
Cream puff or eclair batter		1 oz (small), 2 oz (large)
Cream puff or eclair filling		1½ oz, No. 20 scoop
Ice box cake	12¾ x 23 in.	Cut 5 x 10
Ice box pudding		No. 20 scoop
Jello	12¾ x 23 in.	Cut 5 by 9
	12 x 20 in.	Cut 6 by 8
Whipped cream topping		2 T, 2 qt whipped tops 100 portions
Ice Cream, etc		
Brick	quart	Cut 8
Bulk		No. 12 scoop
Sundae		No. 16, 2 oz sauce
(See also portioning information in frozen desserts)		
Miscellaneous		
Graham craker roll, etc	Loaf 9⅝ x 5½ x 3¼ in.	Cut 16
Pineapple delicious		½ c, No. 10 scoop rounded
Shortcake		2½ in. diameter biscuit, ⅓ c fruit, 2 T whipped cream
Steamed pudding	1 qt mold	Cut into 12 (3½ oz); 2 oz sauce
	12 x 20 in.	Cut 6 by 10
Meringues		⅓ c, 2 oz ladle sirup or sauce, 2 T whipped cream
Sauces for topping		3 T, vary with richness

Table 15-17
Canned Foods: Servings Per Can or Jar

PRODUCT	Content — Can or Jar (Approx.)			Size of Each Serving (Approx.)
	Net Weight or Volume	Cups or Pieces	Servings	
FRUITS				
Apples; Applesauce; Berries; Cherries; Grapes; Grapefruit and Orange Sections; Fruit Cocktail; Fruits for Salad; Sliced Peaches; Pears; Pineapple Chunks, Crushed, Tidbits	8½ to 8¾ oz	1 c	2	½ c
	16 to 17 oz	1¾ to 2 c	4	½ c
	1 lb 4 oz	2¼ to 2½ c	5	½ c
	1 lb 13 oz	3¼ to 3½ c	7	½ c
	6 lb 2 oz to 6 lb 12 oz	12 to 13 c	25	½ c
Apricots, Whole (Medium Size)	16 to 17 oz	8 to 14	4	2 to 3 apricots
	1 lb 13 oz	15 to 18	7	2 to 3 apricots
	6 lb 10 oz	50 to 60	25	2 to 3 apricots
Apricots, Halves (Medium Size)	8¾ oz	6 to 12	2	3 to 5 halves
	16 to 17 oz	12 to 20	4	3 to 5 halves
	1 lb 13 oz	26 to 35	7	3 to 5 halves
	6 lb 10 oz	95 to 130	25	3 to 5 halves
Peaches, Halves or Pears, Halves	16 to 17 oz	6 to 10	3	2 medium halves
	1 lb 13 oz	7 to 12	7	1 large half
	6 lb 10 oz	45 to 65	25	2 medium halves
Pineapple, Sliced	9 oz	4	2	2 slices
	1 lb 4 oz	10	5	2 slices
	1 lb 14 oz	8	8	1 large slice
	6 lb 12 oz	28 to 50	25	1 large or 2 small slices
Plums; Prunes	8¾ oz	7 to 9	2	2 to 3 plums
	16 to 17 oz	10 to 14	4	2 to 3 plums
	1 lb 14 oz	12 to 20	7	2 to 3 plums
	6 lb 10 oz	40 to 60	25	2 to 3 plums
Figs	8 to 9 oz	6 to 12	2	3 to 4 figs
	16 to 17 oz	12 to 20	4	3 to 4 figs
	1 lb 14 oz	18 to 24	7	3 to 4 figs
	7 lb	70 to 90	25	3 to 4 figs

Item	Net Weight	Approx. Cups	Approx. Servings	Serving Size
Cranberry Sauce	6 to 8 oz	¾ to 1 c	4	¼ c
	1 lb	2 c	8	¼ c
	7 lb 5 oz	12 to 13 c	50	¼ c
*Olives, Ripe	4½ oz	—	—	3 olives
	9 oz	—	—	3 olives
	1 lb 2 oz	—	—	3 olives
	4 lb 2 oz	—	—	3 olives

VEGETABLES

Item	Net Weight	Approx. Cups	Approx. Servings	Serving Size
Asparagus Cuts; Beans, Green and Wax, Kidney, Lima; Beets; Carrots; Corn; Hominy; Okra; Onions; Peas; Peas and Carrots; Black-Eyed Peas; Pumpkin; Sauerkraut; Spinach and Other Greens; Squash; Succotash; **Sweet Potatoes; Tomatoes; Mixed Vegetables; Potatoes, White, Cut, Sliced	8 to 8½ oz	1 c	2	½ c
	12 oz	1½ to ¾ c	4	½ c
	16 to 17 oz	2 c	4	½ c
	1 lb 4 oz	2¼ to 2½ c	5	½ c
	1 lb 13 oz	3¼ to 3½ c	7	½ c
	6 lb 2 oz to 6 lb 12 oz	12 to 13 c	25	½ c
Asparagus Spears (Medium Size) (Count in spears)	10½ oz	9 to 12	2	4 to 6 spears
	14½ to 16 oz	16 to 28	3	4 to 6 spears
	1 lb 3 oz	20 to 30	5	4 to 6 spears
	4 lb 4 oz	115 to 145	25	4 to 6 spears
Potatoes, White, Peeled, Whole, Small	16 to 17oz	8 to 12	4	2 to 3 potatoes
	6 lb 6 oz	55 to 65	25	2 to 3 potatoes
Beans; Baked; with Pork; in Sauce	8¾ oz	1 c	1 to 2	½ to ¾ c
	1 lb	1¾ c	3 to 4	½ to ¾ c
	1 lb 10 oz	3 c	4 to 6	½ to ¾ c
	6 lb 14 oz	12 to 13 c	16 to 25	½ to ¾ c
Mushrooms	2 oz	⅓ c	1	⅓ c
	4 oz	⅔ c	2	⅓ c
	8 oz	1½ c	4	⅓ c
	6 lb 7 oz	12 to 13 c	36	⅓ c
Pimientos; Peppers, Red, Sweet	2 oz	¼ c	—	—
	4 oz	½ c	—	—
	7 oz	1 c	—	—
	6 lb 13 oz	12 to 13 c	—	—

Table 15-17 — Continued
Canned Foods: Servings Per Can or Jar

PRODUCT	Net Weight or Volume	Cups or Pieces	Servings	Size of Each Serving (Approx.)
JUICES				
Apple; Cherry; Cranberry; Grape; Grapefruit; Grapefruit-Orange; Loganberry; Nectars; Orange; Pineapple; Prune; Tangerine; Carrot; Sauerkraut; Tomato; Vegetable Cocktail; Vegetable	6 to 8 oz	¾ to 1 c	1 to 2	4 to 6 oz
	12 fl oz	1½ c	3	4 oz
	1 pint	2 c	2	6 oz
			4	4 oz
	1 pt 2 fl oz	2¼ to 2½ c	3	6 oz
			5	4 oz
	1 pt 7 fl oz	3 c	3	6 oz
			6	4 oz
	1 quart	4 c	4	6 oz
			8	4 oz
	1 qt 14 fl oz	5¾ c	5	6 oz
			12	4 oz
	3 quarts	12 c	8	6 oz
			24	4 oz
			16	6 oz
Lemon; Lime	5½ to 6 oz	¾ c	—	—
SOUPS				
Condensed	10½ to 12 oz	1¼ c (2½ c prepared soup)	3	¾ c
	3 lb 2 oz	5¾ c (11½ c prepared soup)	12 to 16	¾ c
Ready-to-serve	8 fl oz indv	1 c	1	1 c
	12 fl oz	1½ c	2	¾ c
	15 fl oz	2 c	3	¾ c
	1 pt 5 fl oz to 1 pt 9 fl oz	2½ to 3 c	4	¾ c
	3 qt	12 c	20	¾ c

MEATS & POULTRY

Chili Con Carne; Chili Con Carne with Beans	15 to 16 oz	2 c	3 to 4	½ to ⅔ c
	1½ lb	3 c	4 to 5	½ to ⅔ c
	6 lb 12 oz	12 to 13 c	18 to 24	½ to ⅔ c
Corned Beef	12 oz	—	4	3 oz
	6 lb		30	3 oz
Corned Beef Hash	8 oz	1 c	1 to 2	½ to ⅔ c
	1 lb	2 c	3 to 4	½ to ⅔ c
	1½ lb	3 c	5 to 6	½ to ⅔ c
	5 lb 8 oz to 5 lb 14 oz	12 to 13 c	18 to 24	½ to ⅔ c
Deviled Ham	2¼ to 3 oz	⅓ c	3 to 4	1½ T
	4½ oz	½ c	5 to 6	1½ T
Deviled Meat; Potted Meat; Meat Spreads	2 to 3¼ oz	⅓ c	3 to 4	1½ T
	5½ oz	¾ c	8	1½ T
Luncheon Meat	12 oz	—	4	2 slices (3½" x 1¾" x ⅜")
	6 lb	—	32	
Tongue: Beef; Lamb; Pork	6 oz	—	2	3 oz
	12 oz	—	4	3 oz
	1 to 2 lb	—	5 to 10	3 oz
Hams, Whole (Small)	1½ to 4 lb	—	3 to 4 per pound	2 slices (4" x 3" x ⅛")
(Medium)	6 to 8 lb	—		
(Large)	9 to 14 lb	—		
Poultry, Boned: Chicken; Turkey	5 to 6 oz	—	2	3 oz
	12 oz	—	4	3 oz
	1 lb 14 oz	—	10	3 oz
	2 lb 3 oz	—	12	3 oz
Sausage, Pork; Frankfurters	8 oz	11 to 12	3 to 4	3 sausages
	12 oz	8 to 9 large	4	2 sausages
Stew: Beef, Lamb	1 lb	2 c	2	¾ c
	1 lb 4 oz	2½ c	3	¾ c
	1½ lb	3 c	4	¾ c
Vienna Sausage	4 oz	8 to 10	2	4 to 5 sausages
	9 oz	16 to 20	4	4 to 5 sausages

Table 15-17 — Continued
Canned Foods: Servings Per Can or Jar

PRODUCT	Content — Can or Jar (Approx.)			Size of Each Serving (Approx.)
	Net Weight or Volume	Cups or Pieces	Servings	
FISH AND SEAFOOD				
Clams	7½ oz	1 c	2	½ c
Crab Meat	5½ to 7½ oz	¾ to 1 c	2 to 3	⅓ to ½ c
Mackerel	1 lb	2 c	4	½ c
Oysters	8 oz	1 c	2	½ c
Salmon	7¾ oz	1 c	2	½ c
	1 lb	2 c	4	½ c
Sardines	3¼ to 4 oz	6 to 10	1½	5 to 7 sardines
Sardines, Pilchards	15 oz	6 to 7 large	4	1½ sardines
*Shrimp	4½ to 6½ oz	25 to 35	3 to 4	10 to 12 medium size
				6 to 8 jumbo size
Tuna in Oil	6 to 7 oz	1 c	2	½ c
	13 oz	1¾ c	4	½ c
INFANT FOODS				
VEGETABLES AND FRUITS				
Infant: Strained; Homogenized	4¾ oz	½ c	—	—
Junior Chopped	6½ oz	¾ c	—	—
	8 oz	⅞ c	—	—
MEATS				
Infant: Strained	3½ oz	7 T	—	—
Junior: Chopped	3½ oz	7 T	—	—

SOUPS

Infant	4¾ oz	½ c	— —
Junior	8 oz	⅞ c	— —

*Declared as drained weight. (The number of olives per container varies as to size of the olives.)

**Sweet potatoes also come in 1 lb 2 oz to 1 lb 7 oz cans.

NOTE: The net weight of various foods in the same size can or glass jar will vary with the density of the food. For the most part only minimum weights are shown in the table.

Cups or pieces and servings in the table have been given in approximates; and sizes of servings are given in rounded numbers in order to furnish a practical guide.

Table 15-18
Can Sizes

Size Can	Approximate Quantity		Products Contained
	Net Weight	Cups	
8 oz	8 oz	1	
Picnic	10½ to 12 oz	1¼	Fruits, vegetables, specialties
12 oz (vacuum)	12 oz	1½	Soups, fruits, vegetables, meat and fish specialties
No. 300	14 to 16 oz	1¾	Pork and beans, baked beans, meat products, cranberry sauce, blueberries, specialties
No. 303	16 to 17 oz	2	Fruits, vegetables, meats, ready-to-serve soups, specialties
No. 2	1 lb 4 oz or 1 pt 2 fl oz	2½	Juices, ready to serve soups, fruits and vegetables, specialties.
No. 2½	1 lb 13 oz	3½	Fruits, vegetables such as pumpkin, sauerkraut, pork and beans, greens, tomatoes
No. 3 cylinder or 46 oz	3 lb 3 oz or 1 qt 14 fl oz	5¾	Fruit and vegetable juices, pork and beans, condensed soup and some vegetables
No. 10	6½ lb to 7 lb 5 oz*	12 to 13	Fruits and vegtables for institutional use

*Jellies and jams and other heavy items will weight more than this.

Table 15-19
Can Substitutions for No. 10 Size

Net Weight of No. 10	Number Cans to Substitute	Net Weight Substituted
6 lb 10 oz	7 No. 303's	7 lb
6 lb 10 oz	5 No. 2's	6 lb 2 oz
6 lb 10 oz	4 No. 2½'s	7 lb 2 oz
6 lb 10 oz	2 No. 46 oz or 2 No. 3 cylinder	5 lb 12 oz to 6 lb 4 oz

Table 15-20

Dishes Stored on 14 x 18 in. Trays or 18 x 26 in. Baking Sheets

Item	Diameter (inches)	Height (inches)	Items per Tray	Items per Sheet	Weights* Dishes and Tray	Weights* Dishes and Sheet
		(China and Glassware)				
Glass, juice, 5 oz	2⅛	3⅝	35	84	9 lb 12 oz	23 lb 7 oz
Glass, water, 10 oz	3¼	3⅞	20	40	7 lb 11 oz	16 lb 4 oz
Glass, sherbet	3	2⅞	20	40	8 lb 2 oz	16 lb 14 oz
Plate	6⅜	¾	5	11	4 lb 6 oz	9 lb 15 oz
Plate	7⅜	¾	4	8	5 lb 2 oz	10 lb 14 oz
Fruit nappie	4⅝	1¼	8	21	4 lb 9 oz	11 lb 10 oz
Oatmeal bowl	5	1⅞	5	15	6 lb 5 oz	15 lb
Bouillon cup	3¾	2⅜	12	28	6 lb	16 lb 7 oz
Salad bowl	5⅞	1½	5	11	2 lb 10 oz	6 lb 2 oz
Creamer	1⅞	2	48	126	10 lb 4 oz	27 lb 4 oz
Custard cup (Hall)	3	2½	20	40	12 lb 3 oz	25 lb
		(Paper Goods)				
Creamer, 1 oz	1¾	1⅝	63	135		
Portion cup, ¾ oz	1½	1⅛	80	176		
Portion cup, 5 oz	3¾	1¼	12	28		
Portion cup, 6 oz	3¾	1⅞	12	28		
Juice cup, 5 oz	2½	2⅞	30	60		
Butter patty	2¼	½	30	77		

*Weights will vary according to type of china and glassware; to obtain total weight add weight of individual item times number of items on the container.

Source of basic data: Koch Refrigerators, Inc.

Table 15-21

Paper Containers Stored on 14 x 18 in. Trays or 18 x 26 in. Baking Sheets and Portions Obtained in Common-Sized Cans

Portion Size (oz)	Cup Height	Cups per Tray	Cups per Sheet	Number of Portions Obtained From Can* No. 2	No. 2½	Qt	46 oz	No. 10	Gal	10 lb
½	⅞ in.	88	187	36	52	64	92	224	256	320
½	1 in.	108	260	36	52	64	92	224	256	320
¾	1⅛ in.	80	187	24	34	43	61	148	171	212
1	1¼ in.	63	135	18	26	32	46	112	128	160
1¼	1¼ in.	48	117	14	20	26	37	90	102	128
2	1¼ in.	42	84	9	13	16	23	56	64	80
2	1⅜ in.	48	96	9	13	16	23	56	64	80
2½	1 7/16 in.	35	77	7	10	13	18	45	51	64
3¼	1½ in.	30	60	5	8	10	14	34	39	50
4	1⅝ in.	24	54	5	6	8	11	28	32	40
5½	1¾ in.	20	40	3	5	6	8	20	22	29
6	1⅞ in.	12	28	3	4	5	7	19	21	27
8	2¾ in.	12	28	2	3	4	6	14	16	20
10	2½ in.	12	24	2	3	3	4	11	13	16

*Approximate only; will depend upon fill of the container and portioning loss.

Source of basic data: Koch Refrigerators, Inc.

Table 15-22 through 15-24

Tables 15-22 through 15-24 were originally developed by the Nutrition Services Division of the New York State Department of Mental Health under Mrs. Kathryn Flack and adapted by Pearl J. Aldrich and Grace A. Miller in *Standardizing Recipes for Institutional Use.* Circular Bulletin 233, Agr. Experiment Station, Michigan State University, 1963.

Instructions for Using Table 15-22:

1. Locate column which corresponds to the original yield of the recipe you wish to adjust. For example, let us assume your original recipe for meat loaf yields 100 portions. Locate the **100** column.

2. Run your finger **down** this column until you come to the amount of the ingredient required (or closest to this figure) in the recipe you wish to adjust. Say that your original recipe for 100 portions of meat loaf requires 21 pounds of ground beef. Run your finger down the column headed 100 until you come to **21 pounds.**

3. Next, run your finger **across** the page, in line with that amount, until you come to the column which is headed to correspond with **the yield you desire.** Suppose you want to make 75 portions of meat loaf. Starting with your finger under the 21 lb. (in the 100 column), slide it across to the column headed 75 and read the figure. You see you need 15 lb. 12 oz. ground beef to make 75 portions with your recipe.

4. Record this figure as the amount of the ingredient required for the new yield of your recipe. Repeat Steps 1, 2, 3 for each ingredient in your original recipe to obtain the adjusted ingredient weight needed of each for your new yield. You can increase or decrease yield in this manner.

5. If you need to combine two columns to obtain your desired yield, follow the above procedure and **add together** the amounts given in the two columns to get the amount required for your adjusted yield. For example, to find the amount of ground beef for 225 portions of meat loaf (using the same basic recipe for 100 we used above) locate the figures in columns headed 200 and 25 and add them. In this case they would be: 42 lb. + 5 lb. 4 oz., and the required total would be 47 lb. 4 oz.

6. The figures in Table 1 are given in **exact** weights including fractional ounces. After you have made yield adjustments for every ingredient, refer to Table 4 for "rounding-off" fractional amounts which are not of sufficient proportion to change product quality. No "rounding-off" is required for amounts needed for adjusted ingredients in the examples we have used here.

TABLE 15-22

Direct-reading table for adjusting yield of recipes with ingredient amounts. (This table is primarily for adjusting recipes with original and desired portion yields which can be divided by 25. It may be used along with Table 15-23, which is similarly constructed for measures.)

ABBREVIATIONS IN TABLE:
oz. = ounce
# = pound

BASIC INFORMATION:
1 pound = 16 ounces

25	50	75	100	200	300	400	500	600	700	800	900	1000
(a)	(a)	(a)	¼ oz.	½ oz.	¾ oz.	1 oz.	1¼ oz.	1½ oz.	1¾ oz.	2 oz.	2¼ oz.	2½ oz.
(a)	(a)	(a)	½ oz.	1 oz.	1½ oz.	2 oz.	2½ oz.	3 oz.	3½ oz.	4 oz.	4½ oz.	5 oz.
(a)	(a)	(a)	¾ oz.	1½ oz.	2¼ oz.	3 oz.	3¾ oz.	4½ oz.	5¼ oz.	6 oz.	6¾ oz.	7½ oz.
¼ oz	½ oz.	¾ oz.	1 oz.	2 oz.	3 oz.	4 oz.	5 oz.	6 oz.	7 oz.	8 oz.	9 oz.	10 oz.
(a)	(a)	(a)	1¼ oz.	2½ oz.	3¾ oz.	5 oz.	6¼ oz.	7½ oz.	8¾ oz.	10 oz.	11¼ oz.	12½ oz.
(a)	¾ oz.	(a)	1½ oz.	3 oz.	4½ oz.	6 oz.	7½ oz.	9 oz.	10½ oz.	12 oz.	13½ oz.	15 oz.
(a)	(a)	(a)	1¾ oz.	3½ oz.	5¼ oz.	7 oz.	8¾ oz.	10½ oz.	12¼ oz.	14 oz.	15¾ oz.	1# 1½ oz.
½ oz	1 oz.	1½ oz.	2 oz.	4 oz.	6 oz.	8 oz.	10 oz.	12 oz.	14 oz.	1#	1# 2 oz.	1# 4 oz.
(a)	(a)	1¾ oz.	2¼ oz.	4½ oz.	6¾ oz.	9 oz.	11¼ oz.	13½ oz.	15¾ oz.	1# 2 oz.	1# 4¼ oz.	1# 6½ oz.
(a)	1¼ oz.	2 oz.	2½ oz.	5 oz.	7½ oz.	10 oz.	12½ oz.	15 oz.	1# 1½ oz.	1# 4 oz.	1# 6½ oz.	1# 9 oz.
(a)	(a)	2 oz.	2¾ oz.	5½ oz.	8¼ oz.	11 oz.	13¾ oz.	1# ½ oz.	1# 3¼ oz.	1# 6 oz.	1# 8¾ oz.	1# 11½ oz.
¾ oz	1½ oz.	2¼ oz.	3 oz.	6 oz.	9 oz.	12 oz.	15 oz.	1# 2 oz.	1# 5 oz.	1# 8 oz.	1# 11 oz.	1# 14 oz.
(a)	(a)	2½ oz.	3¼ oz.	6½ oz.	9¾ oz.	13 oz.	1# ¼ oz.	1# 3½ oz.	1# 6¾ oz.	1# 10 oz.	1# 13¼ oz.	2# ½ oz.
(a)	1¾ oz.	2¾ oz.	3½ oz.	7 oz.	10½ oz.	14 oz.	1# 1½ oz.	1# 5 oz.	1# 8½ oz.	1# 12 oz.	1# 15½ oz.	2# 3 oz.
1 oz	2 oz.	2¾ oz.	3¾ oz.	7½ oz.	11¼ oz.	15 oz.	1# 2¾ oz.	1# 6½ oz.	1# 10¼ oz.	1# 14 oz.	2# 1¾ oz.	2# 5½ oz.
1 oz	2 oz.	3 oz.	4 oz.	8 oz.	12 oz.	1#	1# 4 oz.	1# 8 oz.	1# 12 oz.	2#	2# 4 oz.	2# 8 oz.
1 oz	2¼ oz.	3¼ oz.	4¼ oz.	8½ oz.	12¾ oz.	1# 1 oz.	1# 5¼ oz.	1# 9½ oz.	1# 13¾ oz.	2# 2 oz.	2# 6¼ oz.	2# 10½ oz.
(a)	2½ oz.	3½ oz.	4½ oz.	9 oz.	13½ oz.	1# 2 oz.	1# 6½ oz.	1# 11 oz.	1# 15½ oz.	2# 4 oz.	2# 8½ oz.	2# 13 oz.
(a)	2½ oz.	3½ oz.	4¾ oz.	9½ oz.	14¼ oz.	1# 3 oz.	1# 7¾ oz.	1# 12½ oz.	2# 1¼ oz.	2# 6 oz.	2# 10¾ oz.	2# 15½ oz.
1¼ oz	2½ oz.	3¾ oz.	5 oz.	10 oz.	15 oz.	1# 4 oz.	1# 9 oz.	1# 14 oz.	2# 3 oz.	2# 8 oz.	2# 13 oz.	3# 2 oz.
(a)	2¾ oz.	4¼ oz.	5½ oz.	11 oz.	1# ½ oz.	1# 6 oz.	1# 11½ oz.	2# 1 oz.	2# 6½ oz.	2# 12 oz.	3# 1½ oz.	3# 7 oz.
1½ oz.	3 oz.	4½ oz.	6 oz.	12 oz.	1# 2 oz.	1# 8 oz.	1# 14 oz.	2# 4 oz.	2# 10 oz.	3#	3# 6 oz.	3# 12 oz.
(a)	3¼ oz.	4¾ oz.	6½ oz.	13 oz.	1# 3½ oz.	1# 10 oz.	2# ½ oz.	2# 7 oz.	2# 13½ oz.	3# 4 oz.	3# 10½ oz.	4# 1 oz.
1¾ oz.	3½ oz.	5¼ oz.	7 oz.	14 oz.	1# 5 oz.	1# 12 oz.	2# 3 oz.	2# 10 oz.	3# 1 oz.	3# 8 oz.	3# 15 oz.	4# 6 oz.
2 oz.	3¾ oz.	5¾ oz.	7½ oz.	15 oz.	1# 6½ oz.	1# 14 oz.	2# 5½ oz.	2# 13 oz.	3# 4½ oz.	3# 12 oz.	4# 3½ oz.	4# 11 oz.
2 oz.	4 oz.	6 oz.	8 oz.	1#	1# 8 oz.	2#	2# 8 oz.	3#	3# 8 oz.	4#	4# 8 oz.	5#
2¼ oz	4¼ oz.	6½ oz.	8½ oz.	1# 1 oz.	1# 9½ oz.	2# 2 oz.	2# 10½ oz.	3# 3 oz.	3# 11½ oz.	4# 4 oz.	4# 12½ oz.	5# 5 oz.
2¼ oz	4½ oz.	6¾ oz.	9 oz.	1# 2 oz.	1# 11 oz.	2# 4 oz.	2# 13 oz.	3# 6 oz.	3# 15 oz.	4# 8 oz.	5# 1 oz.	5# 10 oz.
2½ oz	4¾ oz.	7¼ oz.	9½ oz.	1# 3 oz.	1# 12½ oz.	2# 6 oz.	2# 15½ oz.	3# 9 oz.	4# 2½ oz.	4# 12 oz.	5# 5½ oz.	5# 15 oz.
2½ oz.	5 oz.	7½ oz.	10 oz.	1# 4 oz.	1# 14 oz.	2# 8 oz.	3# 2 oz.	3# 12 oz.	4# 6 oz.	5#	5# 10 oz.	6# 4 oz.
2¾ oz.	5½ oz.	8¼ oz.	11 oz.	1# 6 oz.	2# 1 oz.	2# 12 oz.	3# 7 oz.	4# 2 oz.	4# 13 oz.	5# 8 oz.	6# 3 oz.	6# 14 oz.
3 oz.	6 oz.	9 oz.	12 oz.	1# 8 oz.	2# 4 oz.	3#	3# 12 oz.	4# 8 oz.	5# 4 oz.	6#	6# 12 oz.	7# 8 oz.
3¼ oz	6½ oz.	9¾ oz.	13 oz.	1# 10 oz.	2# 7 oz.	3# 4 oz.	4# 1 oz.	4# 14 oz.	5# 11 oz.	6# 8 oz.	7# 5 oz.	8# 2 oz.
3½ oz.	7 oz.	10½ oz.	14 oz.	1# 12 oz.	2# 10 oz.	3# 8 oz.	4# 6 oz.	5# 4 oz.	6# 2 oz.	7#	7# 14 oz.	8# 12 oz.
3¾ oz.	7½ oz.	11¼ oz.	15 oz.	1# 14 oz.	2# 13 oz.	3# 12 oz.	4# 11 oz.	5# 10 oz.	6# 9 oz.	7# 8 oz.	8# 7 oz.	[illegible]# 6 oz.
4 oz.	8 oz.	12 oz.	1#	2#	3#	4#	5#	6#	7#	8#	9#	10#
4½ oz	9 oz.	13½ oz.	1# 2 oz.	2# 4 oz.	3# 6 oz.	4# 8 oz.	5# 10 oz.	6# 12 oz.	7# 14 oz.	9#	10# 2 oz.	11# 4 oz.

(a) The amounts cannot be weighed accurately without introducing errors. Change to measurement by using conversion table.

Table 15-22 — Concluded

25	50	75	100	200	300	400	500	600	700	800	900	1000
5 oz.	10 oz.	15 oz.	1# 4 oz.	2# 8 oz.	3# 12 oz.	5#	6# 4 oz.	7# 8 oz.	8# 12 oz.	10#	11# 4 oz.	12# 8 oz.
5½ oz.	11 oz.	1# ½ oz.	1# 6 oz.	2# 12 oz.	4# 2 oz.	5# 8 oz.	6# 14 oz.	8# 4 oz.	9# 10 oz.	11#	12# 6 oz.	13# 12 oz.
6 oz.	12 oz.	1# 2 oz.	1# 8 oz.	3#	4# 8 oz.	6#	7# 8 oz.	9#	10# 8 oz.	12#	13# 8 oz.	15#
6½ oz.	13 oz.	1# 3½ oz.	1# 10 oz.	3# 4 oz.	4# 14 oz.	6# 8 oz.	8# 2 oz.	9# 12 oz.	11# 6 oz.	13#	14# 10 oz.	16# 4 oz.
7 oz.	14 oz.	1# 5 oz.	1# 12 oz.	3# 8 oz.	5# 4 oz.	7#	8# 12 oz.	10# 8 oz.	12# 4 oz.	14#	15# 12 oz.	17# 8 oz.
7½ oz.	15 oz.	1# 6½ oz.	1# 14 oz.	3# 12 oz.	5# 10 oz.	7# 8 oz.	9# 6 oz.	11# 4 oz.	13# 2 oz.	15#	16# 14 oz.	18# 12 oz.
8 oz.	1#	1# 8 oz.	2#	4#	6#	8#	10#	12#	14#	16#	18#	20#
8½ oz.	1# 1 oz.	1# 9½ oz.	2# 2 oz.	4# 4 oz.	6# 6 oz.	8# 8 oz.	10# 10 oz.	12# 12 oz.	14# 14 oz.	17#	19# 2 oz.	21# 4 oz.
9 oz.	1# 2 oz.	1# 11 oz.	2# 4 oz.	4# 8 oz.	6# 12 oz.	9#	11# 4 oz.	13# 8 oz.	15# 12 oz.	18#	20# 4 oz.	22# 8 oz.
9½ oz.	1# 3 oz.	1# 12½ oz.	2# 6 oz.	4# 12 oz.	7# 2 oz.	9# 8 oz.	11# 14 oz.	14# 4 oz.	16# 10 oz.	19#	21# 6 oz.	23# 12 oz.
10 oz.	1# 4 oz.	1# 14 oz.	2# 8 oz.	5#	7# 8 oz.	10#	12# 8 oz.	15#	17# 8 oz.	20#	22# 8 oz.	25#
11 oz.	1# 6 oz.	2# 1 oz.	2# 12 oz.	5# 8 oz.	8# 4 oz.	11#	13# 12 oz.	16# 8 oz.	19# 4 oz.	22#	24# 12 oz.	27# 8 oz.
12 oz.	1# 8 oz.	2# 4 oz.	3#	6#	9#	12#	15#	18#	21#	24#	27#	30#
13 oz.	1# 10 oz.	2# 7 oz.	3# 4 oz.	6# 8 oz.	9# 12 oz.	13#	16# 4 oz.	19# 8 oz.	22# 12 oz.	26#	29# 4 oz.	32# 8 oz.
14 oz.	1# 12 oz.	2# 10 oz.	3# 8 oz.	7#	10# 8 oz.	14#	17# 8 oz.	21#	24# 8 oz.	28#	31# 8 oz.	35#
15 oz.	1# 14 oz.	2# 13 oz.	3# 12 oz.	7# 8 oz.	11# 4 oz.	15#	18# 12 oz.	22# 8 oz.	26# 4 oz.	30#	33# 12 oz.	37# 8 oz.
1#	2#	3#	4#	8#	12#	16#	20#	24#	28#	32#	36#	40#
1# 1 oz.	2# 2 oz.	3# 3 oz.	4# 4 oz.	8# 8 oz.	12# 12 oz.	17#	21# 4 oz.	25# 8 oz.	29# 12 oz.	34#	38# 4 oz.	42# 8 oz.
1# 2 oz.	2# 4 oz.	3# 6 oz.	4# 8 oz.	9#	13# 8 oz.	18#	22# 8 oz.	27#	31# 8 oz.	36#	40# 8 oz.	45#
1# 3 oz.	2# 6 oz.	3# 9 oz.	4# 12 oz.	9# 8 oz.	14# 4 oz.	19#	23# 12 oz.	28# 8 oz.	33# 4 oz.	38#	42# 12 oz.	47# 8 oz.
1# 4 oz.	2# 8 oz.	3# 12 oz.	5#	10#	15#	20#	25#	30#	35#	40#	45#	50#
1# 5 oz.	2# 10 oz.	3# 15 oz.	5# 4 oz.	10# 8 oz.	15# 12 oz.	21#	26# 4 oz.	31# 8 oz.	36# 12 oz.	42#	47# 4 oz.	52# 8 oz.
1# 6 oz.	2# 12 oz.	4# 2 oz.	5# 8 oz.	11#	16# 8 oz.	22#	27# 8 oz.	33#	38# 8 oz.	44#	49# 8 oz.	55#
1# 7 oz.	2# 14 oz.	4# 5 oz.	5# 12 oz.	11# 8 oz.	17# 4 oz.	23#	28# 12 oz.	34# 8 oz.	40# 4 oz.	46#	51# 12 oz.	57# 8 oz.
1# 8 oz.	3#	4# 8 oz.	6#	12#	18#	24#	30#	36#	42#	48#	54#	60#
1# 10 oz.	3# 4 oz.	4# 14 oz.	6# 8 oz.	13#	19# 8 oz.	26#	32# 8 oz.	39#	45# 8 oz.	52#	58# 8 oz.	65#
1# 12 oz.	3# 8 oz.	5# 4 oz.	7#	14#	21#	28#	35#	42#	49#	56#	63#	70#
1# 14 oz.	3# 12 oz.	5# 10 oz.	7# 8 oz.	15#	22# 8 oz.	30#	37# 8 oz.	45#	52# 8 oz.	60#	67# 8 oz.	75#
2#	4#	6#	8#	16#	24#	32#	40#	48#	56#	64#	72#	80#
2# 2 oz.	4# 4 oz.	6# 6 oz.	8# 8 oz.	17#	25# 8 oz.	34#	42# 8 oz.	51#	59# 8 oz.	68#	76# 8 oz.	85#
2# 4 oz.	4# 8 oz.	6# 12 oz.	9#	18#	27#	36#	45#	54#	63#	72#	81#	90#
2# 6 oz.	4# 12 oz.	7# 2 oz.	9# 8 oz.	19#	28# 8 oz.	38#	47# 8 oz.	57#	66# 8 oz.	76#	85# 8 oz.	95#
2# 8 oz.	5#	7# 8 oz.	10#	20#	30#	40#	50#	60#	70#	80#	90#	100#
2# 12 oz.	5# 8 oz.	8# 4 oz.	11#	22#	33#	44#	55#	66#	77#	88#	99#	110#

3#	6#	9#	12#	24#	36#	48#	60#	72#	84#	96#	108#	120#
3# 4 oz.	6# 8 oz.	9# 12 oz.	13#	26#	39#	52#	65#	78#	91#	104#	117#	130#
3# 8 oz.	7#	10# 8 oz.	14#	28#	42#	56#	70#	84#	98#	112#	126#	140#
3# 12 oz.	7# 8 oz.	11# 4 oz.	15#	30#	45#	60#	75#	90#	105#	120#	135#	150#
4#	8#	12#	16#	32#	48#	64#	80#	96#	112#	128#	144#	160#
4# 4 oz.	8# 8 oz.	12# 12 oz.	17#	34#	51#	68#	85#	102#	119#	136#	153#	170#
4# 8 oz.	9#	13# 8 oz.	18#	36#	54#	72#	90#	108#	126#	144#	162#	180#
4# 12 oz.	9# 8 oz.	14# 4 oz.	19#	38#	57#	76#	95#	114#	133#	152#	171#	190#
5#	10#	15#	20#	40#	60#	80#	100#	120#	140#	160#	180#	200#
5# 4 oz.	10# 8 oz.	15# 12 oz.	21#	42#	63#	84#	105#	126#	147#	168#	189#	210#
5# 8 oz.	11#	16# 8 oz.	22#	44#	66#	88#	110#	132#	154#	176#	198#	220#
5# 12 oz.	11# 8 oz.	17# 4 oz.	23#	46#	69#	92#	115#	138#	161#	184#	207#	230#
6# 4 oz.	12# 8 oz.	18# 12 oz.	25#	50#	75#	100#	125#	150#	175#	200#	225#	250#
7# 8 oz.	15#	22# 8 oz.	30#	60#	90#	120#	150#	180#	210#	240#	270#	300#
8# 12 oz.	17# 8 oz.	26# 4 oz.	35#	70#	105#	140#	175#	210#	245#	280#	315#	350#
10#	20#	30#	40#	80#	120#	160#	200#	240#	280#	320#	360#	400#
11# 4 oz.	22# 8 oz.	33# 12 oz.	45#	90#	135#	180#	225#	270#	315#	360#	405#	450#
12# 8 oz.	25#	37# 8 oz.	50#	100#	150#	200#	250#	300#	350#	400#	450#	500#

Instructions for Using Table 15-23:

1. Locate column which corresponds to the original yield of the recipe you wish to adjust. For example, let us assume your original sour cream cookie recipe yields 300 cookies. Locate the **300 column.**

2. Run your finger **down** this column until you come to the amount of the ingredient required (or closest to this figure) in the recipe you wish to adjust. Say that your original recipe for 300 cookies required 2¼ c. fat. Run your finger down the column **headed 300** until you come to 2¼ c.

3. Next, run your finger **across** the page, in line with that amount, until you come to the column which is headed to correspond with **the yield you desire.** Suppose you want to make 75 cookies. Starting with your finger under the 2¼ c. (in the 300 column), slide it across to the column headed 75 and read the figure. You see you need ½ c. + 1 T. fat to make 75 cookies from your recipe.

4. Record this figure as the amount of the ingredient required for the new yield of your recipe. Repeat Steps 1, 2, 3 for each ingredient in your original recipe to obtain the adjusted measure needed of each for your new yield. You can increase or decrease yield in this manner.

5. If you need to combine two columns to obtain your desired yield, follow the above procedure and **add** together the amounts given in the two columns to get the amount required for your adjusted yield. For example, to find the amount of fat needed to make 550 cookies (using the same basic recipe as above) locate the figures in columns headed 500 and 50 and add them. In this case they would be 3¾ c. + 6 T. and the required total would be 1 qt. + 2 T. fat.

6. The figures in Table 2 are given in measurements which provide absolute accuracy. After you have made yield adjustments for each ingredient, refer to Table 4 for "rounding-off" odd fractions and complicated measurements. You can safely "round-off" to 1 qt. as shown in Table 4, for the amount of fat needed in the recipe for 550 cookies.

Table 15-23

Direct-reading table for adjusting yield of recipes with ingredient amounts given in measurement. (This table is primarily for adjusting recipes with original and desired portion yields which can be divided by 25. It is intended for use along with Table 15-22, which is similarly constructed for adjusting weights.)

ABBREVIATIONS IN TABLE:

t. = teaspoon
T. = Tablespoon
c. = cup
qt. = quart
gal. = gallon
(r) = slightly rounded
(s) = scant

BASIC INFORMATION:

Measuring spoons
1 T.
1 t.
½ t.
¼ t.
for ¾ t. combine ½ t. + ¼ t.
for ⅛ t. use half of the ¼ t.

Equivalents
3 t. = 1 T.
4 T. = ¼ c.
5 T. + 1 t. = ⅓ c.
8 T. = ½ c.
10 T. + 2 t. = ⅔ c.
12 T. = ¾ c.
16 T. = 1 c.
4 c. = 1 qt.
4 qt. = 1 gal.

Measurement needed for number of portions indicated below.

25	50	75	100	200	300	400	500	600	700	800	900	1000
¼ t.	½ t.	¾ t.	1 t.	2 t.	1 T.	1 T. +1 t.	1 T. +2 t.	2 T.	2 T. +1 t.	2 T. +2 t.	3 T.	3 T. +1 t.
¼ t. (r)	½ t. (r)	1 t. (s)	1¼ t.	2½ t.	1 T. +¾ t.	1 T. +2 t.	2 T. +¼ t.	2½ T.	2 T. +2¾ t.	3 T. +1 t.	3 T. +2¼ t.	4 T. +½ t.
¼ t. +⅛ t.	¾ t.	1 t. +⅛ t.	1½ t.	1 T.	1½ T.	2 T.	2½ T.	3 T.	3½ T.	4 T.	4 T. +1½ t.	5 T.
½ t. (s)	¾ t. (r)	1¼ t. (r)	1¾ t.	1 T. +½ t.	1 T. +2¼ t.	2 T. +1 t.	2 T. +2¾ t.	3½ T.	4 T. +¼ t.	4 T. +2 t.	5 T. +¾ t.	5 T. +2½ t.
½ t.	1 t.	1½ t.	2 t.	1 T. +1 t.	2 T.	2 T. +2 t.	3 T. +1 t.	4 T.	4 T. +2 t.	5 T. +1 t.	6 T.	6 T. +2 t.
½ t. (r)	1 t +⅛ t	1¾ t. (s)	2¼ t.	1½ T.	2 T. +¾ t.	3 T.	3 T. +2¼ t.	4½ T.	5 T. +¾ t.	6 T.	6 T. +2¼ t.	7½ T.
½ t. +⅛ t.	1¼ t.	2 t. (s)	2½ t.	1 T. +2 t.	2½ T.	3 T. +1 t.	4 T. +½ t.	5 T.	5½ T.	6 T. +2 t.	7½ T.	8 T. +1 t.
¾ t. (s)	1¼ t. +⅛ t.	2 t. (r)	2¾ t.	1 T. +2½ t.	2 T. +2¼ t.	3 T. +2 t.	4 T. +1¾ t.	5½ T.	6 T. +1¼ t.	7 T. +1 t.	8 T. +¾ t.	9 T. +½ t.
¾ t.	1½ t.	2¼ t.	1 T.	2 T.	3 T.	¼ c.	5 T.	6 T.	7 T.	½ c.	½ c. +1 T.	½ c. +2 T.
1 t. +⅛ t.	2¼ t.	1 T. +¼ t. +⅛ t.	1½ T.	3 T.	¼ c. +1½ t.	⅓ c. +2 t.	¼ c. +3½ T.	½ c. +1 T.	½ c. +2½ T.	¾ c.	¾ c. +1½ T.	¾ c. +3 T.
1½ t.	1 T.	1½ T.	2 T.	¼ c.	¼ c. +2 T.	½ c.	½ c. +2 T.	¾ c.	¾ c. +2 T.	1 c.	1 c. +2 T.	1¼ c.
1¾ t. +⅛ t.	1 T. +¾ t.	1 T. +2½ t. +⅛ t.	2½ T.	¼ c. +1 T.	¼ c. +3½ T.	½ c. +2 T.	¾ c. +½ t.	¾ c. +3 T.	1 c +1½ T.	1¼ c.	1¼ c. +2½ T.	1½ c. +1 T.
2¼ t.	1½ T.	2 T. +¾ t.	3 T.	⅓ c. +2 t.	½ c. +1 T.	¾ c.	¾ c. +3 T.	1 c. +2 T.	1¼ c. +1 T.	1½ c.	1½ c. +3 T.	1¾ c. +2 T.
2¼ t. +⅛ t.	1 T. +2¼ t.	2 T. +1½ t. +⅛ t.	3½ T.	¼ c. +3 T.	½ c. +2½ T.	¾ c. +2 T.	1 c. +1½ T.	1¼ c. +1 T.	1½ c. +⅓ T.	1¾ c.	1¾ c. +3½ T.	2 c. +3 T.
1 T.	2 T.	3 T.	¼ c.	½ c.	¾ c.	1 c.	1¼ c.	1½ c.	1¾ c.	2 c.	2¼ c.	2½ c.
1 T. +1 t.	2 T. +2 t.	¼ c.	⅓ c.	⅔ c.	1 c.	1⅓ c.	1⅔ c.	2 c.	2⅓ c.	2⅔ c.	3 c.	3⅓ c.
2 T.	¼ c.	¼ c. +2 T.	½ c.	1 c.	1½ c.	2 c.	2½ c.	3 c.	3½ c.	1 qt.	1 qt. +½ c.	1¼ qt.
2 T. +2 t.	⅓ c.	½ c.	⅔ c.	1⅓ c.	2 c.	2⅔ c.	3⅓ c.	1 qt.	1 qt. +⅔ c.	1¼ qt. +⅓ c.	1½ qt.	1½ qt. +⅔ c.
3 T.	6 T.	½ c. +1 T.	¾ c.	1½ c.	2¼ c.	3 c.	3¾ c.	1 qt. +½ c.	1¼ qt. +¼ c.	1½ qt.	1½ qt. +¾ c.	1¾ qt. +½ c.
¼ c.	½ c.	¾ c.	1 c.	2 c.	3 c.	1 qt.	1¼ qt.	1½ qt.	1¾ qt.	2 qt.	2¼ qt.	2½ qt.
¼ c. +1 T.	½ c. +2 T.	¾ c. +3 T.	1¼ c.	2½ c.	3¾ c.	1¼ qt.	1½ qt. +¼ c.	1¾ qt. +½ c.	2 qt. +¾ c.	2½ qt.	2¾ qt. +¼ c.	3 qt. +½ c.
⅓ c.	⅔ c.	1 c.	1⅓ c.	2⅔ c.	1 qt.	1¼ qt. +⅓ c.	1½ qt. +⅔ c.	2 qt.	2¼ qt. +⅓ c.	2½ qt. +⅔ c.	3 qt.	3¼ qt. +⅓ c.
⅓ c. +2 t.	¾ c.	1 c. +2 T.	1½ c.	3 c.	1 qt. +½ c.	1½ qt.	1¾ qt. +½ c.	2¼ qt.	2½ qt. +½ c.	3 qt.	3¼ qt. +½ c.	3¾ qt.

Table 15-23 — Concluded

25	50	75	100	200	300	400	500	600	700	800	900	1000
6 T.+2 t.	¾ c.+4 t.	1¼ c.	1⅔ c.	3⅓ c.	1¼ qt.	1½ qt. +⅔ c.	2 qt.+⅓ c.	2½ qt.	2¾ qt. +⅔ c.	3¼ qt. +⅓ c.	3¾ qt.	1 gal.+⅔ c.
¼ c.+3 T.	¾ c.+2 T.	1¼ c. +1 T.	1¾ c.	3½ c.	1¼ qt. +¼ c.	1¾ qt.	2 qt.+¾ c.	2½ qt. +½ c.	3 qt.+¼ c.	3½ qt.	3¾ qt. +¾ c.	1 gal. +1½ c.
½ c.	1 c.	1½ c.	2 c.	1 qt.	1½ qt.	2 qt.	2½ qt.	3 qt.	3½ qt.	1 gal.	1 gal.+2 c.	1 gal.+1 qt.
½ c.+1 T.	1 c.+2 T.	1½ c. +3 T.	2¼ c.	1 qt. +½ c.	1½ qt. +¾ c.	2¼ qt.	2¾ qt. +¼ c.	3¼ qt. +½ c.	3¾ qt. +¾ c.	1 gal. +2 c.	1¼ gal. +¼ c.	1¼ gal. +2½ c.
½ c.+4 t.	1 c.+2 T. +2 t.	1¾ c.	2⅓ c.	1 qt. +⅔ c.	1¾ qt.	2¼ qt. +⅓ c.	2¾ qt. +⅔ c.	3½ qt.	1 gal. +⅓ c.	1 gal. +2⅔ c.	1¼ gal. +1 c.	1¼ gal. +3⅓ c.
½ c.+2 T.	1¼ c.	1¾ c. +2 T.	2½ c.	1¼ qt.	1¾ qt. +½ c.	2½ qt.	3 qt. +½ c.	3¾ qt.	1 gal. +1½ c.	1¼ gal.	1¼ gal. +2½ c.	1½ gal. +1 c.
⅔ c.	1⅓ c.	2 c.	2⅔ c.	1¼ qt. +⅓ c.	2 qt.	2½ qt. +⅔ c.	3 qt. +1⅓ c.	1 gal.	1 gal. +2⅔ c.	1¼ gal. +1⅓ c.	1½ gal.	1½ gal. +2⅔ c.
½ c.+3 T.	1¼ c. +2 T.	2 c.+1 T.	2¾ c.	1¼ qt. +½ c.	2 qt.+¼ c.	2¾ qt.	3¼ qt. +¾ c.	1 gal. +½ c.	1 gal. +3¼ c.	1¼ gal. +2 c.	1½ gal. +¾ c.	1½ gal. +3½ c.
¾ c.	1½ c.	2¼ c.	3 c.	1½ qt.	2¼ qt.	3 qt.	3¾ qt.	1 gal. +2 c.	1¼ gal. +1 c.	1½ gal.	1½ gal. +3 c.	1¾ gal. +2 c.
¾ c.+1 T.	1½ c. +2 T.	2¼ c. +3 T.	3¼ c.	1½ qt. +½ c.	2¼ qt. +¾ c.	3¼ qt.	1 gal. +¼ c.	1 gal. +3½ c.	1¼ gal. +2¾ c.	1½ gal. +2 c.	1¾ gal. +1¼ c.	2 gal. +½ c.
3 c.+4 t.	1⅔ c.	2½ c.	3⅓ c.	1½ qt. +⅔ c.	2½ qt.	3¼ qt. +⅓ c.	1 gal. +⅔ c.	1¼ gal.	1¼ gal. +3⅓ c.	1½ gal. +2⅔ c.	1¾ gal. +2 c.	2 gal. +1⅓ c.
¾ c.+2 T.	1¾ c.	2½ c. +2 T.	3½ c.	1¾ qt.	2½ qt. +½ c.	3½ qt.	1 gal. +1½ c.	1¼ gal. +1 c.	1½ gal. +½ c.	1¾ gal.	1¾ gal. +3½ c.	2 gal. +2½ c.
¾ c.+2 T. +2½ t.	1¾ c. +4 t.	2¾ c. +½ t.	3⅔ c.	1¾ qt. +⅓ c.	2¾ qt.	3½ qt. +⅔ c.	1 gal. +1⅔ c.	1¼ gal. +1⅓ c.	1½ gal. +2 c.	1¾ gal. +1⅔ c.	2 gal. +1⅓ c.	2¼ gal. +1 c.
¾ c.+3 T.	1¾ c. +2 T.	2¾ c. +1 T.	3¾ c.	1¾ qt. +½ c.	2½ qt. +¼ c.	3 qt. +3 c.	1 gal. +2¾ c.	1¼ gal. +2½ c.	1½ gal. +2¼ c.	1¾ gal. +2 c.	2 gal. +1¾ c.	2¼ gal. +1½ c.
1 c.	2 c.	3 c.	1 qt.	2 qt.	3 qt.	1 gal.	1¼ gal.	1½ gal.	1¾ gal.	2 gal.	2¼ gal.	2½ gal.
1¼ c.	2½ c.	3¾ c.	1¼ qt.	2½ qt.	3¾ qt.	1¼ gal.	1½ gal. +1 c.	1¾ gal. +2 c.	2 gal. +3 c.	2½ gal.	2¾ gal. +1 c.	3 gal. +2 c.
1½ c.	3 c.	1 qt. +½ c.	1½ qt.	3 qt.	1 gal. +2 c.	1½ gal.	1¾ gal. +2 c.	2¼ gal.	2½ gal. +2 c.	3 gal.	3¼ gal. +2 c.	3¾ gal.
1¾ c.	3½ c.	1¼ qt. +¼ c.	1¾ qt.	3½ qt.	1¼ gal. +1 c.	1¾ gal.	2 gal. +3 c.	2½ gal. +2 c.	3 gal. +1 c.	3½ gal.	3¾ gal. +3 c.	4¼ gal. +2 c.
2 c.	1 qt.	1½ qt.	2 qt.	1 gal.	1½ gal.	2 gal.	2½ gal.	3 gal.	3½ gal.	4 gal.	4½ gal.	5 gal.
2¼ c.	1 qt. +½ c.	1½ qt. +¾ c.	2¼ qt.	1 gal. +2 c.	1½ gal. +3 c.	2¼ gal.	2¾ gal. +1 c.	3¼ gal. +2 c.	3¾ gal. +3 c.	4½ gal.	5 gal. +1 c.	5½ gal. +2 c.
2½ c.	1¼ qt.	1¾ qt. +½ c.	2½ qt.	1¼ gal.	1¾ gal. +2 c.	2½ gal.	3 gal. +2 c.	3¾ gal.	4¼ gal. +2 c.	5 gal.	5½ gal. +2 c.	6¼ gal.
2¾ c.	1¼ qt. +½ c.	2 qt. +¼ c.	2¾ qt.	1¼ gal. +2 c.	2 gal. +1 c.	2¾ gal.	3¼ gal. +3 c.	4 gal. +2 c.	4¾ gal. +1 c.	5½ gal.	6 gal. +3 c.	6¾ gal. +2 c.
3 c.	1½ qt.	2¼ qt.	3 qt.	1½ gal.	2¼ gal.	3 gal.	3¾ gal.	4½ gal.	5¼ gal.	6 gal.	6¾ gal.	7½ gal.
3¼ c.	1½ qt. +½ c.	2¼ qt. +¾ c.	3¼ qt.	1½ gal. +2 c.	2¼ gal. +3 c.	3¼ gal.	4 gal. +1 c.	4¾ gal. +2 c.	5½ gal. +3 c.	6½ gal.	7¼ gal. +1 c.	8 gal. +2 c.
3½ c.	1¾ qt.	2½ qt. +½ c.	3½ qt.	1¾ gal.	2½ gal. +2 c.	3½ gal.	4¼ gal. +2 c.	5¼ gal.	6 gal. +2 c.	7 gal.	7¾ gal. +2 c.	8¾ gal.

3¾ c.	1¾ qt. +½ c.	2¾ qt. +¼ c.	3¾ qt.	1¾ gal. +2 c.	2¾ gal. +1 c.	3¾ gal.	4½ gal. +3 c.	5½ gal. +2 c.	6½ gal. +1 c.	7½ gal.	8¼ gal. +3 c.	9¼ gal. +2 c.
1 qt.	2 qt.	3 qt.	1 gal.	2 gal.	3 gal.	4 gal.	5 gal.	6 gal.	7 gal.	8 gal.	9 gal.	10 gal.
1¼ qt.	2½ qt.	3¾ qt.	1¼ gal.	2½ gal.	3¾ gal.	5 gal.	6¼ gal.	7½ gal.	8¾ gal.	10 gal.	11¼ gal.	12½ gal.
1½ qt.	3 qt.	1 gal. +2 c.	1½ gal.	3 gal.	4½ gal.	6 gal.	7½ gal.	9 gal.	10½ gal.	12 gal.	13½ gal.	15 gal.
1¾ qt.	3½ qt.	1¼ gal. +1 c.	1¾ gal.	3½ gal.	5¼ gal.	7 gal.	8¾ gal.	10½ gal.	12¼ gal.	14 gal.	15¾ gal.	17½ gal.
2 qt.	1 gal.	1½ gal.	2 gal.	4 gal.	6 gal.	8 gal.	10 gal.	12 gal.	14 gal.	16 gal.	18 gal.	20 gal.
2¼ qt.	1 gal. +2 c.	1½ gal. +3 c.	2¼ gal.	4½ gal.	6¾ gal.	9 gal.	11¼ gal.	13½ gal.	15¾ gal.	18 gal.	20¼ gal.	22½ gal.
2½ qt.	1¼ gal.	1¾ gal. +2 c.	2½ gal.	5 gal.	7½ gal.	10 gal.	12½ gal.	15 gal.	17½ gal.	20 gal.	22½ gal.	25 gal.
2¾ qt.	1¼ gal. +2 c.	2 gal. +1 c.	2¾ gal.	5½ gal.	8¼ gal.	11 gal.	13¾ gal.	16½ gal.	19¼ gal.	22 gal.	24¾ gal.	27½ gal.
3 qt.	1½ gal.	2¼ gal.	3 gal.	6 gal.	9 gal.	12 gal.	15 gal.	18 gal.	21 gal.	24 gal.	27 gal.	30 gal.
3 qt. +1 c.	1½ gal. +2 c.	2¼ gal. +3 c.	3¼ gal.	6½ gal.	9¾ gal.	13 gal.	16¼ gal.	19½ gal.	22¾ gal.	26 gal.	29¼ gal.	32½ gal.
3½ qt.	1¾ gal.	2½ gal. +2 c.	3½ gal.	7 gal.	10½ gal.	14 gal.	17½ gal.	21½ gal.	24½ gal.	28 gal.	31½ gal.	35 gal.
3½ qt. +1 c.	1¾ gal. +2 c.	2¾ gal. +1 c.	3¾ gal.	7½ gal.	11¼ gal.	15 gal.	18¾ gal.	22½ gal.	26¼ gal.	30 gal.	33¾ gal.	37½ gal.
1 gal.	2 gal.	3 gal.	4 gal.	8 gal.	12 gal.	16 gal.	20 gal.	24 gal.	28 gal.	32 gal.	36 gal.	40 gal.
1 gal. +1 c.	2 gal. +2 c.	3 gal. +3 c.	4¼ gal.	8½ gal.	12¾ gal.	17 gal.	21¼ gal.	25½ gal.	29¾ gal.	34 gal.	38¼ gal.	42½ gal.
1 gal. +2 c.	2¼ gal.	3¼ gal. +2 c.	4½ gal.	9 gal.	13½ gal.	18 gal.	22½ gal.	27 gal.	31½ gal.	36 gal.	40½ gal.	45 gal.
1 gal. +3 c.	2¼ gal. +2 c.	3½ gal. +1 c.	4¾ gal.	9½ gal.	14¼ gal.	19 gal.	23¾ gal.	28½ gal.	33¼ gal.	38 gal.	42¾ gal.	47½ gal.
1¼ gal.	2½ gal.	3¾ gal.	5 gal.	10 gal.	15 gal.	20 gal.	25 gal.	30 gal.	35 gal.	40 gal.	45 gal.	50 gal.
1¼ gal. +1 c.	2½ gal. +2 c.	3¾ gal. +3 c.	5¼ gal.	10½ gal.	15¾ gal.	21 gal.	26¼ gal.	31½ gal.	36¾ gal.	42 gal.	47½ gal.	52½ gal.
1¼ gal. +2 c.	2¾ gal.	4 gal. +2 c.	5½ gal.	11 gal.	16½ gal.	22 gal.	27½ gal.	33 gal.	38½ gal.	44 gal.	49½ gal.	55 gal.
1¼ gal. +3 c.	2¾ gal. +2 c.	4¼ gal. +1 c.	5¾ gal.	11½ gal.	17¼ gal.	23 gal.	28¾ gal.	34½ gal.	40¼ gal.	46 gal.	51¾ gal.	57½ gal.
1½ gal.	3 gal.	4½ gal.	6 gal.	12 gal.	18 gal.	24 gal.	30 gal.	36 gal.	42 gal.	48 gal.	54 gal.	60 gal.
1½ gal. +1 c.	3 gal. +2 c.	4½ gal. +3 c.	6¼ gal.	12½ gal.	18¾ gal.	25 gal.	31¼ gal.	37¼ gal.	43¾ gal.	50 gal.	56¼ gal.	62½ gal.
1½ gal. +2 c.	3¼ gal.	4¾ gal. +2 c.	6½ gal.	13 gal.	19½ gal.	26 gal.	32½ gal.	39 gal.	45½ gal.	52 gal.	58½ gal.	65 gal.
1½ gal. +3 c.	3¼ gal. +2 c.	5 gal. +1 c.	6¾ gal.	13½ gal.	20¼ gal.	27 gal.	33¾ gal.	40½ gal.	47¼ gal.	54 gal.	60¾ gal.	67½ gal.
1¾ gal.	3½ gal.	5¼ gal.	7 gal.	14 gal.	21 gal.	28 gal.	35 gal.	42 gal.	49 gal.	56 gal.	63 gal.	70 gal.

Instructions for Using Table 15-24:

1. Locate column which corresponds to the original yield of the recipe you wish to adjust. For example, let us assume your original custard sauce recipe yields 24 portions. Locate the **24 column.**

2. Run your finger down this column until you come to the amount of the ingredient required (or closest to this figure) in the recipe you wish to adjust. Say that your original recipe for 24 portions requires 1½ T. cornstarch and 1¼ qt. milk. Run your finger down the column **headed 24** until you come to 1½ T. (for cornstarch) and then 1¼ qt. (for milk), etc.

3. Next, run your finger **across** the page, in line with that amount, until you come to the column which is headed to correspond with **the yield you desire.** Suppose you want to make 64 portions. Starting with your finger under the 1½ T. (in the 24 column), slide it across to the column headed 64 and read the figure. You need ¼ c. cornstarch for 64 portions. Repeat the procedure starting with 1¼ qt. in the 24 column; tracing across to the 64 column, you find you need 3¼ qt. + ⅓ c. milk.

4. Read this figure as the amount of the ingredient required for the new yield of your recipe. Repeat Steps 1, 2, 3 for each ingredient in your original recipe to obtain the adjusted measure needed of each for your new yield. You can increase or decrease yield in this manner.

5. If you need to combine two columns to obtain your desired yield, follow the above procedure and **add together** the amounts given in the two columns to get the amount required for your adjusted yield. For example, to find the amount of cornstarch needed for 124 portions of pudding (using the same basic recipe as above) locate the figures in colufns 60 and 64 and add them. In this case you would add 3 T. + 2¼ t. and ¼ c.

6. The figures in Table 15-23 are in measurements which give absolute accuracy. After making yield adjustments for all ingredients, go to Table 15-24 for "rounding-off" awkward fractions and complicated measurements. In our example (increasing from 24 to 64 portions) you can "round" the adjusted amount of milk to 3¼ qt. without upsetting proportions. The total amount of cornstarch in our example need not be "rounded-off" since it can be measured easily (¼ c.).

Table 15-24

Direct-reading table for adjusting yield of recipes with ingredient amounts given in measurement. (This table is primarily for use with recipes with original or desired yields which can be divided by 8; yields of 20 and 60 portions are also included.)

ABBREVIATIONS IN TABLE:

t. = teaspoon
T. = tablespoon
c. = cup
qt. = quart
gal. = gallon
(r) = slightly rounded
(s) = scant

(a) = too small for accurate measure; use caution

BASIC INFORMATION

Measuring Spoons
1 T.
1 t.
½ t.
¼ t.
for ¾ t. combine ½ t. + ¼ t.
for ⅛ t. use half of the ¼ t.

Equivalents
3 t. = 1 T.
4 T. = ¼ c.
5 T. + 1 t. = ⅓ c.
8 T. = ½ c.
10 T. + 2 t. = ⅔ c.
12 T. = ¾ c.
16 T. = 1 c.
4 c. = 1 qt.
4 qt. = 1 gal.

8	16	20	24	32	40	48	56	60	64	72	80	88	96
(a)	(a)	⅛ t.(s)	⅛ t.	⅛ t.(r)	¼ t.(s)	¼ t.	¼ t.(r)	¼ t.(r)	¼ t.(r)	¼ t.+⅛ t.	½ t.(s)	½ t.(s)	½ t.
(a)	⅛ t.(r)	¼ t.(s)	¼ t.	¼ t.(r)	½ t.(r)	½ t.	½ t.(r)	½ t.(r)	¾ t.(s)	¾ t.	¾ t.(r)	1 t.(r)	1 t.
¼ t.(s)	¼ t.(r)	½ t.(s)	½ t.	¾ t.(s)	¾ t.(r)	1 t.	1¼ t.(s)	1¼ t.	1¼ t.(r)	1½ t.	1¾ t.(s)	1¾ t.(r)	2 t.
¼ t.	½ t.	½ t.(r)	¾ t.	1 t.	1¼ t.	1½ t.	1¾ t.	1¾ t.(r)	2 t.	2¼ t.	2½ t.	2¾ t.	1 T.
¼ t.(r)	¾ t.(s)	¾ t.(r)	1 t.	1¼ t.(r)	1¾ t.(s)	2 t.	2¼ t.(r)	2½ t.	2¾ t.(s)	1 T.	1 T.+¼ t.	1 T.+¾ t.	1 T.+1 t.
½ t.(s)	¾ t.(r)	1 t.	1¼ t.	1¾ t.(s)	2 t.	2½ t.	1 T.(s)	1 T.+⅛ t.	1 T.+¼ t.	1 T.+¾ t.	1 T.+1¼ t.	1½ T.	1 T.+2 t.
½ t.	1 t.	1¼ t.	1½ t.	2 t.	2½ t.	1 T.	1 T.+½ t.	1 T.+¾ t.	1 T.+1 t.	1½ T.	1 T.+2 t.	1 T.+2½ t.	2 T.
½ t.(r)	1¼ t.(s)	1½ t.	1¾ t.	2¼ t.(r)	1 T.(s)	1 T.+½ t.	1 T.+1 t.	1 T.+1¼ t. +⅛ t.	1 T.+1¾ t.	1 T.+2¼ t.	1 T.+2¾ t.	2 T.+½ t.	2 T.+1 t.
¾ t.(s)	1¼ t.(r)	1¾ t.(s)	2 t.	2¾ t.(r)	1 T.+¼ t.	1 T.+1 t.	1 T.+1¾ t.	1 T.+2 t.	1 T.+2¼ t.	2 T.	2 T.+¾ t.	2 T.+1¼ t.	2 T.+2 t.
¾ t.	1½ t.	1¾ t.(r)	2¼ t.	1 T.	1 T.+¾ t.	1 T.+1½ t.	1 T.+2¼ t.	1 T.+2½ t.	2 T.	2 T.+¾ t.	2½ T.	2 T.+2¼ t.	3 T.
¾ t.(r)	1¾ t.(s)	2 t.	2½ t.	1 T.+¼ t. (r)	1 T.+1¼ t.	1 T.+2 t.	1 T.+2¾ t. (r)	2 T.+¼ t.	2 T.+¾ t.	2 T.+1½ t.	2 T.+2¼ t.	3 T.	3 T.+1 t.
1 t.(s)	1¾ t.(r)	2¼ t.(r)	2¾ t.	1 T.+¾ t. (s)	1 T.+1½ t.	1 T.+2½ t.	2 T.+½ t.	2 T.+¾ t.	2 T.+1¼ t.	2 T.+2¼ t.	3 T.	3 T.+1 t.	3 T.+2 t.
1 t.	2 t.	2½ t.	1 T.	1 T.+1 t.	1 T.+2 t.	2 T.	2 T.+1 t.	2½ T.	2 T.+2 t.	3 T.	3 T.+1 t.	3 T.+2 t.	¼ c.
1½ t.	1 T.	1 T.+¾ t.	1½ T.	2 T.	2½ T.	3 T.	3½ T.	3 T.+2¼ t.	¼ c.	¼ c. +1½ t.	¼ c. + 1 T.	⅓ c. + ½ t.	⅓ c. + 2t.
2 t.	1 T.+1 t.	1 T.+2 t.	2 T.	2 T.+2 t.	3 T.+1 t.	¼ c.	¼ c.+2 t.	¼ c.+1 T.	⅓ c.	⅓ c.+2 t.	⅓ c.+4 t.	⅓ c.+2 T.	½ c.
2½ t.	1 T.+2 t.	2 T.+¼ t.	2½ T.	3 T.+1 t.	¼ c.+½ t.	¼ c.+1 T.	⅓ c. +½ T.	⅓ c. +2¾ t.	⅓ c. +4 t.	¼ c. +3½ T.	½ c.+1 t.	½ c. +3½ t.	½ c.+2 T.
1 T.	2 T.	2½ T.	3 T.	¼ c.	¼ c.+1 T.	⅓ c.+2 t.	¼ c.+3 T.	¼ c. +3½ T.	½ c.	½ c.+1 T.	½ c.+2 T.	½ c.+3 T.	¾ c.
1 T.+½ t.	2 T.+1 t.	2 T. +2¾ t.	3½ T.	¼ c.+2 t.	⅓ c. +½ T.	¼ c.+3 T.	½ c.+½ t.	½ c. +2¼ t.	½ c.+4 t.	½ c. +2½ T.	⅔ c.+1 T.	¾ c. +2½ t.	¾ c.+2 T.
1 T.+1 t.	2 T.+2 t.	3 T.+1 t.	¼ c.	⅓ c.	⅓ c.+4 t.	½ c.	½ c.+4 t.	½ c.+2 T.	⅔ c.	¾ c.	¾ c.+4 t.	¾ c. +2½ T.	1 c.

Table 15-24 — Concluded

8	16	20	24	32	40	48	56	60	64	72	80	88	96
1 T. +2¼ t.	3 T. +2¾ t.	¼ c. +1¼ t.	⅓ c.	¼ c. + 3 T.	½ c. +2½ t.	⅔ c.	¾ c. +½ T.	¾ c. +4 t.	¾ c. +2 T.	1 c.	1 c. +5 t.	1 c. +3½ T.	1⅓ c.
2 T.+2 t.	⅓ c.	⅓ c. +2 T.	½ c.	⅔ c.	¾ c. +4 t.	1 c.	1 c. +2½ T.	1¼ c.	1⅓ c.	1½ c.	1⅔ c.	1¾ c. +4 t.	2 c.
3 T. +1¾ t.	⅓ c. +5 t.	½ c. +2¾ t.	⅔ c.	¾ c. +2 T.	1 c. +5½ t.	1⅓ c.	1½ c. +1 T.	1⅔ c.	1¾ c.	2 c.	2 c. +3½ T.	2¼ c. +3 T.	2⅔ c.
¼ c.	½ c.	½ c. +2 T.	¾ c.	1 c.	1¼ c.	1½ c.	1¾ c.	1¾ c. +2 T.	2 c.	2¼ c.	2½ c.	2¾ c.	3 c.
⅓ c.	⅔ c.	¾ c.+2 t.	1 c.	1⅓ c.	1⅔ c.	2 c.	2⅓ c.	2½ c.	2⅔ c.	3 c.	3⅓ c.	3⅔ c.	1 qt.
⅓ c.+4 t.	¾ c.+4 t.	1 c.+2 t.	1¼ c.	1⅔ c.	2 c.+4 t.	2½ c.	2¾ c. +2½ T.	3 c.+2 T.	3⅓ c.	3¾ c.	1 qt. +2½ T.	4½ c.+4 t.	1¼ qt.
⅓ c. +5¼ t.	⅔ c. +3½ T.	1 c. +5¼ t.	1⅓ c.	1¾ c. +1¼ t.	2 c. +3½ T.	2⅔ c.	3 c. +2 T.	3⅓ c.	3½ c. +2½ t.	1 qt.	4¼ c. +3 T.	4¾ c. +2 T.+1 t.	1¼ qt. +⅓ c.
½ c.	1 c.	1¼ c.	1½ c.	2 c.	2½ c.	3 c.	3½ c.	3¾ c.	1 qt.	1 qt. +½ c.	1¼ qt.	1¼ qt. +½ c.	1½ qt.
½ c. +2¼ t.	1 c. +5¼ t.	1⅓ c.	1⅔ c.	2 c. +3½ T.	2⅔ c.	3⅓ c.	3¾ c. +2 T.	1 qt. +2½ T.	4¼ c. +3 T.	1¼ qt.	1¼ qt. +⅓ c.	1½ qt. +5 t.	1½ qt. +⅔ c.
½ c. +4 t.	1 c. +3 T.	1⅓ c. +2 T.	1¾ c.	2⅓ c.	2¾ c. +1½ T.	3½ c.	1 qt. +4 t.	1 qt.+ ¼ c.+2 T.	1 qt. +⅔ c.	1¼ qt. +¼ c.	5½ c. +3 T.	1½ qt.+ ¼ c.+2½T.	1¾ qt.
⅔ c.	1⅓ c.	1⅔ c.	2 c.	2⅔ c.	3⅓ c.	1 qt.	1 qt. +⅔c.	1¼ qt.	1¼ qt. +⅓ c.	1½ qt.	1½ qt. +⅔ c.	1¾ qt. +⅓ c.	2 qt.
¾ c.	1½ c.	1¾ c. +2 T.	2¼ c.	3 c.	3¾ c.	1 qt. +½ c.	1¼ qt. +¼ c.	1¼ qt. +⅔ c.	1½ qt.	1½ qt. +¾ c.	1¾ qt. +½ c.	2 qt. +¼ c.	2¼ qt.
¾ c. +1¼ t.	1½ c. +2¾ t.	1¾ c. +3 T.	2⅓ c.	3 c. +2 T.	3¾ c. +2 T.	1 qt. +⅔ c.	5¼ c. +3 T.	5¾ c. +1½ T.	1½ qt. +¼ c.	1¾ qt.	1¾ qt. +¾ c.	2 qt.+ ½ c.+1 T.	2¼ qt. +⅓ c.
¾ c. +4 t.	1⅔ c.	2 c. +4 t.	2½ c.	3⅓ c.	1 qt. +2½ T.	1¼ qt.	5¾ c. +1 T.	1½ qt. +¼ c.	1½ qt. +⅔ c.	1¾ qt. +½ c.	2 qt. +5 T.	2¼ qt. +3 T.	2½ qt.
⅔ c. +3½ T.	1¾ c. +1¼ t.	2 c. +3½ T.	2⅔ c.	3½ c. +1 T.	4¼ c. +3 T.	1¼ qt. +⅓ c.	1½ qt. +¼ c.	1½ qt. +⅔ c.	1¾ qt. +2 T.	2 qt.	2 qt.+ ¾ c.+2 T.	2¼ qt.+ ¾ c.+½ T.	2½ qt. +⅔ c.
⅔ c. +¼ c.	1¾ c. +4 t.	2¼ c. +2 t.	2¾ c.	3⅔ c.	4¼ c. +4 t.	1¼ qt. +½ c.	1½ qt.+ ¼ c.+3 T.	1½ qt.+ ¾ c.+2 T.	1¾ qt. +⅓ c.	2 qt. +¼ c.	2¼ qt. +2½ T.	2½ qt. +1½ T.	2¾ qt.
1 c.	2 c.	2½ c.	3 c.	1 qt.	1¼ qt.	1½ qt.	1¾ qt.	1¾ qt. +½ c.	2 qt.	2¼ qt.	2½ qt.	2¾ qt.	3 qt.
1 c. +4 t.	2 c. +2½ T.	2⅔ c. +2 t.	3¼ c.	1 qt. +⅓ c.	5⅓ c. +4 t.	1½ qt. +½ c.	1¾ qt.+ ⅓ c.+¼ c.	2 qt. +2 T.	2 qt. +⅔ c.	2¼ qt. +¾ c.	2½ qt.+ ¾ c.+1½ T.	2¾ qt.+ ¾ c.+3 T.	3¼ qt.
1 c. +5¼ t.	2 c. +3½ T.	2¾ c. +½ T.	3⅓ c.	4¼ c. +3 T.	5½ c. +1 T.	1½ qt. +⅔ c.	1¾ qt. +¾ c.	2 qt. +⅓ c.	2 qt.+ ¾ c.+2 T.	2½ qt.	2¾ qt. +2 T.	3 qt. +¼ c.	3¼ qt. +⅓ c.
1 c.+ 2 T.+2 t.	2¼ c. +4 t.	2¾ c. +2½ T.	3½ c.	1 qt. +⅔ c.	5¾ c. +1 T.	1¾ qt.	2 qt. +3 T.	2 qt. +¾ c.	2¼ qt. +⅓ c.	2½ qt. +½ c.	2¾ qt.+ ½ c.+2 T.	3 qt.+ ¾ c.+1½T.	3½ qt.

1 c. +3½ T.	2¼ c. +3 T.	3 c. +1 T.	3⅔ c.	4¾ c. +2 T.	1½ qt. +2 T.	1¾ qt. +⅓ c.	2 qt. + ½ c. +1 T.	2¼ qt. +2½ T.	2¼ qt. +¾ c.	2¾ qt.	3 qt. +¼ c.	3¼ qt. + ¼ c. +3 T.	3 qt. 2⅔ c.
1¼ c.	2½ c.	3 c. +2 T.	3¾ c.	1¼ qt.	1½ qt. +¼ c.	1¾ qt. +½ c.	2 qt. +¾ c.	2¼ qt. + ¼ c. +2 T.	2½ qt.	2¾ qt. +¼ c.	3 qt. +½ c.	3 qt. +1¾ c.	3 qt. +3 c.
1⅓ c.	2⅔ c.	3⅓ c.	1 qt.	1¼ qt. +⅓ c.	1½ qt. +⅔ c.	2 qt.	2 qt. +1⅓ c.	2½ qt.	2¾ qt. +⅓ c.	3 qt.	3 qt. +1⅓ c.	3 qt. +2⅔ c.	1 gal.
1⅔ c.	3⅓ c.	1 qt. +2½ T.	1¼ qt.	1½ qt. +⅔ c.	2 qt. + ¼ c. +1 T.	2½ qt.	2¾ qt. +⅔ c.	3 qt. +½ c.	3¼ qt. +⅓ c.	3¾ qt.	1 gal. +⅔ c.	1 gal. +2⅓ c.	1¼ gal.
2 c.	1 qt.	1¼ qt.	1½ qt.	2 qt.	2½ qt.	3 qt.	3½ qt.	3¾ qt.	1 gal.	1 gal. +2 c.	1¼ gal.	1¼ gal. +2 c.	1½ gal.
2⅓ c.	1 qt. +⅔ c.	5¾ c. +1½ T.	1¾ qt.	2¼ qt. +⅓ c.	2¾ qt. +⅔ c.	3½ qt.	1 gal. +⅓ c.	1 gal. +1½ c.	1 gal. +2⅔ c.	1¼ gal. +1 c.	1¼ gal. +3⅓ c.	1½ gal. +1⅔ c.	1¾ gal.
2⅔ c.	1¼ qt. +⅓ c.	1½ qt. +⅔ c.	2 qt.	2½ qt. +⅔ c.	3¼ qt. +⅓ c.	1 gal.	1 gal. +2⅔ c.	1¼ gal.	1¼ gal. +1⅓ c.	1½ gal.	1½ gal. +2⅔ c.	1¾ gal. +1⅓ c.	2 gal.
3 c.	1½ qt.	1¾ qt. +½ c.	2¼ qt.	3 qt.	3¾ qt.	1 gal. +2 c.	1¼ gal. +1 c.	1¼ gal. +2½ c.	1½ gal.	1½ gal. +3 c.	1¾ gal. +2 c.	2 gal. +1 c.	2¼ gal.
3⅓ c.	1½ qt. +⅔ c.	2 qt. +⅓ c.	2½ qt.	3¼ qt. +⅓ c.	1 gal. +⅔ c.	1¼ gal.	1¼ gal. +3⅓ c.	1½ gal. +1 c.	1½ gal. +2⅔ c.	1¾ gal. +2 c.	2 gal. +1⅓ c.	2¼ gal. +⅔ c.	2½ gal.
3⅔ c.	1¾ qt. +⅓ c.	2¼ qt. +2½ T.	2¾ qt.	3½ qt. +⅔ c.	1 gal. +2⅓ c.	1¼ gal. +2 c.	1½ gal. +1⅔ c.	1½ gal. +3½ c.	1¾ gal. +1⅓ c.	2 gal. +1 c.	2¼ gal. +⅔ c.	2½ gal. +⅓ c.	2¾ gal.
1 qt.	2 qt.	2½ qt.	3 qt.	1 gal.	1¼ gal.	1½ gal.	1¾ gal.	1¾ gal. +2 c.	2 gal.	2¼ gal.	2½ gal.	2¾ gal.	3 gal.
1 qt. +⅓ c.	2 qt. +⅔ c.	2½ qt. + ¾ c. +1½ T.	3¼ qt.	1 gal. +1⅓ c.	1¼ gal. +1⅔ c.	1½ gal. +2 c.	1¾ gal. +2⅓ c.	2 gal. +½ c.	2 gal. +2⅔ c.	2¼ gal. +3 c.	2½ gal. +3⅓ c.	2¾ gal. +3⅔ c.	3¼ gal.
1 qt. +⅔ c.	2¼ qt. +⅓ c.	2¾ qt. +⅔ c.	3½ qt.	1 gal. +2⅔ c.	1¼ gal. +3⅓ c.	1¾ gal.	2 gal. +⅔ c.	2 gal. +3 c.	2¼ gal. +1⅓ c.	2½ gal. +2 c.	2¾ gal. +2⅔ c.	3 gal. +3⅓ c.	3½ gal.
1¼ qt.	2½ qt.	3 qt. +½ c.	3¾ qt.	1¼ gal.	1½ gal. +1 c.	1¾ gal. +2 c.	2 gal. +3 c.	2¼ gal. +1½ c.	2½ gal.	2¾ gal. +1 c.	3 gal. +2 c.	3¼ gal. +3 c.	3¾ gal.
1¼ qt. +½ c.	2½ qt. +⅔ c.	3 qt. +1⅓ c.	1 gal.	1¼ gal. +1⅓ c.	1½ gal. +2⅔ c.	2 gal.	2¼ gal. +1⅓ c.	2½ gal.	2½ gal. +2⅔ c.	3 gal.	3¼ gal. +1⅓ c.	3½ gal. +2⅔ c.	4 gal.
1½ qt. +⅔ c.	3¼ qt. +⅓ c.	1 gal. +⅔ c.	1¼ gal.	1½ gal. +2⅔ c.	2 gal. +1⅓ c.	2½ gal.	2¾ gal. +2⅔ c.	3 gal. +2 c.	3¼ gal. +1⅓ c.	3¾ gal.	4 gal. +2⅔ c.	4½ gal. +1⅓ c.	5 gal.
2 qt.	1 gal.	1¼ gal.	1½ gal.	2 gal.	2½ gal.	3 gal.	3½ gal.	3¾ gal.	4 gal.	4½ gal.	5 gal.	5½ gal.	6 gal.

Table 15-25
Guide for Rounding-off Weights and Measures

These values for rounding have been calculated to be within the limits of error normally introduced in the handling of ingredients in preparing foods. They are intended to aid in "rounding" fractions and complex measurements and weights into amounts which are as simple as possible to weigh or measure while maintaining the accuracy needed for quality control in products.

Scan your adjusted recipe yields for measurements or weights which would be difficult to handle with the equipment you have. Check the table to see how to "round' these amounts safely without changing the quality of the product.

WEIGHTS

Item	If the total amount of an ingredient is	Round it to
	less than 2 oz.	measure unless wt. is in $\frac{1}{4}$, $\frac{1}{2}$, $\frac{3}{4}$ oz. amounts
Various Miscellaneous Ingredients	2 oz. to 10 oz.	closest $\frac{1}{4}$ oz. or convert to measure
	more than 10 oz. but less than 2 lb. 8 oz.	closest $\frac{1}{2}$ oz.
	2 lb. 8 oz. to 5 lb.	closest full oz.
	more than 5 lb.	closest $\frac{1}{4}$ lb.

MEASURES

Item	If the total amount of an ingredient is	Round it to
	less than 1 tbsp.	closest $= \frac{1}{8}$ tsp.
Primarily spices seasonings flavorings condiments leavenings and similar items	{more than 1 tbsp. but less than 3 tabsp.	closest $\frac{1}{4}$ tsp.
	3 tbsp. to $\frac{1}{2}$ cup	closest $\frac{1}{2}$ tsp. or convert to weight
	{more than $\frac{1}{2}$ cup but less than $\frac{3}{4}$ cup	closest full tsp. or convert to weight
	{more than $\frac{3}{4}$ cup but less than 2 cups	closest full tbsp. or convert to weight
	2 cups to 2 qt.	nearest $\frac{1}{4}$ cup
Primarily milk water eggs juice oil syrup molasses etc.	{more than 2 qt. but less than 4 qt.	nearest $\frac{1}{2}$ cup
	1 to 2 gal.	nearest full cup or $\frac{1}{4}$ qt.
	{more than 2 gal. but less than 10 gal.	nearest full qt.
	{more than 10 gal. but less than 20 gal.	closest $\frac{1}{2}$ gal.
	over 20 gal.	closest full gal.

Source: *Standardizing Recipes for Institutional Use;* Circular 233, Agr. Ex. Station, Michigan State University.

Table 15-26
Ounces and Their Decimal Equivalents of a Pound

When you use the FACTOR method for adjusting your recipe yields, you may find this table helpful if you prefer to work with pounds and decimal parts of a pound instead of multiplying pounds and ounces by the FACTOR. For example, ingredient A might appear in your recipe as 5 pounds 10 ounces. To change the ounces to decimal parts of a pound, read the value across from 10 ounces on the table. Your value is, thus 5.625 pounds.

This table will also be useful in adjusting yield figures for operations which may have scales and recipes set up in decimal parts of a pound (tenths and hundredths).

Ounces	Decimal part of a pound	Ounces	Decimal part of a pound	Ounces	Decimal part of a pound	Ounces	Decimal part of a pound
¼	.016	4¼	.266	8¼	.516	12¼	.766
½	.031	4½	.281	8½	.531	12½	.781
¾	.047	4¾	.297	8¾	.547	12¾	.797
1	.063	5	.313	9	.563	13	.813
1¼	.078	5¼	.328	9¼	.578	13¼	.828
1½	.094	5½	.344	9½	.594	13½	.844
1¾	.109	5¾	.359	9¾	.609	13¾	.859
2	.125	6	.375	10	.625	14	.875
2¼	.141	6¼	.391	10¼	.641	14¼	.891
2½	.156	6½	.406	10½	.656	14½	.906
2¾	.172	6¾	.422	10¾	.672	14¾	.922
3	.188	7	.438	11	.688	15	.938
3¼	.203	7¼	.453	11¼	.703	15¼	.953
3½	.219	7½	.469	11½	.719	15½	.969
3¾	.234	7¾	.484	11¾	.734	15¾	.984
4	.250	8	.500	12	.750	16	1.000

Source: *Standardizing Recipes for Institutional Use*, Circular 233, Agr. Ex. Station, Michigan State University.

Index